BD Chaurasia's
Human
Anatomy

Regional and Applied   Dissection and Clinical

Seventh Edition

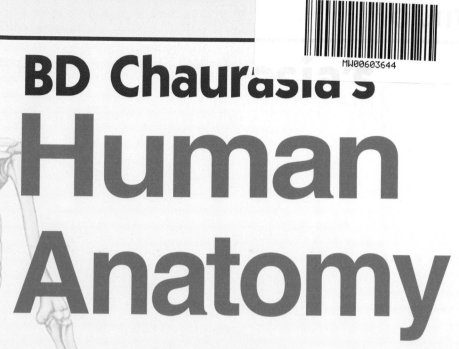

Upper Limb
Thorax

Dr BD Chaurasia (1937–1985)

was Reader in Anatomy at GR Medical College, Gwalior.
He received his MBBS in 1960, MS in 1965 and PhD in 1975.
He was elected fellow of National Academy of Medical Sciences (India) in 1982.
He was a member of the Advisory Board of the *Acta Anatomica* since 1981,
member of the editorial board of *Bionature*, and in addition
member of a number of scientific societies.
He had a large number of research papers to his credit.

Volume 1

BD Chaurasia's
Human
Anatomy

Regional and Applied   Dissection and Clinical

Seventh Edition

Upper Limb
Thorax

Chief Editor

Krishna Garg
MBBS MS PhD FIMSA FIAMS FAMS FASI

Member and Fellow, Academy of Medical Sciences
Fellow, Indian Academy of Medical Specialists
Fellow, International Medical Science Academy
Fellow, Anatomical Society of India
Life Time Achievement Awardee
DMA Distinguished Service Award

Ex-Professor and Head, Department of Anatomy
Lady Hardinge Medical College
New Delhi

Editors

Pragati Sheel Mittal MBBS MS
Associate Professor, Department of Anatomy
KD Medical College, Hospital and Research Centre
Mathura, UP

Mrudula Chandrupatla MBBS MD
Associate Professor, Department of Anatomy
Apollo Institute of Medical Sciences
Hyderabad, AP

CBS

CBS Publishers & Distributors Pvt Ltd

New Delhi • Bengaluru • Chennai • Kochi • Kolkata • Mumbai
Hyderabad • Nagpur • Patna • Pune • Vijayawada

Volume 1

BD Chaurasia's
Human
Anatomy

Regional and Applied Dissection and Clinical

Seventh Edition

ISBN: 978-93-85915-46-8

Copyright © Publisher and author

Seventh Edition: 2016

First Edition: 1979
 Reprinted: 1980, 1981, 1982, 1983, 1984, 1985, 1986, 1987, 1988

Second Edition: 1989
 Reprinted: 1990, 1991, 1992, 1993, 1994

Third Edition: 1995
 Reprinted: 1996, 1997, 1998, 1999, 2000, 2001, 2002, 2003, 2004

Fourth Edition: 2004
 Reprinted: 2005, 2006, 2007, 2008, 2009

Fifth Edition: 2010
 Reprinted: 2011, 2012

Sixth Edition: 2013
 Reprinted: 2014, 2015

Published by Satish Kumar Jain and produced by Varun Jain for

CBS Publishers & Distributors Pvt Ltd
4819/XI Prahlad Street, 24 Ansari Road, Daryaganj, New Delhi 110 002
Ph: 23289259, 23266861, 23266867 Fax: 011-23243014 Website: www.cbspd.com
e-mail: delhi@cbspd.com; cbspubs@airtelmail.in

Corporate Office: 204 FIE, Industrial Area, Patparganj, Delhi 110 092
Ph: 4934 4934   Fax: 4934 4935   e-mail: publishing@cbspd.com; publicity@cbspd.com

Branches

- **Bengaluru:** Seema House 2975, 17th Cross, K.R. Road,
  Banasankari 2nd Stage, Bengaluru 560 070, Karnataka
  Ph: +91-80-26771678/79   Fax: +91-80-26771680   e-mail: bangalore@cbspd.com
- **Chennai:** 7, Subbaraya Street, Shenoy Nagar, Chennai 600 030, Tamil Nadu
  Ph: +91-44-26260666, 26208620   Fax: +91-44-42032115   e-mail: chennai@cbspd.com
- **Kochi:** Ashana House, No. 39/1904, AM Thomas Road, Valanjambalam, Eranakulam 682 018, Kochi, Kerala
  Ph: +91-484-4059061-65   Fax: +91-484-4059065   e-mail: kochi@cbspd.com
- **Kolkata:** No. 6/B, Ground Floor, Rameswar Shaw Road, Kolkata-700014 (West Bengal), India
  Ph: +91-33-2289-1126, 2289-1127, 2289-1128   e-mail: kolkata@cbspd.com
- **Mumbai:** 83-C, Dr E Moses Road, Worli, Mumbai-400018, Maharashtra
  Ph: +91-22-24902340/41   Fax: +91-22-24902342   e-mail: mumbai@cbspd.com

Representatives

- **Hyderabad** 0-9885175004   • **Nagpur** 0-9021734563   • **Patna** 0-9334159340
- **Pune**   0-9623451994   • **Vijayawada** 0-9000660880

Printed at Thomson Press (India) Ltd.

to

_____

my teacher
Shri Uma Shankar Nagayach

— BD Chaurasia

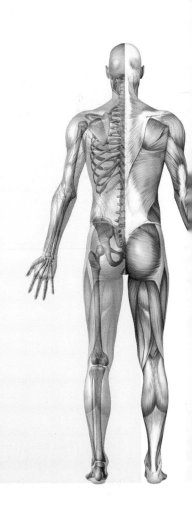

Volume **1**

UPPER LIMB and THORAX

Volume **2**

LOWER LIMB, ABDOMEN and PELVIS

Volume **3**

HEAD and NECK

Volume **4**

BRAIN–NEUROANATOMY

This human anatomy is not systemic but regional
Oh yes, it is theoretical as well as practical
Besides the gross features, it is chiefly clinical
Clinical too is very much diagrammatical.

Lots of tables for the muscles are provided
Even methods for testing are incorporated
Improved colour illustrations are added
So that right half of brain gets stimulated

Tables for muscles acting on joints are given
Tables for branches of nerves and arteries are given
Hope these volumes turn highly useful
Editor's hardwork under Almighty's guidance prove fruitful

Preface to the Seventh Edition

Suggestions from our esteemed readers to add line diagrams based on the concepts followed in the earlier editions of this monumental book have enthused us to move ahead with the seventh edition. A large number of line diagrams in each volume have been modified and redrawn to bring in simplicity. New figures of histology with three points as Facts to Remember have been added, to provide a holistic understanding of a particular topic. Many flowcharts are prepared to make learning easier, faster and interesting. Some real dissection photographs have been given to give a virtual look of anatomy. Anatomy is a visual subject and ideal means of visual recall are simple line diagrams drawn in colour thematically.

The reining feature of this edition is splitting up of the earlier last edition into two: Volume 3 containing head and neck, and Volume 4 brain and neuroanatomy. The material on brain and neuroanatomy has been extensively revised, reinforced and presented with fresh visual and textual appeals to help the students understand and retain the topics with ease and clarity. The topic of neuroanatomy has been given crisply, yet adequate enough to meet all the requirements of the medical students.

Volume 4 will also serve as a useful text for the students of dental sciences, physiotherapy, occupational therapy and other concerned courses. Postgraduate students in neurology, neurosurgery, ophthalmology and otorhinolaryngology will find it as a convenient handbook before embarking upon the study of advanced topics in their respective specialties.

The wall charts accompanying Volumes 1–3 are like ready-reckoner to recollect the numerous names in anatomy. Nomenclature of various structures has been prepared by senior anatomists after profound thoughts. Just the name tells us very important aspect of the part concerned.

Table of contents has been compiled extensively; and Index elaborated upon and improved with addition of keywords on dissection, histology and development. It would make search for a particular component easier.

Steps of dissection, actual dissection photographs, paper models, spots, videos, X-rays, etc. will help and guide the students in their practical training. Anatomy is a practical subject: Feeling various structures in one's own body, marking arteries, nerves, veins, viscera, etc., with sketch-pens (containing washable inks) make strategic understanding of landmark features in human anatomy.

As we are aware that examinations are an extension of teaching so the knowledge acquired is tested by Multiple Choice Questions (MCQs). To these MCQs, we have now added Frequently Asked Questions (FAQs) to judge their writing skills and power of expression.

As human anatomy is the fundamental subject of clinical practice, clinical anatomy with relevant text, clinicoanatomical problems at the end of each chapter, and clinical terms at the end of every section, written in easy and lucid language, have been given.

We are encouraged by the fact that the volumes have been translated into other international langauges and the publishers are being approached for translation rights globally.

I am hopeful that the volumes would satisfy the requirements of most of the teachers and students. Suggestions are welcome for further improvement of the volumes.

Any suggestions from the teachers and readers for rectification and improvement are welcome at our email ID editors_bdc@cbspd.com.

Krishna Garg
Chief Editor

Preface to the First Edition
(Excerpts)

The necessity of having a simple, systematized and complete book on anatomy has long been felt. The urgency for such a book has become all the more acute due to the shorter time now available for teaching anatomy, and also to the falling standards of English language in the majority of our students in India. The national symposium on "Anatomy in Medical Education" held at Delhi in 1978 was a call to change the existing system of teaching the unnecessary minute details to the undergraduate students.

This attempt has been made with an object to meet the requirements of a common medical student. The text has been arranged in small classified parts to make it easier for the students to remember and recall it at will. It is adequately illustrated with simple line diagrams which can be reproduced without any difficulty, and which also help in understanding and memorizing the anatomical facts that appear to defy memory of a common student. The monotony of describing the individual muscles separately, one after the other, has been minimised by writing them out in tabular form, which makes the subject interesting for a lasting memory. The relevant radiological and surface anatomy have been treated in separate chapters. A sincere attempt has been made to deal, wherever required, the clinical applications of the subject. The entire approach is such as to attract and inspire the students for a deeper dive in the subject of anatomy.

The book has been intentionally split in three parts for convenience of handling. This also makes a provision for those who cannot afford to have the whole book at a time.

It is quite possible that there are errors of omission and commission in this mostly single-handed attempt. I would be grateful to the readers for their suggestions to improve the book from all angles.

I am very grateful to my teachers and the authors of numerous publications, whose knowledge has been freely utilised in the preparation of this book. I am equally grateful to my professor and colleagues for their encouragement and valuable help. My special thanks are due to my students who made me feel their difficulties, which was a great incentive for writing this book. I have derived maximum inspiration from Prof. Inderbir Singh (Rohtak), and learned the decency of work from Shri SC Gupta (Jiwaji University, Gwalior).

I am deeply indebted to Shri KM Singhal (National Book House, Gwalior) and Mr SK Jain (CBS Publishers & Distributors, Delhi), who have taken unusual pains to get the book printed in its present form. For giving it the desired get-up, Mr VK Jain and Raj Kamal Electric Press are gratefully acknowledged. The cover page was designed by Mr Vasant Paranjpe, the artist and photographer of our college; my sincere thanks are due to him. I acknowledge with affection the domestic assistance of Munne Miyan and the untiring company of my Rani, particularly during the odd hours of this work.

BD Chaurasia

Acknowledgements

Foremost acknowledgment is the extreme gratefulness to almighty for "All Time Guidance" during the preparation of the seventh edition. I am blessed to have Dr Pragati Sheel Mittal and Dr Mrudula Chandrupatla as editors of this book and am thankful to them for their continuous help in compiling and modifying the text and illustrations, and their expert opinions. Dr Mittal has given many sittings with the graphic designers despite his busy schedule.

The suggestions provided by Dr DC Naik, Dr NA Faruqui, Dr SN Kazi, Dr Ved Prakash, Dr Mohini Kaul, Dr Indira Bahl, Dr SH Singh, Dr Rewa Choudhary, Dr Shipra Paul, Dr Anita Tuli, Dr Shashi Raheja, Dr Sneh Aggarwal, Dr Mangala Kohli, Dr Gayatri Rath, Dr RK Suri, Dr Vadana Mehta, Dr Veena Bharihoke, Dr Mahindra Nagar, Dr Renu Chauhan, Dr Sunita Kalra, Dr Vivek Parashar, Mr Buddhadev Ghosh, Mr Kaushik Saha, Dr Neelam Vasudeva, Dr Sabita Mishra, Dr Dinesh Kumar, Dr Nisha Kaul, Dr Satyam Khare, Dr AK Garg, Dr Archana Sharma, Dr Shipli Jain, Dr Poonam Kharab, Dr Mahindra K Anand, Dr Daisy Sahni, Dr Kiran Vasudeva, Dr Rashmi Bhardwaj, Dr Azmi Mohsin, Dr Arqam Miraj, Dr Joseph, Dr Harsh Piumal, HA Buch, Umang Sharma and many friends and colleagues is gratefully acknowledged. They have been providing help and guidance to sustain the responsibility of upkeeping the standard of these volumes.

Videos of bones and soft parts of human body, prepared at Kathmandu University School of Medical Sciences, have been added in the CDs along with the Frequently Asked Questions. I am grateful to Dr R Koju, CEO of KUSMS and Dhulikhel Hospital, for his generosity.

The moral support of the family members is appreciated. The members are Dr DP Garg, Mr Satya Prakash Gupta, Mr Ramesh Gupta, Dr Suvira Gupta, Dr JP Gupta, Mr Manoj, Ms Rekha, Master Shikhar, Mr Sanjay, Mrs Meenakshi, Kriti, Kanika, Dr Manish, Dr Shilpa, Meera, Raghav. Dr Surbhi Garg, the granddaughter has been giving continuous input for improvement of text and diagrams. Dr Medha Joshi has always found solutions to my myriad problems. Dr Shilpa Mittal (KDMC and RC, Mathura, UP), Ms Madhu Chhanda Mohanty (DDUIPH, New Delhi) and Dr Sushant Rit have been encouraging and inspiring us in the preparation of the volumes.

Many students have been assisting in various ways. They are Simral Behl (SAMC and PGI, Indore, MP), Shweta Yadav, Sushmita Rana, Chetan Sood, Gaurav Gupta, Anjali Gupta, Himanshi Gupta, Himakshi Eklaviya and many others of DDUIPH, New Delhi.

The magnanimity shown by Mr SK Jain (Chairman) and Mr Varun Jain (Director), CBS Publishers & Distributors Pvt Ltd, has been ideal and always forthcoming.

The unquestionable support of Mr YN Arjuna (Senior Vice-President Publishing, Editorial and Publicity) and his entire team comprising Ms Ritu Chawla (AGM Production), Sanjay Chauhan (graphic artist) with his untiring efforts on drawings, Ms Jyoti Kaur (DTP operator) for excellent formatting, Mr S Jha and Mr Kshirod Sahoo (proof-readers), and Ms Sugandha have done excellent work to bring out the seventh edition. I am really obliged to all of them.

Krishna Garg
Chief Editor

Thus spoke the cadaver

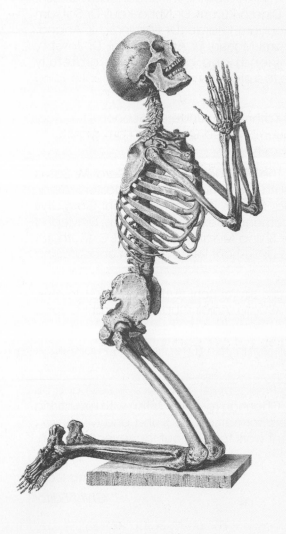

Handle me with little love and care
As I had missed it in my life affair
Was too poor for cremation or burial
That is why am lying in dissection hall

You dissect me, cut me, section me
But your learning anatomy should be precise
Worry not, you would not be taken to court
As I am happy to be with the bright lot

Couldn't dream of a fridge for cold water
Now my body parts are kept in refrigerator
Young students sit around me with friends
A few dissect, rest talk, about food, family and movies
How I enjoy the dissection periods
Don't you? Unless you are interrogated by a teacher

When my parts are buried post-dissection
Bones are taken out for the skeleton
Skeleton is the crown glory of the museum
Now I am being looked up by great enthusiasm

If not as skeletons as loose bones
I am in their bags and in their hostel rooms
At times, I am on their beds as well
Oh, what a promotion to heaven from hell

I won't leave you, even if you pass anatomy
Would follow you in forensic medicine and pathology
Would be with you even in clinical teaching
Medicine line is one where dead teach the living

One humble request I'd make
Be sympathetic to persons with disease
Don't panic, you'll have enough money
And I bet, you'd be singularly happy

Contents

Section 1 UPPER LIMB

10. Joints of Upper Limb   143

11. Surface Marking, Radiological Anatomy and Comparison of Upper and Lower Limbs   167

Appendix 1   178

Section 2 THORAX

1

Upper Limb

*Ichchak dana, bichchak dana, dane upar dana
Hands naache, feet naache, brain hai khushnama
Ichchak dana
Ulna upar radius ghoome—Ulna upar radius ghoome,
haath hai anjana
Ichchak dana
Pronators prone kare, supinators reverse kare,
midprone mai haath jud jayen aakhon ka lajana
Ichchak dana
Bolo kya—pronation, supination
Bolo kya—pronation, supination*

Introduction

One pronates while giving, and supinates while getting

The fore- and hind limbs were evolved basically for bearing the weight of the body and for locomotion as is seen in quadrupeds, e.g. cows or dogs. The two pairs of limbs are, therefore, built on the same basic principle.

Each limb is made up of a basal segment or girdle, and a free part divided into proximal, middle and distal segments. The girdle attaches the limb to the axial skeleton. The distal segment carries five digits. Table 1.1 shows homologous parts of upper and lower limbs.

However, with the evolution of the erect posture in man, the function of weight-bearing was taken over by the lower limbs. Thus the upper limbs, especially the hands, became free and gradually evolved into organs having great manipulative skills.

This has become possible because of a wide range of mobility at the shoulder. The whole upper limb works as a jointed lever. The human hand is a grasping tool. It is exquisitely adaptable to perform various complex functions under the control of a large area of the brain. The unique position of man as a master mechanic of the animal world is because of the skilled movements of his hands.

PARTS OF THE UPPER LIMB

It has been seen that the upper limb is made up of four parts: (1) Shoulder region; (2) arm or brachium; (3) forearm or antebrachium; and (4) hand or manus. Further subdivisions of these parts are given in Table 1.2 and Fig. 1.1.

1 The *shoulder region* includes:
   a. The *pectoral* or *breast region* on the front of the chest;
   b. The *axilla* or *armpit;* and
   c. The *scapular region* on the back comprising parts around the scapula.

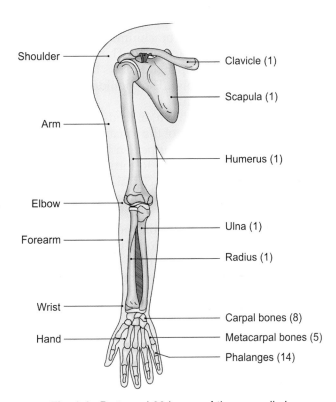

Fig. 1.1: Parts and 32 bones of the upper limb

Table 1.1: Homologous parts of the limbs

Upper limb	Lower limb
1. Shoulder girdle	Hip girdle
2. Shoulder joint	Hip joint
3. Arm with humerus	Thigh with femur
4. Elbow joint	Knee joint
5. Forearm with radius and ulna	Leg with tibia and fibula
6. Wrist joint	Ankle joint
7. Hand with	Foot with
a. Carpus	a. Tarsus
b. Metacarpus	b. Metatarsus and
c. 5 digits	c. 5 digits

Table 1.2: Parts of the upper limb

Parts	Subdivision	Bones	Joints
1. Shoulder region	a. Pectoral region on the front of the chest b. Axilla or armpit c. Scapular region on the back	Bones of the shoulder girdle a. Clavicle b. Scapula	• Sternoclavicular joint • Acromioclavicular joint
2. Upper arm (arm or brachium) from shoulder to the elbow	—	Humerus (scapulohumeral joint)	Shoulder joint
3. Forearm (antebrachium) from elbow to the wrist	—	a. Radius b. Ulna	• Elbow joint • Radioulnar joints
4. Hand	a. Wrist	• Carpus, made up of 8 carpal bones	• Wrist joint (radiocarpal joint) • Intercarpal joints
	b. Hand proper	• Metacarpus, made up of 5 metacarpal bones	• Carpometacarpal joints
	c. Five digits, numbered from lateral to medial side First = Thumb or pollex Second = Index or forefinger Third = Middle finger Fourth = Ring finger Fifth = Little finger	• 14 phalanges—two for the thumb, and three for each of the four fingers	• Intermetacarpal joints • Metacarpophalangeal joints • Proximal and distal interphalangeal joints

The bones of the shoulder girdle are the clavicle and the scapula.

Of these, only the clavicle articulates with the axial skeleton at the sternoclavicular joint. The scapula is mobile and is held in position by muscles. The clavicle and scapula articulate with each other at the acromioclavicular joint.

2 The *arm* (upper arm or brachium) extends from the shoulder to the elbow (cubitus). The bone of the arm is the humerus. Its upper end meets the scapula and forms the shoulder joint. The shoulder joint permits movements of the arm.

3 The *forearm* (antebrachium) extends from the elbow to the wrist. The bones of the forearm are the radius and the ulna. At their upper ends, they meet the lower end of the humerus to form the elbow joint. Their lower ends meet the carpal bones to form the wrist joint. The radius and ulna meet each other at the radioulnar joints.

The elbow joint permits movements of the forearm, namely flexion and extension. The radioulnar joints permit rotatory movements of the forearm called pronation and supination. In a mid-flexed elbow, the palm faces upwards in supination and downwards in pronation. During the last movement, the radius rotates around the ulna (*see* Fig. 10.23).

4 The *hand* (manus) includes:
  a. The *wrist* or carpus, supported by eight carpal bones arranged in two rows.
  b. The *hand proper* or metacarpus, supported by five metacarpal bones.
  c. *Five digits* (thumb and four fingers). Each finger is supported by three phalanges, but the thumb has only two phalanges (there being 14 phalanges in all).

The carpal bones form the wrist joint with the radius, intercarpal joints with one another, and carpometacarpal joints with the metacarpals.

The phalanges form metacarpophalangeal joints with the metacarpals and interphalangeal joints with one another.

Movements of the hand are permitted chiefly at the wrist joint. The thumb moves at the first carpometacarpal joint; where an exclusive movement of opposition besides the other usual movements are permitted. Each of the second to fifth digits move at metacarpophalangeal, proximal and distal interphalangeal joints. Figure 1.2 and Flowchart 1.1 show the lines of force transmission.

EVOLUTION OF UPPER LIMBS

The forelimbs have evolved from the pectoral fins of fishes. In tetrapods (terrestrial/land vertebrates), all the four limbs are used for supporting body weight, and for locomotion. In arboreal (tree-dwelling) human ancestors, the forelimbs have been set free from their weight-bearing function. The forelimbs, thus 'emancipated', acquired a wide range of mobility and were used for prehension or grasping, feeling, picking, holding, sorting, breaking, fighting, etc. These functions became possible only after necessary structural modifications such as the following, were done:

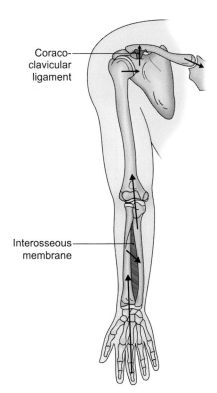

Fig. 1.2: Scheme of skeleton of upper limb showing lines of force transmission

a. Appearance of joints permitting rotatory movements of the forearms (described as supination and pronation), as a result of which food could be picked up and taken to the mouth.
b. Addition of the clavicle, which has evolved with the function of prehension.
c. Rotation of the thumb through 90 degrees, so that it can be opposed to other digits for grasping.
d. Appropriate changes for free mobility of the fingers and hand.

The primitive pentadactyl limb of amphibians, terminating in five digits, has persisted through evolution and is seen in man. In some other species, however, the limbs are altogether lost, as in snakes; while in others the digits are reduced in number as in ungulates. The habit of brachiation, i.e. suspending the

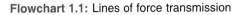

Flowchart 1.1: Lines of force transmission

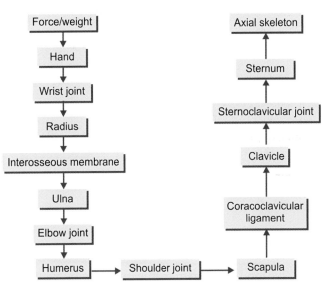

body by the arms, in anthropoid apes resulted in disproportionate lengthening of the forearms, and also in elongation of the palm and fingers.

Study of Anatomy

Before studying the anatomy of any region, it is usual to begin by learning general features of the skin, the superficial fascia and its contents, the deep fascia the bones, the muscles, joints, blood vessels and nerves. All these are provided in BD Chaurasia's Handbook of General Anatomy, 5th edition. This is followed by the study of the muscles of the region, and finally, the blood vessels and nerves. These descriptions should be read only after the part has been dissected with the help of the steps of dissection provided in the book.

Before undertaking the study of any part of the body, it is essential for the students to acquire some knowledge of the bones of the region. It is for this reason that a chapter on bones (osteology) is given at the beginning of each section. While reading the chapter, the students should palpate the various parts of bones on themselves. The next chapter must be studied with the help of loose human bones.

FREQUENTLY ASKED QUESTIONS

1. Make a flow chart to show lines of force transmission in upper limb.
2. Tabulate the homologous parts upper and lower limb.
3. Enumerate:
   a. Subdivisions of shoulder region
   b. Joints related to the forearm
   c. Name of carpal bones in order
   d. Joints of the hand

Bones of Upper Limb

Palpation of ulnar nerve behind medial epicondyle of humerus makes some persons smile, that is why the bone is called humerus

INTRODUCTION

Out of 206 total bones in man, the upper limbs contain as many as 64 bones. Each side consists of 32 bones, the distribution of which is shown in Table 1.2 and Fig. 1.1 (*see* Chapter 1). Since bones of the two upper limbs are similar, one needs to learn only 32 bones out of a total 64 bones. This applies to soft parts as well. One learns only one upper limb, the other upper limb gets learnt on its own. This is true for the whole body except parts of abdomen. Actually, one needs to master only 50% of the body and other gets mastered itself. The individual bones of the upper limb will be described one by one. Their features and attachments should be read with the bones before undertaking the dissection of the part concerned. The paragraphs on attachments should be revised when the dissection of a particular region has been completed.

CLAVICLE

The clavicle (Latin *a small key*) is a long bone. It supports the shoulder so that the arm can swing clearly away from the trunk. The clavicle transmits the weight of the limb to the sternum. The bone has a cylindrical part called the shaft, and two ends, lateral and medial.

Side Determination

The side to which a clavicle belongs can be determined from the following characters.
1 The lateral end is flat, and the medial end is large and quadrilateral.
2 The shaft is slightly curved, so that it is convex forwards in its medial two-thirds, and concave forwards in its lateral one-third.
3 The inferior surface is grooved longitudinally in its middle one-third.

Peculiarities of the Clavicle

1 It is the only long bone that lies horizontally.

2 It is subcutaneous throughout.
3 It is the first bone to start ossifying.
4 It is the only long bone which ossifies in membrane.
5 It is the only long bone which has two primary centres of ossification.
6 There is no medullary cavity.
7 It is occasionally pierced by the middle supraclavicular nerve.

It receives weight of upper limb via lateral one-third through coracoclavicular ligament and transmits weight of upper limb to the axial skeleton via medial two-thirds part (*see* Flowchart 1.1).

Features

Shaft

The shaft (Figs 2.1a and b) is divisible into the lateral one-third and the medial two-thirds.

The *lateral one-third of the shaft* is flattened from above downwards. It has two borders, anterior and posterior. The *anterior border* is concave forwards. The *posterior border* is convex backwards. This part of the bone has two surfaces, superior and inferior. The *superior surface* is subcutaneous and the inferior surface presents an elevation called the *conoid* (Greek *cone*) *tubercle* and a ridge called the *trapezoid ridge.*

The *medial two-thirds of the shaft* is rounded and is said to have four surfaces. The anterior surface is convex forwards. The posterior surface is smooth. The superior surface is rough in its medial part. The inferior surface has a rough oval impression at the medial end. The lateral half of this surface has a longitudinal *subclavian groove.* The nutrient foramen lies at the lateral end of the groove.

Lateral and Medial Ends

1 The lateral or acromial (Greek *peak of shoulder*) end is flattened from above downwards. It bears a facet that articulates with the acromion process of the scapula to form the acromioclavicular joint.

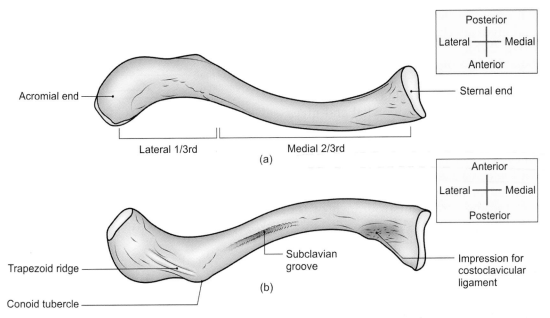

Figs 2.1a and b: General features of right clavicle: (a) Superior aspect, and (b) inferior aspect

2 The medial or sternal end is quadrangular and articulates with the clavicular notch of the manubrium sterni to form the sternoclavicular joint. The articular surface extends to the inferior aspect, for articulation with the first costal cartilage.

Attachments

1 *At the lateral end,* the margin of the articular surface for its acromioclavicular joint gives attachment to the joint capsule.

2 *At the medial end,* the margin of the articular surface for the sternum gives attachment to:

a. Fibrous capsule of sternoclavicular joint all around (Figs 2.2a and b).

b. Articular disc posterosuperiorly.

c. Interclavicular ligament superiorly.

3 *Lateral one-third of shaft*

a. The anterior border gives origin to the *deltoid* (Fig. 2.2a).

b. The posterior border provides insertion to the *trapezius.*

c. The conoid tubercle and trapezoid ridge give attachment to the conoid and trapezoid parts of the *coracoclavicular ligament* (Fig. 2.2b).

4 *Medial two-thirds of the shaft*

a. Most of the anterior surface gives origin to the *pectoralis major* (Figs 2.2a and b).

b. Half of the rough superior surface gives origin to the clavicular head of the *sternocleidomastoid* (Fig. 2.2a).

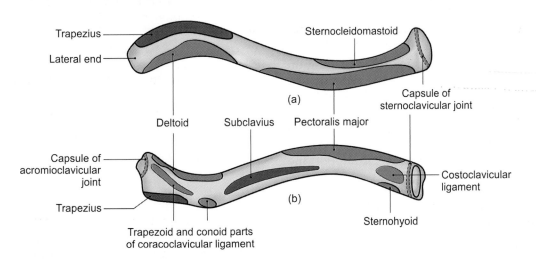

Figs 2.2a and b: Attachments of right clavicle: (a) Superior aspect, and (b) inferior aspect

c. The oval impression on the inferior surface at the medial end gives attachment to the *costoclavicular ligament* (Fig. 2.2b).

d. The subclavian groove gives insertion to the *subclavius muscle*. The margins of the groove give attachment to the clavipectoral fascia.

e. The posterior surface close to medial end gives origin to *sternohyoid muscle*.

f. The *subclavian* vessels and *cords of brachial plexus* pass towards the axilla lying between the inferior surface of the clavicle and upper surface of first rib. Subclavius muscle acts as a cushion.

The nutrient foramen transmits a branch of the suprascapular artery.

OSSIFICATION

The clavicle is the first bone in the body to ossify (Fig. 2.3). Except for its medial end, it ossifies in membrane. It ossifies from two primary centres and one secondary centre.

The two primary centres appear in the shaft between the fifth and sixth weeks of intrauterine life, and fuse about the 45th day. The secondary centre for the medial end appears during 15–17 years, and fuses with the shaft during 21–22 years. Occasionally, there may be a secondary centre for the acromial end.

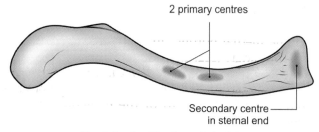

Fig. 2.3: Ossification of clavicle

CLINICAL ANATOMY

- The clavicle is commonly fractured by falling on the outstretched hand (indirect violence). The most common site of fracture is the junction between the two curvatures of the bone, which is the weakest point. The lateral fragment is displaced downwards by the weight of the limb as trapezius muscle alone is unable to support the weight of upper limb (Fig. 2.4).

- The clavicles may be congenitally absent, or imperfectly developed in a disease called *cleidocranial dysostosis*. In this condition, the shoulders droop, and can be approximated anteriorly in front of the chest (Figs 2.5a and b).

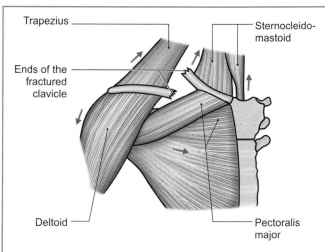

Fig. 2.4: Fracture of clavicle

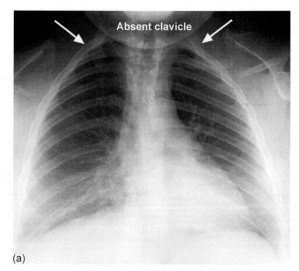

(a)

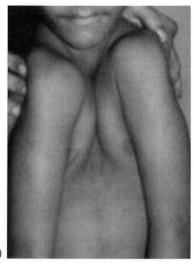

(b)

Figs 2.5a and b: Cleidocranial dysostosis: (a) Clavicles absent on both sides, and (b) shoulders approximated

SCAPULA

The scapula (Latin *shoulder blade*) is a thin bone placed on the posterolateral aspect of the thoracic cage. The scapula has two surfaces, three borders, three angles, and three processes (Fig. 2.6).

Side Determination

1 The lateral or glenoid (Greek *socket*) angle is large and bears the glenoid cavity.
2 The dorsal surface is convex and is divided by the triangular spine into the supraspinous and infraspinous fossae. The costal surface is occupied by the concave subscapular fossa to fit on the convex chest wall (Figs 2.6 and 2.7).
3 The thickest lateral border runs from the glenoid cavity above to the inferior angle below.

Features

Surfaces

1 The *costal surface* or subscapular fossa is concave and is directed medially and forwards. It is marked by three longitudinal ridges. Another thick ridge adjoins the lateral border. This part of the bone is almost rod-like. It acts as a lever for the action of the *serratus anterior* in overhead abduction of the arm.
2 The *dorsal surface* gives attachment to the spine of the scapula which divides the surface into a smaller *supraspinous fossa* and a larger *infraspinous fossa*. The two fossae are connected by the *spinoglenoid notch*, situated lateral to the root of the spine.

Borders

1 The *superior border* is thin and shorter. Near the root of the coracoid process, it presents the *suprascapular notch*.
2 The *lateral border* is thick. At the upper end, it presents the *infraglenoid tubercle*.
3 The *medial border* is thin. It extends from the superior angle to the inferior angle.

Angles

1 The *superior angle* is covered by the trapezius.
2 The *inferior angle* is covered by the *latissimus dorsi*. It moves forwards round the chest when the arm is abducted.
3 The *lateral* or *glenoid angle* is broad and bears the glenoid cavity or fossa, which is directed forwards, laterally and slightly upwards (Fig. 2.7).

Processes

1 The *spine* or *spinous process* is a triangular plate of bone with three borders and two surfaces. It divides the dorsal surface of the scapula into the supraspinous and infraspinous fossae. Its posterior border is called the *crest of the spine*. The crest has upper and lower lips.
2 The *acromion* has two borders, medial and lateral; two surfaces, superior and inferior; and a facet for the clavicle (Fig. 2.7).
3 The *coracoid* (Greek *like a crow's beak*) *process* is directed forwards and slightly laterally. It is bent and finger-like. It is atavistic type of epiphysis.

Attachments

1 The multipennate *subscapularis* arises from the medial two-thirds of the subscapular fossa (Figs 2.8 and 6.4).
2 The *supraspinatus* arises from the medial two-thirds of the supraspinous fossa including the upper surface of the spine (Fig. 2.9).
3 The *infraspinatus* arises from the medial two-thirds of the infraspinous fossa, including the lower surface of the spine (Fig. 2.9).
4 The *deltoid* arises from the lower border of the crest of the spine and from the lateral border of the acromion (Fig. 2.10). The acromial fibres are *multipennate*.
5 The *trapezius* is inserted into the upper border of the crest of the spine and into the medial border of the acromion (Fig. 2.10).
6 The *serratus anterior* is inserted along the medial border of the costal surface: One digitation from the superior angle to the root of spine, two digitations to the medial border, and five digitations to the inferior angle (Fig. 2.8).
7 The *long head of the biceps brachii* arises from the supraglenoid tubercle; and the *short head* from the lateral part of the tip of the coracoid process (Fig. 2.9).
8 The *coracobrachialis* arises from the medial part of the tip of the coracoid process.
9 The *pectoralis minor* is inserted into the medial border and superior surface of the coracoid process (Fig. 2.8).
10 The *long head of the triceps brachii* arises from the infraglenoid tubercle.
11 The *teres minor* arises by 2 slips from the upper two-thirds of the rough strip on the dorsal surface along the lateral border (Fig. 2.9). Circumflex scapular artery lies between the two slips.
12 The *teres major* arises from the lower one-third of the rough strip on the dorsal aspect of the lateral border (Fig. 2.9).
13 The *levator scapulae* is inserted along the dorsal aspect of the medial border, from the superior angle up to the root of the spine (Fig. 2.9).

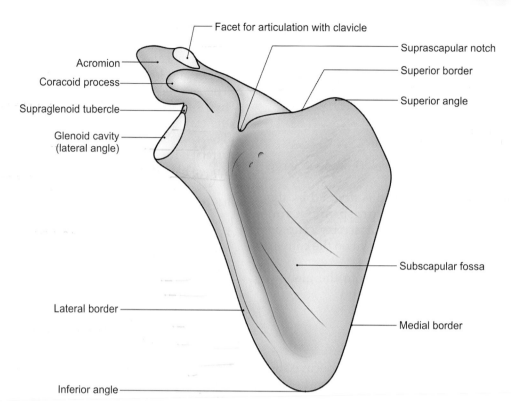

Fig. 2.6: General features of right scapula: Costal surface

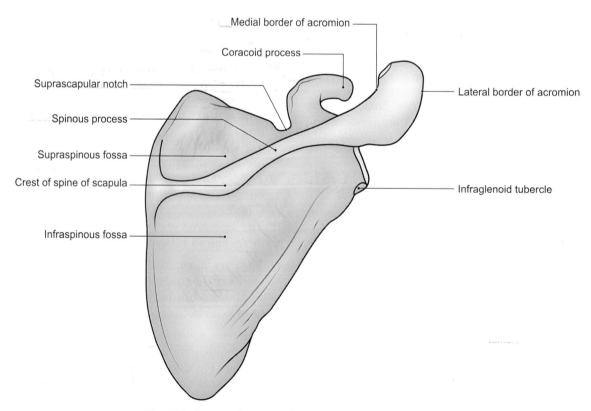

Fig. 2.7: General features of right scapula: Dorsal surface

Rotator cuff muscles ① Supraspinatus ② infraspinatus ③ Teres minor ④ Subscapularis

(Clavical attaches to make ACL joint)

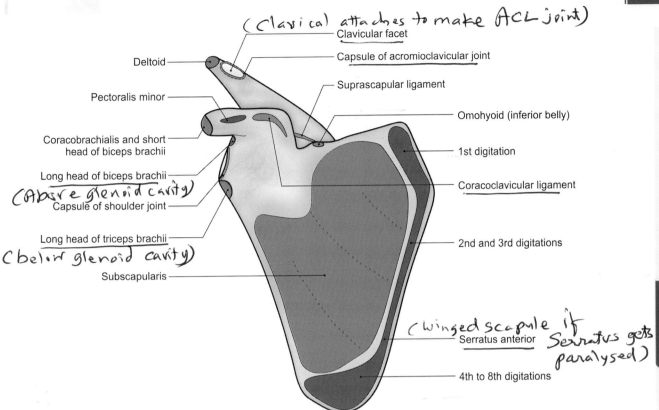

Clavicular facet
Capsule of acromioclavicular joint
Deltoid
Suprascapular ligament
Pectoralis minor
Omohyoid (inferior belly)
Coracobrachialis and short head of biceps brachii
1st digitation
Long head of biceps brachii
Coracoclavicular ligament
(Above glenoid cavity)
Capsule of shoulder joint
Long head of triceps brachii
2nd and 3rd digitations
(below glenoid cavity)
Subscapularis
(Winged scapule if Serratus gets paralysed)
Serratus anterior
4th to 8th digitations

Fig. 2.8: Attachments of right scapula: Costal aspect (Ventral or anterior aspect)

Upper Limb
Section 1

(top part of Acromion)

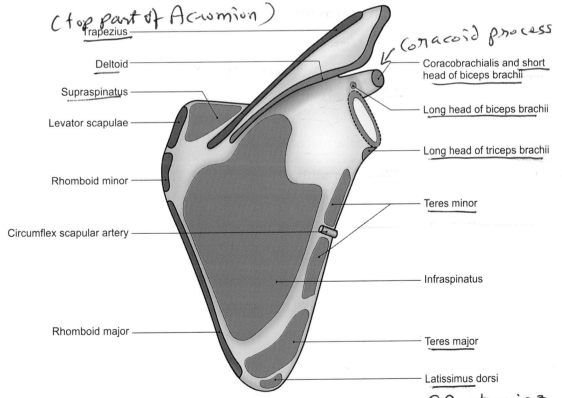

Trapezius
Coracoid process
Deltoid
Coracobrachialis and short head of biceps brachii
Supraspinatus
Levator scapulae
Long head of biceps brachii
Rhomboid minor
Long head of triceps brachii
Teres minor
Circumflex scapular artery
Infraspinatus
Rhomboid major
Teres major
Latissimus dorsi

Fig. 2.9: Attachments of right scapula: Dorsal aspect (Posterior aspect)

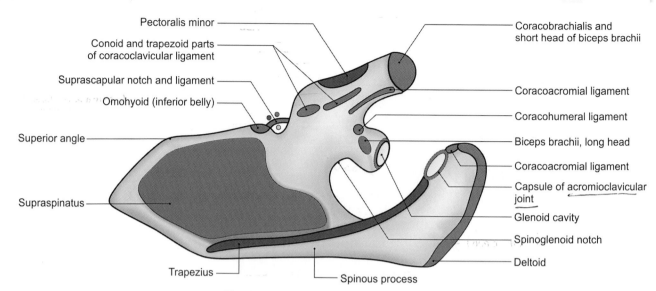

Fig. 2.10: Right scapula: Superior aspect

14 The *rhomboid minor* is inserted into the medial border (dorsal aspect) opposite the root of the spine (Fig. 2.9).

15 The *rhomboid major* is inserted into the medial border (dorsal aspect) between the root of the spine and the inferior angle.

16 The *inferior belly of the omohyoid* arises from the upper border near the suprascapular notch (Fig. 2.8).

17 The margin of the glenoid cavity gives attachment to the capsule of the shoulder joint and to the *glenoidal labrum* (Latin *lip*) (Fig. 2.8).

18 The margin of the facet on the medial aspect of the acromion gives attachment to the *capsule of the acromioclavicular joint* (Fig. 2.10).

19 The *coracoacromial ligament* is attached: (a) to the lateral border of the coracoid process, and (b) to the medial side of the tip of the acromion process (Figs 2.10 and 6.7).

20 The *coracohumeral ligament* is attached to the root of the coracoid process (Fig. 2.10).

21 The coracoclavicular ligament is attached to the coracoid process: The trapezoid part on the superior aspect, and the conoid part near the root (Fig. 2.10).

22 *The transverse ligament* bridges across the suprascapular notch and converts it into a foramen which transmits the suprascapular nerve. The suprascapular vessels lie above the ligament (Fig. 2.10).

23 *The spinoglenoid ligament* may bridge the spinoglenoid notch. The suprascapular vessels and nerve pass deep to it (Fig. 10.3).

OSSIFICATION

The scapula ossifies from one primary centre and seven secondary centres. The primary centre appears near the glenoid cavity during the eighth week of development. The first secondary centre appears in the middle of the coracoid process during the first year and fuses by the 15th year. The subcoracoid centre appears in the root of the coracoid process during the 10th year and fuses by the 16th to 18th years (Fig. 2.11). The other centres, including two for the acromion, one for the lower two-thirds of the margin of the glenoid cavity, one for the medial border and one for the inferior angle, appear at puberty and fuse by the 25th year.

The fact of practical importance is concerned with the acromion. If the two centres appearing for acromion fail to unite, it may be interpreted as a fracture on radiological examination. In such cases, a radiograph of the opposite acromion will mostly reveal similar failure of union.

CLINICAL ANATOMY

- Paralysis of the serratus anterior causes 'winging' of the scapula. The medial border of the bone becomes unduly prominent, and the arm cannot be abducted beyond 90 degrees (Fig. 2.12).
- The *scaphoid* scapula is a developmental anomaly, in which the medial border is concave.

HUMERUS

The humerus is the bone of the arm. It is the longest bone of the upper limb. It has an upper end, a lower end and a shaft (Figs 2.13 and 2.14).

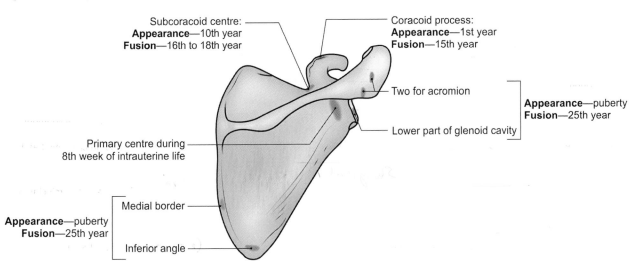

Subcoracoid centre:
Appearance—10th year
Fusion—16th to 18th year

Coracoid process:
Appearance—1st year
Fusion—15th year

Two for acromion

Appearance—puberty
Fusion—25th year

Primary centre during
8th week of intrauterine life

Lower part of glenoid cavity

Medial border

Appearance—puberty
Fusion—25th year

Inferior angle

Fig. 2.11: Ossification of scapula

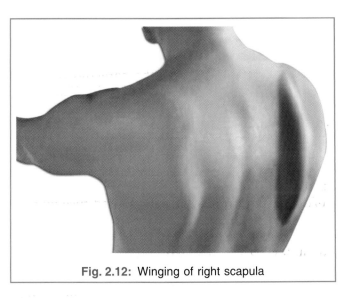

Fig. 2.12: Winging of right scapula

Side Determination

1 The upper end is rounded to form the head. The lower end is expanded from side to side and flattened from before backwards.
2 The head is directed medially, upwards and backwards.
3 The lesser tubercle projects from the front of the upper end and is limited laterally by the intertubercular sulcus or bicipital groove.

Features

Upper End

1 The *head* is directed medially, backwards and upwards. It articulates with the glenoid cavity of the scapula to form the shoulder joint. The head forms about one-third of a sphere and is much larger than the glenoid cavity.

2 The line separating the head from the rest of the upper end is called the *anatomical neck*.
3 The *lesser tubercle* (Latin *lump*) is an elevation on the anterior aspect of the upper end (Fig. 2.13a).
4 The *greater tubercle* is an elevation that forms the lateral part of the upper end. Its posterior aspect is marked by three impressions—upper, middle and lower.
5 The *intertubercular sulcus* or bicipital groove separates the lesser tubercle medially from the anterior part of the greater tubercle. The sulcus has medial and lateral lips that represent downward prolongations of the lesser and greater tubercles.
6 The narrow line separating the upper end of the humerus from the shaft is called the *surgical neck* (Fig. 2.13b).
7 Morphological neck lies 0.5 cm above surgical neck. It shows the position of epiphyseal line (Fig. 2.13b).

Shaft

The shaft is rounded in the upper half and triangular in the lower half. It has three borders and three surfaces.

Borders

1 The upper one-third of the *anterior border* forms the lateral lip of the intertubercular sulcus. In its middle part, it forms the anterior margin of the *deltoid tuberosity*. The lower half of the anterior border is smooth and rounded.
2 The *lateral border* is prominent only at the lower end where it forms the *lateral supracondylar ridge*. In the upper part, it is barely traceable up to the posterior surface of the greater tubercle. In the middle part, it is interrupted by the *radial* or *spiral groove* (Fig. 2.13b).
3 The upper part of the *medial border* forms the medial lip of the intertubercular sulcus. About its middle, it

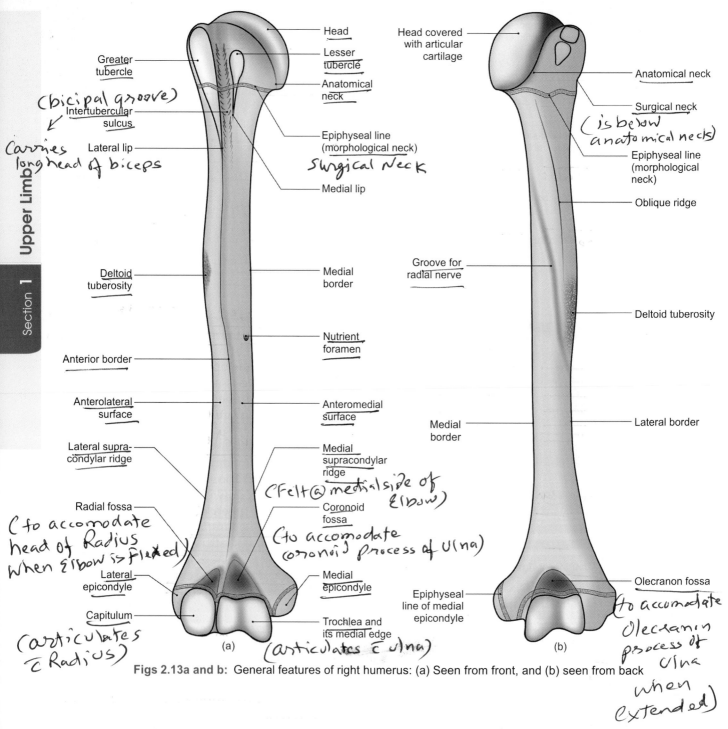

Figs 2.13a and b: General features of right humerus: (a) Seen from front, and (b) seen from back

Handwritten annotations:

(bicipal groove)

Carries long head of biceps

Surgical Neck

(is below anatomical neck)

(to accomodate head of Radius when Elbow is Flexed)

(Felt @ medial side of Elbow)

(to accomodate coronoid Process of U(na)

(articulates c Radius)

(articulates c ulna)

Olecranon fossa (to accomodate Olecranon process of Ulna when extended)

presents a rough strip. It is continuous below with the *medial supracondylar ridge*.

Surfaces

1 The *anterolateral surface* lies between the anterior and lateral borders. The upper half of this surface is covered by the deltoid. A little above the middle, it is marked by a V-shaped *deltoid* (Greek *triangular-shaped*) *tuberosity*. Behind the deltoid tuberosity, the *radial groove* runs downwards and forwards across the surface.

2 The *anteromedial surface* lies between the anterior and medial borders. Its upper one-third is narrow and forms the floor of the intertubercular sulcus. A nutrient foramen is seen near the medial border below its middle part (Fig. 2.13a).

3 The *posterior surface* lies between the medial and lateral borders. Its upper part is marked by an oblique ridge. The middle one-third is crossed by the *radial groove* (Fig. 2.13b).

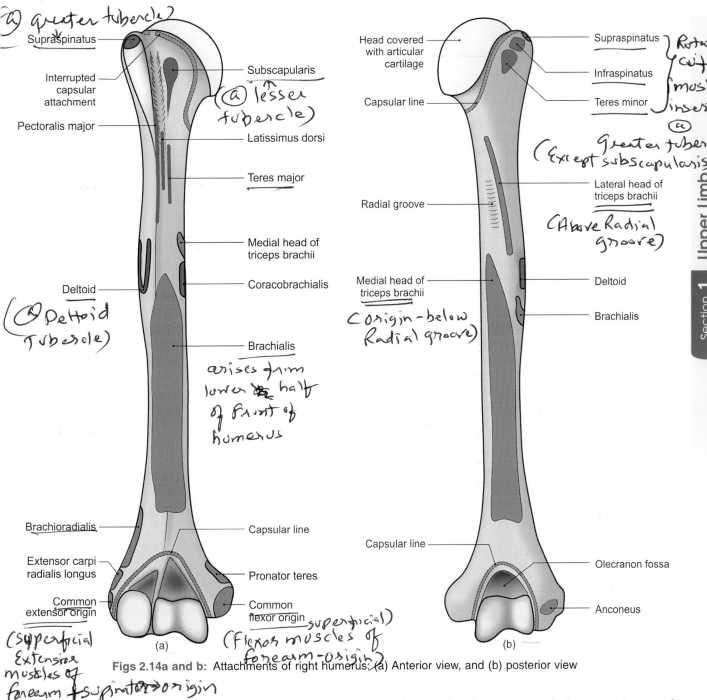

(a) greater tubercle?

Suprasinatus

Interrupted capsular attachment

Pectoralis major

@ lesser tubercle)

Subscapularis

Latissimus dorsi

Teres major

Medial head of triceps brachii

Deltoid

(@ Deltoid Tubercle)

Coracobrachialis

Brachialis

arises from lower half of front of humerus

Brachioradialis

Extensor carpi radialis longus

Common extensor origin

(Superficial Extensor muscles of forearm + supinator → origin

Capsular line

Pronator teres

Common flexor origin superficial)

(Flexor muscles of forearm - origin)

Head covered with articular cartilage

Capsular line

Suprasinatus

Infraspinatus

Teres minor

Rotator cuff muscles inserts

@
(Except greater tubercle subscapularis)

Radial groove

Lateral head of triceps brachii

(Above Radial groove)

Medial head of triceps brachii

(Origin - below Radial groove)

Deltoid

Brachialis

Capsular line

Olecranon fossa

Anconeus

Section 1 | Upper Limb

Figs 2.14a and b: Attachments of right humerus: (a) Anterior view, and (b) posterior view

Lower End

The lower end of the humerus forms the condyle which is expanded from side to side, and has articular and nonarticular parts. The *articular part* includes the following.

1 The *capitulum* (Latin *little head*) is a rounded projection which articulates with the head of the radius (Fig. 2.13a).

2 The *trochlea* (Greek *pulley*) is a pulley-shaped surface. It articulates with the trochlear notch of the ulna. The medial edge of the trochlea projects down 6 mm more than the lateral edge—this

results in the formation of the *carrying angle* (*see* Fig. 10.13).

The *nonarticular part* includes the following.

1 The *medial epicondyle* is a prominent bony projection on the medial side of the lower end. It is subcutaneous and is easily felt on the medial side of the elbow (Fig. 2.13a).

2 The *lateral epicondyle* is smaller than the medial epicondyle. Its anterolateral part has a muscular impression.

3 The sharp lateral margin just above the lower end is called the *lateral supracondylar ridge*.

4 The *medial supracondylar ridge* is a similar ridge on the medial side.

5 The *coronoid fossa* is a depression just above the anterior aspect of the trochlea. It accommodates the coronoid process of the ulna when the elbow is flexed (Fig. 2.13a).

6 The *radial fossa* is a depression present just above the anterior aspect of the capitulum. It accommodates the head of the radius when the elbow is flexed.

7 The *olecranon* (Greek *ulna head*) *fossa* lies just above the posterior aspect of the trochlea. It accommodates the olecranon process of the ulna when the elbow is extended (Fig. 2.13b).

Attachments

1 The multipennate *subscapularis* is inserted into the lesser tubercle (Fig. 2.14a).

2 The *supraspinatus* is inserted into the uppermost impression on the greater tubercle.

3 The *infraspinatus* is inserted into the middle impression on the greater tubercle (Fig. 2.14b).

4 The *teres minor* is inserted into the lower impression on the greater tubercle (Fig. 2.14b).

5 The *pectoralis major* is inserted into the lateral lip of the intertubercular sulcus. The insertion is *bilaminar* (Fig. 2.14a).

6 The *latissimus dorsi* is inserted into the floor of the intertubercular sulcus.

7 The *teres major* is inserted into the medial lip of the intertubercular sulcus.

8 The contents of the intertubercular sulcus are:
   a. The *tendon of the long head of the biceps brachii*, and its synovial sheath.
   b. The ascending branch of the anterior circumflex humeral artery.

9 The *deltoid* is inserted into the deltoid tuberosity (Fig. 2.14a).

10 The *coracobrachialis* is inserted into the rough area on the middle of the medial border.

11 The *brachialis* arises from the lower halves of the anteromedial and anterolateral surfaces of the shaft. Part of the area extends onto the posterior aspect (Fig. 2.14a).

12 The *brachioradialis* arises from the upper two-thirds of the lateral supracondylar ridge (Fig. 2.14a).

13 The *extensor carpi radialis longus* arises from the lower one-third of the lateral supracondylar ridge.

14 The *pronator teres* (humeral head) arises from the lower one-third of the medial supracondylar ridge.

15 The *superficial flexor muscles* of the forearm arise by a common origin from the anterior aspect of the medial epicondyle. This is called the *common flexor origin*.

16 The *superficial extensor muscles* of the forearm and supinator have a common origin from the lateral epicondyle. This is called the *common extensor origin*.

17 The *anconeus* (Greek *elbow*) arises from the posterior surface of the lateral epicondyle (Fig. 2.14b).

18 Lateral head of *triceps brachii* arises from oblique ridge on the upper part of posterior surface above the radial groove, while its *medial head* arises from posterior surface below the radial groove.

19 The *capsular ligament of the shoulder joint* is attached to the anatomical neck except on the medial side where the line of attachment dips down by about two centimetres to include a small area of the shaft within the joint cavity. The line is interrupted at the intertubercular sulcus to provide an aperture through which the tendon of the long head of the biceps brachii leaves the joint cavity (Fig. 2.14a).

20 The *capsular ligament of the elbow joint* is attached to the lower end along a line that reaches the upper limits of the radial and coronoid fossae anteriorly; and of the olecranon fossa posteriorly; so that these fossae lie within the joint cavity. Medially, the line of attachment passes between the medial epicondyle and the trochlea. On the lateral side, it passes between the lateral epicondyle and the capitulum (Figs 2.14a and 2.14b).

21 Three nerves are directly related to the humerus and are, therefore, liable to injury—the *axillary at the surgical neck, the radial at the radial groove, and the ulnar behind the medial epicondyle* (Fig. 2.15).

OSSIFICATION

The humerus ossifies from one primary centre and seven secondary centres. The primary centre appears in the middle of the diaphysis during the 8th week of development.

The upper end ossifies from three secondary centres—one for the head (first year), one for the greater tubercle (second year), and one for the lesser tubercle (fifth year). The three centres fuse together during the sixth year to form one *compound epiphysis*, which fuses with the shaft during the 20th year. The epiphyseal line encircles the bone at the level of the lowest margin of the head. This is the growing end of the bone (remember that the nutrient foramen is always directed away from the growing end).

The lower end ossifies from four centres which form two epiphyses. The centres include one for the capitulum and the lateral flange of the trochlea (first year), one for the medial flange of the trochlea (9th year), and one for the lateral epicondyle (12th year). All three fuse during the 14th year to form another compound epiphysis, which fuses with the shaft at about 16 years. The centre for the medial epicondyle appears during 4–6 years, forms a separate epiphysis, and fuses with the shaft during the 20th year.

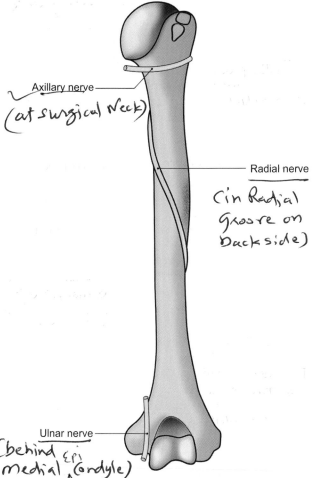

Axillary nerve
(at surgical neck)

Radial nerve
(in Radial groove on backside)

Ulnar nerve
(behind Epi medial condyle)

Fig. 2.15: Relation of axillary, radial and ulnar nerves to the back of humerus

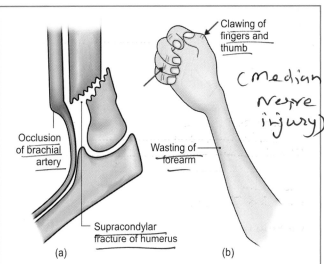

Occlusion of brachial artery

Supracondylar fracture of humerus

Clawing of fingers and thumb

Wasting of forearm

(median Nerve injury)

(a)   (b)

Figs 2.16a and b: (a) Supracondylar fracture of humerus, and (b) Volkmann's ischaemic contracture

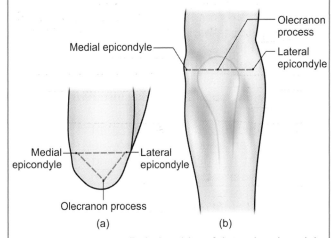

Medial epicondyle

Olecranon process

Lateral epicondyle

Medial epicondyle

Lateral epicondyle

Olecranon process

(a)   (b)

Figs 2.17a and b: Relationship of lateral epicondyle, olecranon process and medial epicondyle in: (a) Flexed elbow, and (b) extended elbow

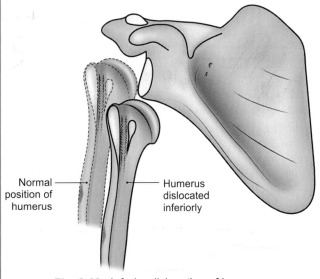

Normal position of humerus

Humerus dislocated inferiorly

Fig. 2.18: Inferior dislocation of humerus

CLINICAL ANATOMY

- The common sites of fracture of humerus are the surgical neck, shaft, and supracondylar region.
- *Supracondylar fracture* is common in young age. It is produced by a fall on the outstretched hand. The lower fragment is mostly displaced backwards, so that the elbow is unduly prominent, as in dislocation of the elbow joint. This fracture may cause injury to the median nerve. It may also lead to *Volkmann's ischaemic contracture* caused by occlusion of the brachial artery (Figs 2.16a and b).
- The three bony points of the normal elbow form the equilateral triangle in a flexed elbow and are in one line in an extended elbow (Figs 2.17a and b).
- The humerus has a poor blood supply at the junction of its upper and middle thirds. Fractures at this site show delayed union or nonunion.
- The head of the humerus commonly dislocates anteroinferiorly (Fig. 2.18).

RADIUS

The radius is the lateral bone of the forearm, and is homologous with the tibia of the lower limb. It has an upper end, a lower end and a shaft.

Side Determination

1 Upper end is having disc-shaped head while lower end is expanded with a styloid process.
2 At the lower end, the anterior surface is in the form of thick prominent ridge. While the posterior surface presents four grooves for the extensor tendons.
3 The sharpest border of the shaft is the medial border. Close to neck, it presents a radial tuberosity.
4 Lower end presents a tubercle on the posterior surface called as dorsal tubercle of Lister.

Features

Upper End

1 The *head* is disc-shaped and is covered with hyaline cartilage (Fig. 2.19). It has a superior concave surface which articulates with the capitulum of the humerus at the elbow joint. The circumference of the head is also articular. It fits into a socket formed by the radial notch of the ulna and the *annular ligament*, thus forming the superior radioulnar joint.
2 The *neck* is enclosed by the narrow lower margin of the annular ligament. The head and neck are free from capsular attachment and can rotate freely within the socket.
3 The *tuberosity* lies just below the medial part of the neck. It has a rough posterior part and a smooth anterior part.

Shaft

It has three borders and three surfaces (Fig. 2.20).

Borders

1 The *anterior border* extends from the anterior margin of the radial tuberosity down close to the styloid process. It is oblique in the upper half of the shaft, and vertical in the lower half. The lowest part is sharp and crest-like. The oblique part is called the *anterior oblique line*. The lower vertical part is crest-like (Fig. 2.19).
2 The *posterior border* is the mirror image of the anterior border, but is clearly defined only in its middle one-third. The upper oblique part is known as the posterior oblique line (Fig. 2.20).
3 The *medial* or *interosseous border* is the sharpest of the three borders. It extends from the radial tuberosity above to the posterior margin of the ulnar notch below. The interosseous membrane is attached to its lower three-fourths. In its lower part, it forms the

posterior margin of an elongated triangular area (Fig. 2.21a).

Surfaces

1 The *anterior surface* lies between the anterior and interosseous borders. A nutrient foramen opens in its upper part, and is directed upwards. The nutrient artery is a branch of the anterior interosseous artery (Fig. 2.21a).
2 The *posterior surface* lies between the posterior and interosseous borders.
3 The *lateral surface* lies between the anterior and posterior borders. It shows a roughened area in its middle part.

Lower End

The lower end is the widest part of the bone. It has five surfaces.

1 The anterior surface is in the form of a thick prominent ridge. The *radial artery* is palpated against this surface.
2 The posterior surface presents four grooves for the extensor tendons. The dorsal tubercle of Lister lies lateral to an oblique groove (Fig. 2.20).
3 The medial surface is occupied by the *ulnar notch* for the head of the ulna (Fig. 2.20).
4 The lateral surface is prolonged downwards to form the styloid (Greek *pillar*) process (Fig. 2.20).
5 The inferior surface bears a triangular area for the scaphoid bone, and a medial quadrangular area for the lunate bone. This surface takes part in forming the wrist joint.

Attachments

1 The *biceps* (Latin *two heads*) *brachii* is inserted into the rough posterior part of the radial tuberosity. The anterior part of the tuberosity is covered by a bursa (Figs 2.22 and 8.4).
2 The *supinator* (Latin *to bend back*) is inserted into the upper part of the lateral surface (Fig. 2.24).
3 The *pronator teres* is inserted into the middle of the lateral surface (Fig. 2.22).
4 The *brachioradialis* is inserted into the lowest part of the lateral surface just above the styloid process (Fig. 2.22).
5 The radial head of the *flexor digitorum superficialis* takes origin from the anterior oblique line and the upper part of anterior border (Fig. 2.22).
6 The *flexor pollicis* (Latin *thumb*) *longus* takes origin from the upper two-thirds of the anterior surface (Fig. 2.22).
7 The *pronator quadratus* is inserted into the lower part of the anterior surface and into the triangular area on the medial side of the lower end. The radial artery

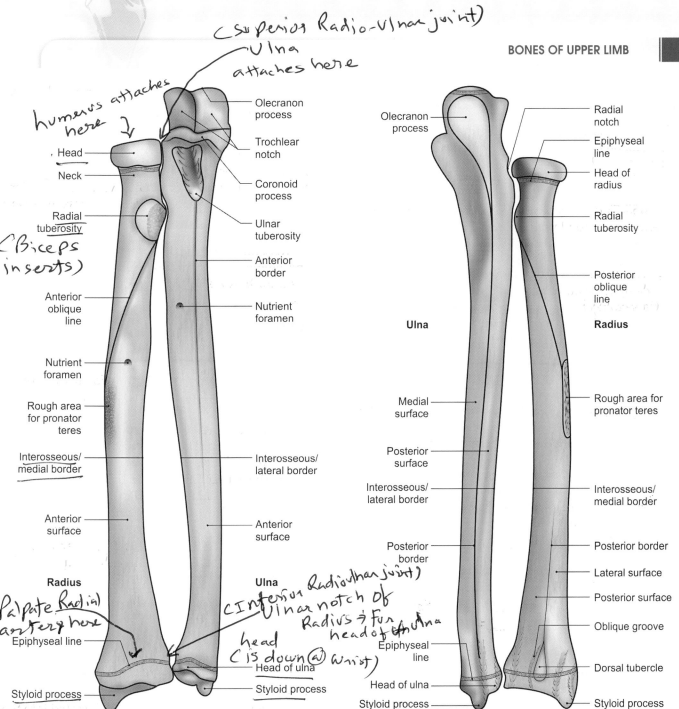

Handwritten annotations (Fig. 2.19):
- (Superior Radio-Ulnar joint) Ulna attaches here
- Humerus attaches here
- (Biceps inserts) [Radial tuberosity]
- Interosseous/medial border
- Palpate Radial artery here
- (Inferior Radioulnar joint) Ulnar notch of Radius → for head of ulna (is down @ wrist)

Labels (Fig. 2.19), radius side: Head, Neck, Radial tuberosity, Anterior oblique line, Nutrient foramen, Rough area for pronator teres, Interosseous/medial border, Anterior surface, Radius, Epiphyseal line, Styloid process

Labels (Fig. 2.19), ulna side: Olecranon process, Trochlear notch, Coronoid process, Ulnar tuberosity, Anterior border, Nutrient foramen, Interosseous/lateral border, Anterior surface, Ulna, Head of ulna, Styloid process

Fig. 2.19: Features of anterior surfaces of radius and ulna

Labels (Fig. 2.20), ulna side: Olecranon process, Ulna, Medial surface, Posterior surface, Interosseous/lateral border, Posterior border, Epiphyseal line, Head of ulna, Styloid process

Labels (Fig. 2.20), radius side: Radial notch, Epiphyseal line, Head of radius, Radial tuberosity, Posterior oblique line, Radius, Rough area for pronator teres, Interosseous/medial border, Posterior border, Lateral surface, Posterior surface, Oblique groove, Dorsal tubercle, Styloid process

Fig. 2.20: Features of right radius and ulna, posterior aspect

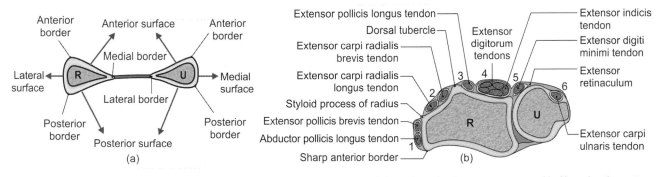

Labels (Fig. 2.21a): Anterior border, Anterior surface, Anterior border, Medial border, Lateral surface, R, U, Medial surface, Lateral border, Posterior border, Posterior surface, Posterior border

Labels (Fig. 2.21b): Extensor pollicis longus tendon, Dorsal tubercle, Extensor carpi radialis brevis tendon, Extensor carpi radialis longus tendon, Styloid process of radius, Extensor pollicis brevis tendon, Abductor pollicis longus tendon, Sharp anterior border, Extensor digitorum tendons, Extensor indicis tendon, Extensor digiti minimi tendon, Extensor retinaculum, R, U, Extensor carpi ulnaris tendon

Figs 2.21a and b: (a) Radius (R) and ulna (U) in transverse section, and (b) tendons in six compartments (1–6) under the extensor retinaculum

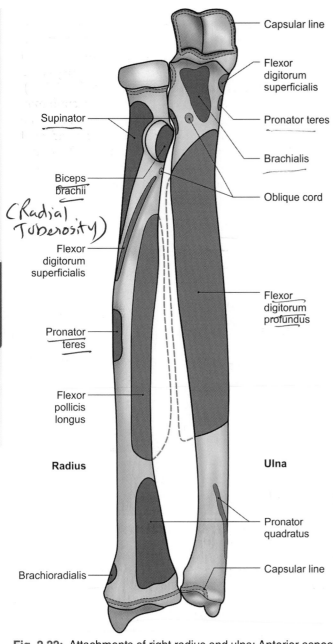

(Radial Tuberosity)

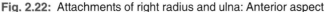

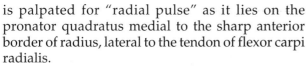

Fig. 2.22: Attachments of right radius and ulna: Anterior aspect

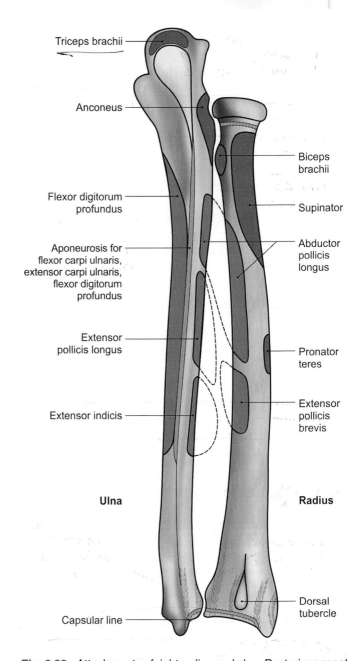

Fig. 2.23: Attachments of right radius and ulna: Posterior aspect

is palpated for "radial pulse" as it lies on the pronator quadratus medial to the sharp anterior border of radius, lateral to the tendon of flexor carpi radialis.

8 The *abductor pollicis longus* and the *extensor pollicis brevis* arise from the posterior surface (Fig. 2.23).

9 The *quadrate ligament* is attached to the medial part of the neck.

10 The *oblique cord* is attached on the medial side just below the radial tuberosity.

11 The *articular capsule of the wrist joint* is attached to the anterior and posterior margins of the inferior articular surface (Figs 2.19 and 2.20).

12 The *articular disc* of the inferior radioulnar joint is attached to the lower border of the ulnar notch.

13 The *extensor retinaculum* is attached to the lower part of the sharp anterior border.

14 The *interosseous membrane* is attached to the lower three-fourths of the interosseous border.

15 The first groove between sharp crest-like lowest part of anterior border and styloid process gives passage to *abductor pollicis longus and extensor pollicis brevis.*

16 The second groove between styloid process and dorsal tubercle gives way to *extensor carpi radialis longus* and *extensor carpi radialis brevis* tendons.

17 The third oblique groove medial to dorsal tubercle gives passage to *extensor pollicis longus* tendon.

18 The fourth groove on the medial aspect gives passage to tendons of *extensor digitorum*, *extensor indicis*, *posterior interosseous nerve* and *anterior interosseous artery*.

19 In addition, at the junction of lower ends of radius and ulna, passes the tendon of *extensor digiti minimi*.

20 Lastly in relation to ulna, between its head and styloid process, traverses the tendon of *extensor carpi ulnaris* (Fig. 2.21b).

These are six compartments under extensor retinaculum of wrist, four are in relation to radius, 5th at the junction of radius and ulna and 6th on the ulna itself between its head and styloid process (Fig. 2.21b).

OSSIFICATION

- The shaft ossifies from a primary centre which appears during the 8th week of development.
- The lower end ossifies from a secondary centre which appears during the first year and fuses at 20 years; it is the growing end of the bone.
- The upper end (head) ossifies from a secondary centre which appears during the 4th year and fuses at 18 years (Table 2.1).

CLINICAL ANATOMY

- The radius commonly gets fractured about 2 cm above its lower end (Colles' fracture). This fracture is caused by a fall on the outstretched hand (Fig. 2.24a). The distal fragment is displaced

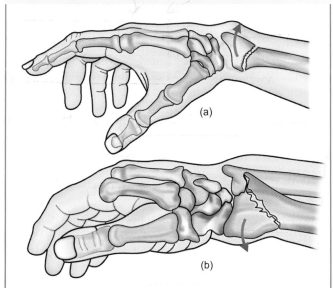

Figs 2.24a and b: (a) Colles' fracture with dinner fork deformity, and (b) Smith's fracture

upwards and backwards, and the radial styloid process comes to lie proximal to the ulnar styloid process. (It normally lies distal to the ulnar styloid process.) If the distal fragment gets displaced anteriorly, it is called Smith's fracture (Fig. 2.24b).

- A sudden powerful jerk on the hand of a child may dislodge the head of the radius from the grip of the annular ligament. This is known as subluxation of the head of the radius (*pulled elbow*) (Figs 2.25a and b). The head can normally be felt in a hollow behind the lateral epicondyle of the humerus.

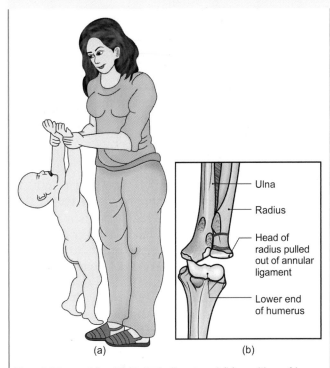

Ulna

Radius

Head of radius pulled out of annular ligament

Lower end of humerus

(a) (b)

Figs 2.25a and b: (a) Pulled elbow, and (b) position of bones

ULNA

The ulna is the medial bone of the forearm, and is homologous with the fibula of the lower limb. It has an upper end, a shaft and a lower end.

Side Determination

1 The upper end is hook-like, with its concavity directed forwards.

2 The lateral border of the shaft is sharp and crest-like.

3 Pointed styloid process lies posteromedial to the rounded head of ulna at its lower end.

Features

Upper End

The upper end presents the olecranon and coronoid processes, and the trochlear and radial notches (Fig. 2.19).

1 The *olecranon process* projects upwards from the shaft. It has superior, anterior, posterior, medial and lateral surfaces.

- The *anterior surface* is articular, it forms the upper part of the trochlear notch (Fig. 2.19).
- The *posterior surface* forms a triangular sub-cutaneous area which is separated from the skin by a *bursa*. Inferiorly, it is continuous with the posterior border of the shaft of the ulna (Fig. 2.20). Its upper part forms the point of the elbow.
- The *medial surface* is continuous inferiorly with the *medial surface* of the shaft.
- The *lateral surface* is smooth, continues as posterior surface of shaft.
- The *superior surface* in its posterior part shows a roughened area.

2 The *coronoid* (Greek *like crow's beak*) *process* projects forwards from the shaft just below the olecranon and has four surfaces, namely superior, anterior, medial and lateral.

- The *superior surface* forms the lower part of the trochlear notch.
- The *anterior surface* is triangular and rough. Its lower corner forms the ulnar tuberosity.
- The upper part of its *lateral surface* is marked by the radial notch for the head of the radius. The annular ligament is attached to the anterior and posterior margins of the notch. The lower part of the lateral surface forms a depressed area to accommodate the radial tuberosity. It is limited behind by a ridge called the *supinator crest* (Fig. 2.26).
- *Medial surface* is continuous with medial surface of the shaft.

3 The *trochlear notch* forms an articular surface that articulates with the trochlea of the humerus to form the elbow joint.

4 The *radial notch* articulates with the head of the radius to form the superior radioulnar joint (Fig. 2.26).

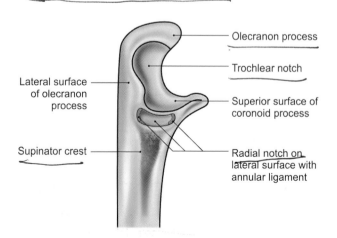

Lateral surface of olecranon process

Supinator crest

Olecranon process

Trochlear notch

Superior surface of coronoid process

Radial notch on lateral surface with annular ligament

Fig. 2.26: Features of upper end of ulna

Shaft

The shaft has three borders and three surfaces (Fig. 2.21).

Borders

1 The *interosseous* or *lateral border* is the sharpest in its middle two-fourths. Inferiorly, it can be traced to the lateral side of the head. Superiorly, it is continuous with the supinator crest.

2 The *anterior border* is thick and rounded. It begins above on the medial side of the ulnar tuberosity, passes backwards in its lower one-third, and terminates at the medial side of the styloid process.

3 The *posterior border* is subcutaneous. It begins, above, at the apex of the triangular subcutaneous area at the back of the olecranon, and terminates at the base of the styloid process (Fig. 2.20).

Surfaces

1 The *anterior surface* lies between the anterior and interosseous borders. A nutrient foramen is seen on the upper part of this surface. It is directed upwards. The nutrient artery is derived from the anterior interosseous artery (Fig. 2.19).

2 The *medial surface* lies between the anterior and posterior borders (Fig. 2.19).

3 The *posterior surface* lies between the posterior and interosseous borders. It is subdivided into three areas by two lines. An oblique line divides it into upper and lower parts. The lower part is further divided by a vertical line into a medial and a lateral area (Fig. 2.20).

Lower End

The lower end is made up of the head and the styloid process. The head articulates with the ulnar notch of the radius to form the *inferior radioulnar joint*. It is separated from the wrist joint by the articular disc (*see* Fig. 10.24a and b). Ulnar artery and nerve lie on the anterior aspect of head of ulna.

The styloid process projects downwards from posteromedial side of lower end of the ulna. Posteriorly, between the head and the styloid process, there is groove for the tendon of the extensor carpi ulnaris (*see* Fig. 9.52).

Attachments

1 The *triceps brachii* is inserted into the rough posterior part of the superior surface of the olecranon (Fig. 2.23). The anterior part of the surface is covered by a bursa.

2 The *brachialis* is inserted into the anterior surface of the coronoid process including the tuberosity of the ulna (Fig. 2.22).

3 The *supinator* arises from the supinator crest and from the triangular area in front of the crest (Fig. 2.22).

4 The ulnar head of the *flexor digitorum superficialis* arises from a tubercle at the upper end of the medial margin of the coronoid process.

5 The ulnar head of the *pronator teres* arises from the medial margin of the coronoid process.

6 The *flexor digitorum profundus* (Latin *deep*) arises from:
   a. The upper three-fourths of the anterior and medial surfaces of the shaft.
   b. The medial surfaces of the coronoid and olecranon processes.
   c. The posterior border of the shaft through an aponeurosis which also gives origin to the flexor carpi ulnaris and the extensor carpi ulnaris (Fig. 2.23).

7 The *pronator quadratus* takes origin from the oblique ridge on the lower part of the anterior surface (Fig. 2.22).

8 The *flexor carpi ulnaris* (ulnar head) arises from the medial side of the olecranon process and from the posterior border.

9 The *extensor carpi ulnaris* arises from the posterior border (Fig. 2.23).

10 The *anconeus* is inserted into the lateral aspect of the olecranon process and the upper one-fourth of the posterior surface (Fig. 2.23) of the shaft.

11 The lateral part of the posterior surface gives origin from above downwards to the *abductor pollicis longus,* the *extensor pollicis longus* and the *extensor indicis.*

12 The *interosseous membrane* is attached to the interosseous border.

13 The *oblique cord* is attached to the ulnar tuberosity.

14 The *capsular ligament of the elbow joint* is attached to the margins of the trochlear notch, i.e. to the coronoid and olecranon processes (Fig. 2.22).

15 The *annular ligament* of the superior radioulnar joint is attached to the two margins of radial notch of ulna (Fig. 2.26).

16 The *ulnar collateral ligament* of the wrist is attached to the styloid process.

17 The *articular disc* of the inferior radioulnar joint is attached by its apex to a small rough area just lateral to the styloid process.

OSSIFICATION

The shaft and most of the upper end ossify from a primary centre which appears during the 8th week of development.

The superior part of the olecranon process ossifies from a secondary centre which appears during the 10th year. It forms a scale-like epiphysis which joins the rest of the bone by 16th year.

The lower end ossifies from a secondary centre which appears during the 5th year, and joins with the shaft by 18th year. This is the growing end of the bone (Table 2.1).

CLINICAL ANATOMY

- The ulna is the stabilising bone of the forearm, with its trochlear notch gripping the lower end of the humerus. On this foundation, the radius can pronate and supinate for efficient working of the upper limb.
- The shaft of the ulna may fracture either alone or along with that of the radius. Cross-union between the radius and ulna must be prevented to preserve pronation and supination of the hand.
- *Dislocation of the elbow* is produced by a fall on the outstretched hand with the elbow slightly flexed. The olecranon shifts posteriorly and the elbow is fixed in slight flexion.
  Normally, in an extended elbow, the tip of the olecranon lies in a horizontal line with the two epicondyles of the humerus; and in the flexed elbow (Figs 2.17a and b), the three bony points form an equilateral triangle. These relations are disturbed in dislocation of the elbow.
- *Fracture of the olecranon* is common and is caused by a fall on the point of the elbow. Fracture of the coronoid process is uncommon, and usually accompanies dislocation of the elbow.
- *Madelung's deformity* is dorsal subluxation (displacement) of the lower end of the ulna, due to retarded growth of the lower end of the radius (Fig. 2.27).

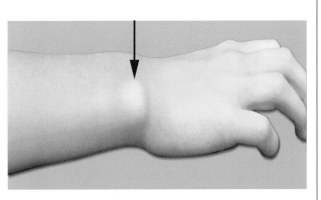

Fig. 2.27: Madelung's deformity

Ossification of Humerus, Radius and Ulna

Law of Ossification

In long bones possessing epiphyses at both their ends, the epiphysis of that end which appears first is last to join with the shaft. As a corollary, epiphysis which appears last is first to join.

These ends of long bones which unite last with the shaft are designated as *growing end* of the bone. In case of long bones of the upper limb, growing ends are at shoulder and wrist joints. This implies that the upper end of humerus and lower ends of both radius and ulna are growing ends; and each will, therefore, unite with its shaft at a later period than its corresponding other ends.

The direction of the nutrient foramen in these bones, as a rule, is opposite to the growing end.

The time of appearance and time of fusion (either of various parts at one end, or with the shaft) are given in Table 2.1.

Importance of Capsular Attachments and Epiphyseal Lines

Metaphysis is the epiphyseal end of the diaphysis. It is actively growing part of the bone with rich blood supply. Infections in this part of the bone are most common in the young age. The epiphyseal line is the line of union of metaphysis with the epiphysis. At the end of the bone, besides the epiphyseal line, is the attachment of the capsule of the respective joints.

So infection in the joint may affect the metaphysis of the bone, if it is partly or completely inside the joint capsule. As a corollary, the disease of the metaphysis, if inside a joint, may affect the joint. So it is worthwhile to know the intimate relation of the capsular attachment and the epiphyseal line at the ends of humeral, radial and ulnar bones as shown in Table 2.2.

CLINICAL ANATOMY

Relation of capsular attachments and epiphyseal lines: If epiphyseal line, i.e. site of union of epiphysis and metaphyseal end of diaphysis, is intracapsular, the infections of the joints are likely to affect the metaphysis, the actively growing part of the bone especially in young age.

CARPAL BONES

The carpus is (Greek *Karpos, wrist*) made up of 8 carpal bones, which are arranged in two rows (Fig. 2.28).

Table 2.1: Ossification of humerus, radius and ulna

Name of bone and parts	Primary centre	Secondary centres		Time of fusion together	Time of fusion with shaft
Humerus					
• Shaft	8 wk IUL	—		—	—
• Upper end	(intrauterine life)				
Head		1st yr			
Greater tubercle		2nd yr		6th yr	20th yr
Lesser tubercle		5th yr			
• Lower end					
Capitulum + lateral part of trochlea		1st yr			
Medial part of trochlea		9th yr		14th yr	16th yr
Lateral epicondyle		12th yr			
• Medial epicondyle		5th yr		—	20th yr
Radius					
• Shaft	8 wk IUL	—		—	—
• Lower end	—	1st yr		—	20th yr
• Upper end	—	4th year			18th yr
Ulna					
• Shaft	8 wk IUL	—		—	—
• Lower end	—	5th yr		—	18th yr
• Upper end	—	10th yr			16th yr

Table 2.2: Relation of capsular attachment and epiphyseal lines

	Capsular attachment (CA)	Epiphyseal line (EL)	Metaphysis
Humerus, upper end	Laterally to the anatomical neck, medially 2 cm below the shaft and deficient at bicipital grove	At the lowest part of articular surface of the head	Metaphysis is partly intracapsular
Humerus, lower end	Follows the margins of radial and coronoid fossae and the olecranon fossa. Both epicondyles are extracapsular	A horizontal line at the level of lateral epicondyle. Medial epicondyle owns a separate epiphyseal line	Metaphysis is partly intracapsular
Radius, upper end	Attached to the neck of the radius	The head forms the epiphysis	Metaphysis is intracapsular
Radius, lower end	Close to the articular margin all around	Horizontal line at the level of the upper part of ulnar notch	Metaphysis is completely extracapsular
Ulna, upper end	Near the articular surface of ulna	Scale-like epiphysis on the upper surface of olecranon	Metaphysis and part of diaphysis are related to capsular line. The epiphysis is extracapsular
Ulna, lower end	Around the head of ulna	Horizontal line at the level of articulating surface of radius	Metaphysis is partly intracapsular

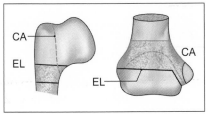  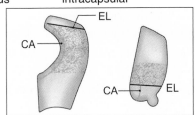

1 The proximal row contains (from lateral to medial side):
  i. The *scaphoid* (Greek *boat, wrist*),
  ii. The *lunate* (Latin *moon-shaped*),
  iii. The *triquetral* (Latin *three-cornered*), and
  iv. The *pisiform* (Greek *pea*)
2 The distal row contains in the same order:
  i. The *trapezium* (Greek *four-sided geometric figure*),
  ii. The *trapezoid* (Greek *baby's shoe*),
  iii. The *capitate* (Latin *head*), and
  iv. The *hamate* (Latin *hook*).

Identification

1 The *scaphoid* is boat-shaped and has a tubercle on its lateral side.
2 The *lunate* is half-moon-shaped or crescentic.
3 The *triquetral* is pyramidal in shape and has an isolated oval facet on the distal part of the palmar surface.
4 The *pisiform* is pea-shaped and has only one oval facet on the proximal part of its dorsal surface.
5 The *trapezium* is quadrangular in shape, and has a crest and a groove anteriorly. It has a sellar (concavoconvex) articular surface distally.

6 The *trapezoid* resembles the shoe of a baby.
7 The *capitate* is the largest carpal bone, with a rounded head.
8 The *hamate* is wedge-shaped with a hook near its base.

Side Determination

General Points

1 The proximal row is convex proximally, and concave distally.
2 The distal row is convex proximally and flat distally.
3 Each bone has 6 surfaces.
  i. The palmar and dorsal surfaces are nonarticular, except for the triquetral and pisiform.
  ii. The lateral surfaces of the two lateral bones (scaphoid and trapezium) are nonarticular.
  iii. The medial surfaces of the three medial bones (triquetral, pisiform and hamate) are nonarticular.
4 The dorsal nonarticular surface is always larger than the palmar nonarticular surface, except for the *lunate*, in which the palmar surface is larger than the dorsal.

The general points help in identifying the proximal, distal, palmar and dorsal surfaces in most of the bones. The side can be finally determined with the help of the specific points.

Specific Points

1 The *scaphoid:* The tubercle is directed laterally, forward and downwards.

2 The *lunate:*
   i. A small semilunar articular surface for the scaphoid is on the lateral side.
   ii. A quadrilateral articular surface for the triquetral is on the medial side.

3 The *triquetral:*
   i. The oval facet for the pisiform lies on the distal part of the palmar surface.
   ii. The medial and dorsal surfaces are continuous and nonarticular.

4 The *pisiform:*
   i. The oval facet for the triquetral lies on the proximal part of the dorsal surface.
   ii. The lateral surface is grooved by the ulnar nerve.

5 The *trapezium:*
   i. The palmar surface has a vertical groove for the tendon of the flexor carpi radialis.
   ii. The groove is limited laterally by the crest of the trapezium.
   iii. The distal surface bears a sellar concavo-convex articular surface for the base of the first metacarpal bone.

6 The *trapezoid:*
   i. The distal articular surface is bigger than the proximal.
   ii. The palmar nonarticular surface is prolonged laterally.

7 The *capitate:* The dorsomedial angle is the distal-most projection from the body of the capitate. It bears a small facet for the 4th metacarpal bone.

8 The *hamate:* The hook projects from the distal part of the palmar surface, and is directed laterally.

Attachments

There are four bony pillars at the four corners of the carpus. All attachments are to these four pillars (Fig. 2.28).

1 The tubercle of the scaphoid:
   i. The flexor retinaculum,
   ii. A few fibres of the abductor pollicis brevis.

2 The pisiform gives:
   i. Flexor carpi ulnaris,
   ii. Flexor retinaculum and its superficial slip,
   iii. Abductor digiti minimi (Fig. 2.32a),
   iv. Extensor retinaculum (*see* Fig. 9.15).

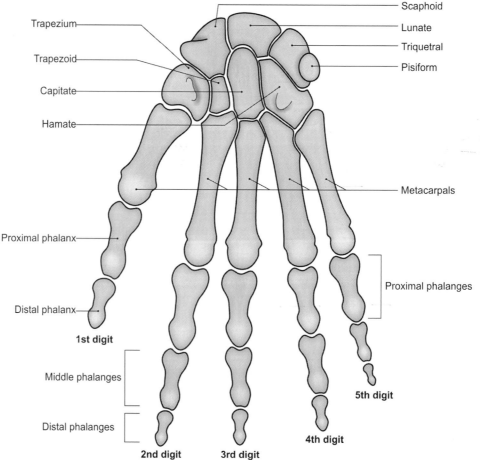

Fig. 2.28: Skeleton of the right hand: Palmar aspect

3 The trapezium:
   i. The crest gives origin to the *abductor pollicis brevis, flexor pollicis brevis,* and *opponens pollicis.* These constitute muscles of thenar eminence (Fig. 2.32a).
   ii. The edges of the groove give attachment to the two layers of the *flexor retinaculum.*
   iii. The lateral surface gives attachment to the lateral ligament of the wrist joint.
   iv. The groove lodges the tendon of the *flexor carpi radialis.*

4 The hamate:
   i. The tip of the hook gives attachment to the *flexor retinaculum* (*see* Fig. 9.15).
   ii. The medial side of the hook gives attachment to the *flexor digiti minimi* and the *opponens digiti minimi.*

Articulations

1 The scaphoid: Radius, lunate, trapezium, trapezoid capitate (Figs 2.32a and b).

2 The lunate: Radius, scaphoid, capitate, hamate and triquetral.
3 The triquetral: Pisiform, lunate, hamate and articular disc of the inferior radioulnar joint.
4 The pisiform articulates only with the triquetral.
5 The trapezium: Scaphoid, 1st and 2nd metacarpals and trapezoid.
6 The trapezoid: Scaphoid, trapezium, 2nd metacarpal and capitate.
7 The capitate: Scaphoid, lunate, hamate, 2nd, 3rd and 4th metacarpals and trapezoid.
8 The hamate: Lunate, triquetral, capitate, and 4th and 5th metacarpals.

OSSIFICATION

The year of appearance of centre of ossification in the carpal bones is shown in Fig. 2.29.

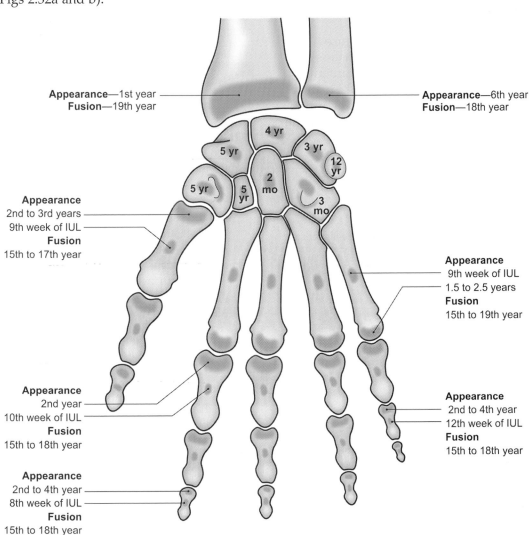

Fig. 2.29: Ossification of lower ends of radius, ulna, carpal bones, metacarpals and phalanges

Upper Limb

Section 1

Upper Limb

Section 1

CLINICAL ANATOMY

- *Fracture of the scaphoid* is quite common. The bone fractures through the waist at right angles to its long axis. The fracture is caused by a fall on the outstretched hand, or on the tips of the fingers. This causes tenderness and swelling in the anatomical snuff box, and pain on longitudinal percussion of the thumb and index finger. The residual disability is more marked in the midcarpal joint than in the wrist joint. The importance of the fracture lies in its liability to nonunion, and avascular necrosis of the body of the bone. Normally, the scaphoid has two nutrient arteries, one entering the palmar surface of the tubercle and the other the dorsal surface of the body. Occasionally (13% of cases), both vessels enter through the tubercle or through the distal half of the bone. In such cases, fracture may deprive the proximal half of the bone of its blood supply leading to avascular necrosis (Fig. 2.30).
- Dislocation of the lunate may be produced by a fall on the acutely dorsiflexed hand with the elbow joint flexed. This displaces the lunate anteriorly, also leading to *carpal tunnel syndrome* like features (Figs 2.31a to c).
- During scaphoid fracture, pain is felt in the *anatomical snuff box*.

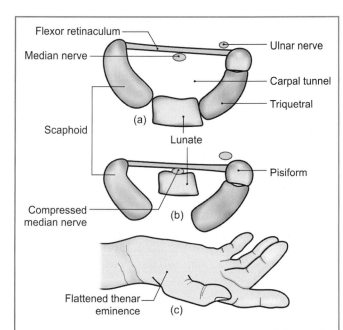

Figs 2.31a to c: (a) Normal position of nerves, (b) dislocation of lunate leading to carpal tunnel syndrome, and (c) Ape-like deformity of the hand

METACARPAL BONES

1. The metacarpal bones are 5 miniature long bones, which are numbered from lateral to the medial side (Fig. 2.28).
2. Each bone has a head placed distally, a shaft and a base at the proximal end.
   i. The head is round. It has an articular surface which extends more anteroposteriorly than laterally. It extends more on the palmar surface than on the dorsal surface. The heads of the metacarpal bones form the knuckles during flexion.
   ii. The shaft is concave on the palmar surface. Its dorsal surface bears a flat triangular area in its distal part.
   iii. The base is irregularly expanded.
3. A metacarpal bone can be distinguished from a metatarsal bone because of the differences given in Table 2.3.

Characteristics of Individual Metacarpal Bones

1st
- a. It is the shortest and stoutest of all metacarpal bones (Fig. 2.32a).
- b. The base is occupied by a convexo-concave articular surface for the trapezium.
- c. The dorsal surface of the shaft is uniformly convex (Fig. 2.32b).
- d. The head is less convex and broader from side to side than the heads of other metacarpals. The ulnar and radial corners of the palmar surface show impressions for sesamoid bones.

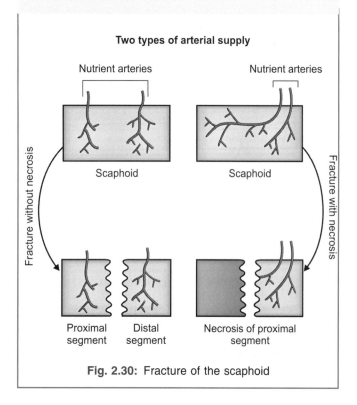

Fig. 2.30: Fracture of the scaphoid

Table 2.3: Differences between metacarpals and metatarsals

Metacarpal	Metatarsal
1. The head and shaft are prismoid	1. The head and shaft are flattened from side to side
2. The shaft is of uniform thickness	2. The shaft tapers distally
3. The dorsal surface of the shaft has an elongated, flat triangular area	3. The dorsal surface of the shaft is uniformly convex
4. The base is irregular	4. The base appears to be cut sharply and obliquely

e. The first metacarpal bone (lying on a more anterior plane) is rotated medially through 90° relative to the other metacarpals. As a result of this rotation, the movements of the thumb take place at right angles to those of other digits.

f. It *does not* articulate with any other metacarpal bone.

2nd The base is grooved from before backwards. The medial edge of the groove is larger.

3rd The base has a styloid process projecting up from the dorsolateral corner.

4th The base has two small oval facets on its lateral side for the third metacarpal, and on its medial side it has a single elongated facet for the 5th metacarpal.

5th The base has an elongated articular strip on its lateral side for the 4th metacarpal. The medial side of the base is nonarticular and bears a tubercle.

Side Determination of Metacarpals

The proximal, distal, palmar and dorsal aspects of each metacarpal bone can be made out from what has been stated above. The lateral and medial sides can be confirmed by the following criteria.

1st The anterolateral surface is larger than the anteromedial (Fig. 2.32a).

2nd a. The medial edge of the groove on the base is deeper than the lateral edge.

b. The medial side of the base bears an articular strip which is constricted in the middle.

3rd a. The styloid process is dorsolateral.

b. The lateral side of the base bears an articular strip which is constricted in the middle.

c. The medial side of the base has two small oval facets for the 4th metacarpal.

4th a. The lateral side of the base has two small oval facets for the 3rd metacarpal.

b. The medial side of the base has an elongated articular strip for the 5th metacarpal.

5th a. The lateral side of the base has an elongated articular strip for the 4th metacarpal.

b. The medial side of the base is nonarticular and has a tubercle.

Main Attachments of Metacarpals

The main attachments from shaft of metacarpals are of palmar and dorsal interossei muscles. Palmar interossei arise from one bone each except the 3rd metacarpal (Fig. 2.32a). Dorsal interossei arise from adjacent sides of two metacarpals (Fig. 2.32b). The other attachments are listed below.

1st a. The *opponens pollicis* is inserted on the radial border and the anterolateral surface of the shaft (Fig. 2.32a).

b. The *abductor pollicis longus* is inserted on the lateral side of the base.

c. The first *palmar interosseous* muscle arises from the ulnar side of the base.

2nd a. The *flexor carpi radialis* is inserted on a tubercle on the palmar surface of the base.

b. The *extensor carpi radialis longus* is inserted on the dorsal surface of the base (Fig. 2.32b).

c. The *oblique head of the adductor pollicis* arises from the palmar surface of the base.

3rd a. A slip from the *flexor carpi radialis* is inserted on the palmar surface of the base.

b. The *extensor carpi radialis brevis* is inserted on the dorsal surface of the base, immediately beyond the styloid process.

c. The *oblique head of the adductor pollicis* arises from the palmar surface of the base (Fig. 2.32a).

d. The *transverse head of the adductor pollicis* arises from the distal two-thirds of the palmar surface of the shaft (Fig. 2.32a)

4th Only the interossei arise from it (Figs 2.32a and b).

5th a. The *extensor carpi ulnaris* is inserted on the tubercle at the base.

b. The *opponens digiti minimi* is inserted on the medial surface of the shaft (Fig. 2.32a).

Articulations at the Bases

1st : With the trapezium forms saddle-shaped joint.

2nd : With the trapezium, the trapezoid, the capitate and the 3rd metacarpal.

3rd : With the capitate and the 2nd and 4th metacarpals.

4th : With the capitate, the hamate and the 3rd and 5th metacarpals.

5th : With the hamate and the 4th metacarpal.

OSSIFICATION

The shafts ossify from one primary centre each, which appears during the 9th week of development. A secondary centre for the head appears in the 2nd–5th metacarpals, and for the *base* in the 1st metacarpal. It appears during the 2nd–3rd year and fuses with the shaft at about 16–18 years (Fig. 2.29).

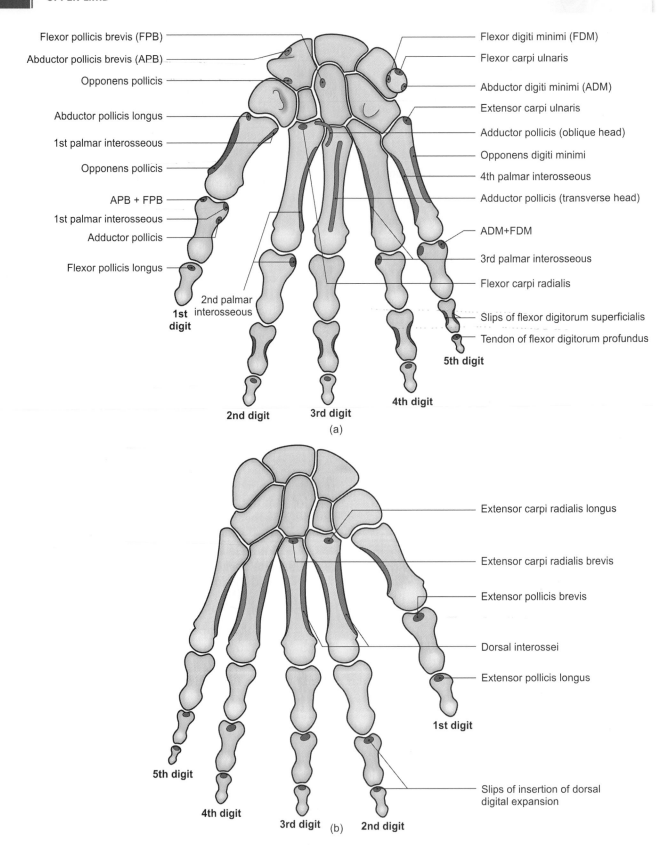

Figs 2.32a and b: Attachments on the skeleton of hand: (a) Anterior aspect, and (b) posterior aspect

CLINICAL ANATOMY

- Fracture of the base of the first metacarpal is called *Bennett's fracture*. It involves the anterior part of the base, and is caused by a force along its long axis. The thumb is forced into a semiflexed position and cannot be opposed. The fist cannot be clenched (Fig. 2.33).
- The other metacarpals may also be fractured by direct or indirect violence. Direct violence usually displaces the fractured segment forwards. Indirect violence displaces them backwards (Fig. 2.34).
- Tubercular or syphilitic disease of the metacarpals or phalanges in a child is located in the middle of the diaphysis rather than in the metaphysis because the nutrient artery breaks up into a plexus immediately upon reaching the medullary cavity. In adults, however, the chances of infection are minimised because the nutrient artery is replaced (as the major source of supply) by periosteal vessels.
- When the thumb possesses three phalanges, the first metacarpal has two epiphyses one at each end. Occasionally, the first metacarpal bifurcates distally. Then the medial branch has no distal epiphysis, and has only two phalanges. The lateral branch has a distal epiphysis and three phalanges (Fig. 2.35). Total digits are six in such case.

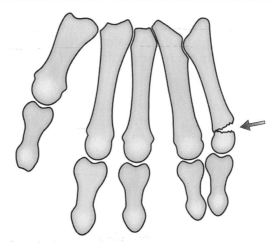

Fig. 2.34: Fracture through the neck of metacarpal (usually angulated)

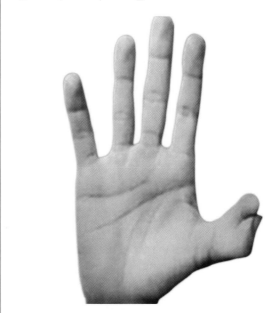

Fig. 2.35: Six digits (polydactyly)

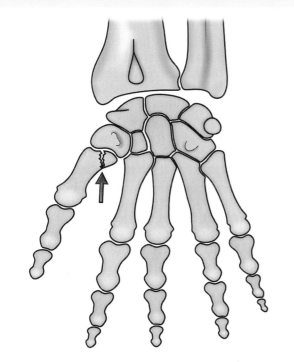

Fig. 2.33: Bennett's fracture

PHALANGES

There are 14 phalanges in each hand, 3 for each finger and 2 for the thumb. Each phalanx has a base, a shaft and a head.

Base

In the proximal phalanx, the base is marked by a concave oval facet for articulation with the head of the metacarpal bone. In the middle phalanx, or a distal phalanx, it is marked by two small concave facets separated by a smooth ridge.

Shaft

The shaft tapers towards the head. The dorsal surface is convex from side to side. The palmar surface is flattened from side to side, but is gently concave in its long axis.

Head

In the proximal and middle phalanges, the head has a pulley-shaped articular surface. In the distal phalanges, the head is nonarticular, and is marked anteriorly by a rough horseshoe-shaped tuberosity which supports the sensitive pulp of the finger/tip.

Attachments

1 *Base of the distal phalanx*
   a. The *flexor digitorum profundus* is inserted on the palmar surface (Fig. 2.32a).
   b. Two-side slips of digital expansion fuse to be inserted on the dorsal surface. These also extend the insertion of lumbrical and interossei muscles (Fig. 2.32b).
2 *The middle phalanx*
   a. The *two slips or flexor digitorum superficialis* are inserted on each side of the shaft (Fig. 2.32a).
   b. The fibrous *flexor sheath* is also attached to the side of the shaft.
   c. A major part of the *extensor digitorum* is inserted on the dorsal surface of the base (Fig. 2.32b).
3 *The proximal phalanx*
   a. The fibrous *flexor sheath* is attached to the sides of the shaft.
   b. On each side of the base, parts of the *lumbricals* and *interossei* are inserted.
4 In the thumb, the base of the proximal phalanx provides attachments to the following structures (Fig. 2.32a).
   a. The *abductor pollicis brevis* and *flexor pollicis brevis* are inserted on the lateral side.
   b. The *adductor pollicis* and the *first palmar interosseous* are inserted on the medial side.
   c. The *extensor pollicis brevis* is inserted on the dorsal surface (Fig. 2.32b).
5 In the little finger, the medial side of the base of the proximal phalanx provides insertion to the *abductor digiti minimi* and the *flexor digiti minimi.*

OSSIFICATION

The shaft of each phalanx ossifies from a primary centre which appears during the 8th week of development in the distal phalanx, 10th week in the proximal phalanx and 12th week in the middle phalanx.

The secondary centre appears for the base during 2–4 years and fuses with the shaft during 15–18 years (Fig. 2.29).

CLINICAL ANATOMY

Fracture of distal phalanx of middle finger is commonest. It is treated by splinting the injured phalanx to the adjacent normal finger. This is called "buddy splint". Figure 2.36 shows buddy splint of the fingers.

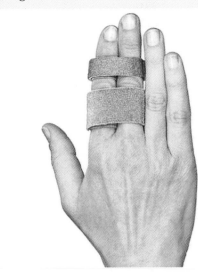

Fig. 2.36: Buddy splint of the fingers

SESAMOID BONES OF THE UPPER LIMB

Sesamoid bones (Latin *sesum, seed-like*) are small rounded masses of bones located in some tendons at points where they are subjected to great pressure. They are variable in their occurrence. These are as follows.

1 The pisiform is often regarded as a sesamoid bone lying within the tendon of the flexor carpi ulnaris.
2 Two sesamoid bones are always found on the palmar surface of the head of the first metacarpal bone.
3 One sesamoid bone is found in the capsule of the interphalangeal joint of the thumb, in 75% of subjects.
4 One sesamoid bone is found on the ulnar side of the capsule of the metacarpophalangeal joint of the little finger, in about 75% of subjects.
5 Less frequently, there is a sesamoid bone on the lateral side of the metacarpophalangeal joint of the index finger.
6 Sometimes sesamoid bone may be found at other metacarpophalangeal joints.

Mnemonics

Carpal bones
"She Looks Too Pretty, Try To Catch Her"
Lateral to medial, proximal row
– **S**caphoid

- **L**unate
- **T**riquetral
- **P**isiform

Distal row
- **T**rapezium
- **T**rapezoid
- **C**apitate
- **H**amate

Elbow
Which side has common flexor origin

FM (as in FM Radio)
Flexor medial, so common flexor origin is on the medial side.

Bicipital groove of humerus "Lady between 2 majors"
Lateral lip—pectoralis major
Medial lip—teres major
Floor—latissimus dorsi

FACTS TO REMEMBER

- Axillary, radial and ulnar nerves are intimately related to humerus and are liable to be injured.
- Radial pulse is felt close to the lower end of shaft of radius.

- Pisiform bone is a sesamoid bone in the tendon of flexor carpi ulnaris muscle.
- First metacarpal is the shortest, and strongest of metacarpals. It is situated at an angle to the other bones, this permitting opposition of the thumb.
- Third metacarpal is the longest and the axis of abduction and adduction passes through its centre.

CLINICOANATOMICAL PROBLEM

A 50-year-old man fell off his bicycle. He heard a cracking noise and felt severe pain in his right shoulder region. He noted that the lateral part of the shoulder drooped and medial end of clavicle was elevated.

- Which is the common site of fracture of clavicle and why?
- Why did his shoulder droop down?

Ans: The clavicle gets fractured at the junction of medial two-thirds and lateral one-third. This is the weak point as it lies at the junction of two opposing curvatures.

The shoulder drooped down, because of the weight of the unsupported shoulder.

FREQUENTLY ASKED QUESTIONS

1. Muscles attached to greater and lesser tubercles of humerus
2. Muscles attached to medial border of scapula on the dorsal and costal surfaces
3. Tendons present on the posterior surface of lower end of radius
4. Muscles arising from the aponeurosis attached to the posterior border of ulna
5. Attachment of deltoid and trapezius on the clavicle
6. Attachment of flexor digitorum superficialis and flexor digitorum profundus muscles on the phalanges.

MULTIPLE CHOICE QUESTIONS

1. Which of the following bones is the first one to start ossification?
   a. Ulna
   b. Scapula
   c. Clavicle
   d. Humerus
2. Fracture of humerus at midshaft is likely to cause injury to which of the following nerves?
   a. Median
   b. Radial
   c. Ulnar
   d. Musculocutaneous
3. Attachments of biceps brachii are to all of the following, *except*:
   a. Tip of coracoid process
   b. Supraglenoid tubercle
   c. Shaft of humerus
   d. Radial tuberosity
4. All the following muscles are flexors of the wrist, *except*:
   a. Flexor carpi radialis
   b. Flexor digitorum superficialis
   c. Pronator teres
   d. Flexor carpi ulnaris
5. The axis of abduction/adduction of digits passes through centre of which digit?
   a. 2nd
   b. 3rd
   c. 4th
   d. 5th
6. All are heads of triceps brachii, *except*:
   a. Long head
   b. Short head
   c. Lateral head
   d. Medial head

ANSWERS

1. c   2. b   3. c   4. c   5. b   6. b

Pectoral Region

Who ever thought of the word "Mammogram?". Every time I hear it, I think
I'm supposed to put my breast in an envelope and send it to someone
—Jan Kingz

INTRODUCTION

The pectoral region lies on the front of the chest. It essentially consists of structures which connect the upper limb to the anterolateral chest wall. Mammary gland lies in this region.

SURFACE LANDMARKS

The following features of the pectoral region can be seen or felt on the surface of body.

1 The *clavicle* lies horizontally at the root of the neck, separating it from the front of the chest. The bone is subcutaneous, and therefore, palpable throughout its length. Medially, it articulates with the sternum at the *sternoclavicular joint,* and laterally with the acromion at the *acromioclavicular joint*. Both the joints are palpable because of the upward projecting ends of the clavicle (Fig. 3.1). The sternoclavicular joint may be masked by the sternocleidomastoid muscle.

2 The *jugular notch* (interclavicular or suprasternal notch) lies between the medial ends of the clavicles, at the superior border of the manubrium sterni.

3 The *sternal angle* (angle of Louis) is felt as a transverse ridge about 5 cm below the jugular notch (Fig. 3.1). It marks the manubriosternal joint. Laterally, on either side, the *second costal cartilage* joins the sternum at this level. The sternal angle thus serves as a landmark for identification of the second rib. Other ribs can be identified by counting downwards from the second rib.

4 The *epigastric fossa* (pit of the stomach) is the depression in the infrasternal angle. The fossa overlies the xiphoid process, and is bounded on each side by the seventh costal cartilage.

5 The *nipple* is markedly variable in position in females. In males, and in immature females, it

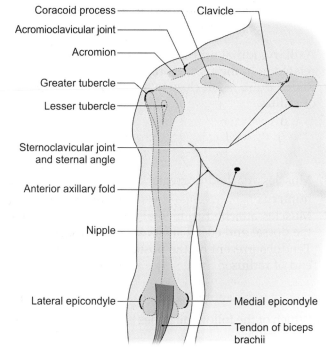

Fig. 3.1: Surface landmarks: Shoulder, axilla, arm and elbow regions (anterior aspect)

usually lies in the fourth intercostal space just medial to the midclavicular line; or 10 cm from the midsternal line. In fact, the position of the nipple is variable even in males.

6 The *midclavicular line* passes vertically through the middle of clavicle, the tip of the ninth costal cartilage and the midinguinal point.

7 The *infraclavicular fossa* (deltopectoral triangle) is a triangular depression below the junction of the lateral and middle thirds of the clavicle. It is bounded medially by the pectoralis major, laterally

by the anterior fibres of the deltoid, and superiorly by the clavicle.

8 The tip of the *coracoid process* of the scapula lies 2–3 cm below the clavicle, overlapped by the anterior fibres of the deltoid. It can be felt on deep palpation just lateral to the infraclavicular fossa.

9 The *acromion* of the scapula (*acron* = summit; *omos* = shoulder) is a flattened piece of bone that lies subcutaneously forming the top of the shoulder. The posterior end of its lateral border is called the *acromial angle*, where it is continuous with the lower lip of the crest of the spine of the scapula. The anterior end of its medial border articulates with the clavicle at the acromioclavicular joint.

10 The *deltoid* is triangular muscle with its apex directed downwards. It forms the rounded contour of the shoulder, extending vertically from the acromion to the deltoid tuberosity of the humerus.

11 The *axilla* (Latin *armpit*) is a pyramidal space between the arm and chest. When the arm is raised (abducted), the floor of the axilla rises, the anterior and posterior folds stand out, and the space becomes more prominent. The *anterior axillary fold* contains the lower border of the *pectoralis major*, and *posterior axillary fold* contains the tendon of the *latissimus dorsi* winding round the fleshy *teres major*.

The *medial wall of the axilla* is formed by the upper 4 ribs covered by the *serratus anterior*. The narrow *lateral wall* presents the upper part of the humerus covered by the *short head of the biceps, and the coracobrachialis*. Axillary arterial pulsations can be felt by pressing the artery against the humerus. The cords of the brachial plexus can also be rolled against the humerus. The head of the humerus can be felt by pressing the fingers upwards into the axilla.

12 The *midaxillary line* is a vertical line drawn midway between the anterior and posterior axillary folds.

PECTORAL REGION

DISSECTION

Mark the following points.
 i. Centre of the suprasternal notch,
 ii. Xiphoid process,
 iii. 7 o'clock position at the margin of areola,
 iv. Lateral end of clavicle (Fig. 3.2).

Give an incision vertically down from the first point to the second which joins the centre of the suprasternal notch to the xiphoid process in the midsagittal plane. From the lower end of this line, extend the incision upward and laterally till you reach to the third point on the areolar margin.

Encircle the areola and carry the incision upwards and laterally till the anterior axillary fold is reached.

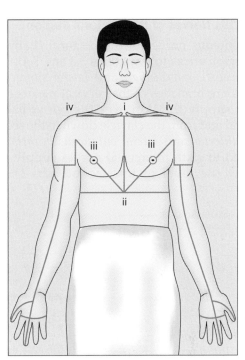

Fig. 3.2: Points and lines of incision

Continue the line of incision downwards along the medial border of the upper arm till its junction of upper one-third and lower two-thirds. Extend this incision transversely across the arm.

Make another incision horizontally from the xiphoid process across the chest wall till the posterior axillary fold.

Lastly, give horizontal incision from the centre of suprasternal notch to the lateral (acromial) end of the clavicle.

Reflect the two flaps of skin towards the upper limb.

SUPERFICIAL FASCIA

The superficial fascia (Latin *a band*) of the pectoral region is visualised after the skin has been incised. It contains moderate amount of fat, and is continuous with that of surrounding regions. The *mammary gland,* which is well developed in females, is the most important of all contents of this fascia. The fibrous septa given off by the fascia support the lobes of the gland, and the skin covering the gland.

Contents

In addition to fat, the superficial fascia of the pectoral region contains the following.
 i. Cutaneous nerves derived from the cervical plexus and from the intercostal nerves.
 ii. Cutaneous branches from the internal thoracic and posterior intercostal arteries.
 iii. The platysma (Greek *broad*)
 iv. The breast.

Cutaneous Nerves of the Pectoral Region

The cutaneous nerves of the pectoral (Latin *pectus, chest*) region are as follows (Figs 3.3 and 3.4).

1 The *medial, intermediate* and *lateral supraclavicular nerves* are branches of the cervical plexus (C3, C4). They supply the skin over the upper half of the deltoid and from the clavicle down to the second rib.

2 The *anterior* and *lateral cutaneous branches* of the second to sixth intercostal nerves supply the skin below the level of the second rib. The inter-

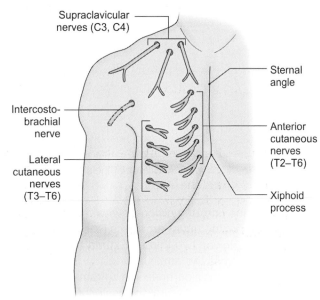

Fig. 3.3: Cutaneous nerves of the pectoral region

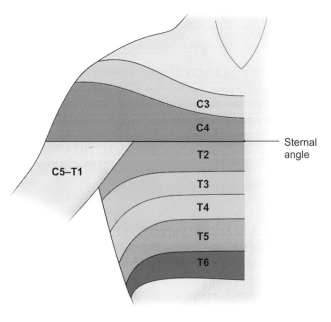

Fig. 3.4: Areas supplied by cutaneous nerves of the pectoral region

costobrachial nerve of T2 supplies the skin of the floor of the axilla and the upper half of the medial side of the arm (Fig. 3.3).

It is of interest to note that the area supplied by spinal nerves C3 and C4 directly meets the area supplied by spinal nerves T2 and T3. This is because of the fact that the intervening nerves (C5–C8 and T1) have been 'pulled away' to supply the upper limb. It may also be noted that normally the areas supplied by *adjoining spinal nerves* overlap, but because of what has been said above there is hardly any overlap between the areas supplied by C3 and C4 above and T2 and T3 below (Fig. 3.4).

Cutaneous Vessels

The cutaneous vessels are very small. The anterior cutaneous nerves are accompanied by the *perforating branches of the internal thoracic artery*. The second, third and fourth of these branches are large in females for supplying the breast. The lateral cutaneous nerves are accompanied by the *lateral cutaneous branches of the posterior intercostal arteries* (Fig. 3.8).

Platysma

The platysma (Greek *broad*) is a thin, broad sheet of subcutaneous muscle. The fibres of the muscle arise from the deep fascia covering the pectoralis major; run upwards and medially, crossing the clavicle and the side of the neck; and are inserted into the base of the mandible, and into skin over the posterior and lower part of the face. The platysma is supplied by a branch of the *facial nerve*. When the angle of the mouth is pulled down, the muscle contracts and wrinkles the skin of the neck. The platysma may protect the external jugular vein (which underlies the muscle) from external pressure.

BREAST/MAMMARY GLAND

The breast, or mammary gland (Latin *breast*) is the most important structure present in the pectoral region. Its anatomy is of great practical importance and has to be studied in detail.

The breast is found in both sexes, but is rudimentary in the male. It is well developed in the female after puberty. The breast is a *modified sweat gland*. It forms an important accessory organ of the female reproductive system, and provides nutrition to the newborn in the form of milk. Its shape is hemispherical.

Situation

The breast lies in the superficial fascia of the pectoral region. It is divided into four quadrants, i.e. upper medial, upper lateral, lower medial and lower lateral.

A small extension of the upper lateral quadrant, called the *axillary tail of Spence*, passes through an opening in the deep fascia and lies in the axilla (Fig. 3.5). The opening is called *foramen of Langer*.

Extent of the Base

i. Vertically, it extends from the second to the sixth ribs.

ii. Horizontally, it extends from the lateral border of the sternum to the midaxillary line.

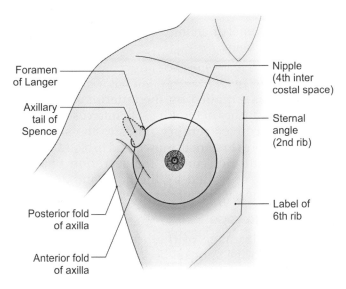

Fig. 3.5: Extent of the breast

Deep Relations

The deep surface of the breast is related to the following structures in that order (Fig. 3.6).

1 The breast lies on the deep fascia (pectoral fascia) covering the pectoralis major.

2 Still deeper there are the parts of three muscles, namely the *pectoralis major, the serratus anterior, and the external oblique muscle of the abdomen*.

3 The breast is separated from the pectoral fascia by loose areolar tissue, called the *retromammary space*. Because of the presence of this loose tissue, the normal breast can be moved freely over the pectoralis major.

Structure of the Breast

The structure of the breast may be conveniently studied by dividing it into the skin, the parenchyma, and the stroma.

Skin

It covers the gland and presents the following features.

1 A conical projection, called the *nipple*, is present just below the centre of the breast at the level of the fourth intercostal space 10 cm from the midline. The nipple is pierced by 15 to 20 lactiferous ducts. It contains circular and longitudinal smooth muscle fibres which can make the nipple stiff or flatten it, respectively. It has a few modified sweat and sebaceous glands. It is rich in nerve supply and has many sensory end organs at the termination of nerve fibres.

2 The skin surrounding the base of the nipple is pigmented and forms a circular area called the *areola*.

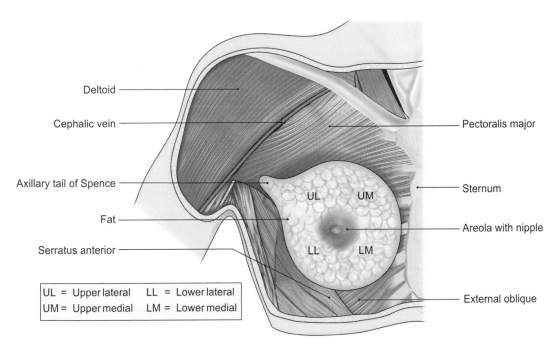

| UL = Upper lateral | LL = Lower lateral |
| UM = Upper medial | LM = Lower medial |

Fig. 3.6: Axillary tail and the four quadrants of breast and the muscles situated deep to the breast

This region is rich in modified *sebaceous glands*, particularly at its outer margin. These become enlarged during pregnancy and lactation to form raised *tubercles of Montgomery*. Oily secretions of these glands lubricate the nipple and areola, and prevent them from cracking during lactation. Apart from sebaceous glands, the areola also contains some sweat glands, and accessory mammary glands. The skin of the areola and nipple is devoid of hair, and there is no fat subjacent to it. Below the areola lie lactiferous sinus where stored milk is seen.

Parenchyma

It is a compound tubuloalveolar gland which secretes milk. The gland consists of 15 to 20 lobes. Each lobe is a cluster of alveoli, and is drained by a lactiferous duct. The lactiferous ducts converge towards the nipple and open on it. Near its termination, each duct has a dilatation called a *lactiferous sinus* (Figs 3.7a and b).

Stroma

It forms the supporting framework of the gland. It is partly fibrous and partly fatty.

The fibrous stroma forms septa, known as the *suspensory ligaments of Cooper,* which anchor the skin and gland to the pectoral fascia (Fig. 3.7a).

The fatty stroma forms the main bulk of the gland. It is distributed all over the breast, except beneath the areola and nipple.

Blood Supply

The mammary gland is extremely vascular. It is supplied by branches of the following arteries (Fig. 3.8).
1 Internal thoracic artery, a branch of the subclavian artery, through its perforating branches.
2 The lateral thoracic, superior thoracic and acromiothoracic (thoracoacromial) branches of the axillary artery.
3 Lateral branches of the posterior intercostal arteries.

The arteries converge on the breast and are distributed from the anterior surface. The posterior surface is relatively avascular.

The veins follow the arteries. They first converge towards the base of the nipple where they form an anastomotic venous circle, from where veins run in superficial and deep sets.
1 The superficial veins drain into the internal thoracic vein and into the superficial veins of the lower part of the neck.
2 The deep veins drain into the axillary and posterior intercostal veins.

Nerve Supply

The breast is supplied by the anterior and lateral cutaneous branches of the 4th to 6th intercostal nerves. The nerves convey sensory fibres to the skin, and autonomic fibres to smooth muscle and to blood vessels. The nerves do not control the secretion of milk. Secretion is controlled by the hormone *prolactin*, secreted by the *pars anterior* of the *hypophysis cerebri*.

Lymphatic Drainage

Lymphatic drainage of the breast assumes great importance to the surgeon because carcinoma of the breast spreads mostly along lymphatics to the regional lymph nodes. The subject can be described under two heads, the lymph nodes, and the lymphatic vessels.

Lymph Nodes

Groups of lymph nodes are shown in Fig. 3.9.

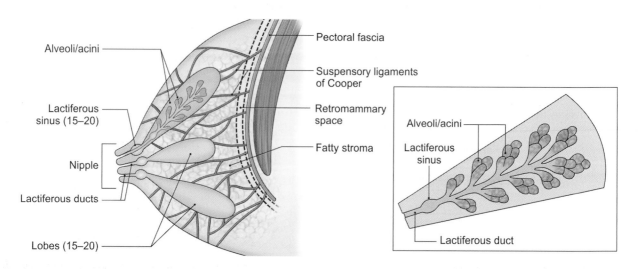

Figs 3.7a and b: (a) Suspensory ligaments of the breast and its lobes, and (b) structure of one lobe of the mammary gland

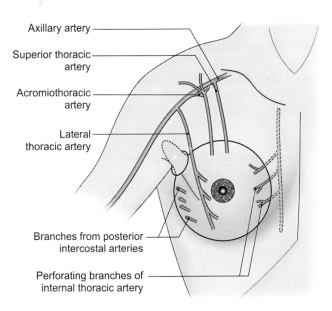

Fig. 3.8: Arterial supply of the breast

Lymph from the breast drains into the following lymph nodes (Fig. 3.9).

1. The axillary lymph nodes, chiefly the anterior (or pectoral) group. The posterior, lateral, central and apical groups of nodes also receive lymph from the breast either directly or indirectly.
2. The internal mammary (parasternal) nodes which lie along the internal thoracic vessels (Fig. 3.10)
3. Some lymph from the breast also reaches the supraclavicular nodes, the cephalic (deltopectoral) node, the posterior intercostal nodes (lying in front of the heads of the ribs), the subdiaphragmatic and subperitoneal lymph plexuses.

Lymphatic Vessels

1. The *superficial lymphatics* drain the skin over the breast except for the nipple and areola. The lymphatics pass radially to the surrounding lymph nodes (axillary, internal mammary, supraclavicular and cephalic).
2. The *deep lymphatics* drain the parenchyma of the breast. They also drain the nipple and areola (Fig. 3.11).

Some further points of interest about the lymphatic drainage are as follows.

1. About 75% of the lymph from the breast drains into the axillary nodes; 20% into the internal mammary nodes; and 5% into the posterior intercostal nodes. Among the axillary nodes, the lymphatics end mostly in the anterior group (closely related to the axillary tail) and partly in the posterior and apical groups. Lymph from the anterior and posterior groups passes to the central and lateral groups, and through them to the apical group. Finally, it reaches the supra-clavicular nodes.
2. The internal mammary nodes drain the lymph not only from the inner half of the breast, but from the outer half as well.
3. A plexus of lymph vessels is present deep to the areola. This is the subareolar plexus of Sappey (Fig. 3.11). Subareolar plexus and most of lymph from the breast drains into the anterior or pectoral group of lymph nodes.
4. The lymphatics from the deep surface of the breast pass through the pectoralis major muscle and the clavipectoral fascia to reach the apical nodes, and also to the internal mammary nodes (Figs 3.12a and b).

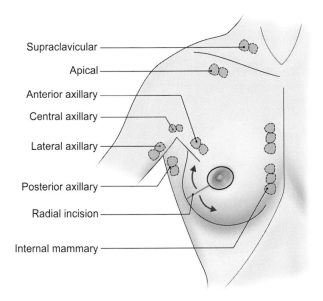

Fig. 3.9: Lymph nodes draining the breast. Radial incision is shown to drain breast abscess

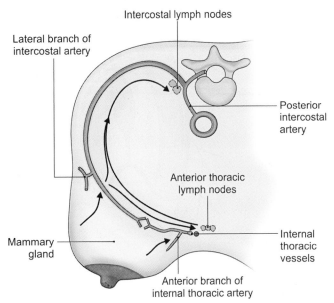

Fig. 3.10: The routes of lymph from the breast. The arrows show the direction of lymph flow

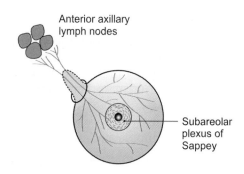

Fig. 3.11: Subareolar lymph plexus of Sappey

5 Lymphatics from the lower and inner quadrants of the breast may communicate with the subdiaphragmatic and subperitoneal lymph plexuses after crossing the costal margin and then piercing the anterior abdominal wall through the upper part of the linea alba.

Development of the Breast

1 The breast develops from an ectodermal thickening, called the *mammary ridge, milk* line, or *line of Schultz* (Fig. 3.13). This ridge extends from the axilla to the groin. It appears during the fourth week of intrauterine life, but in human beings, it disappears over most of its extent persisting only in the pectoral region. The gland is ectodermal, and the stroma mesodermal in origin.

2 The persisting part of the mammary ridge is converted into a *mammary pit*. Secondary buds

(15–20) grow down from the floor of the pit. These buds divide and subdivide to form the lobes of the gland. The entire system is first solid, but is later canalised. At birth or later, the nipple is everted at the site of the original pit.

3 Growth of the mammary glands, at puberty, is caused by oestrogens. Apart from oestrogens, development of secretory alveoli is stimulated by progesterone and by the prolactin hormone of the hypophysis cerebri.

4 Developmental anomalies of the breast are:
   a. *Amastia* (absence of the breast),
   b. *Athelia* (absence of nipple),
   c. *Polymastia* (supernumerary breasts),
   d. *Polythelia* (supernumerary nipples),
   e. *Gynaecomastia* (development of breasts in a male) which occurs in Klinefelter's syndrome.

Histology of Breast

The mammary glands are specialised accessory glands of the skin, which have evolved in mammals to provide nourishment to the young ones. Mammary gland consists of 15–20 lobes with the same number of ducts. Each lobe is made up of many lobules containing acini. Histologically, only lobules are discernible in the gland.

Resting Phase in Non-pregnant Adult Female

The mammary gland in this phase consists mainly of ducts and their branches (Fig. 3.14). The stroma has connective tissue and fat cells.

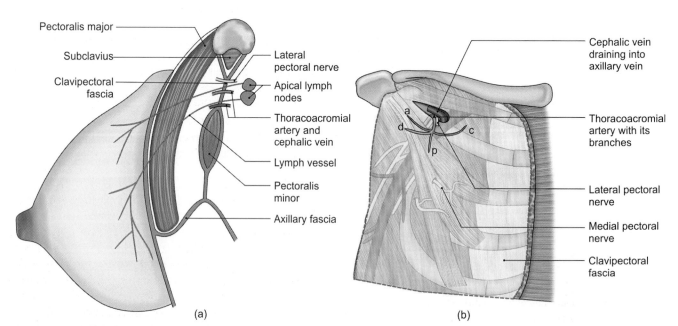

(a)   (b)

Figs 3.12a and b: (a) Deep lymphatics of the breast passing to the apical lymph nodes and the structures piercing the clavipectoral fascia, and (b) structures piercing the clavipectoral fascia. Branches of thoracoacromial artery: a—acromial, p—pectoral, c—clavicular, d—deltoid

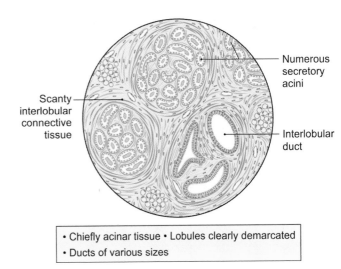

• Chiefly acinar tissue • Lobules clearly demarcated
• Ducts of various sizes

Fig. 3.15: Mammary gland—lactating phase

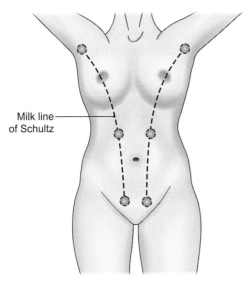

Fig. 3.13: Milk line with possible positions of accessory nipples

The intralobular ducts are usually lined by *low columnar epithelium* resting on a basement membrane. The intralobular connective tissue which is derived from the papillary layer of the dermis is more cellular, containing fibroblasts.

The interlobular connective tissue, which lies between the ducts of adjacent lobules, is derived from the reticular layer of the dermis, and is more fibroreticular in nature. It contains fat lobules.

Lactating Phase

The gland is full of acini with minimum amount of connective tissue. Some acini are lined by tall columnar cells, others by normal columnar cells. The nucleus may be round or oval and is seen in the middle of the cell (Fig. 3.15). Droplets of fat accumulate near the free

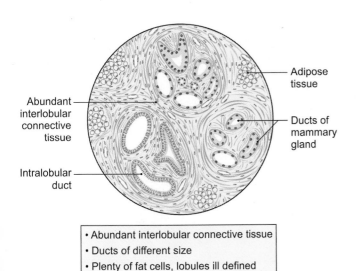

• Abundant interlobular connective tissue
• Ducts of different size
• Plenty of fat cells, lobules ill defined

Fig. 3.14: Mammary gland—resting phase

surface of the cell. Myoepithelial cells may be seen between the basement membrane and secretory cells.

Ducts are also seen but they are fewer in number as compared to the acini. The bigger ducts are lined by stratified columnar or columnar epithelium.

CLINICAL ANATOMY

The upper and outer quadrant of breast is a frequent site of carcinoma (cancer). Several anatomical facts are of importance in diagnosis and treatment of this condition. Abscesses may also form in the breast and may require drainage. The following facts are worthy of note.

- Incisions of breast are usually made radially to avoid cutting the lactiferous ducts (Fig. 3.9).
- Cancer cells may infiltrate the suspensory ligaments. The breast then becomes fixed. Contraction of the ligaments can cause retraction or puckering (folding) of the skin.
- Infiltration of lactiferous ducts and their consequent fibrosis can cause retraction of the nipple.
- Obstruction of superficial lymph vessels by cancer cells may produce oedema of the skin giving rise to an appearance like that of the skin of an orange (*peau d'orange* appearance) (Fig. 3.16).
- Because of communications of the superficial lymphatics of the breast across the midline, cancer may spread from one breast to the other (Fig. 3.17).
- Because of communications of the lymph vessels with those in the abdomen, cancer of the breast may spread to the liver, and cancer cells may 'drop' into the pelvis producing secondaries there (Fig. 3.17).

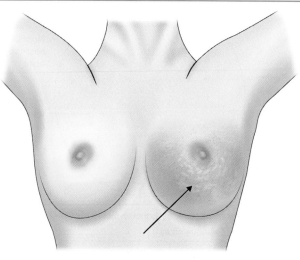

Fig. 3.16: Peau d'orange appearance

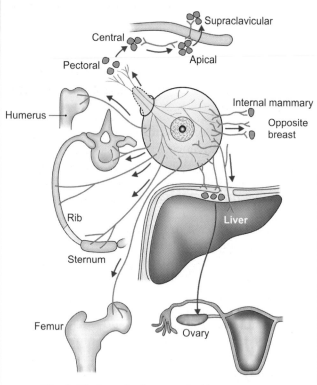

Fig. 3.17: Lymphatic spread of breast cancer

- Apart from the lymphatics, cancer may spread through the segmental veins. In this connection, it is important to know that the veins draining the breast communicate with the vertebral venous plexus of veins. Through these communications, cancer can spread to the vertebrae and to the brain (Fig. 3.18).

- Self-examination of breasts:
  a. Inspect: Symmetry of breasts and nipples.
  b. Change in colour of skin.
  c. Retraction of nipple is a sign of cancer.
  d. Discharge from nipple on squeezing it.
  e. Palpate all four quadrants with palm of hand. Note any palpable lump.
  f. Raise the arm to feel lymph nodes in axilla.
- Mammogram may reveal cancerous mass (Fig. 3.19).
- Fine needle aspiration cytology is safe and quick method of diagnosis of lesion of breast.
- Retracted nipple is a sign of tumour in the breast.
- Size of mammary gland can be increased by putting an implant inside the gland.

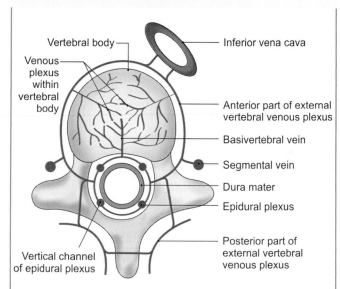

Fig. 3.18: Vertebral system of veins

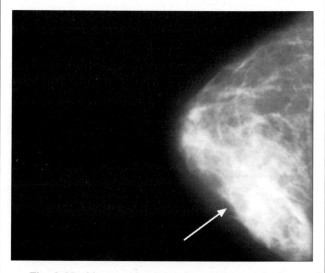

Fig. 3.19: Mammogram showing cancerous lesion

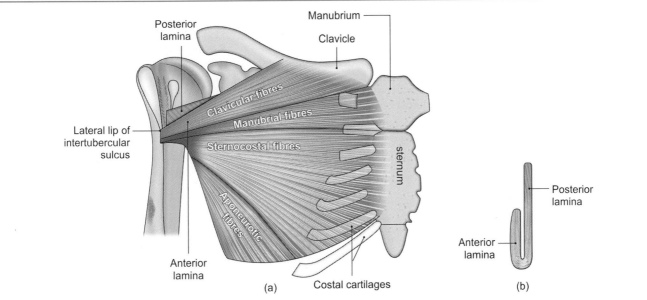

Figs 3.20a and b: (a) The origin and insertion of the pectoralis major muscle, and (b) the bilaminar insertion of the pectoralis major. The anterior lamina is formed by the clavicular and manubrial fibres; the rest of the sternocostal and aponeurotic fibres form the posterior lamina. Part of the posterior lamina is twisted upside down

- Cancer of the mammary glands is the most common cancer in females of all ages. It is more frequently seen in postmenopausal females due to lack of oestrogen hormones.
- Self-examination of the mammary gland is the only way for early diagnosis and appropriate treatment.

DEEP PECTORAL FASCIA

The deep fascia covering the pectoralis major muscle is called the pectoral fascia. It is thin and closely attached to the muscle by numerous septa passing between the fasciculi of the muscle. It is attached *superiorly* to the clavicle, and *anteriorly* to the sternum. *Superolaterally*, it passes over the infraclavicular fossa and deltopectoral groove to become continuous with the fascia covering the deltoid. *Inferolaterally*, the fascia curves round the inferolateral border of the pectoralis major to become continuous with the axillary fascia. *Inferiorly*, it is continuous with the fascia over the thorax and the rectus sheath.

MUSCLES OF THE PECTORAL REGION

DISSECTION

Identify the extensive pectoralis major muscle in the pectoral region and the prominent deltoid muscle on the lateral aspect of the shoulder joint and upper arm.

Demarcate the deltopectoral groove by removing the deep fascia. Now identify the cephalic vein, a small artery and few lymph nodes in the groove.

Clean the fascia over the pectoralis major muscle and look for its attachments. Divide the clavicular head of the muscle and reflect it laterally. Medial and lateral pectoral nerves will be seen supplying the muscle.

Make a vertical incision 5 to 6 cm from the lateral border of sternum and reflect its sternocostal head laterally.

Identify the pectoralis minor muscle under the central part of the pectoralis major. Note clavipectoral fascia extending between pectoralis minor muscle and the clavicle bone.

Identify the structures piercing the clavipectoral fascia: These are cephalic vein, thoracoacromial artery and lateral pectoral nerve. If some fine vessels are also seen, these are the lymphatic channels.

Also, identify the serratus anterior muscle showing serrated digitations on the side of the chest wall.

Introduction

Muscles of the pectoral region are described in Tables 3.1 and 3.2. Some additional features are given below.

Pectoralis Major

Structures under Cover of Pectoralis Major

a. *Bones and cartilages:* Sternum, costal cartilages and ribs.

Table 3.1: Muscles of the pectoral region

Muscle	Origin	Insertion
Pectoralis major (Fig. 3.20)	• Anterior surface of medial two-thirds of clavicle • Half the breadth of anterior surface of manubrium and sternum up to 6th costal cartilages • Second to sixth costal cartilages, sternal end of 6th rib • Aponeurosis of the external oblique muscle of abdomen	It is inserted by a bilaminar tendon on the lateral lip of the bicipital groove in form of 'U' The two laminae are continuous with each other inferiorly
Pectoralis minor (Fig. 3.21a)	• 3, 4, 5 ribs, near the costochondral junction • Intervening fascia covering external intercostal muscles	Medial border and upper surface of the coracoid process
Subclavius (Fig. 3.21b)	First rib at the costochondral junction	Subclavian groove in the middle one-third of the clavicle

Table 3.2: Nerve supply and actions of muscles

Muscle	Nerve supply	Actions

Pectoralis major (Fig. 3.20)	Medial and lateral pectoral nerves
	Medial pectoral reaches it after piercing pectoralis minor. The lateral pectoral reaches the muscle by piercing clavipectoral fascia
		• Acting as a whole the muscle causes: Adduction and medial rotation of the shoulder joint (arm)
		• Clavicular part produces: Flexion of the arm
		• Sternocostal part is used in
		  – Extension of flexed arm against resistance
		  – Climbing
		• Acts as an accessory muscle during inspiration when the humerus is fixed in abduction.

Pectoralis minor (Fig. 3.21a)	Medial and lateral pectoral nerves (Fig. 3.22a)	• Draws the scapula forward (with serratus anterior) • Depresses the point of the shoulder • Helps in forced inspiration
Subclavius (Fig. 3.21b)	Nerve to subclavius from upper trunk of brachial plexus	Steadies the clavicle during movements of the shoulder joint. Forms a cushion for axillary vessels and divisions of trunks of brachial plexus

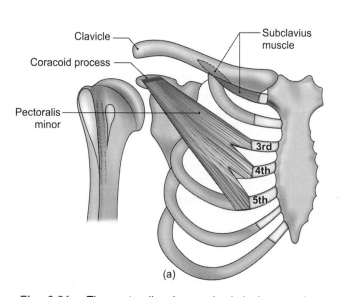

Figs 3.21a: The pectoralis minor and subclavius muscles

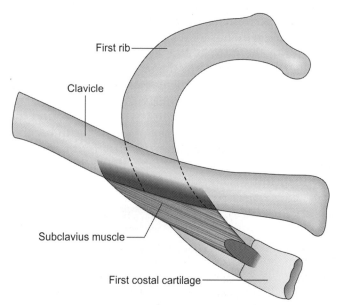

Fig. 3.21b: Subclavius muscle

b. *Fascia:* Clavipectoral.
c. *Muscles:* Subclavius, pectoralis minor, serratus anterior, intercostals and upper parts of the biceps brachii and coracobrachialis.
d. *Vessels:* Axillary.
e. *Nerves:* Cords of brachial plexus with their branches.

Bilaminar Tendon of Pectoralis Major

The muscle is inserted by a bilaminar tendon into the lateral lip of the intertubercular sulcus of the humerus.

The anterior lamina is thicker and shorter than the posterior. It receives two strata of muscle fibres: Superficial fibres arising from the clavicle and deep fibres arising from the manubrium (Fig. 3.20).

The posterior lamina is thinner and longer than the anterior lamina. It is formed by fibres from the front of the sternum, 2nd–6th costal cartilages, sternal end of 6th rib and from the aponeurosis of the external oblique muscle of the abdomen. Out of these only the fibres from the sternum and aponeurosis are twisted around the lower border of the rest of the muscle. The twisted fibres form the anterior axillary fold. The costal fibres do not twist.

These fibres pass upwards and laterally to get inserted successively higher into the posterior lamina of the tendon. Fibres arising lowest, find an opportunity to get inserted the highest and form a crescentic fold which fuses with the capsule of the shoulder joint.

Clinical Testing

i. The clavicular head of the pectoralis major can be tested by attempting to lift a heavy table/rod. The sternocostal head can be tested by trying to depress a heavy table/rod.
ii. The clavicular head is made prominent by flexing the arm to a right angle. The sternocostal head can be tested by extending the flexed arm against resistance.
iii. Sternocostal head is made prominent by abducting arm to 60° and then touching the opposite hip.
iv. Pressing the fists against each other makes the whole muscle prominent (Fig. 3.22b).

Clavipectoral Fascia

Clavipectoral fascia is a fibrous sheet situated deep to the clavicular portion of the pectoralis major muscle. It extends from the clavicle above to the axillary fascia below. Its upper part splits to enclose the *subclavius muscle* (Fig. 3.12a). The posterior lamina is fused to the investing layer of the deep cervical fascia and to the *axillary sheath*. Inferiorly, the clavipectoral fascia splits to enclose the pectoralis minor muscle (Fig. 3.12a). Medially, it is attached to external intercostal muscle of upper intercostal spaces and laterally to coracoid process. Below this muscle, it continues as the

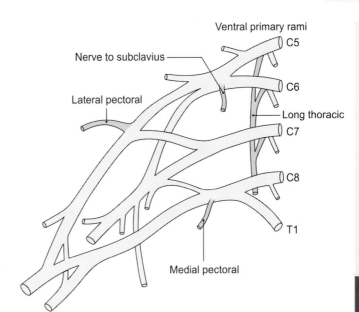

Fig. 3.22a: Nerve supply of pectorals, subclavius and serratus anterior

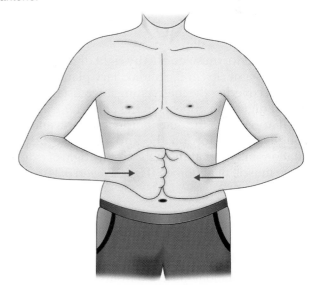

Fig. 3.22b: Pectoralis major being tested

suspensory ligament which is attached to the dome of the axillary fascia, and helps to keep it pulled up.

The clavipectoral fascia is pierced by the following structures.

i. Lateral pectoral nerve (Figs 3.12a and b).
ii. Cephalic vein.
iii. Thoracoacromial artery.
iv. Lymphatics passing from the breast and pectoral region to the apical group of axillary lymph nodes (Fig. 3.12a).

Serratus Anterior

Serratus anterior muscle is not strictly muscle of the pectoral region, but it is convenient to consider it here. It is also called boxer's muscle.

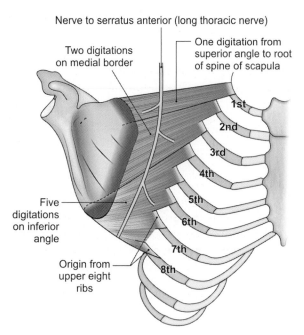

Fig. 3.23: The serratus anterior

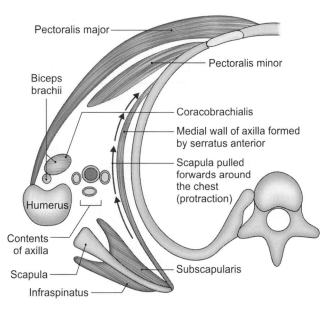

Fig. 3.24: Horizontal section through the axilla showing the position of the serratus anterior

Origin

Serratus anterior muscle arises by eight digitations from the upper eight ribs in the midaxillary plane and from the fascia covering the intervening intercostal muscles. The first digitation appears in the posterior triangle of neck. It arises from the outer border of 1st rib and from a rough impression on the 2nd rib. Also 5th–8th digitations interdigitate with the costal origin of external oblique muscle of abdomen (Figs 3.23 and 3.24).

Insertion

All 8 digitations pass backwards around the chest wall.

The muscle is inserted into the costal surface of the scapula along its medial border.

The first digitation is inserted from the superior angle to the root of the spine.

The next two digitations are inserted lower down on the medial border.

The lower five digitations are inserted into a large triangular area over the inferior angle.

Nerve Supply

The nerve to the serratus anterior is a branch of the brachial plexus. It arises from roots C5, C6 and C7 and is also called long thoracic nerve. The nerve enters through the apex of axilla behind 1st part of axillary artery to reach the medial wall of axilla. It lies on the surface of the muscle (Figs 3.22a and 3.23).

• C5 root supplies 1st and 2nd digitations
• C6 root supplies 3rd and 4th digitations
• C7 root supplies 5th to 8th digitations

Actions

1 Along with the pectoralis minor, the muscle pulls the scapula forwards around the chest wall to protract the upper limb (in pushing and punching movements).
2 The fibres inserted into the inferior angle of the scapula pull it forwards and rotate the scapula so that the glenoid cavity is turned upwards. In this action, the serratus anterior is helped by the trapezius which pulls the acromion upwards and backwards (see Fig. 10.6c).
3 The muscle steadies the scapula during weight carrying.
4 It helps in forced inspiration.

Additional Features

1 Paralysis of the serratus anterior produces 'winging of scapula' in which the inferior angle and the medial border of the scapula are unduly prominent. The patient is unable to do any pushing action, nor can he raise his arm above the head. Any attempt to do these movements makes the inferior angle of the scapula still more prominent.

Mnemonics

Branches of any artery/nerve M-CAT

M—Muscular
C—Cutaneous
A—Articular
T—Terminal

2 *Clinical testing:* Forward pressure with the hands against a wall, or against resistance offered by the examiner, makes the medial border and the inferior angle of the scapula prominent (winging of scapula) if the serratus anterior is paralysed (*see* Fig. 2.12).

FACTS TO REMEMBER

- Pectoralis major forms part of the bed for the mammary gland. 75% of lymph from mammary gland drains into axillary; 20% into parasternal and 5% into intercostal lymph nodes.
- The sternocostal head of pectoralis major causes extension of the flexed arm against resistance.
- Pectoralis minor divides the axillary artery into three parts.

CLINICOANATOMICAL PROBLEM

A 45-year-old women complained of a firm painless mass in the upper lateral quadrant of her left breast. The nipple was also raised. Axillary lymph nodes were palpable and firm. It was diagnosed as cancer breast.
- Where does the lymph from upper lateral quadrant drain?
- What causes the retraction of the nipple?

Ans: The lymph from the upper lateral quadrant drains mainly into the pectoral group of axillary lymph nodes. The lymphatics also drain into supraclavicular and infraclavicular lymph nodes.

Blockage of some lymph vessels by the cancer cells causes oedema of skin with dimpled appearance. This is called *peau d'orange*. When cancer cells invade the suspensory ligaments, glandular tissue or the ducts, there is retraction of the nipple.

FREQUENTLY ASKED QUESTIONS

1. Describe mammary gland under following headings: Extent, relations, blood supply, lymphatic drainage and clinical anatomy.
2. Describe pectoralis major muscle under following headings: Origin, insertion, nerve supply, structures deep to it, actions and clinical anatomy

3. Write short notes/enumerate
   a. Structures piercing clavipectoral fascia
   b. Winging of scapula
   c. Origin and insertion of pectoralis minor muscle
   d. Root value of long thoracic nerve

MULTIPLE CHOICE QUESTIONS

1. Which of the following muscle does not form deep relation of the mammary gland?
   a. Pectoralis major
   b. Pectoralis minor
   c. Serratus anterior
   d. External oblique of abdomen

2. One of the following structures does not pierce clavipectoral fascia:
   a. Cephalic vein
   b. Thoracoacromial artery
   c. Medial pectoral nerve
   d. Lateral pectoral nerve

3. Which of the following arteries does not supply the mammary gland?
   a. Superior thoracic
   b. Thoracodorsal branch of subscapular artery
   c. Lateral thoracic artery
   d. Thoracoacromial artery

4. Axillary sheath is derived from which fascia?
   a. Pretracheal
   b. Prevertebral
   c. Investing layer of cervical
   d. Pharyngobasilar

5. Winging of scapula occurs in paralysis of:
   a. Pectoralis major
   b. Pectoralis minor
   c. Latissimus dorsi
   d. Serratus anterior

ANSWERS

1. b   2. c   3. b   4. b   5. d

Axilla

Tailors know about the asymmetry of the arm and stitch the right sleeve a little looser than left

INTRODUCTION

The axilla (Latin *armpit*) is a pyramidal space situated between the upper part of the arm and the chest wall. It resembles a four-sided pyramid, and has the following.

i. An apex
ii. A base
iii. Four walls: Anterior, posterior, medial and lateral.

The axilla is disposed obliquely in such a way that the apex is directed upwards and medially towards the root of the neck, and the base is directed downwards.

DISSECTION

Place a rectangular wooden block under the neck and shoulder region of cadaver (Fig. 4.1). Ensure that the block supports the body firmly. Abduct the limb at right angles to the trunk; and strap the wrist firmly on block projecting towards your side. In continuation with earlier dissection, reflect the lower skin flap till the posterior axillary fold made up by the subscapularis, teres major, and latissimus dorsi muscles is seen. Clean the fat, and remove the lymph nodes and superficial veins to reach depth of the armpit. Identify two muscles arising from the tip of the coracoid process of scapula; out of these, the short head of biceps brachii muscle lies on the lateral side and the coracobrachialis on the medial side.

The pectoral muscles with the clavipectoral fascia form anterior boundary of the region.

Look for upper three intercostal muscles and serratus anterior muscle which make the medial wall of axilla.

Clean and identify the axillary vessels. Trace the course of the branches of the axillary artery.

Reflect the upper skin flap on the arm till the incision already given at its junction of upper one-third and lower two-thirds.

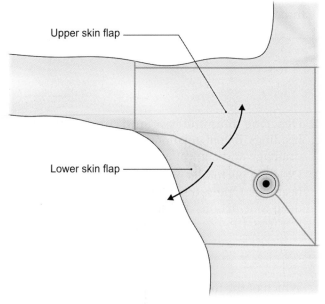

Fig. 4.1: Dissection of axilla

BOUNDARIES

Apex/Cervicoaxillary Canal

It is directed upwards and medially towards the root of the neck.

It is truncated (not pointed), and corresponds to a triangular interval bounded

i. Anteriorly, by the posterior surface of clavicle.
ii. Posteriorly, by the superior border of the scapula and medial aspect of coracoid process.
iii. Medially, it is bounded by the outer border of the first rib.

This oblique passage is called the cervicoaxillary canal (Figs 4.2a to c). The axillary artery, axillary vein and the brachial plexus enter the axilla through this canal.

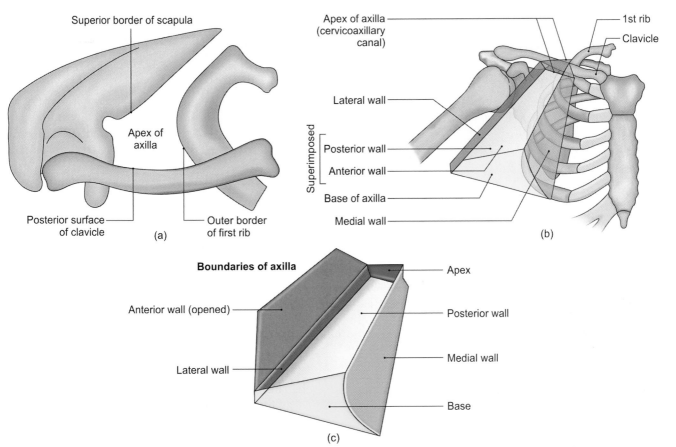

Figs 4.2a to c: (a) Boundaries of the apex of the axilla, (b) walls of the axilla, and (c) opened up axilla

Base or Floor

It is directed downwards, and is formed by skin, superficial and axillary fasciae. It is convex upwards in congruence with concavity of axilla.

Anterior Wall

It is formed by the following.
  i. The pectoralis major in front (Fig. 4.3).
 ii. The clavipectoral fascia
iii. Pectoralis minor.

Posterior Wall

It is formed by the following.
  i. Subscapularis above (Fig. 4.4),
 ii. Teres major and
iii. Latissimus dorsi below.

Medial Wall

It is convex laterally and formed by the following.
  i. Upper four ribs with their intercostal muscles.
 ii. Upper part of the serratus anterior muscle (Fig. 4.5).

Lateral Wall

It is very narrow because the anterior and posterior walls converge on it. It is formed by the following.

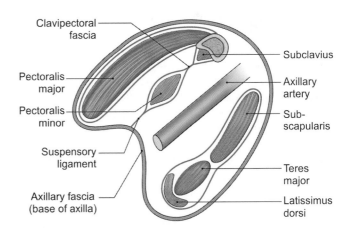

Fig. 4.3: Anterior and posterior walls of the axilla with the axillary artery

  i. Upper part of the shaft of the humerus in the region of the bicipital groove, and
 ii. Coracobrachialis and short head of the biceps brachii (Fig. 4.5).

CONTENTS OF AXILLA

1 Axillary artery and its branches (Fig. 4.5).
2 Axillary vein and its tributaries.
3 Infraclavicular part of the brachial plexus.

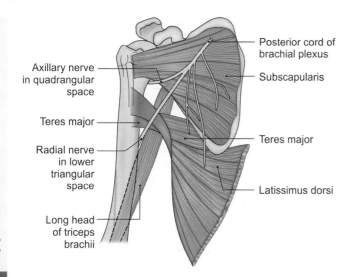

Fig. 4.4: Muscles forming the posterior wall of axilla with their nerve supply

4 Five groups of axillary lymph nodes and the associated lymphatics.
5 The long thoracic and intercostobrachial nerves.
6 Axillary fat and areolar tissue in which the other contents are embedded.

Layout

1 Axillary artery and the brachial plexus of nerves run from the apex to the base along the lateral wall of the axilla, nearer the anterior wall than the posterior wall.
2 The thoracic branches of the axillary artery lie in contact with the pectoral muscles, the lateral thoracic vessels running along the lower border of the pectoralis minor.

3 a. The subscapular vessels run along the lower border of the subscapularis.
  b. The subscapular nerve and the thoracodorsal nerve (nerve to latissimus dorsi) cross the anterior surface of the subscapularis (Fig. 4.4).
  c. The circumflex scapular vessels wind round the lateral border of the scapula (*see* Fig. 6.12).
  d. The axillary nerve and the posterior circumflex humeral vessels pass backwards close to the surgical neck of the humerus.
4 a. The medial wall of the axilla is avascular, except for a few small branches from the superior thoracic artery.
  b. The long thoracic nerve (nerve to the serratus anterior) descends on the surface of the muscle (Fig. 4.5).
  c. The intercostobrachial nerve pierces the antero-superior part of the medial wall and crosses the spaces to reach the medial side of the arm (*see* Fig. 3.3).
5 The axillary lymph nodes are 20 to 30 in number, and are arranged in five sets.
  a. The anterior group lies along the lower border of the pectoralis minor, on the lateral thoracic vessels.
  b. The posterior group lies along the lower margin of the posterior wall along the subscapular vessels (Fig. 4.11).
  c. The lateral group lies posteromedial to the axillary vein.
  d. The central group lies in the fat of the axilla.
  e. The apical group lies behind and above the pectoralis minor, medial to the axillary vein.

AXILLARY ARTERY

Axillary artery is the continuation of the subclavian artery. It extends from the outer border of the first rib

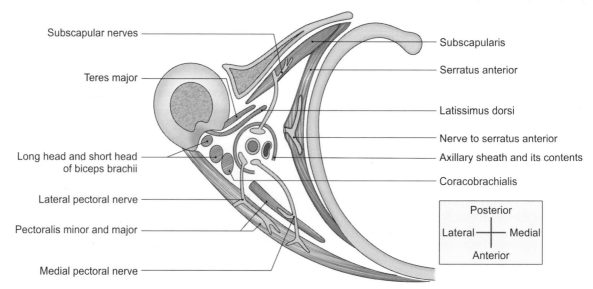

Fig. 4.5: Walls and contents of axilla

to the lower border of the teres major muscle where it continues as the brachial artery. Its direction varies with the position of the arm.

The pectoralis minor muscle crosses the artery and divides it into three parts (Fig. 4.6).

 i. First part, superior (proximal) to the muscle.
 ii. Second part, posterior (deep) to the muscle.
 iii. Third part, inferior (distal) to the muscle.

RELATIONS OF AXILLARY ARTERY

Relations of First Part

Anterior

1 Skin
2 Superficial fascia, platysma and supraclavicular nerves
3 Deep fascia
4 Clavicular part of the pectoralis major (Fig. 4.7a)

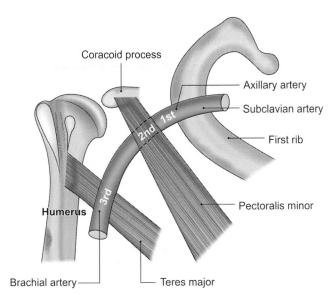

Fig. 4.6: The extent and parts of the axillary artery

5 Clavipectoral fascia with cephalic vein, lateral pectoral nerve, and thoracoacromial artery.
6 Loop of communication between the lateral and medial pectoral nerves.

Posterior

1 First intercostal space with the external intercostal muscle.
2 First and second digitations of the serratus anterior with the nerve to serratus anterior.
3 Medial cord of brachial plexus with its medial pectoral branch.

Lateral

Lateral and posterior cords of the brachial plexus.

Medial

Axillary vein: The first part of the axillary artery is enclosed (together with the brachial plexus) in the axillary sheath, derived from the prevertebral layer of deep cervical fascia.

Relations of Second Part

Anterior

1 Skin
2 Superficial fascia
3 Deep fascia
4 Pectoralis major
5 Pectoralis minor (Fig. 4.7b)

Posterior

1 Posterior cord of brachial plexus
2 Subscapularis

Lateral

1 Lateral cord of brachial plexus
2 Coracobrachialis (Fig. 4.8)

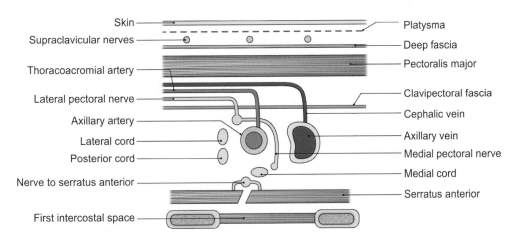

Fig. 4.7a: Relations of first part of axillary artery

Upper Limb

Section 1

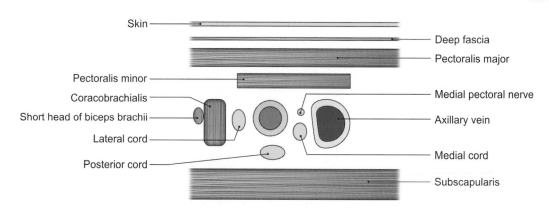

Fig. 4.7b: Relations of second part of axillary artery

Medial

1 Medial cord of brachial plexus
2 Medial pectoral nerve
3 Axillary vein

Relations of Third Part

Anterior

1 Skin
2 Superficial fascia

3 Deep fascia
4 In the upper part, there are the pectoralis major and the medial root of the median nerve (Fig. 4.7c).

Posterior

1 Radial nerve (Fig. 4.9)
2 Axillary nerve in the upper part
3 Subscapularis in the upper part
4 Tendons of the latissimus dorsi and the teres major in the lower part (Fig. 4.7d).

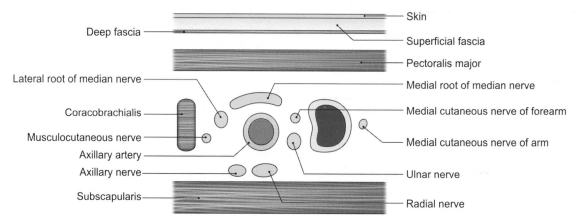

Fig. 4.7c: Relations of third part of axillary artery (upper part)

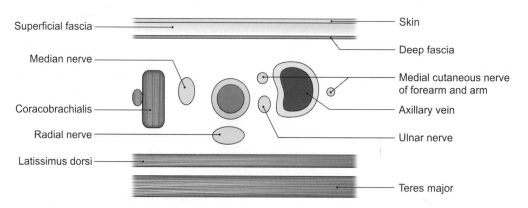

Fig. 4.7d: Relations of third part of axillary artery (lower part)

Lateral

1 Coracobrachialis
2 Musculocutaneous nerve in the upper part (Fig. 4.8)
3 Lateral root of median nerve in the upper part
4 Trunk of median nerve in the lower part.

Medial

1 Axillary vein
2 Medial cutaneous nerve of the forearm and ulnar nerve, between the axillary artery and the axillary vein
3 Medial cutaneous nerve of arm, medial to the axillary vein (Fig. 4.9).

Branches

The axillary artery gives six branches. One branch arises from the first part, two branches from the second part, and three branches from the third part. These are as follows (Fig. 4.10).

Superior Thoracic Artery

Superior thoracic artery is a very small branch which arises from the first part of the axillary artery (near the subclavius). It runs downwards, forwards and medially, passes between the two pectoral muscles, and ends by supplying these muscles and the thoracic wall (Fig. 4.10).

Thoracoacromial (Acromiothoracic) Artery

Thoracoacromial artery is a branch from the second part of the axillary artery. It emerges at the upper border of

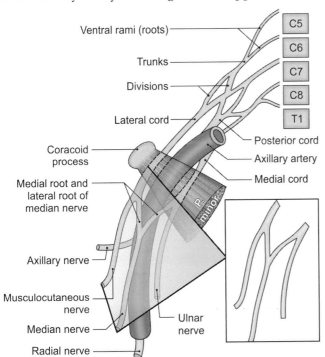

Fig. 4.8: Relation of the brachial plexus to the axillary artery. C5–C8 and T1 are anterior primary rami of respective spinal segments

Ventral rami (roots) — C5, C6
Trunks
Divisions — C7, C8, T1
Lateral cord
Posterior cord
Coracoid process
Axillary artery
Medial root and lateral root of median nerve
Medial cord
P. minor
Axillary nerve
Musculocutaneous nerve
Median nerve
Ulnar nerve
Radial nerve

the pectoralis minor, pierces the clavipectoral fascia, and soon divides into the following four terminal branches.

a. The *pectoral branch* passes between the pectoral muscles, and supplies these muscles as well as the breast.
b. The *deltoid branch* runs in the deltopectoral groove, along with the cephalic vein.
c. The *acromial branch* crosses the coracoid process and ends by joining the anastomoses over the acromion.
d. The *clavicular branch* runs superomedially deep to the pectoralis major, and supplies the acromioclavicular joint and subclavius.

Lateral Thoracic Artery

Lateral thoracic artery is a branch of the second part of the axillary artery. It emerges at, and runs along, the lower border of the pectoralis minor in close relation with the anterior group of axillary lymph nodes.

In females, the artery is large and gives off the lateral mammary branches to the breast.

Anterior Circumflex Humeral Artery

Anterior circumflex humeral artery is a small branch arising from the third part of the axillary artery, at the lower border of the subscapularis.

It passes laterally in front of the intertubercular sulcus of the humerus, and anastomoses with the posterior circumflex humeral artery, to form an arterial circle round the surgical neck of the humerus.

It gives off an ascending branch which runs in the intertubercular sulcus, and supplies the head of the humerus and shoulder joint.

Posterior Circumflex Humeral Artery

Posterior circumflex humeral artery is much larger than the anterior artery. It arises from the third part of the axillary artery at the lower border of the subscapularis. It runs backwards, accompanied by the axillary nerve, passes through the *quadrangular intermuscular* space, and ends by anastomosing with the anterior circumflex humeral artery around the surgical neck of the humerus (*see* Figs 6.6 and 6.12).

It supplies the shoulder joint, the deltoid, and the muscles bounding the quadrangular space.

It gives off a descending branch which anastomoses with the ascending branch of the *profunda brachii artery*.

Subscapular Artery

Subscapular artery is the largest branch of the axillary artery, arising from its third part. It runs along the lower border of the subscapularis to terminate near the inferior angle of the scapula. It supplies the latissimus dorsi and the serratus anterior.

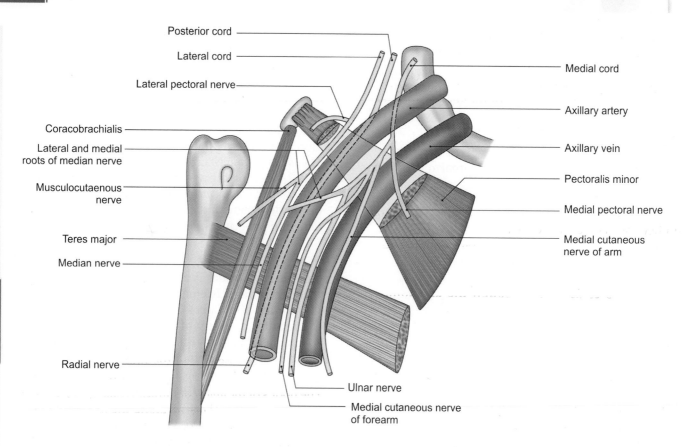

Fig. 4.9: Relations of branches of brachial plexus to the axillary vessels

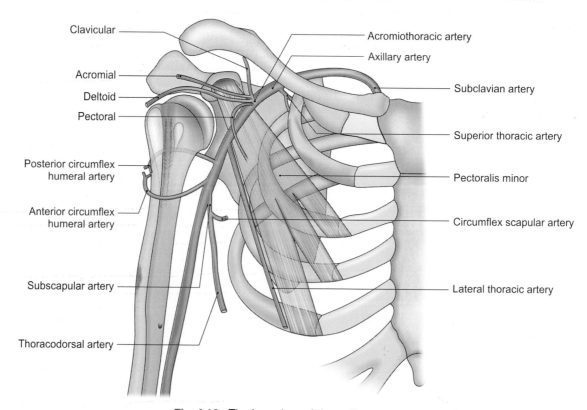

Fig. 4.10: The branches of the axillary artery

It gives off a large branch, the *circumflex scapular artery*, which is larger than the continuation of the main artery. This branch passes through the upper triangular intermuscular space, winds round the lateral border of the scapula between two slips of the teres minor, and gives a branch to the subscapular fossa, and another branch to the infraspinous fossa, both of which take part in the anastomoses around the scapula (*see* Fig. 6.12).

Anastomoses and Collateral Circulation

The branches of the axillary artery anastomose with one another and with branches derived from neighbouring arteries (internal thoracic, intercostal, suprascapular, deep branch of transverse cervical, profunda brachii). When the axillary artery is blocked, a collateral circulation is established through the anastomoses around the scapula which links the first part of the subclavian artery with the third part of the axillary artery (apart from communications with the posterior intercostal arteries) (*see* Fig. 6.12).

AXILLARY VEIN

The axillary vein is the continuation of the basilic vein. The axillary vein is joined by the venae comitantes of the brachial artery a little above the lower border of the teres major. It lies on the medial side of the axillary artery (Fig. 4.9). At the outer border of the first rib, it becomes the subclavian vein. It receives 5 out of 6 tributaries corresponding to the branches of axillary artery and the cephalic vein. Veins accompanying branches of thoracoacromial artery drain directly into the cephalic vein. Lateral thoracic vein of UL is joined to superficial epigastric vein of LL by thoracoepigastric vein enabling blood to return to heart in blockage of inferior vena cava (*see* Flowcharts 14.1 and 14.2).

AXILLARY LYMPH NODES

The axillary lymph nodes are scattered in the fibrofatty tissue of the axilla. They are divided into five groups.

1 The nodes of the *anterior (pectoral) group* lie along the lateral thoracic vessels, i.e. along the lower border of the pectoralis minor. They receive lymph from the upper half of the anterior wall of the trunk, and from the major part of the breast (Fig. 4.11).

2 The nodes of the *posterior (scapular) group* lie along the subscapular vessels, on the posterior fold of the axilla. They receive lymph from the posterior wall of the upper half of the trunk, and from the axillary tail of the breast.

3 The nodes of the *lateral group* lie along the upper part of the humerus, medial to the axillary vein. They receive lymph from the upper limb.

4 The nodes of the *central group* lie in the fat of the upper axilla. They receive lymph from the preceding

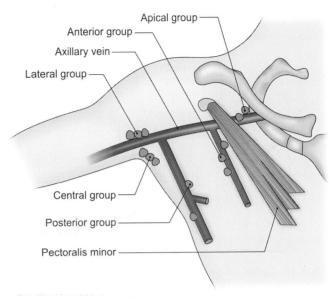

Fig. 4.11: The axillary lymph nodes

groups and drain into the apical group. They receive some direct vessels from the floor of the axilla. The intercostobrachial nerve is closely related to them.

5 The nodes of the *apical* or *infraclavicular group* lie deep to the clavipectoral fascia, along the axillary vessels. They receive lymph from the central group, from the upper part of the breast, and from the thumb and its web. The lymphatics from the thumb accompany the cephalic vein.

CLINICAL ANATOMY

- The axilla has abundant axillary hair. Infection of the hair follicles and sebaceous glands gives rise to boils which are common in this area.
- The axillary lymph nodes drain lymph not only from the upper limb but also from the breast and the anterior and posterior body walls above the level of the umbilicus. Therefore, infections or malignant growths in any part of their territory of drainage give rise to involvement of the axillary lymph nodes (Fig. 4.12). Bimanual examination of these lymph nodes is, therefore, important in clinical practice. Left axillary nodes to be palpated by right hand. Right axillary nodes have to be palpated by left hand.
- An axillary abscess should be incised through the floor of the axilla, midway between the anterior and posterior axillary folds, and nearer to the medial wall in order to avoid injury to the main vessels running along the anterior, posterior and lateral walls.
- Axillary arterial pulsations can be felt against the lower part of the lateral wall of the axilla.
  In order to check bleeding from the distal part of

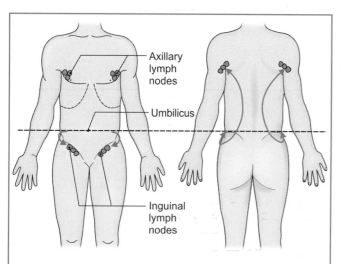

Fig. 4.12: Lymph above umbilicus drains into axillary lymph nodes while below umbilicus drains into inguinal group

the limb (in injuries, operations and amputations), the artery can be effectively compressed against the humerus in the lower part of the lateral wall of the axilla.

SPINAL NERVE

Each spinal nerve is formed by union of dorsal root and ventral root. Dorsal root is sensory and is characterised by the presence of spinal or dorsal root ganglion and enters the dorsal horn and posterior funiculus of spinal cord. Ventral root is motor, arises from anterior horn cells of spinal cord.

The motor and sensory fibres get united in the spinal nerve which divides into short dorsal ramus and

long ventral ramus. Both the rami thus contain motor and sensory fibres. In addition, these also manage to obtain sympathetic fibres via grey ramus communicans (Fig. 4.13).

Only the ventral primary rami form plexuses. Brachial plexus is formed by ventral primary rami or ventral rami of C5–C8 and T1 segments of spinal cord.

BRACHIAL PLEXUS

DISSECTION

After cleaning the branches of the axillary artery, proceed to clean the brachial plexus. It is formed by the ventral primary rami of the lower four cervical (C5–C8) and the first thoracic (T1) nerves. The first and second parts of the axillary artery are related to the cords; and third part is related to the branches of the plexus. Study the description of the brachial plexus before proceeding further.

The plexus consists of roots, trunks, divisions, cords and branches (Fig. 4.14).

Roots

These are constituted by the anterior primary rami of spinal nerves C5–C8 and T1, with contributions from the anterior primary rami of C4 and T2 (Fig. 4.8).

The origin of the plexus may shift by one segment either upward or downward, resulting in a prefixed or postfixed plexus respectively.

In a prefixed plexus, the contribution by C4 is large and that from T2 is often absent.

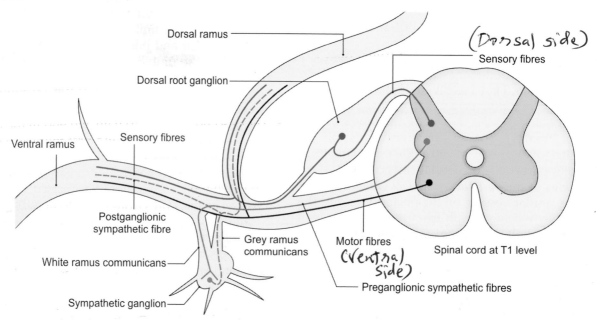

Fig. 4.13: Mixed fibres of root of brachial plexus

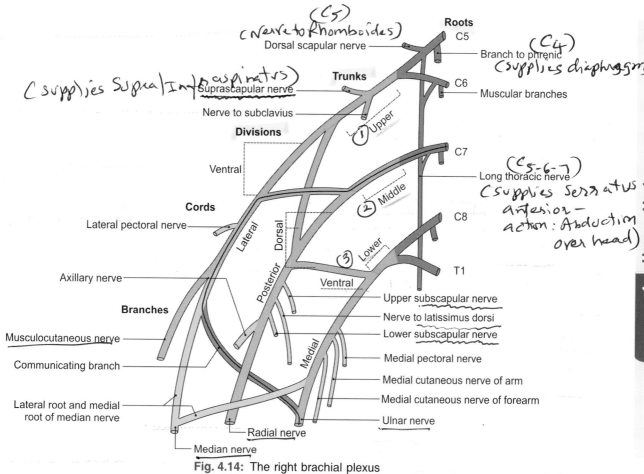

Fig. 4.14: The right brachial plexus

Handwritten annotations on figure:
(C5) (Nerve to Rhomboides) Dorsal scapular nerve
(C4) (supplies diaphragm) Branch to phrenic
(supplies Supra|Infraspinatus) Suprascapular nerve
(C5-6-7) (supplies Serratus anterior – action: Abduction over head) Long thoracic nerve

Upper Limb — Section 1

In a postfixed plexus, the contribution by T1 is large, T2 is always present, C4 is absent, and C5 is reduced in size. The roots join to form trunks as follows:

Roots and Trunks—Supraclavicular Part

Roots C5 and C6 join to form the *upper* trunk. Root C7 forms the *middle* trunk. Roots C8 and T1 join to form the *lower* trunk.

Divisions of the Trunks—Retroclavicular Part

Each trunk (three in number) divides into ventral and dorsal divisions (which ultimately supply the anterior and posterior aspects of the limb). These divisions join to form cords.

Cords and Branches—Infraclavicular Part

i. The lateral cord is formed by the union of ventral divisions of the upper and middle trunks (two divisions).

ii. The medial cord is formed by the ventral division of the lower trunk (one division).

iii. The posterior cord is formed by union of the dorsal divisions of all the three trunks (three divisions).

Sympathetic Innervation

1 Sympathetic nerves for the upper limb are derived from spinal segments T2 to T6. Most of the vasoconstrictor fibres supplying the arteries emerge from segments T2 and T3.

2 The preganglionic fibres arise from lateral horn cells and emerge from the spinal cord through ventral nerve roots.

3 Passing through white rami communicantes, they reach the sympathetic chain.

4 They ascend within the chain and end in the middle cervical, inferior cervical and first thoracic ganglia.

5 Postganglionic fibres from middle cervical ganglion pass through grey rami communicantes to reach C5, C6 nerve roots.

6 Postganglionic fibres from inferior cervical ganglion pass through grey rami communicantes to reach C7, and C8 nerve roots.

7 Postganglionic fibres from first thoracic sympathetic ganglion pass through grey rami communicantes to reach T1 nerve roots.

8 The arteries of skeletal muscles are dilated by sympathetic activity. For the skin, however, these nerves are vasomotor, sudomotor and pilomotor.

Vasomotor: Constricts the arterioles of skin.

Sudomotor: Increases the sweat secretion.

Pilomotor: Contracts the arrector pilorum muscle to cause erection of the hair.

Branches

The roots value of each branch is given in brackets.

Branches of the Roots

The roots value of each branch is given in brackets.

1 Nerve to serratus anterior (long thoracic nerve) (C5–C7). It only supplies serratus anterior muscle, one of the key muscles, for overhead abduction.
2 Nerve to rhomboids (dorsal scapular nerve) (C5). This nerve supplies rhomboid minor and rhomboid major muscles, responsible for retraction of the shoulder girdle.
3 Branches to longus colli and scaleni muscles (C5–C8) and branch to phrenic nerve (C4). The root of phrenic nerve from C5 is small one, the main root is from C4. Phrenic nerve is the sole motor nerve supply of thoracoabdominal diaphragm. In addition, it carries afferent fibres from mediastinal pleura, fibrous pericardium and part of the parietal peritoneum.

Branches of the Trunks

These arise only from the upper trunk which gives two branches:

1 Suprascapular (C5, C6). This nerve supplies supraspinatus and infraspinatus muscles.
2 Nerve to subclavius (C5, C6). It supplies the small subclavius muscles. It may give a root for phrenic nerve.

Branches of the Cords

Branches of lateral cord

1 Lateral pectoral (C5, C7). This nerve supplies both pectoralis major and pectoralis minor muscles.
2 Musculocutaneous (C5, C7). This is the nerve of muscles of front of forearm, i.e. coracobrachialis both the long and short heads of biceps brachii and the brachialis muscles.
3 Lateral root of median (C5–C7). It joins the medial root of median nerve. Median nerve is the chief nerve of the muscles of front of forearm and of muscles of thenar eminence.

Branches of medial cord

1 Medial pectoral (C8, T1). It also supplies both the pectoralis minor and pectoralis major muscles.
2 Medial cutaneous nerve of arm (C8, T1). Carries sensory impulses from a small area of medial side of arm.

3 Medial cutaneous nerve of forearm (C8, T1) carries sensory impulses from large area of medial side of the forearm.
4 Ulnar (C7, C8, T1). C7 fibres reach by a communicating branch from lateral root of median nerve. This is the nerve of one and a half muscles of front of forearm and 15 intrinsic muscles of the palm.
5 Medial root of median (C8, T1). It joins the lateral root and gets distributed with branches of median nerve.

Branches of posterior cord (Supplies back of Upper limb)

1 Upper subscapular (C5, C6): This nerve supplies large multipennate subscapularis muscles.
2 Nerve to latissimus dorsi (C6–C8). Only supplies muscles of its name. It is also called thoracodorsal nerve.
3 Lower subscapular (C5, C6). It helps upper subscapular nerve in supplying of the subscapularis muscles. In addition, it supplies the teres major muscles.
4 Axillary (circumflex) (C5, C6). It is responsible for supplying one of the important muscles of the shoulder, the deltoid, It also supplies small teres minor muscle.
5 Radial (C5–C8, T1). This is the thickest branch of brachial plexus. It supplies all the three heads of triceps brachii muscle. Then it supplies 12 muscles on the back of forearm.

In addition to the branches of the brachial plexus, the upper limb is also supplied, near the trunk, by the supraclavicular branches of the cervical plexus, and by the intercostobrachial branch of the second intercostal nerve. Sympathetic nerves are distributed through the brachial plexus. The arrangement of the various nerves in the axilla was studied with the relations of the axillary artery.

Special Features

The lateral cord, medial cord and their branches form the letter "M" with the three corners extended (Fig. 4.8 inset). Lateral cord gives musculocutaneous and lateral root of median.

Medial cord gives ulnar and medial root of median. The lateral root and medial root of median nerve join to form the median nerve.

Blood Supply of Brachial Plexus

Vertebral artery and thyrocervical trunk with its branches, the suprascapular and transverse cervical arteries, supply blood to the brachial plexus. These are the life line of this important plexus.

CLINICAL ANATOMY

Erb's Paralysis *Upper Trunk (C5, C6) injury)*

Site of injury: One region of the upper trunk of the brachial plexus is called Erb's point (Fig. 4.15). Six nerves meet here. Injury to the upper trunk causes Erb's paralysis.

Causes of injury: Undue separation of the head from the shoulder, which is commonly encountered in the following.

    i. Birth injury
    ii. Fall on the shoulder
    iii. During anaesthesia.

Nerve roots involved: Mainly C5 and partly C6.

Muscles paralysed: Mainly biceps brachii, deltoid, brachialis and brachioradialis. Partly supraspinatus, infraspinatus and supinator.

Deformity and position of the limb:

Arm: Hangs by the side; it is adducted and medially rotated.

Forearm: Extended and pronated.

The deformity is known as 'policeman's tip hand' or waiter's tip hand or 'porter's tip hand' (Fig. 4.16).

Disability: The following movements are lost.

- Abduction and lateral rotation of the arm at shoulder joint.
- Flexion and supination of the forearm.
- Biceps and supinator jerks are lost.
- Sensations are lost over a small area over the lower part of the deltoid.

Klumpke's Paralysis

Site of injury: Lower trunk of the brachial plexus.

Cause of injury: Undue abduction of the arm, as in clutching something with the hands after a fall from a height, or sometimes in birth injury.

Nerve roots involved: Mainly T1 and partly C8.

Muscles paralysed

- Intrinsic muscles of the hand (T1).
- Ulnar flexors of the wrist and fingers (C8).

Deformity and position of the hand: Claw hand due to the unopposed action of the long flexors and extensors of the fingers. In a claw hand, there is hyperextension at the metacarpophalangeal joints and flexion at the interphalangeal joints.

Disability

- Biceps and supinator jerks are lost.
- Complete claw hand (Fig. 4.17).
- Cutaneous anaesthesia and analgesia in a narrow zone along the ulnar border of the forearm and hand.

- *Horner's syndrome:* If T1 is injured proximal to white ramus communicans to first thoracic sympathetic ganglion, there is ptosis, miosis, anhydrosis, enophthalmos, and loss of cilio-spinal reflex—may be associated. This is because of injury to sympathetic fibres to the head and neck that leave the spinal cord through nerve T1.
- *Vasomotor changes:* The skin area with sensory loss is warmer due to arteriolar dilation. It is also drier due to the absence of sweating as there is loss of sympathetic activity.
- *Trophic changes:* Long-standing case of paralysis leads to dry and scaly skin. The nails crack easily with atrophy of the pulp of fingers.

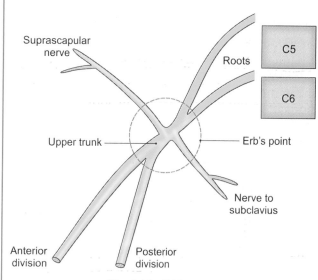

Fig. 4.15: Erb's point

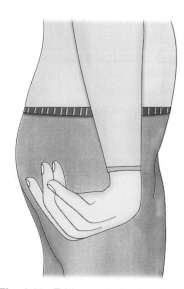

Fig. 4.16: Erb's paralysis of right arm

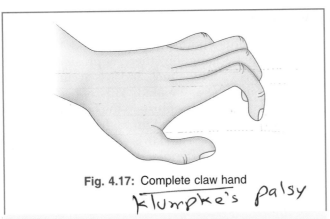

Fig. 4.17: Complete claw hand

Klumpke's palsy

Injury to the Nerve to Serratus Anterior (Nerve of Bell)

Causes

1 Sudden pressure on the shoulder from above.
2 Carrying heavy loads on the shoulder.

Deformity

Winging of the scapula, i.e. excessive prominence of the medial border of the scapula. Normally, the pull of the muscle keeps the medial border against the thoracic wall.

Disability

- Loss of pushing and punching actions. During attempts at pushing, there occurs winging of the scapula (*see* Fig. 2.12).
- Arm cannot be raised beyond 90°, i.e. overhead abduction is not possible as it is performed by the serratus anterior muscle.

Mnemonics

Axillary artery branches "Slap The Lawyer Save A Patient":

1st part gives 1 branch; 2nd part 2 branches; and 3rd part 3 branches.

Superior thoracic branch of 1st part
Thoracoacromial branch of 2nd part
Lateral thoracic branch of 2nd part
Subscapular branch of 3rd part
Anterior circumflex humeral branch of 3rd part
Posterior circumflex humeral branch of 3rd part

Thoracoacromial artery branches "ABCD":

Acromial
Breast (pectoral)
Clavicular
Deltoid

Brachial plexus branches: "My Aunt Ragged My Uncle":

From lateral to medial:

- **M**usculocutaneous
- **A**xillary
- **R**adial
- **M**edian
- **U**lnar

Brachial plexus "Ramu Tailor Drinks Cold Bear": *Beer*

Roots (ventral rami) C5–T1
Trunks (upper, middle, lower)
Divisions (3 anterior and 3 posterior)
Cords (lateral, posterior, medial)
Branches

🔑 FACTS TO REMEMBER

- Sternoaponeurotic part of pectoralis major twist around the upper fibres of same muscle. Latissimus dorsi twists around the teres major. Thus the smooth anterior and posterior walls of the axilla are formed.
- Infraclavicular part of brachial plexus lies in the axilla.
- Apex of the axilla is known as cervico-axillary canal and gives passage to axillary vessels and lower part of brachial plexus.
- Axillary sheath is derived from prevertebral fascia.

✓ CLINICOANATOMICAL PROBLEM

A patient came with inability to: (i) abduct right shoulder, (ii) flex elbow joint and (iii) supinate the forearm

- What is the site of injury of the nerves?
- What is the point called?
- What nerves are affected?

Ans: The site of injury is called Erb's point.
Six nerves are involved:

   i. Ventral ramus of cervical five segment of spinal cord
  ii. Ventral ramus of cervical six segment of spinal cord

    These two rami join to form the upper trunk

 iii. Suprascapular nerve from upper trunk
 iv. Nerve to subclavius from upper trunk
  v. Anterior division of upper trunk
 vi. Posterior division of upper trunk

    These divisions give fibres to deltoid, brachialis, biceps brachii, supinator, so the arm cannot be abducted. The elbow is extended and forearm is pronated. This paralysis is called Erb's paralysis.

FREQUENTLY ASKED QUESTIONS

1. Describe mammary gland under following headings: Extent, relations, blood supply, lymphatic drainage and clinical anatomy
2. Describe pectoralis major muscle under following headings: Origin, insertion, nerve supply, structures deep to it, actions and clinical anatomy

3. Write short notes/enumerate:
   a. Structures piercing clavipectoral fascia
   b. Winging of scapula
   c. Origin and insertion of pectoralis minor muscle
   d. Root value of long thoracic nerve

MULTIPLE CHOICE QUESTIONS

1. Which of the following is not a branch of posterior cord of brachial plexus?
   a. Upper subscapular   b. Lower subscapular
   c. Suprascapular   d. Axillary
2. Porter's tip or policeman's tip deformity occurs due to:
   a. Klumpke's paralysis
   b. Paralysis of median nerve
   c. Paralysis of radial nerve
   d. Erb's paralysis
3. Which is not a branch of lateral cord of brachial plexus

   a. Musculocutaneous
   b. Lateral root of median
   c. Medial root of median
   d. Lateral pectoral

4. Erb's paralysis causes weakness of all muscles, *except:*
   a. Supraspinatus   b. Deltoid
   c. Biceps brachii   d. Triceps brachii
5. Posterior wall of axilla is formed by all except one muscle:
   a. Teres major   b. Teres minor
   c. Latissimus dorsi   d. Subscapularis

ANSWERS

1. c   **2.** d   **3.** c   **4.** d   **5.** b

Back

A little learning is a dangerous thing
—Alexander Pope

INTRODUCTION

This chapter deals mainly with structures which connect the upper limb with the back of the trunk.

SURFACE LANDMARKS

1 The scapula (shoulder blade) is placed on the posterolateral aspect of the upper part of the thorax. It extends from the second to seventh ribs. Although it is thickly covered by muscles, most of its outline can be felt in the living subject. The *acromion* lies at the top of the shoulder. The *crest of the spine* of the scapula runs from the acromion medially and slightly downwards to the medial border of the scapula. The *medial border* and the *inferior angle* of the scapula can also be palpated (Fig. 5.1).
2 The *eighth rib* is just below the inferior angle of the scapula. The lower ribs can be identified on the back by counting down from the eighth rib.
3 The *iliac crest* is a curved bony ridge lying below the waist. The anterior end of the crest is the *anterior superior iliac spine*. The *posterior superior iliac spine* is felt in a shallow dimple above the buttock, about 5 cm from the median plane.
4 The *sacrum* lies between the right and left dimples mentioned above. Usually three *sacral spines* are palpable in the median plane.
5 The *coccyx* lies between the two buttocks in the median plane.
6 The spine of the seventh cervical vertebra or *vertebra prominens* is readily felt at the root of the neck. Higher up on the back of the neck, the *second cervical spine* can be felt about 5 cm below the *external occipital protuberance*. Other spines that can be recognised are T3 at the level of root of the spine of the scapula, L4 at the level of the highest point of the iliac crest, and S2 at the level of the posterior superior iliac spine.

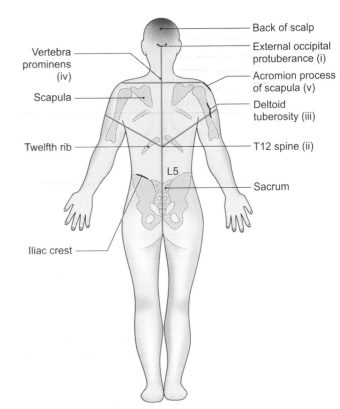

Fig. 5.1: Surface landmarks and lines of dissection

7 The junction of the back of the head with that of the neck is indicated by the external occipital protuberance and the superior nuchal lines. The *external occipital protuberance* is a bony projection felt in the median plane on the back of the head at the upper end of the nuchal furrow (running vertically on the back of the neck). The *superior nuchal lines* are indistinct curved ridges which extend on either side from the protuberance to the mastoid process. The nuchal furrow extends to the external occipital protuberance above and to the spine of C7 below.

SKIN AND FASCIAE OF THE BACK

DISSECTION

Identify the external occipital protuberance (i) of the skull. Draw a line in the midline from the protuberance to the spine of the last thoracic (T12) vertebra (ii). Make incision along this line (Fig. 5.1). Extend the incision from its lower end to the deltoid tuberosity (iii) on the humerus which is present on lateral surface about the middle of the arm. Note that the arm is placed by the side of the trunk.

Make another incision along a horizontal line from seventh cervical spine—vertebra prominens (iv) to the acromion process of scapula (v). Reflect the skin flap laterally.

Position

Human being mostly lies on his back. Therefore, the skin and fasciae of the back are adapted to sustain pressure of the body weight. Accordingly, the skin is thick and fixed to the underlying fasciae; the superficial fascia containing variable amount of fat, is thick and strong and is connected to overlying skin by connective tissue; and the deep fascia is dense in texture.

Cutaneous Nerves

The cutaneous nerves of the back are derived from the posterior primary rami of the spinal nerves. Their distribution extends up to the posterior axillary lines. The following points may be noted.

1   The posterior primary rami of the spinal nerves C1, C7, C8, L4 and L5 do not give off any cutaneous branches. All twelve thoracic, L1–L3 and five sacral nerves, however, give cutaneous branches.

2   Each posterior/dorsal primary ramus divides into medial and lateral branches, both of which supply the erector spinae muscles, but only one of them, either medial or lateral, continues to become the cutaneous nerves. In the upper half of the body (up to T6), the medial branches, and in the lower half of the body (below T6) the lateral branches, of the posterior primary rami provide the cutaneous branches. Each cutaneous nerve divides into a smaller medial and a larger lateral branch before supplying the skin (Fig. 5.2).

3   The posterior primary rami supply the intrinsic muscles of the back and the skin covering them. The cutaneous distribution extends further laterally than the extensor muscles.

4   No posterior primary ramus *ever* supplies skin or muscles of a limb. The cutaneous branches of the posterior primary rami of nerves L1, L2, L3 and S1–S3 are exceptions in this respect: they turn downwards unlike any other nerve and supply the skin of the gluteal region.

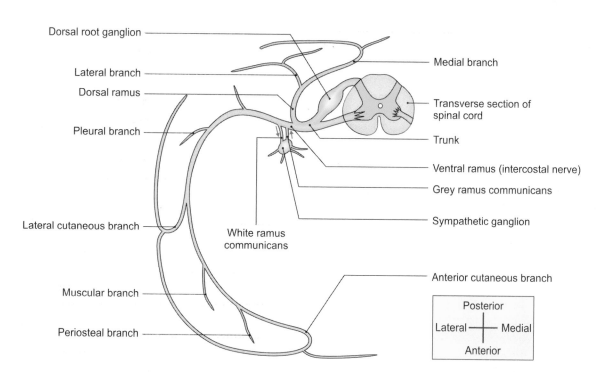

Fig. 5.2: Typical thoracic spinal nerve. The ventral primary ramus is the intercostal nerve

MUSCLES CONNECTING THE UPPER LIMB WITH THE VERTEBRAL COLUMN

DISSECTION

Identify the attachments of trapezius muscle in the upper part of back; and that of latissimus dorsi in the lower part. Cut vertically through trapezius 5 cm lateral to the vertebral spines. Divide the muscle horizontally between the clavicle and spine of scapula; and reflect it laterally to identify the *accessory nerve* and its accompanying blood vessels, the *superficial cervical artery* and *vein*.

Look for the *suprascapular vessels* and *nerve*, deep to trapezius muscle, towards the scapular notch.

Cut through levator scapulae muscle midway between its two attachments and clean the dorsal scapular nerve (supplying the rhomboids) and accompanying blood vessels. Identify rhomboid minor from rhomboid major muscle.

Pull the medial or inner scapular border away from the chest wall for looking at the serratus anterior muscle.

Define attachments of latissimus dorsi muscle.

Features

Muscles connecting the upper limb with the vertebral column are the trapezius (Figs 5.3a to c), the latissimus dorsi, the levator scapulae, and the rhomboid minor and rhomboid major. The attachments of these muscles are given in Table 5.1, and their nerve supply and actions are shown in Table 5.2.

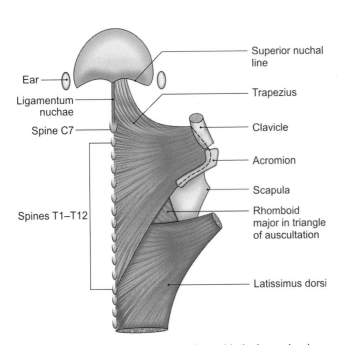

Fig. 5.3a: The trapezius muscle and latissimus dorsi

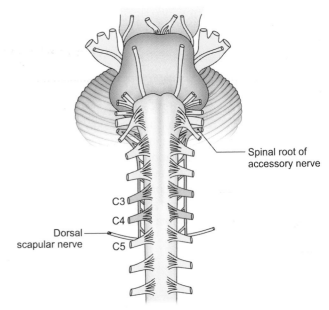

Fig. 5.3b: Nerve supply of trapezius

Additional Features of Muscles of the Back

Trapezius

1 Developmentally, the trapezius is related to the sternocleidomastoid. Both of them develop from branchial arch mesoderm and are supplied by the spinal accessory nerve.
2 The principal action of the trapezius is to rotate the scapula during abduction of the arm beyond 90°. Clinically, the muscle is tested by asking the patient to shrug his shoulder against resistance.

Structures under Cover of the Trapezius

A large number of structures lies immediately under cover of the trapezius. They are shown in Figs 5.6 to 5.8 and are listed below.

A. *Muscles*
  1 Semispinalis capitis.
  2 Splenius capitis.
  3 Levator scapulae (Fig. 5.4).
  4 Inferior belly of omohyoid.
  5 Rhomboid minor.
  6 Rhomboid major.
  7 Supraspinatus.
  8 Infraspinatus.
  9 Latissimus dorsi.
  10 Serratus posterior superior.

B. *Vessels*
  1 Suprascapular artery and vein
  2 Superficial branch of the transverse cervical artery (superficial cervical) (Fig. 5.5) and accompanying veins
  3 Deep branch of transverse cervical artery (Fig. 5.6) (dorsal scapular) and accompanying veins.

Table 5.1: Attachments of muscles connecting the upper limb to the vertebral column (Figs 5.4 and 5.6)

Muscle	Origin	Insertion
Trapezius The right and left muscles together form a trapezium that covers the upper half of the back (Figs 5.3a and c)	• Medial one-third of superior nuchal line • External occipital protuberance • Ligamentum nuchae • C7 spine • T1–T12 spines • Corresponding supraspinous ligaments	• Upper fibres into the posterior border of lateral one-third of clavicle • Middle fibres, into the medial margin of the acromion and upper lip of the crest of spine of the scapula • Lower fibres, on the apex of triangular area at the medial end of the spine, with a bursa intervening
Latissimus dorsi It covers a large area of the lower back, and is overlapped by the trapezius (Fig. 5.4)	• Posterior one-third of the outer lip of iliac crest • Posterior layer of lumbar fascia; thus attaching the muscle to the lumbar and sacral spines • Spines of T7–T12, Lower four ribs • Inferior angle of the scapula	The muscle winds round the lower border of the teres major, and forms the posterior fold of the axilla The tendon is twisted upside down and is inserted into floor of the intertubercular sulcus
Levator scapulae (Fig. 5.4)	• Transverse processes of C1, C2 • Posterior tubercles of the transverse processes of C3, C4	Superior angle and upper part of medial border (up to triangular area) of the scapula
Rhomboid minor	• Lower part of ligamentum nuchae • Spines C7 and T1	Base of the triangular area at the root of the spine of the scapula
Rhomboid major	• Spines of T2–T5 • Supraspinous ligaments	Medial border of scapula below the root of the spine

Table 5.2: Nerve supply and actions of muscles connecting the upper limb to the vertebral column

Muscle	Nerve supply	Actions
Trapezius	• Spinal part of accessory nerve • Branches from C3, C4	• Upper fibres act with levator scapulae, and elevate the scapula, as in shrugging. Upper fibres of both sides extend the neck • Middle fibres act with rhomboids, and retract the scapula • Upper and lower fibres act with serratus anterior, and rotate the scapula forwards round the chest wall thus playing an important role in abduction of the arm beyond 90° (Fig. 5.7) • Steadies the scapula
Latissimus dorsi	Thoracodorsal nerve (C6–C8) (nerve to latissimus dorsi)	• Adduction, extension, and medial rotation of the shoulder as in swimming, rowing, climbing, pulling, folding the arm behind the back, and scratching the opposite scapula • Helps in violent expiratory effort like coughing, sneezing, etc. • Essentially a climbing muscle • Hold inferior angle of the scapula in place
Levator scapulae	• A branch from dorsal scapular nerve (C5) • Branches from C3, C4	• Helps in elevation of scapula • Steadies the scapula during movements of the arm
Rhomboid minor	Dorsal scapular nerve (C5)	• Retraction of scapula
Rhomboid major	Dorsal scapular nerve (C5)	• Retraction of scapula

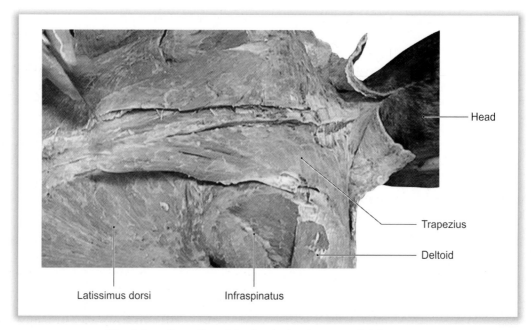

Head

Trapezius

Deltoid

Latissimus dorsi

Infraspinatus

Fig. 5.3c: Dissection of the back showing superficial muscles

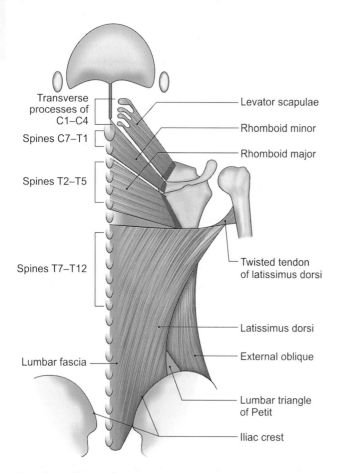

Transverse processes of C1–C4

Spines C7–T1

Spines T2–T5

Spines T7–T12

Lumbar fascia

Levator scapulae

Rhomboid minor

Rhomboid major

Twisted tendon of latissimus dorsi

Latissimus dorsi

External oblique

Lumbar triangle of Petit

Iliac crest

Fig. 5.4: The latissimus dorsi, the levator scapulae, the rhomboid minor and the rhomboid major muscles

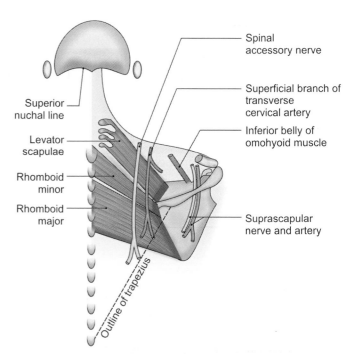

Superior nuchal line

Levator scapulae

Rhomboid minor

Rhomboid major

Outline of trapezius

Spinal accessory nerve

Superficial branch of transverse cervical artery

Inferior belly of omohyoid muscle

Suprascapular nerve and artery

Fig. 5.5: Some of the structures under cover of the right trapezius muscle

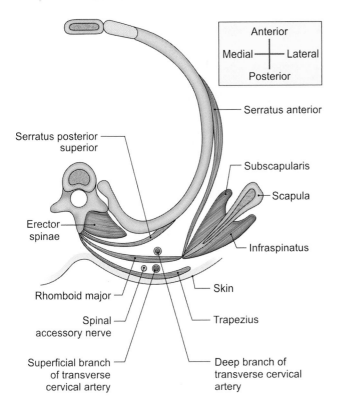

Fig. 5.6: Transverse section showing the arrangement of structures on the back

C. *Nerves*

1 Spinal root of accessory nerve (Fig. 5.3b).
2 Suprascapular nerve.
3 C3, C4 nerves.
4 Posterior primary rami of C2–C6 and T1–T12 pierce the muscle to become cutaneous nerves.

D. *Bursa*

A bursa lies over the smooth triangular area at the root of the spine of the scapula.

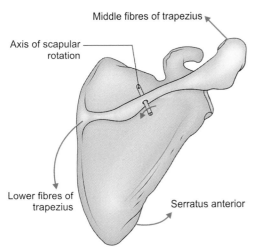

Fig. 5.7: Rotation of the scapula during abduction of the arm beyond 90 degrees, brought about by the trapezius and the serratus anterior muscles

Latissimus Dorsi

1 This is the only muscle which connects the pelvic girdle and vertebral column to upper limb. It possesses extensive origin and narrow insertion.
2 The latissimus dorsi develops in the extensor compartment of the limb. Thereafter, it migrates to its wide attachment on the trunk, taking its nerve supply (thoracodorsal nerve) along with it (latus = wide). It is also called a swimmer's muscle.
3 The latissimus dorsi is tested clinically by feeling the contracting muscle in the posterior fold of the axilla after asking the patient to cough.

Triangle of Auscultation

Triangle of auscultation is a small triangular interval bounded medially by the lateral border of the trapezius, laterally by the medial border of the scapula, and inferiorly by the upper border of the latissimus dorsi. The floor of the triangle is formed by the 6th and 7th rib, and 6th intercostal space (ICS), and the rhomboid major. This is the only part of the back which is not covered by big muscles. Respiratory sounds of apex of lower lobe heard through a stethoscope are better heard over this triangle on each side. On the left side, the cardiac orifice of the stomach lies deep to the triangle, and in days before X-rays were discovered the sounds of swallowed liquids were auscultated over this triangle to confirm the oesophageal tumour (Fig. 5.4).

Lumbar Triangle of Petit

Lumbar triangle of Petit is another small triangle surrounded by muscles. It is bounded medially by the lateral border of the latissimus dorsi, laterally by the posterior border of the external oblique muscle of the abdomen, and inferiorly by the iliac crest (which forms the base). The occasional hernia at this site is called *lumbar hernia* (Fig. 5.4).

After completing the dissection of the back, the limb with clavicle and scapula is detached from the trunk.

DISSECTION

For detachment of the limb, muscles which need to be incised are trapezius, levator scapulae, rhomboid minor and major, serratus anterior, latissimus dorsi and sternocleidomastoid.

The sternoclavicular joint is opened to free clavicle from the sternum. Upper limb with clavicle and scapula are removed en bloc.

🔑 **FACTS TO REMEMBER**

- Trapezius is a shrugging muscle supplied by spinal root of XI nerve.
- Trapezius with serratus anterior causes 90°–180° of abduction at shoulder joints.

Section 1 **Upper Limb**

CLINICOANATOMICAL PROBLEM

A poor young adult felt multiple nodules in the region of his neck above the clavicle. A lymph node biopsy was advised from right side of his neck. A few days after the biopsy he was unable to shrug his right shoulder

• Why was the biopsy advised?

• Why is he not able is shrug his shoulder?

Ans: For proper diagnosis and treatment, a lymph node biopsy was advised from the posterior triangle of neck. The spinal root of accessory nerve got injured during the biopsy procedure. This nerve supplies trapezius muscle, responsible for shrugging of the shoulder. Due to the injury to spinal root of XI nerve, he is unable to shrug his shoulder.

FREQUENTLY ASKED QUESTIONS

1. Describe the axillary artery under following headings: Beginning, course and branches. Add a note on anastomoses around scapula

2. Enumerate the roots, trunks, cords, divisions and branches of brachial plexus

3. Write short notes/enumerate
   a. Boundaries of axilla
   b. Areas draining into axillary lymph nodes
   c. Branches of posterior cord of brachial plexus
   d. Erb's paralysis
   e. Klumpke's paralysis

MULTIPLE CHOICE QUESTIONS

1. Boundaries of triangle of auscultation are not formed by one of the following structures:
   a. Lateral border of trapezius
   b. Medial border of scapula
   c. Upper border of latissimus dorsi
   d. Upper border of teres major

2. Boundaries of lumbar triangle of Petit are formed by all *except*:
   a. Lateral border of latissimus dorsi
   b. Posterior border of external oblique muscle of abdomen
   c. Iliac crest
   d. Quadratus lumborum

3. Trapezius is not attached to:
   a. Clavicle   b. First rib
   c. Occiput   d. Scapula

4. Posterior primary rami of one of the following nerves give cutaneous branch:
   a. C1   b. C7, C8
   c. L4, L5   d. S1

5. Which structure does not lie just deep to trapezius:
   a. Spinal accessory nerve
   b. Superficial branch of transverse cervical artery
   c. Deep branch of transverse cervical artery
   d. C3 and C4 nerves

ANSWERS

1. d   **2.** d   **3.** b   **4.** d   **5.** c

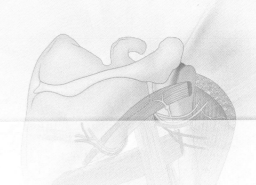

Scapular Region

Action speaks louder than words
—English Proverb

INTRODUCTION

The shoulder or scapular region comprises structures which are closely related to and surround the shoulder joint. For a proper understanding of the region, revise some features of the scapula and the upper end of the humerus.

SURFACE LANDMARKS

1 a. The upper half of the humerus is covered on its anterior, lateral and posterior aspects by the deltoid muscle. This muscle is triangular in shape and forms the rounded contour of the shoulder (Fig. 6.1).

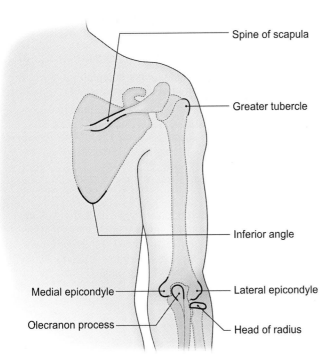

Spine of scapula

Greater tubercle

Inferior angle

Medial epicondyle

Lateral epicondyle

Olecranon process

Head of radius

Fig. 6.1: Surface landmarks: Shoulder, arm and elbow regions

b. The greater tubercle of the humerus forms the most lateral bony point of the shoulder.

2 The *skin* covering the shoulder region is supplied by:

a. The lateral supraclavicular nerve, over the upper half of the deltoid

b. The upper lateral cutaneous nerve of the arm, over the lower half of the deltoid

c. The dorsal rami of the upper thoracic nerves, over the back, i.e. over the scapula.

3 The *superficial fascia* contains (in addition to some fat and cutaneous nerves) the inferolateral part of the platysma arising from the deltoid fascia.

4 The deep fascia covering the deltoid sends numerous septa between its fasciculi. The subscapularis, supraspinatus and infraspinatus fasciae provide origin to a part of the respective muscle.

MUSCLES OF THE SCAPULAR REGION

DISSECTION

Define the margins of the deltoid muscle covering the shoulder joint region. Reflect the part of the muscle arising from spine of scapula downwards. Separate the infraspinatus muscle from teres major and minor muscles which run from the lateral scapular border towards humerus. Axillary nerve accompanied with posterior circumflex humeral vessels lies on the deep aspect of the deltoid muscle.

Features

Muscles of scapular region are the deltoid, the supra-spinatus, the infraspinatus, the teres minor, the subscapu-laris, and the teres major. The deltoid is described below. The other muscles are described in Tables 6.1 and 6.2.

DELTOID

Origin

1 The anterior border and adjoining surface of the lateral one-third of the clavicle (Fig. 6.2).
2 The lateral border of the acromion where four septa of origin are attached (Fig. 6.2).
3 Lower lip of the crest of the spine of the scapula.

Insertion

The deltoid tuberosity of the humerus where three septa of insertion are attached.

Nerve Supply

Axillary nerve (C5, C6).

The acromial part of deltoid is an example of a *multipennate muscle*. Many fibres arise from four septa of origin that are attached above to the acromion. The fibres converge on to three septa of insertion which are attached to the deltoid tuberosity (Fig. 6.2).

Actions

1 The multipennate acromial fibres are powerful abductors of the arm at the shoulder joint from beginning to 90°.

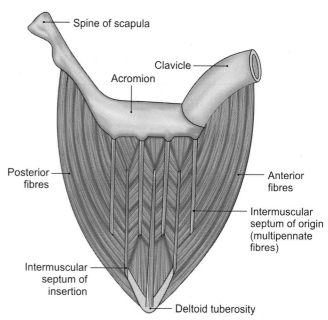

Fig. 6.2: The origin and insertion of the deltoid muscle

A multipennate arrangement allows a large number of muscle fibres to be packed into a relatively small volume. As the strength of contraction of a muscle is

Table 6.1: Attachments of muscles of scapular region (except deltoid)		
Muscle	Origin	Insertion
1. **Supraspinatus** (Fig. 6.3)	Medial two-thirds of the supraspinous fossa of the scapula. The muscle passes as a tendon laterally beneath coracoacromial arch to blend with the capsule of shoulder joint. The tendon is separated from the arch by the subacromial bursa (Fig. 6.7).	Upper impression on the greater tubercle of the humerus
2. **Infraspinatus**	Medial two-thirds of the infraspinous fossa of the scapula	Middle impression on the greater tubercle of the humerus
3. **Teres minor**	Upper two-thirds of the dorsal surface of the lateral border of the scapula as 2 slips	Lowest impression on the greater tubercle of the humerus
4. **Subscapularis** (multipennate)	Medial two-thirds of the subscapular fossa	Lesser tubercle of the humerus
5. **Teres major**	Lower one-third of the dorsal surface of lateral border and inferior angle of the scapula	Medial lip of the bicipital groove of the humerus

Table 6.2: Nerve supply and actions of muscles of scapular region (except deltoid)		
Muscle	Nerve supply	Actions
1. **Supraspinatus** (Fig. 6.3)	Suprascapular nerve (C5, C6)	• Along with other short scapular muscles, it steadies the head of the humerus during movements of the arm. Its action as abductor of shoulder joint from 0–15° is controversial. Both supraspinatus and deltoid are involved in initiation of abduction and continuation of abduction.
2. **Infraspinatus**	Suprascapular nerve (C5, C6)	• Lateral rotator of arm (*see* above)
3. **Teres minor**	Axillary nerve (C5, C6)	Same as infraspinatus
4. **Subscapularis** (Fig. 6.4)	Upper and lower subscapular nerves (C5, C6)	Medial rotator and adductor of arm
5. **Teres major**	Lower subscapular nerve (C5, C6)	Same as subscapularis

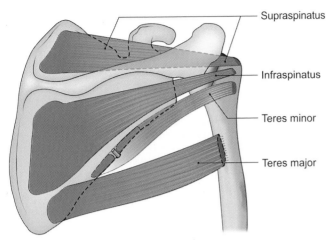

Fig. 6.3: The origin and insertion of the supraspinatus, infraspinatus and teres minor muscles of right side

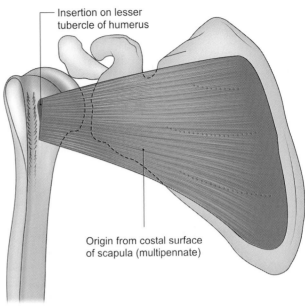

Fig. 6.4: The subscapularis muscle

proportional to the number of muscle fibres present in it (and not on their length), a multipennate muscle is much stronger than other muscles having the same volume.

2 The anterior fibres are flexors and medial rotators of the arm.

3 The posterior fibres are extensors and lateral rotators of the arm.

Structures under Cover of the Deltoid

Bones

i. The upper end of the humerus.
ii. The coracoid process.

Muscles

Insertions of

i. Pectoralis minor on coracoid process.
ii. Supraspinatus, infraspinatus, and teres minor (on the greater tubercle of the humerus) (Fig. 6.3).

iii. Subscapularis on lesser tubercle of humerus (Fig. 6.4).
iv. Pectoralis major, teres major and latissimus dorsi on the intertubercular sulcus of the humerus (Fig. 6.5).

Origin of

i. Coracobrachialis and short head of biceps brachii from the coracoid process (Fig. 6.5).
ii. Long head of the biceps brachii from the supra-glenoid tubercle.
iii. Long head of the triceps brachii from the infra-glenoid tubercle.
iv. The lateral head of the triceps brachii from the upper part of posterior surface of the humerus.

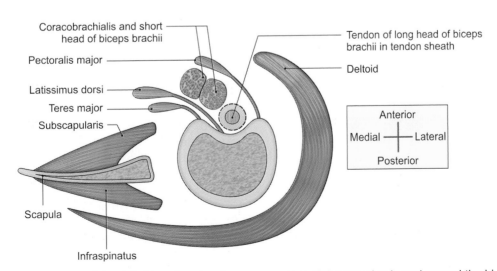

Fig. 6.5: Horizontal section of the deltoid region showing arrangement of the muscles in and around the bicipital groove

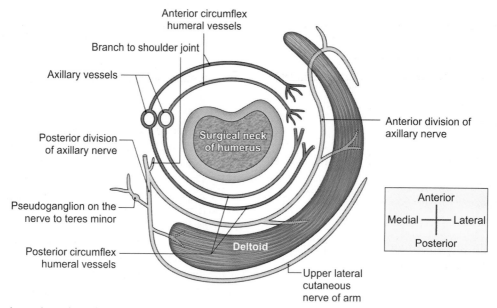

Fig. 6.6: Horizontal section of the deltoid region showing the nerves and vessels around the surgical neck of humerus

Vessels

  i. Anterior circumflex humeral.
  ii. Posterior circumflex humeral (Fig. 6.6).

Nerve

Axillary (Fig. 6.6).

Joints and Ligaments

  i. Musculotendinous cuff of the shoulder (Fig. 6.7).
  ii. Coracoacromial ligament.

Bursae

All bursae around the shoulder joint, including the subacromial or subdeltoid bursa (Fig. 6.8).

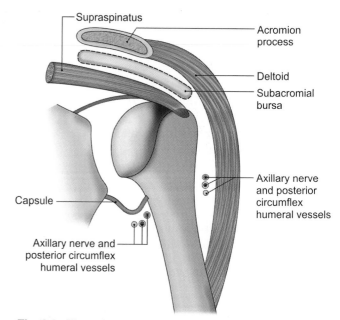

Fig. 6.8: The subacromial bursa as seen in coronal section

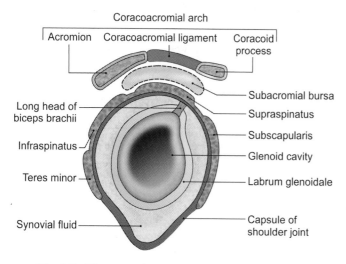

Fig. 6.7: The musculotendinous cuff of the shoulder

CLINICAL ANATOMY

- Intramuscular injections are often given into the deltoid. They should be given in the middle of the muscle to avoid injury to the axillary nerve (Fig. 6.9a).
- The deltoid muscle is tested by asking the patient to abduct the arm against resistance applied with one hand, and feeling for the contracting muscle with the other hand (Fig. 6.9b).
- The axillary nerve may be damaged by dislocation of the shoulder or by the fracture of

the surgical neck of the humerus. The effects produced are:

a. Rounded contour of shoulder is lost; greater tubercle of humerus becomes prominent (Fig. 6.10a).
b. Deltoid is paralysed, with loss of the power of abduction up to 90° at the shoulder.
c. There is sensory loss over the lower half of the deltoid in a badge-like area called regimental badge (Fig. 6.10b).

- The tendon of the supraspinatus may undergo degeneration. This can give rise to calcification and even spontaneous rupture of the tendon.
- In subacromial bursitis, pressure over the deltoid below the acromion with the arm by the side causes pain. However, when the arm is abducted pressure over the same point causes no pain, because the bursa disappears under the acromion (Dawbarn's sign). Subacromial or subdeltoid bursitis is usually secondary to inflammation of the supraspinatus tendon.

Musculotendinous Cuff of the Shoulder or Rotator Cuff

Musculotendinous cuff of the shoulder is a fibrous sheath formed by the four flattened tendons which blend with the capsule of the shoulder joint and strengthen it. The muscles which form the cuff arise from the scapula and are inserted into the lesser and greater tubercles of the humerus. They are the subscapularis, the supraspinatus, the infraspinatus and the teres minor (Fig. 6.7). Their tendons, while crossing the shoulder joint, become flattened and blend with each other on one hand, and with the capsule of the joint on the other hand, before reaching their points of insertion.

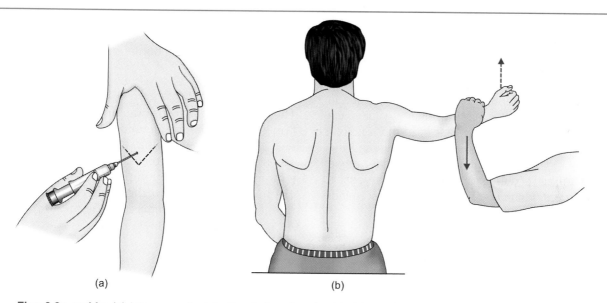

(a)   (b)

Figs 6.9a and b: (a) Intramuscular injection being given in deltoid muscle, and (b) deltoid muscle being tested

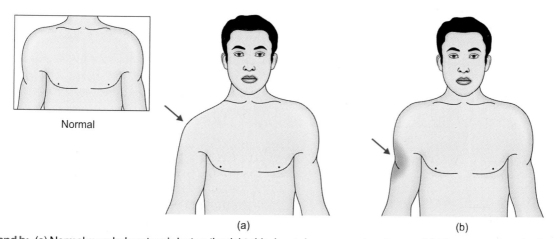

Normal

(a)   (b)

Figs 6.10a and b: (a) Normal rounded contour is lost on the right side. Inset shows normal contour, and (b) the sensory loss (regimental badge)

Upper Limb

Section 1

The cuff gives strength to the capsule of the shoulder joint all around except inferiorly. This explains why dislocations of the humerus occur commonly in a anteroinferior direction.

Subacromial Bursa

Subacromial bursa is the largest bursa of the body, situated below the coracoacromial arch and the deltoid muscle. Below the bursa there are the tendon of the supraspinatus and the greater tubercle of the humerus (Fig. 6.8).

The subacromial bursa is of great value in the abduction of the arm at the shoulder joint.

   i. It protects the supraspinatus tendon against friction with the acromion.

   ii. During overhead abduction the greater tubercle of the humerus passes under the acromion; this is facilitated by the presence of this bursa.

INTERMUSCULAR SPACES

DISSECTION

The quadrangular intermuscular space is a space in between the scapular muscles. The quadrangular space is bounded by teres minor above and teres major below; by the long head of triceps muscle medially and the surgical neck of humerus laterally. The axillary nerve accompanied with posterior circumflex humeral vessels lie in this space. Identify the nerve to the teres minor muscle (Fig. 6.11).

Another intermuscular space, the upper triangular space should be dissected. It is bounded by the teres minor muscle medially, long head of triceps laterally, and teres major muscle below.

Now the remaining two-thirds of deltoid muscle can be reflected towards its insertion. Identify subscapularis muscle anteriorly.

Define the attachments of infraspinatus and cut muscle at the neck of scapula and reflect it on both sides.

Look for the structures covered with deltoid muscle.

Identify a lower triangular space which is bounded above by the lower border of teres major muscle, medially by the long head of triceps brachii and laterally by the medial border of humerus. The radial nerve and profunda brachii vessels pass through the space.

Dissect and identify the arteries taking part in the anastomoses around scapula. These are suprascapular along upper border, deep branch of transverse cervical (dorsal scapular) along medial border and circumflex scapular along lateral border of scapula (Fig. 6.12).

INTRODUCTION

The long head of triceps brachii spans the length of the arm arising from infraglenoid tubercle of scapula to the olecranon process of ulna. It lies medial to humerus. Teres minor crosses posterior aspect of the shoulder joint and origin of the long head as it passes from its origin from scapula to the humerus. The muscle is replaced by subscapularis on the anterior aspect of

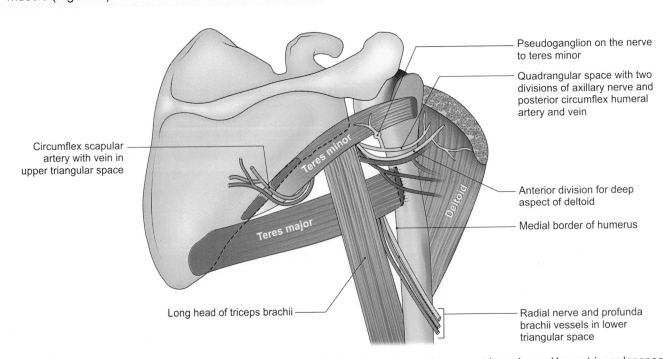

Circumflex scapular artery with vein in upper triangular space

Teres minor

Teres major

Long head of triceps brachii

Pseudoganglion on the nerve to teres minor

Quadrangular space with two divisions of axillary nerve and posterior circumflex humeral artery and vein

Deltoid

Anterior division for deep aspect of deltoid

Medial border of humerus

Radial nerve and profunda brachii vessels in lower triangular space

Fig. 6.11: The intermuscular spaces in the scapular region, including the quadrangular, upper triangular and lower triangular spaces

shoulder joint. Teres major also crosses the long head as it runs to bicipital groove for its insertion.

Thus potential spaces are formed between lateral border of scapula, medial aspect humerus, long head of triceps brachii, teres minor or subscapularis and teres major muscles.

In the upper part there is a quadrangular space laterally and upper triangular space medially. In the lower part is the lower triangular space. Their boundaries are as follows:

Quadrangular Space

Boundaries

Superior
 i. Subscapularis in front.
 ii. Capsule of the shoulder joint. This is the loose inferior part of the capsule of the shoulder joint. In anatomical position, the capsule lies in this space. The capsule is taut and used up during abduction of the shoulder joint.
 iii. Inferior border of teres minor behind.
Inferior: Superior border of teres major.
Medial: Lateral border of long head of the triceps brachii.
Lateral: Surgical neck of the humerus.

Contents

 i. Axillary nerve (Fig. 6.11)
 ii. Posterior circumflex humeral vessels.

Upper Triangular Space

Boundaries

Superior: Inferior border of teres minor.

Lateral: Medial border of long head of the triceps brachii.

Inferior: Superior border of teres major.

Contents

Circumflex scapular artery. It interrupts the origin of the teres minor and reaches the infraspinous fossa for anastomoses with the suprascapular artery and deep branch of transverse cervical artery.

Lower Triangular Space

It is diagonally opposite the upper triangular space.

Boundaries

Medial: Lateral border of long head of the triceps brachii.
Lateral: Medial border of humerus.
Superior: Lower border of teres major (Fig. 6.11).

Contents

 i. Radial nerve.
 ii. Profunda brachii vessels.

AXILLARY OR CIRCUMFLEX NERVE

Axillary or circumflex nerve is an important nerve because it supplies the deltoid muscle which is the main abductor of the arm. Surgically it is important, because it is commonly involved in dislocations of the shoulder and in fractures of the surgical neck of the humerus.

The axillary nerve is a smaller terminal branch of the posterior cord of the brachial plexus (C5, C6).

Root value: Its root value is ventral rami of cervical 5, 6 segments of spinal cord (*see* Fig. 4.14).

Course

Axillary nerve courses through lower part of axilla into the quadrangular space where it terminates by dividing into two branches (Fig. 6.6).

Relations and Branches

a. In the lower part of the axilla, the nerve runs downwards behind the third part of the axillary artery. Here it lies on the subscapularis muscle. It is related medially to the median nerve, and laterally to the coracobrachialis.
 The nerve leaves the axilla by winding round the lower border of the subscapularis in close relation to the lowest part of the capsule of the shoulder joint where it gives a branch to the capsule of the joint and enters the quadrangular space (Fig. 6.8).
b. The nerve then passes backwards through the quadrangular space. Here it is accompanied by the posterior circumflex humeral vessels and has the following relations (Fig. 6.11).
 • *Superiorly:*
  i. Subscapularis or teres minor.
  ii. Lowest part of the capsule of the shoulder joint.
 • *Laterally:* Surgical neck of humerus.
 • *Inferiorly:* Teres major.
 • *Medially:* Long head of the triceps brachii.
 In the quadrangular space, the nerve divides into anterior and posterior branches (Fig. 6.6).
c. The anterior branch is accompanied by the posterior circumflex humeral vessels. It winds round the surgical neck of the humerus, deep to the deltoid, reaching almost up to the anterior border of the muscle. It supplies the deltoid and the skin over its anteroinferior part.
d. The posterior branch supplies the teres minor and the posterior part of the deltoid. The nerve to the teres minor bears a pseudoganglion, i.e. fibrous tissue and fat without any neurons (Fig. 6.6). The posterior branch then pierces the deep fascia at the lower part of the posterior border of the deltoid and continues as the upper lateral cutaneous nerve of the arm.

ANASTOMOSES AROUND SCAPULA

Anastomosis around the Body of the Scapula

The anastomosis occurs in the three fossae, subscapular, supraspinous and infraspinous. It is formed by:

a. The suprascapular artery, a branch of the thyrocervical trunk (Fig. 6.12).

b. The deep branch of the transverse cervical artery, another branch of the thyrocervical trunk.

c. The circumflex scapular artery, a branch of the subscapular artery which arises from the third part of the axillary artery.

Note that it is an anastomosis between branches of the first part of the subclavian artery and the branches of the third part of the axillary artery. These arteries also anastomase with intercostal arteries.

Anastomosis over the Acromion Process

It is formed by:

a. The acromial branch of the thoracoacromial artery (2nd part of axillary).

b. The acromial branch of the suprascapular artery (1st part of subclavian).

c. The acromial branch of the posterior circumflex humeral artery (3rd part of axillary).

Note that this is an anastomosis between the first part of the subclavian artery and the branches of the second and third parts of the axillary artery (Fig. 6.12).

CLINICAL ANATOMY

The arterial anastomoses provide a collateral circulation through which blood can flow to the limb when the distal part of the subclavian artery, or the proximal part of the axillary artery is blocked (Fig. 6.12).

Mnemonics

Rotatory cuff muscles "SITS"

*S*upraspinatus

*I*nfraspinatus

*T*eres minor

*S*ubscapularis

Suprascapular nerve and artery

Army (artery) goes over the bridge

Navy (nerve) goes under the bridge

Artery—suprascapular

Nerve—suprascapular

Bridge—superior transverse scapular ligament.

FACTS TO REMEMBER

• Branches of axillary nerve with accompanying blood vessels pass through the quadrangular intermuscular space

• Loose fold of capsule of shoulder joint forms upper boundary of the quadrangular intermuscular space.

• Radial nerve and profunda brachii vessels course through the lower triangular intermuscular space.

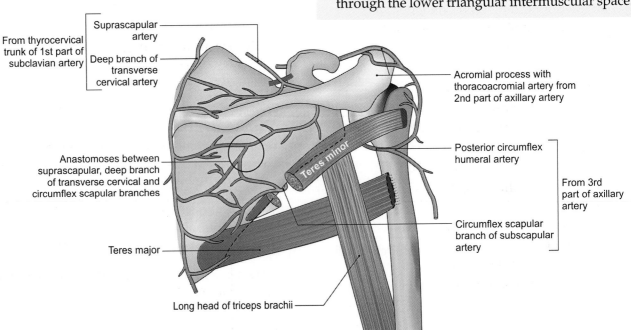

Fig. 6.12: Anastomoses around the scapula (dorsal aspect)

- Only circumflex scapular vessels pass through the upper triangular space.
- Long head of triceps brachii is placed between quadrangular and upper triangular spaces. Lower down it forms a boundary of lower triangular space.

CLINICOANATOMICAL PROBLEM

A patient came with injury on left shoulder region after an accident. He was not able to abduct his shoulder joint

- Which nerve is injured?
- Where is the sensory loss?

Ans: Due to the injury to the surgical to the neck of humerus, the axillary nerve got damaged. Patient feels inability to abduct the shoulder joint.

The sensory loss is over the lower half of deltoid muscle and is called regimental/badge area due to injury to upper lateral cutaneous nerve of the arm, a branch of the axillary nerve.

FREQUENTLY ASKED QUESTIONS

1. Describe deltoid muscle under following headings:
   a. Origin, insertion, action and nerve supply
   b. Structures under cover of deltoid
   c. Effect of paralysis of the muscle
2. Describe the boundaries and contents of quadrangular, upper and lower triangular spaces.

3. Write short notes/enumerate:
   a. Course and branches of axillary nerve
   b. Anastomoses around the body of scapula
   c. Anastomses over the acromion process
   d. Musculotendinous cuff of shoulder/rotator cuff

MULTIPLE CHOICE QUESTIONS

1. Skin of lateral side of arm is supplied by all *except*:
   a. Lateral supraclavicular nerve
   b. Intermediate supraclavicular nerve
   c. Upper lateral cutaneous nerve of arm
   d. Lower lateral cutaneous nerve of arm
2. Which part of deltoid is multipennate?
   a. Clavicular fibres
   b. Acromial fibres
   c. Fibres from spine of scapula
   d. Whole of the muscle
3. Rotator cuff is formed by all *except:*
   a. Supraspinatus   b. Infraspinatus
   c. Teres major   d. Subscapularis
4. Which of the following nerves has a pseudo-ganglion?
   a. Suprascapular nerve
   b. Axillary nerve
   c. Nerve to teres minor
   d. Nerve to serratus anterior

5. Boundaries of quadrangular space is not formed by:
   a. Teres minor
   b. Long head of biceps brachii
   c. Surgical neck of humerus
   d. Teres major
6. Which is not a content of lower triangular space?
   a. Profunda brachii artery
   b. Radial nerve
   c. Superior ulnar collateral artery
   d. Profunda brachii vein
7. Anastomosis around body of scapula is between:
   a. 1st part of subclavian and 3rd part of axillary artery
   b. 2nd part of subclavian artery and 2nd part of axillary artery
   c. 3rd part of subclavian artery and 3rd part of axillary artery
   d. 1st part of subclavian artery and 2nd part of axillary artery

ANSWERS

1. b   **2.** b   **3.** c   **4.** c   **5.** b   **6.** c   **7.** a

Cutaneous Nerves, Superficial Veins and Lymphatic Drainage

Eye, ear, nose and palpating fingers are the gems of a physician. An intact brain is the necklace
—Hippocrates

INTRODUCTION

The superficial fascia seen after the reflection of skin contains cutaneous nerves, cutaneous or superficial veins and lymphatics. The cutaneous nerves are the continuation of the spinal nerves and carry sympathetic fibres for supplying the sweat glands, arterioles in the dermis and arrector pilorum muscles in relation to the hair follicle. Thus, the effects of sympathetic on the skin are sudomotor (increase sweat secretion); vasomotor (narrow the arterioles of skin) and pilomotor (contract arrector pilorum muscle to make the hair erect or straight) respectively. The nerves also carry sensation of pain, touch, temperature and pressure. Superficial veins are seen along with the cutaneous nerves. These are utilised for giving intravenous transfusions, cardiac catheterisation and taking blood samples. Lymphatic vessels are not easily seen in ordinary dissection.

CUTANEOUS NERVES

DISSECTION

Make one horizontal incision in the arm at its junction of upper one-third and lower two-thirds segments (*see* Fig. 3.2) and a vertical incision through the centre of arm and forearm till the wrist where another transverse incision is given.

Reflect the skin on either side on the front as well as on the back of the limb. Use this huge skin flap to cover the limb after the dissection.

Position

The skin of the upper limb is supplied by 15 sets of cutaneous nerves (Table 7.1). Out of these only one set (supraclavicular) is derived from the cervical plexus, and another nerve (intercostobrachial) is derived from the second intercostal nerve. The remaining 13 sets are derived from the brachial plexus through the musculocutaneous, median, ulnar, axillary and radial nerves. Some branches arise directly from the medial cord of the plexus.

It should be noted as follows:
a. The areas of distribution of peripheral cutaneous nerves do not necessarily correspond with those of individual spinal segments (areas of the skin supplied by individual spinal segments are called dermatomes). This is so because each cutaneous nerve contains fibres from more than one ventral ramus (of a spinal nerve); and each ramus gives fibres to more than one cutaneous nerve.
b. Adjacent areas of skin supplied by different cutaneous nerves overlap each other to a considerable extent. Therefore, the area of sensory loss after damage to a nerve is much less than the area of distribution of the nerve. The anaesthetic area is surrounded by an area in which the sensations are somewhat altered.
c. In both the upper and lower limbs, the nerves of the anterior surface have a wider area of distribution than those supplying the posterior surface.

The individual cutaneous nerves, from above downwards, are described below with their root values. Figure 7.1 shows the cutaneous nerves of the upper limb.

1 The *supraclavicular nerves* (C3, C4) are branches of the cervical plexus. They pierce the deep fascia in the neck, descend superficial to the clavicle, and supply:
   a. The skin of the pectoral region up to the level of the second rib.
   b. Skin covering the upper half of the deltoid.
2 The *upper lateral cutaneous nerve of the arm* (C5, C6) is the continuation of the posterior branch of the

Table 7.1: The cutaneous nerves (Figs 7.1a and b)

Region supplied	Nerve(s)	Root value	Derived from
Upper part of pectoral region, and skin over upper part of deltoid	Supraclavicular	C3, C4	Cervical plexus
ARM			
1. Upper medial part	Intercostobrachial (Figs 7.1a and b)	T2	2nd intercostal
2. Lower medial part	Medial cutaneous nerve of arm	T1, T2	Medial cord
3. Upper lateral part (including skin over lower part of deltoid)	Upper lateral cutaneous nerve of arm	C5, C6	Axillary nerve
4. Lower lateral part	Lower lateral cutaneous nerve of arm	C5, C6	Radial nerve
5. Posterior aspect	Posterior cutaneous nerve of arm	C5	Radial nerve
FOREARM			
1. Medial side	Medial cutaneous nerve of forearm	C8, T1	Medial cord
2. Lateral side	Lateral cutaneous nerve of forearm	C5, C6	Musculocutaneous
3. Posterior side	Posterior cutaneous nerve of forearm	C6–C8	Radial nerve
PALM			
1. Lateral two-thirds	Palmar cutaneous branch of median	C6, C7	Median
2. Medial one-third	Palmar cutaneous branch of ulnar	C8	Ulnar
DORSUM OF HAND			
1. Medial half including proximal and middle phalanges of medial 2½ digits	Dorsal branch of ulnar	C8	Ulnar
2. Lateral half including proximal and middle phalanges of lateral 2½ digits	Superficial terminal branch of radial	C6, C7	Radial
DIGITS			
Palmar aspect, and dorsal aspect of distal phalanges			
1. Lateral 3½ digits	Palmar digital branch of median	C7	Median
2. Medial 1½ digits	Palmar digital branch of ulnar	C8	Ulnar

axillary nerve. It supplies the skin covering the lower half of the deltoid.

3 The *lower lateral cutaneous nerve of the arm* (C5, C6) is a branch of the radial nerve given off in the radial groove. It supplies the skin of the lower half of the lateral side of the arm.

4 The *intercostobrachial nerve* (T2) is the lateral cutaneous branch of the second intercostal nerve. It crosses the axilla, and supplies the skin of the upper half of the medial and posterior parts of the arm. It lies amongst the central group of axillary lymph nodes.

5 The *medial cutaneous nerve of the arm* (T1, T2) is the smallest branch of the medial cord of the brachial plexus.

6 The *posterior cutaneous nerve of the arm* (C5) is a branch of the radial nerve given off in the axilla. It supplies the skin of the back of the arm from the insertion of the deltoid to the olecranon.

7 The *lateral cutaneous nerve of the forearm* (C5, C6) is the continuation of the musculocutaneous nerve. It pierces the deep fascia just lateral to the tendon of the biceps 2–3 cm above the bend of the elbow, and supplies the skin of the lateral side of the forearm, extending anteriorly to a small part of the ball of the thumb.

8 The *medial cutaneous nerve of the forearm* (C8, T1) is a branch of the medial cord of the brachial plexus. It runs along the medial side of the axillary and brachial arteries, and supplies the skin of the medial side of the forearm.

9 The *posterior cutaneous nerve of the forearm* (C6–C8) arises from the radial nerve, in the radial groove. It descends posterior to the lateral epicondyle and supplies the skin of the back of the forearm.

10 The *median nerve* gives off two sets of cutaneous branches in the hand.
   a. The *palmar cutaneous branch* (C6–C8) arises a *short distance above the wrist*, lies *superficial to flexor retinaculum* and supplies skin over the lateral two-thirds of the palm including that over the thenar eminence (Fig. 7.1a).

Section 1 | Upper Limb

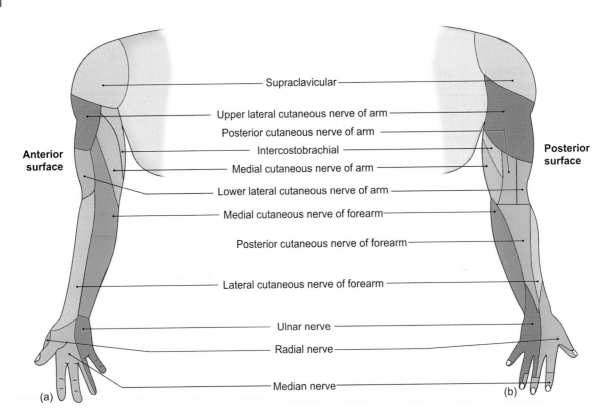

Anterior surface

Posterior surface

Supraclavicular

Upper lateral cutaneous nerve of arm

Posterior cutaneous nerve of arm

Intercostobrachial

Medial cutaneous nerve of arm

Lower lateral cutaneous nerve of arm

Medial cutaneous nerve of forearm

Posterior cutaneous nerve of forearm

Lateral cutaneous nerve of forearm

Ulnar nerve

Radial nerve

Median nerve

(a)   (b)

Fig. 7.1: The cutaneous nerves

b. *Palmar digital branches* (C6–C8) are five in number and arise in the palm. The medial two branches are common palmar digital nerves; each divides near a digital cleft to form two *proper palmar digital nerves*. The lateral three branches are proper palmar digital nerves for the medial and lateral sides of the thumb and for the lateral side of the index finger. The various digital branches of the median nerve supply palmar skin of the lateral three and a half digits, the nail beds, and skin on the dorsal aspect of the distal phalanges of the same digits (Fig. 7.1b).

11 The *ulnar nerve* gives off three sets of cutaneous nerves in hand.

a. The *palmar cutaneous branch* (C7, C8) arises in the middle of the forearm and descends, crossing *superficial to flexor retinaculum* and supplies skin of the medial one-third of the palm.

b. The *palmar digital branches of the ulnar nerve* (C7, C8) are two in number. They arise from the superficial terminal branch of the ulnar nerve just distal to the pisiform bone. The medial of the two branches is a proper palmar digital nerve for the medial side of the little finger. The lateral branch is a common palmar digital nerve which divides into two proper digital

nerves for supply of adjacent sides of the ring and little fingers. Thus it supplies skin of medial one and a half digits, their nail beds and skin on the dorsal aspects of distal phalanges of medial 1½ digits (Fig. 7.1a and b).

c. The *dorsal branch of the ulnar nerve* (C7, C8) arises about 5 cm above the wrist. It descends with the main trunk of the ulnar nerve almost to the pisiform bone. Here it passes backwards to divide into three (sometimes two) dorsal digital nerves. Typically, the region of skin supplied by the dorsal branch covers the medial half of the back of the hand, and the skin on the dorsal aspect of the medial two and a half fingers (*see* Fig. 11.6).

12 The *superficial terminal branch of the radial nerve* (C6–C8) arises in front of the lateral epicondyle of the humerus. It descends through the upper two-thirds of the forearm lateral to the radial artery, and then passes posteriorly about 7 cm above the wrist. While winding round the radius it pierces the deep fascia and divides into four or five small dorsal digital nerves. In all, the superficial terminal branch supplies the skin of the lateral half of the dorsum of the hand, and the dorsal surfaces of the lateral two and a half digits including the thumb, except for the terminal portions supplied by the median nerve.

DERMATOMES

Definition

The area of skin supplied by one spinal segment is called a dermatome. A typical dermatome extends from the posterior median line to the anterior median line around the trunk (*see* Fig. 5.2). However, in the limbs the dermatomes have migrated rather irregularly, so that the original uniform pattern is disturbed.

Embryological Basis

The early human embryo shows regular segmentation of the body. Each segment is supplied by the corresponding segmental nerve. In an adult, all structures, including the skin, developed from one segment, are supplied by their original segmental nerve. The limb may be regarded as an extension of the body wall, and the segments from which they are derived can be deduced from the spinal nerves supplying them. The limb buds arise in the area of the body wall supplied by the lateral branches of anterior primary rami. The nerves to the limbs represent these branches (Fig. 7.2).

Important Features

1 The cutaneous innervation of the upper limb is derived:
   a. Mainly from segments C5–C8 and T1 of the spinal cord, and
   b. Partly from the overlapping segments from above (C3, C4) as well from below (T2, T3). The addi-

tional segments are found only at the proximal end of the limb (Fig. 7.3).

2 Since the limb bud appears on the ventrolateral aspect of the body wall, it is invariably supplied by the anterior primary rami of the spinal nerves. Posterior primary rami do not supply the limb.
   It is possible that the ventral and dorsal divisions of the trunks of the brachial plexus represent the anterior and posterior branches of the lateral cutaneous nerves (*see* Figs 4.14, 5.2 and 7.4).

3 There is varying degree of overlapping of adjoining dermatomes, so that the area of sensory loss following damage to the cord or nerve roots is always less than the area of distribution of the dermatomes (Fig. 7.5).

4 Each limb bud has a cephalic and a caudal border, known as preaxial and postaxial borders, respectively.

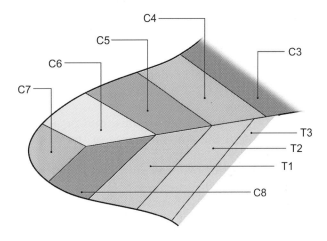

Fig. 7.3: The upper limb bud grows out opposite C5, C6, C7, C8 and T1 segments of the spinal cord

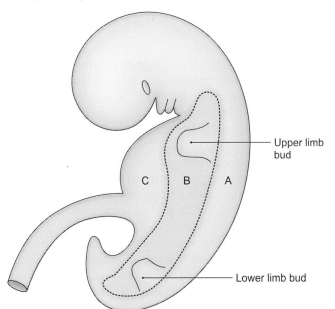

Fig. 7.2: The body wall is supplied by (A) the posterior primary rami, (B) the lateral branches of the anterior primary rami, and (C) the anterior branches of the anterior primary rami of the spinal nerves. The limb buds develop from the area supplied by the lateral branches of the anterior primary rami

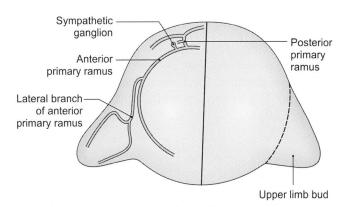

Fig. 7.4: The upper limb bud grows out from the part of the body wall supplied by the lateral cutaneous branches of the anterior primary rami of spinal nerves

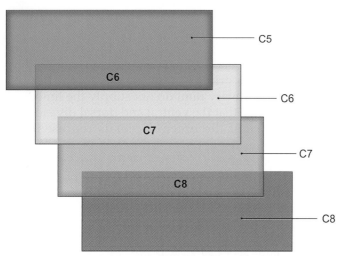

Fig. 7.5: Overlapping of the dermatomes

In the upper limb, the thumb and radius lie along the preaxial border, and the little finger and ulna along the postaxial border.

5 The dermatomes of the upper limb are distributed in an orderly numerical sequence (Figs 7.6a and b).
  a. Along the preaxial border from above downward, by segments C3–C6 with overlapping of the dermatomes.
  b. The middle three digits (index, middle and ring fingers) and the adjoining area of the palm are supplied by segment C7.
  c. The postaxial border is supplied (from below upwards) by segments C8, T1, T2. There is overlapping of the dermatomes.

6 As the limb elongates it rotates laterally and gets adducted and the central dermatome C7 gets pulled in such a way that these are represented only in the distal part of the limb, and are buried proximally.
  On the front of the limb, areas supplied by C5 and C6 segments adjoin the areas supplied by C8, T1 and T2 segments. There is a dividing line between them, known as the *ventral axial line* along which C7 is buried proximally. It reaches the skin just proximal to the wrist (Fig. 7.6a).
  On the back of the limb, C7 reaches the skin just proximal to the elbow. So the *dorsal axial line* ends more proximal to the ventral axial line. There is no overlapping across the ventral and dorsal axial lines (Fig. 7.6b).

CLINICAL ANATOMY

• The area of sensory loss of the skin, following injuries of the spinal cord or of the nerve roots, conforms to the dermatomes. Therefore, the segmental level of the damage to the spinal cord can be determined by examining the dermatomes for touch, pain and temperature. Note that injury to a peripheral nerve produces sensory loss corresponding to the area of distribution of that nerve.

• The spinal segments do not lie opposite the corresponding vertebrae. In estimating the position of a spinal segment in relation to the surface of the body, it is important to remember that a vertebral spine is always *lower* than the corresponding spinal segment. As a rough guide, it may be stated that in the cervical region there is a difference of one segment, e.g. the 5th cervical spine overlies the 6th cervical spinal segment.

Spinal segments	Spine of vertebra
C1–C8	C1–C7
T1–T6	T1–T4
T7–T12	T5–T9
L1–L5	T10–T11
S1–S5 and Co1	T12–L1

SUPERFICIAL VEINS

Superficial veins of the upper limb assume importance in medical practice because these are most commonly used for intravenous injections and for withdrawing blood for testing.

General Remarks

1 Most of the superficial veins of the limb join together to form two large veins, cephalic (preaxial) and basilic (postaxial).

2 The superficial veins run away from pressure points. Therefore, they are absent in the palm (fist area), along the ulnar border of the forearm (supporting border) and in the back of the arm and trapezius region. This makes the course of the veins spiral, from the dorsal to the ventral surface of the limb.

3 The preaxial vein is longer than the postaxial. In other words, the preaxial vein drains into the deep (axillary) vein more proximally (at the root of the limb) than the postaxial vein which becomes deep in the middle of the arm.

4 The earlier a vein becomes deep the better, because the venous return is then assisted by muscular compression. The load of the preaxial (cephalic) vein is greatly relieved by the more efficient postaxial (basilic) vein through a short circuiting channel (the median cubital vein situated in front of the elbow) and partly also by the deep veins through a perforator vein connecting the median cubital to the deep vein.

5 The superficial veins are accompanied by cutaneous nerves and superficial lymphatics, and not by

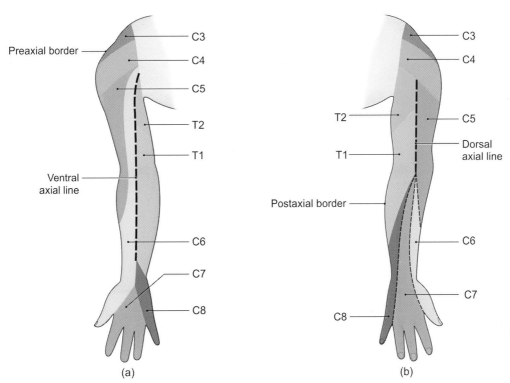

Figs 7.6a and b: Dermatomes: (a) Anterior aspect, and (b) posterior aspect

arteries. The superficial lymph nodes lie along the veins, and the deep lymph nodes along the arteries.

6 The superficial veins are best utilised for intravenous injections.

Individual Veins

Dorsal Venous Arch

Dorsal venous arch lies on the dorsum of the hand (Fig. 7.7a). Its afferents (tributaries) include:

i. Three dorsal metacarpal veins.

ii. A dorsal digital vein from the medial side of the little finger.

iii. A dorsal digital vein from the radial side of the index finger.

iv. Two dorsal digital veins from the thumb.

v. Most of the blood from the palm courses through veins passing around the margins of the hand and also by perforating veins passing through the interosseous spaces. Pressure on the palm during gripping fails to impede the venous return due to the mode of drainage of the palm into the dorsal venous arch. The efferents of dorsal venous arch are the cephalic and basilic veins.

Cephalic Vein

Cephalic vein is the preaxial vein of the upper limb (cf. great saphenous vein of the lower limb).

It begins from the lateral end of the dorsal venous arch.

It runs upwards:

i. Through the roof of the *anatomical snuff box*.

ii. Winds round the lateral border of the distal part of the forearm (Fig. 7.7b).

iii. Continues upwards in front of the elbow and along the lateral border of the biceps brachii.

iv. Pierces the deep fascia at the lower border of the pectoralis major.

v. Runs in the deltopectoral groove up to the infraclavicular fossa.

vi. It pierces the clavipectoral fascia and joins the axillary vein (*see* Fig. 3.12).

At the elbow, the greater part of its blood is drained into the basilic vein through the *median cubital vein*, and partly also into the deep veins through the perforator vein.

It is accompanied by the lateral cutaneous nerve of the forearm, and the terminal part of the radial nerve.

An accessory cephalic vein is sometimes present. It ends by joining the cephalic vein near the elbow.

Basilic Vein

Basilic vein is the postaxial vein of the upper limb (cf. short saphenous vein of the lower limb).

It begins from the medial end of the dorsal venous arch (Fig. 7.7a).

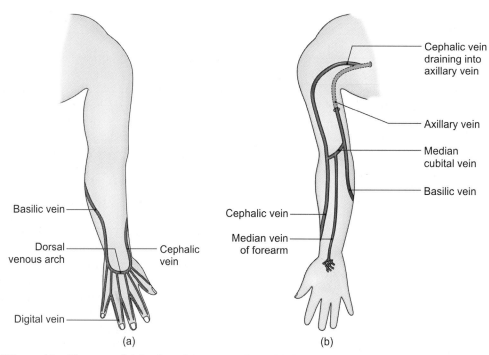

Figs 7.7a and b: The superficial veins of the upper limb: (a) On the back, and (b) on the front of the limb

It runs upwards:
  i. Along the back of the medial border of the forearm,
  ii. Winds round this border near the elbow,
  iii. Continues upwards in front of the elbow (medial epicondyle) and along the medial margin of the biceps brachii up to the middle of the arm, where
  iv. It pierces the deep fascia, and
  v. Runs along the medial side of the brachial artery up to the lower border of teres major where it becomes the axillary vein.

About 2.5 cm above the medial epicondyle of the humerus, it is joined by the median cubital vein.

It is accompanied by the posterior branch of the medial cutaneous nerve of the forearm and the terminal part of the dorsal branch of the ulnar nerve.

Median Cubital Vein

Medial cubital vein is a large communicating vein which shunts blood from the cephalic to the basilic vein (Fig. 7.7b).

It begins from the cephalic vein 2.5 cm below the bend of the elbow, runs obliquely upward and medially, and ends in the basilic vein 2.5 cm above the medial epicondyle. It is separated from the brachial artery by the bicipital aponeurosis.

It may receive tributaries from the front of the forearm (median vein of the forearm) and is connected to the deep veins through a perforator vein which pierces the bicipital aponeurosis. The perforator vein fixes the median cubital vein and thus makes it ideal for intravenous injections.

Median Vein of the Forearm

Median vein of the forearm begins from the palmar venous network, and ends in any one of the veins in front of the elbow mostly in median cubital vein.

Deep Veins

Deep veins start as small venae comitantes running on each side of digital veins. These continue proximally as superficial and deep palmar arches.

Then, these course proximally to continue as venae comitantes of radial and ulnar arteries; which further join to form the brachial veins.

Brachial veins lie on each side of brachial artery. These join the axillary vein at the lower border of teres major. Axillary vein is described in axilla (*see* Ch 4).

CLINICAL ANATOMY

- The median cubital vein is the vein of choice for intravenous injections, for withdrawing blood from donors, and for cardiac catheterisation, because it is fixed by the perforator and does not slip away during piercing. When the median cubital vein is absent, the basilic is preferred over the cephalic because the former is a more efficient channel (Fig. 7.8). Basilic vein runs along straight path, whereas cephalic vein bends acutely to drain into the axillary vein.
- The cephalic vein frequently communicates with the external jugular vein by means of a small vein.

which crosses in front of the clavicle. In operations for removal of the breast (in carcinoma), the axillary lymph nodes are also removed, and it sometimes becomes necessary to remove a segment of the axillary vein also. In these cases, the communication between the cephalic vein and the external jugular vein enlarges considerably and helps in draining blood from the upper limb (Fig. 7.9).

In case of fracture of the clavicle, the rupture of the communicating channel may lead to formation of a large haematoma, i.e. collection of blood.

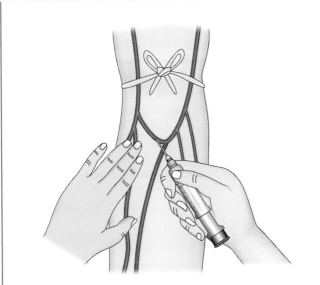

Fig. 7.8: Intravenous injection being given in the median cubital vein

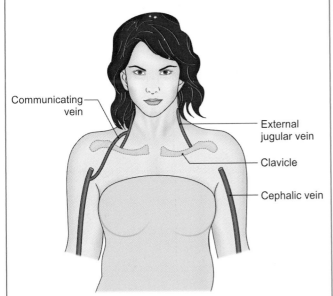

Fig. 7.9: A communicating vein helps in venous drainage from upper limb

Communicating vein

External jugular vein

Clavicle

Cephalic vein

LYMPH NODES AND LYMPHATIC DRAINAGE

When circulating blood reaches the capillaries, part of its fluid content passes through them into the surrounding tissue as *tissue fluid*. Most of this tissue fluid re-enters the capillaries at their venous ends. Some of it is, however, returned to the circulation through a separate set of *lymphatic vessels*. These vessels begin as lymphatic capillaries which drain into larger vessels.

Along the course of these lymph vessels there are groups of *lymph nodes*.

Lymph vessels are difficult to see and special techniques are required for their visualisation.

Lymph nodes are small bean-like structures that are usually present in groups. These are not normally palpable in the living subject.

However, they often become enlarged in disease, particularly by infection or by malignancy in the area from which they receive lymph. They then become palpable and examination of these nodes provides valuable information regarding the presence and spread of disease.

It is, therefore, of importance for the medical student to know the lymphatic drainage of the different parts of the body.

Lymph Nodes

The main lymph nodes of the upper limb are the axillary lymph nodes. These comprise anterior, posterior, lateral, central and apical groups. These have been described in Chapter 4 (*see* Fig. 4.11). Other nodes are as follows:

1 The infraclavicular nodes lie in or on the clavipectoral fascia along the cephalic vein. They drain the upper part of the breast, and the thumb with its web.

2 The deltopectoral node lies in the deltopectoral groove along the cephalic vein. It is a displaced node of the infraclavicular set, and drains similar structures.

3 The superficial cubital or supratrochlear nodes lie just above the medial epicondyle along the basilic vein. They drain the ulnar side of the hand and forearm.

4 A few other deep lymph nodes lie in the following regions:
    i. Along the medial side of the brachial artery.
    ii. At the bifurcation of the brachial artery (deep cubital lymph node).
    iii. Occasionally along the arteries of the forearm.

Lymphatics

Superficial Lymphatics

Superficial lymphatics are much more numerous than the deep lymphatics. They collect lymph from the skin and subcutaneous tissues. Most of them ultimately drain into the axillary nodes, except for:

i. A few vessels from the medial side of the forearm which drain into the superficial cubital nodes.
ii. A few vessels from the lateral side of the forearm which drain into the deltopectoral or infraclavicular nodes.

The dense palmar plexus drains mostly into the lymph vessels on to the dorsum of the hand, where these continue with the vessels of the forearm. Lymph vessels of the back of forearm and arm curve round their medial and lateral surfaces and ascend up to reach the floor of the axilla. Thus, there is a vertical area of *lymph shed* in the middle of back of forearm and arm (Figs 7.10a and b).

Deep Lymphatics

Deep lymphatics are much less numerous than the superficial lymphatics. They drain structures lying deep to the deep fascia. They run along the main blood vessels of the limb, and end in the axillary nodes. Some of the lymph may pass through the deep lymph nodes present along the axillary vein as mentioned above.

CLINICAL ANATOMY

- Inflammation of lymph vessels is known as *lymphangitis.* In acute lymphangitis, the vessels may be seen through the skin as red, tender (painful to touch) streaks (Fig. 7.11).

- Inflammation of lymph nodes is called *lymphadenitis.* It may be acute or chronic. The nodes enlarge and become palpable and painful (Fig. 7.12).
- Obstruction to lymph vessels can result in accumulation of tissue fluid in areas of drainage. This is called *lymphoedema*. This may be caused by carcinoma because of surgical removal of lymph nodes (Fig. 7.13b).
- Pain along the medial side of upper arm is due to pressure on the intercostobrachial nerve by enlarged central group of axillary lymph nodes.

🔑 FACTS TO REMEMBER

- Ventral axial line ends close to wrist joint, while dorsal axial line ends close to elbow joint.
- Dermatome is an area of skin supplied by single spinal segment through a pair of right and left spinal nerves with both its dorsal and ventral rami.
- There is no overlapping of the nerve supply across the axial lines.
- Cephalic vein at its beginning in the 'anatomical snuff box' and median cubital vein near the elbow are the veins of choice for intravenous infusions.
- Median cubital vein is protected from the brachial artery by the bicipital aponeurosis

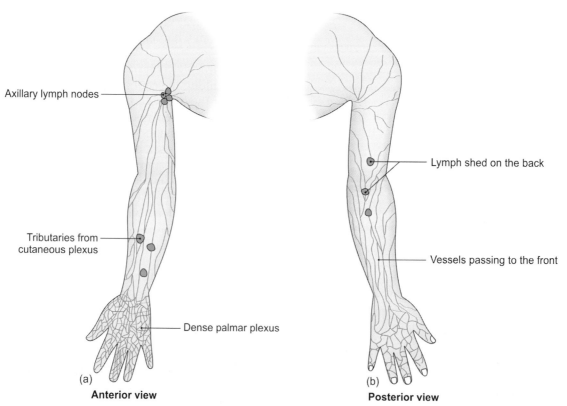

Axillary lymph nodes

Tributaries from cutaneous plexus

Dense palmar plexus

Lymph shed on the back

Vessels passing to the front

(a)
Anterior view

(b)
Posterior view

Figs 7.10a and b: The superficial lymphatics of the upper limb

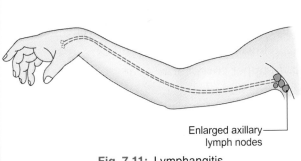

Fig. 7.11: Lymphangitis

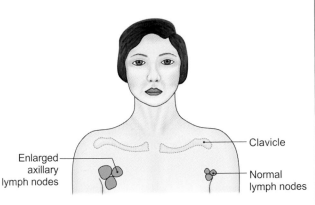

Fig. 7.12: Enlarged axillary lymph nodes

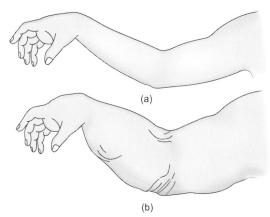

Figs 7.13a and b: (a) Normal upper limb, and (b) lympho-edema due to removal of axillary lymph nodes in case of carcinoma of the breast

CLINICOANATOMICAL PROBLEMS

Case 1

A patient came dehydrated with history of diarrhoea and vomiting. He needed intravenous fluids.

- Which vein is most convenient for intravenous infusion of glucose and why?
- How does one make the vein prominent?

Ans: Median cubital vein is most conveniently placed anterior to the elbow joint.

Deep to the vein is bicipital aponeurosis which mostly prevents the needle from entering into the underlying brachial artery.

The vein is made prominent by tying a tourniquet on the arm or by keeping one's hand tightly around the arm, and asking the patient to do flexion and extension of elbow in a fast mode.

Due to this exercise, the venous return gets increased, but is prevented from drainage into deeper veins due to compression applied to the arm. This makes the superficial veins prominent.

Case 2

A female patient of 60 years felt two nodular swellings in her right axilla.

- What parts of the body have to be examined?
- What is the probable diagnosis of these swellings?

Ans: The parts to be examined are both the mammary glands for any tumour, axilla of both sides for more palpable lymph nodes, supraclavicular and infraclavicular lymph nodes, examination of abdomen and pelvis for any spread in the liver or ovary.

On examination of her right breast, there was a firm mass which she did not feel.

Since there was a firm painless mass in the upper lateral quadrant of her right breast, the diagnosis would be secondary (metastasis) in the axillary lymph node from primary breast tumour. It would be confirmed by fine needle aspiration cytology and other tests.

FREQUENTLY ASKED QUESTIONS

1. Write short notes/enumerate:
   a. Nerve supply of dorsum of hand
   b. Nerve supply nail beds of all 5 digits
   c. Median cubital vein
   d. Ventral axial line

2. Describe the beginning, course, termination of basilic vein

3. Describe the lymphatic drainage of upper limb. Enumerate the groups of lymph nodes of the axilla.

MULTIPLE CHOICE QUESTIONS

1. Skin of nail bed of ring finger is supplied by:
   a. Lateral half by median, medial half by ulnar
   b. Medial half by median, lateral half by radial
   c. Whole by median nerve
   d. Whole by ulnar nerve

2. Skin of anterior, medial and lateral sides of arm is supplied by all *except:*
   a. Medial cutaneous nerve of arm
   b. Lateral supraclavicular nerve
   c. Posterior cutaneous nerve of arm
   d. Intercostobrachial nerve

3. Ventral axial line extends till:
   a. Till wrist joint
   b. Till elbow joint
   c. Middle of forearm
   d. Middle of arm

4. Cephalic vein drains into axillary vein:
   a. In lower part of arm
   b. In upper part of arm
   c. In the forearm
   d. In infraclavicular fossa

5. Lymph shed lies on the:
   a. Lateral side of arm
   b. Medial side of arm
   c. Anterior aspect of arm
   d. Posterior aspect of arm

6. Spinal segments T1–T6 lie opposite:
   a. Spines of 1–4 thoracic vertebrae
   b. Spines of 1–6 thoracic vertebrae
   c. Spines of 2–7 thoracic spines
   d. Spines of 2–8 thoracic spines

ANSWERS

1. a   2. c   3. a   4. d   5. d   6. a

Arm

The man who gets angry, at the right things, with the right people, in the right way, at the right time and for the right length of time is commended
—Aristotle

INTRODUCTION

The arm extends from the shoulder joint till the elbow joint. The skeleton of the arm is a 'solo' bone, the humerus. Medial and lateral intermuscular septa divide the arm into an anterior or flexor compartment and a posterior or extensor compartment, to give each compartment its individuality and freedom of action. Since the structures in the front of arm continue across the elbow joint into the cubital fossa, the cubital fossa is also included in this chapter. The arm is called brachium, so most of the structures in this chapter are named accordingly, like brachialis, coracobrachialis and brachial artery.

SURFACE LANDMARKS

The following landmarks can be felt in the living subject.

1 The *greater tubercle of the humerus* is the most lateral bony point in the shoulder region. It can be felt just below the acromion, deep to the deltoid when the arm is by the side of the trunk (Fig. 8.1).
2 The *shaft of the humerus* is felt only indistinctly because it is surrounded by muscles in its upper half. In the lower half, the humerus is covered anteriorly by the biceps brachii and brachialis, and posteriorly by the triceps brachii.
3 The *medial epicondyle of the humerus* is a prominent bony projection on the medial side of the elbow. It is best seen and felt in a mid-flexed elbow.
4 The *lateral epicondyle of the humerus* is less prominent than the medial. It can be felt in the upper part of the depression on the posterolateral aspect of the elbow in the extended position of the forearm.
5 The medial and lateral *supracondylar ridges* are better defined in the lower portions of the medial and lateral borders of the humerus. They can be felt in

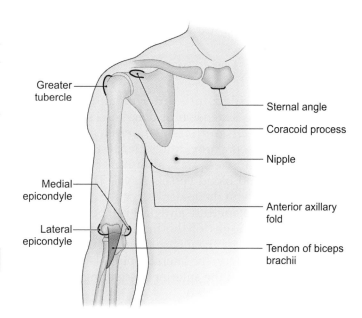

Fig. 8.1: Surface landmarks—front of upper arm

the lower one-fourth of the arm as upward continuations of the epicondyles.
6 The *deltoid* forms the rounded contour of the shoulder. The apex of the muscle is attached to the deltoid tuberosity located at the middle of the anterolateral surface of the humerus.
7 The *coracobrachialis* forms an inconspicuous rounded ridge in the upper part of the medial side of the arm. Pulsations of the brachial artery can be felt in the depression behind it.
8 The *biceps brachii* muscle is overlapped above by the pectoralis major and by the deltoid. Below these muscles the biceps forms a conspicuous elevation on the front of the arm. Upon flexing the elbow, the contracting muscle become still more prominent. The tendon of the biceps can be felt in front of the

elbow. The tendon is a guide to the brachial artery which lies on its medial side.

9 The *brachial artery* can be felt in front of the elbow joint just medial to the tendon of the biceps brachii. Brachial pulsations are used for recording the blood pressure.

10 The *ulnar nerve* can be rolled by the palpating finger behind the medial epicondyle of the humerus. During leprosy this nerve becomes thick and enlarged.

11 The superficial cubital veins can be made more prominent by applying tight pressure round the arm and then contracting the forearm muscles by clenching and releasing the fist a few times. The cephalic vein runs upwards along the lateral border of the biceps. The basilic vein can be seen along the lower half of the medial border of the biceps. The cephalic and basilic veins are connected together in front of the elbow by the median cubital vein which runs obliquely upwards and medially.

COMPARTMENTS OF THE ARM

The arm is divided into anterior and posterior compartments by extension of deep fascia which are called the *medial* and *lateral intermuscular septa* (Fig. 8.2). These septa provide additional surface for the attachment of muscles. They also form planes along which nerves and blood vessels travel. The septa are well defined only in the lower half of the arm and are attached to the medial and lateral borders and supracondylar ridges of the humerus. The medial septum is pierced by the ulnar nerve and the superior ulnar collateral artery; the lateral septum is pierced by the radial nerve and the anterior descending branch of the profunda brachii artery.

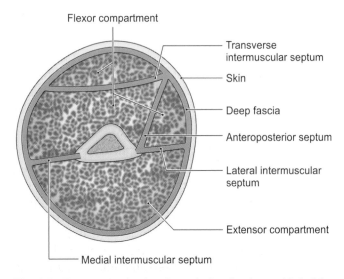

Flexor compartment

— Transverse intermuscular septum

— Skin

— Deep fascia

— Anteroposterior septum

— Lateral intermuscular septum

— Extensor compartment

— Medial intermuscular septum

Fig. 8.2: Transverse section through the distal one-third of the arm, showing the intermuscular septa and the compartments

Two additional septa are present in the anterior compartment of the arm. The *transverse septum* separates the biceps from the brachialis and encloses the musculocutaneous nerve. The *anteroposterior septum* separates the brachialis from the muscles attached to the lateral supracondylar ridge; it encloses the radial nerve and the anterior descending branch of the profunda brachii artery.

ANTERIOR COMPARTMENT

DISSECTION

Make an incision in the middle of deep fascia of the upper arm right down up to the elbow joint. Reflect the flaps sideways.

The most prominent muscle seen is the biceps brachii. Deep to this, another muscle called brachialis is seen easily. In the fascial septum between the two muscles lies the musculocutaneous nerve (a branch of the lateral cord of brachial plexus). Trace the tendinous long head of biceps arising from the supraglenoid tubercle and the short head arising from the tip of the coracoid process of scapula. Identify coracobrachialis muscle on the medial side of biceps brachii. This muscle is easily identified as it is pierced by musculocutaneous nerve. Clean the branches of the nerve supplying all the three muscles dissected.

MUSCLES

Muscles of the anterior compartment of the arm are the coracobrachialis, the biceps brachii and the brachialis. They are described in Tables 8.1 and 8.2.

Changes at the Level of Insertion of Coracobrachialis

1 *Bone*: The circular shaft becomes triangular below this level.

2 *Fascial septa*: The medial and lateral intermuscular septa become better defined from this level down.

3 *Muscles*
   i. Deltoid and coracobrachialis are inserted at this level.
   ii. Upper end of origin of brachialis.
   iii. Upper end of origin of the medial head of triceps brachii.

4 *Arteries*
   i. The brachial artery passes from the medial side of the arm to its anterior aspect.
   ii. The profunda brachii artery runs in the spiral groove and divides into its anterior descending/ radial collateral artery and posterior descending/ middle collateral branches.
   iii. The superior ulnar collateral artery originates from the brachial artery, and pierces the medial intermuscular septum alongwith the ulnar nerve.
   iv. The nutrient artery of the humerus enters the bone.

Table 8.1: Attachments of muscles

Muscle	Origin	Insertion
1. **Coracobrachialis** (*see* Fig. 2.8)	• The tip of the coracoid process with the short head of the biceps brachii	The tendon of long head of biceps brachii undergoes twisting, in a way that anterior surface becomes lateral and posterior surface becomes medial. The middle 5 cm of the medial border of the humerus
2. **Biceps brachii** (Fig. 8.3)	It has two heads of origin • The short head arises with coracobrachialis from the tip of the coracoid process • The long head arises from the supraglenoid tubercle of the scapula and from the glenoidal labrum. The tendon is intracapsular	• Posterior rough part of the radial tuberosity. The tendon is twisted; the anterior fibres become lateral and posterior fibres become medial. The tendon is separated from the anterior part of the tuberosity by a bursa (Fig. 8.4) • The tendon gives off an extension called the bicipital aponeurosis which extends to ulna and it separates median cubital vein from brachial artery
3. **Brachialis** (Fig. 8.5)	• Lower half of the front of the humerus, including both the anteromedial and anterolateral surfaces and the anterior border Superiorly the origin embraces the insertion of the deltoid • Medial and lateral intermuscular septa	• Coronoid process and ulnar tuberosity • Rough anterior surface of the coronoid process of the ulna

Table 8.2: Nerve supply and actions of muscles

Muscle	Nerve supply	Actions
1. **Coracobrachialis** (Fig. 8.6)	Musculocutaneous nerve (C5–C7)	Flexes the arm at the shoulder joint
2. **Biceps brachii**	Musculocutaneous nerve (C5, C6)	• It is strong supinator when the forearm is flexed All screwing movements are done with it • It is a flexor of the elbow • The short head is a flexor of the arm • The long head prevents upwards displacement of the head of the humerus • It can be tested against resistance as shown in Fig. 8.6
3. **Brachialis**	• Musculocutaneous nerve is motor • Radial nerve is proprioceptive	Flexes forearm at the elbow joint

5 *Veins*
  i. The basilic vein pierces the deep fascia.
  ii. Two venae comitantes of the brachial artery may unite to form one brachial vein.
6 *Nerves*
  i. The median nerve crosses the brachial artery from the lateral to the medial side.
  ii. The ulnar nerve pierces the medial intermuscular septum with the superior ulnar collateral artery and goes to the posterior compartment.
  iii. The radial nerve pierces the lateral intermuscular septum with the anterior descending (radial collateral) branch of the profunda brachii artery and passes from the posterior to the anterior compartment.

  iv. The medial cutaneous nerve of the arm pierces the deep fascia.
  v. The medial cutaneous nerve of the forearm pierces the deep fascia.

Morphological Importance of Coracobrachialis

Morphologically, the muscle is very important for following reasons.

The coracobrachialis represents the medial compartment, which is so well developed in the thigh.

In some animals, it is a tricipital muscle. In human, the upper two heads have fused and musculocutaneous nerve passes between the two, and the lowest third head has disappeared. Persistence of the lower head in

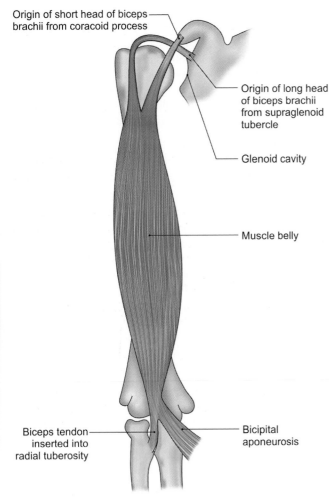

Fig. 8.3: The biceps brachii muscle in extended elbow

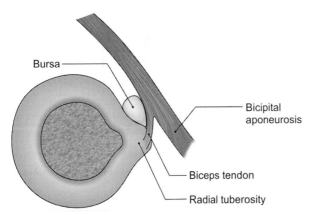

Fig. 8.4: The precise mode of insertion of the biceps brachii muscle

human is associated with the presence of "ligament of Struthers", which is a fibrous band extending from the trochlear spine to the medial epicondyle of the humerus, to which the third head of the coracobrachialis is inserted, and from the lower part of which the pronator teres muscle takes origin. Beneath the ligament pass the median nerve or brachial artery or both.

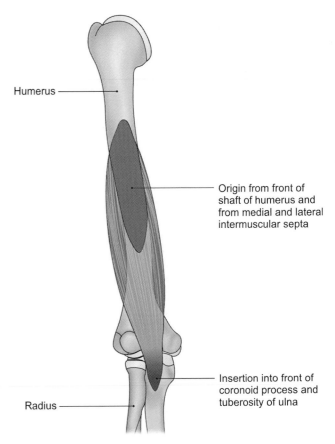

Fig. 8.5: The origin and insertion of the brachialis muscle

The front or anterior compartment of the arm is homologous with flexor and medial compartments of the thigh. The flexor compartments of thigh lies posteriorly because the lower limb bud rotates medially.

MUSCULOCUTANEOUS NERVE

The musculocutaneous nerve is the main nerve of the front of the arm, and continues below the elbow as the lateral cutaneous nerve of the forearm (*see* Fig. 7.1a).

It is a branch of the lateral cord of the brachial plexus, arising at the lower border of the pectoralis minor (*see* Fig. 4.14) in the axilla.

Root Value

The root value of musculocutaneous nerve is ventral rami of C5–C7 segments of spinal cord.

Origin, Course and Termination

Musculocutaneous nerve arises from the lateral cord of brachial plexus in the lower part of the axilla. It accompanies the third part of the axillary artery. It then enters the front of arm, where it pierces coracobrachialis muscle.

Musculocutaneous nerve runs downwards and laterally between biceps brachii and brachialis muscles

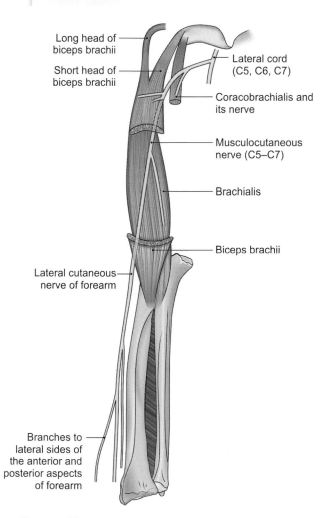

Fig. 8.6: The course of the musculocutaneous nerve

Relations

In the lower part of the axilla: It accompanies the third part of the axillary artery and has the following relations.

Anteriorly: Pectoralis major.

Posteriorly: Subscapularis.

Medially: Axillary artery and lateral root of the median nerve (*see* Fig. 4.9).

Laterally: Coracobrachialis (*see* Fig. 4.9).

Musculocutaneous nerve leaves the axilla, and enters the front of the arm by piercing the coracobrachialis (Fig. 8.6).

In the arm: It runs downward and laterally between the biceps brachii and brachialis to reach the lateral side of the tendon of the biceps. It ends by piercing the fascia 2 cm above the bend of the forearm.

Branches and Distribution

Muscular branches: It supplies the following muscles of the front of the arm.
  i. Coracobrachialis
  ii. Biceps brachii, long and short heads
  iii. Brachialis (Fig. 8.7).

Cutaneous branches: Through the lateral cutaneous nerve of the forearm, it supplies the skin of the lateral side of the forearm from the elbow to the wrist including the ball of the thumb (*see* Fig. 7.1a).

Articular branches:
  i. The elbow joint through its branch to the brachialis.
  ii. The shoulder joint through a separate branch which enters the humerus along with its nutrient artery.

Communicating branches: The musculocutaneous nerve through lateral cutaneous nerve of forearm communicates with the neighbouring nerve, namely the superficial branch of the radial nerve, the posterior

to reach the lateral side of the tendon of biceps brachii. It terminates by continuing as the lateral cutaneous nerve of forearm 2 cm above the bend of the elbow (Fig. 8.6).

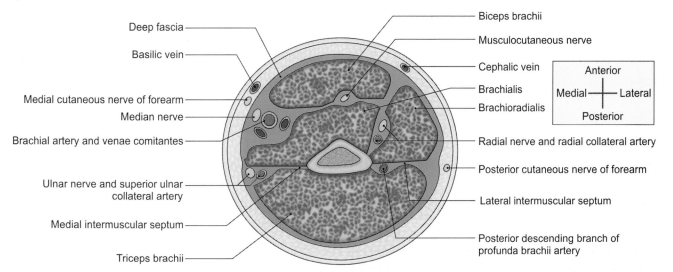

Fig. 8.7: Transverse section passing through the lower one-third of the arm

cutaneous nerve of the forearm, and the palmar cutaneous branch of the median nerve.

CLINICAL ANATOMY

Physician holds the patients wrist firmly, not letting it move. Patient is requested to flex the elbow against the resistance offered by physician's hand. One can see and palpate hardening biceps brachii muscle (Fig. 8.8).

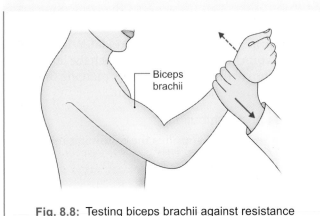

Biceps brachii

Fig. 8.8: Testing biceps brachii against resistance

BRACHIAL ARTERY

DISSECTION

Dissect the brachial artery as it lies on the medial side of the upper part of the arm medial to median nerve and lateral to ulnar nerve (Fig. 8.9).

In the lower half of the upper arm, the brachial artery is seen lateral to the median nerve as the nerve crosses the brachial artery from lateral to medial side. Note that the median nerve and brachial artery are forming together a neurovascular bundle.

Ulnar nerve accompanied by the superior ulnar collateral branch of the brachial artery will be dissected later as it reaches the posterior (extensor) compartment of the upper arm after piercing the medial intermuscular septum.

Look for the radial nerve on the posterior aspect of artery before it enters the radial groove.

Clean the branches of brachial artery and identify other arteries which take part in the arterial anastomoses around the elbow joint.

Features

Brachial artery is the continuation of the axillary artery. It extends from the lower border of the teres major muscle to a point in front of the elbow, at the level of the neck of the radius, just medial to the tendon of the biceps brachii.

Beginning, Course and Termination

Brachial artery begins at the lower border of teres major muscle as continuation of axillary artery. It runs downwards and laterally in the front of arm and crosses the elbow joint. It ends at the level of the neck of radius in the cubital fossa by dividing into its two terminal branches, the radial and ulnar arteries.

Relations

1 It runs downwards and laterally, from the medial side of the arm to the front of the elbow.
2 It is superficial throughout its extent and is accompanied by two venae comitantes.
3 Anteriorly, in the middle of the arm, it is crossed by the median nerve from the lateral to the medial side; and in front of the elbow, it is covered by the bicipital aponeurosis and the median cubital vein (Fig. 8.9).
4 Posteriorly, it is related to:
   i. The triceps brachii
   ii. The radial nerve and the profunda brachii artery.

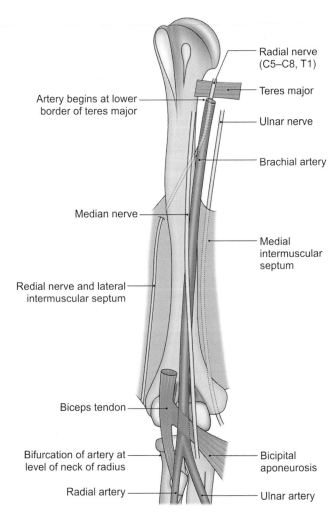

Radial nerve (C5–C8, T1)

Artery begins at lower border of teres major

Teres major

Ulnar nerve

Brachial artery

Median nerve

Medial intermuscular septum

Redial nerve and lateral intermuscular septum

Biceps tendon

Bifurcation of artery at level of neck of radius

Bicipital aponeurosis

Radial artery

Ulnar artery

Fig. 8.9: The course and relations of the brachial artery

5 Medially, in the upper part, it is related to the ulnar nerve and the basilic vein, and in the lower part to the median nerve (Fig. 8.9).

6 Laterally, it is related to the coracobrachialis, the biceps brachii and the median nerve in its upper part; and to the tendon of the biceps brachii at the elbow (Fig. 8.9).

7 At the elbow, the structures from the medial to the lateral side are:
   i. Median nerve.
   ii. Brachial artery.
   iii. Biceps brachii tendon.
   iv. Radial nerve on a deeper plane (MBBR).

Branches

1 Unnamed *muscular* branches.
2 The *profunda brachii artery* arises just below the teres major and accompanies the radial nerve.
3 The *superior ulnar collateral* branch arises in the upper part of the arm and accompanies the ulnar nerve (Figs 8.10a and b).
4 A nutrient artery is given off to the humerus.
5 The *inferior ulnar collateral* (or supratrochlear) branch arises in the lower part and takes part in the anastomoses around the elbow joint.
6 The artery ends by dividing into two terminal branches, the *radial* and *ulnar* arteries.

Anastomoses around the Elbow Joint

Anastomoses around the elbow joint link the brachial artery with the upper ends of the radial and ulnar arteries. They supply the ligaments and bones of the joint. The anastomoses can be subdivided into the following parts.

In front of the lateral epicondyle of the humerus, the anterior descending (radial collateral) branch of the profunda brachii anastomoses with the radial recurrent branch of the radial artery (Fig. 8.10).

Behind the lateral epicondyle of the humerus, the posterior descending branch of the profunda brachii artery (middle collateral) anastomoses with the interosseous recurrent branch of the posterior interosseous artery.

In front of the medial epicondyle of the humerus, the inferior ulnar collateral branch of the brachial artery, anastomoses with the anterior ulnar recurrent branch of the ulnar artery.

Behind the medial epicondyle of the humerus, the superior ulnar collateral branch of the brachial artery anastomoses with the posterior ulnar recurrent branch of the ulnar artery.

CLINICAL ANATOMY

• Brachial pulsations are felt or auscultated in front of the elbow just medial to the tendon of biceps for recording the blood pressure (Fig. 8.11). Figure 8.12 shows other palpable arteries.

Upper Limb

Section 1

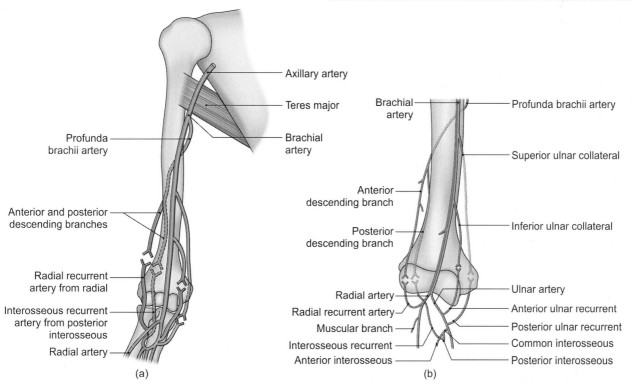

(a)   (b)

Figs 8.10a and b: Anastomoses around the elbow joint

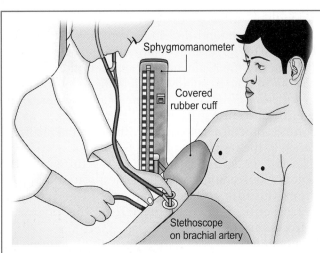

Fig. 8.11: Blood pressure being taken

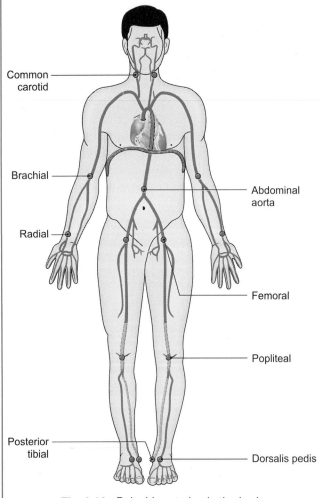

Fig. 8.12: Palpable arteries in the body

- Although the brachial artery can be compressed anywhere along its course, it can be compressed most favourably in the middle of the arm, where it lies on the tendon of the coracobrachialis.

LARGE NERVES

Median Nerve

Median nerve is closely related to the brachial artery throughout its course in the arm (Fig. 8.9).

In the upper part, it is lateral to the artery; in the middle of the arm, it crosses the artery from lateral to the medial side; and remains on the medial side of the artery right up to the elbow.

In the arm, the median nerve gives off a branch to the pronator teres just above the elbow and vascular branches to the brachial artery.

An articular branch to the elbow joint arises at the elbow.

Ulnar Nerve

Ulnar nerve runs on the medial side of the brachial artery up to the level of insertion of the coracobrachialis, where it pierces the medial intermuscular septum and enters the posterior compartment of the arm. It is accompanied by the superior ulnar collateral vessels.

At the elbow, it passes behind the medial epicondyle where it can be palpated with a finger (Fig. 8.13).

Radial Nerve

At the beginning of the brachial artery, the radial nerve lies posterior to the artery (*see* Fig. 4.9). Soon the nerve leaves the artery by entering the radial (spiral) groove

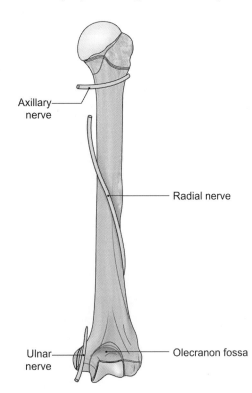

Fig. 8.13: Nerves related to posterior aspect of humerus

on the back of the arm where it is accompanied by the profunda brachii artery (Fig. 8.13).

In the lower part of the arm, the nerve appears again on the front of the arm where it lies between the brachialis (medially); and the brachioradialis and extensor carpi radialis longus (laterally) (Fig. 8.17). Its branches will be discussed with the back of the arm.

CUBITAL FOSSA

DISSECTION

Identify the structures (see text) present in the roof of a shallow cubital fossa located on the front of the elbow. Separate the lateral and medial boundaries formed respectively by the brachioradialis and pronator teres muscles (Figs 8.14 and 8.19). Clean the contents:
i. Median nerve on the medial side of brachial artery.
ii. Terminal part of brachial artery bifurcating into radial and ulnar arteries.
iii. The tendon of biceps brachii muscle between the brachial artery and radial nerve.
iv. The radial nerve on a deeper plane on the lateral side of biceps tendon.
   Identify brachialis and supinator muscles, forming the floor of cubital fossa.

Features

Cubital (Latin *cubitus, elbow*) fossa is a triangular hollow situated on the front of the elbow (it is homologous with the popliteal fossa of the lower limb situated on the back of the knee.)

Boundaries

Laterally – Medial border of the brachioradialis (Fig. 8.14).
Medially – Lateral border of the pronator teres.
Base – It is directed upwards, and is represented by an imaginary line joining the *front of* two epicondyles of the humerus.
Apex – It is directed downwards, and is formed by the area where brachioradialis crosses the pronator teres muscle.

Roof

The roof of the cubital fossa (Fig. 8.15) is formed by:
a. Skin.
b. Superficial fascia containing the median cubital vein joining the cephalic and basilic veins. The lateral cutaneous nerve of the forearm lies along with cephalic vein and the medial cutaneous nerve of the forearm along with basilic vein.
c. Deep fascia.
d. Bicipital aponeurosis.

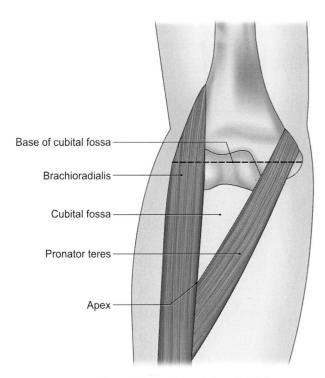

Fig. 8.14: Boundaries of the right cubital fossa

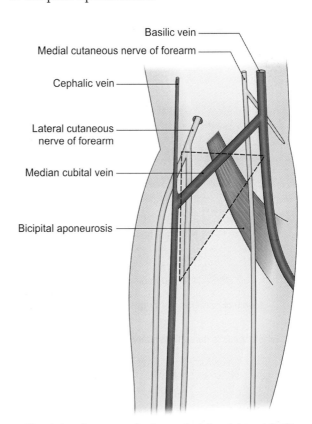

Fig. 8.15: Structures in the roof of the right cubital fossa

Floor

It is formed by:
 i. Brachialis (Figs 8.16a and b)
 ii. Supinator surrounding the upper part of radius

Contents

The fossa is actually very narrow. The contents described are seen after retracting the boundaries. From medial to the lateral side, the contents are as follows:

1 *The median nerve:* It gives branches to flexor carpi radialis, palmaris longus, flexor digitorum superficialis and leaves the fossa by passing between the two heads of pronator teres (Figs 8.17 and 8.18).

2 The termination of the *brachial artery*, and the beginning of the radial and ulnar arteries lie in the fossa.

  The radial artery is smaller and more superficial than the ulnar artery. It gives off the radial recurrent branch. The ulnar artery goes deep to both heads of pronator teres and runs downwards and medially, being separated from the median nerve by the deep head of the pronator teres (Fig. 8.19).

  Ulnar artery gives off the anterior ulnar recurrent, the posterior ulnar recurrent, and the common interosseous branches (Fig. 8.10).

  The common interosseous branch divides into the anterior and posterior interosseous arteries, and latter gives off the interosseous recurrent branch.

3 The tendon of the *biceps brachii*, with the bicipital aponeurosis (*see* Fig. 9.3b).

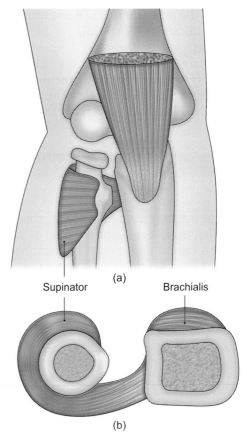

Supinator   (a)   Brachialis

(b)

Figs 8.16a and b: The floor of the cubital fossa is formed by the brachialis and supinator muscles: (a) Surface view, and (b) cross-sectional view

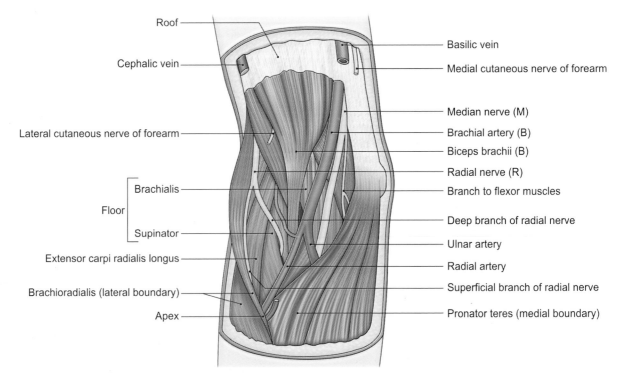

Roof

Cephalic vein

Lateral cutaneous nerve of forearm

Brachialis
Floor
Supinator

Extensor carpi radialis longus

Brachioradialis (lateral boundary)

Apex

Basilic vein

Medial cutaneous nerve of forearm

Median nerve (M)

Brachial artery (B)

Biceps brachii (B)

Radial nerve (R)

Branch to flexor muscles

Deep branch of radial nerve

Ulnar artery

Radial artery

Superficial branch of radial nerve

Pronator teres (medial boundary)

Fig. 8.17: Muscles forming floor of right cubital fossa with its contents; contents shown as mnemonic—MBBR

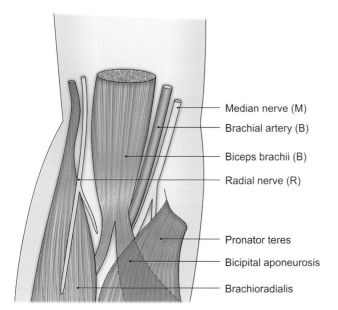

Fig. 8.18: Contents of the right cubital fossa; mnemonic—MBBR

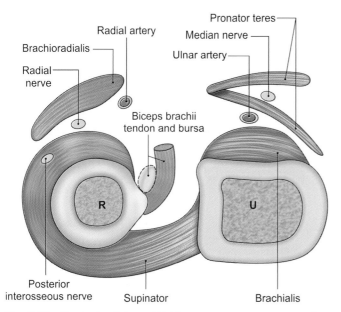

Fig. 8.19: Contents of the cubital fossa as seen a cross-section

4 The *radial nerve:* It desends medial to lateral epicondyle to enter cubital fossa. In the fossa it gives off the posterior interosseous nerve or deep branch of the radial nerve which gives branches to extensor capri radialis brevis and supinator. Then it leaves the fossa by piercing the supinator muscle (Fig. 8.17). The remaining superficial branch runs in the front of forearm for some distance.

CLINICAL ANATOMY

- The cubital region is important for the following reasons:

a. The median cubital vein is often the vein of choice for intravenous injections (*see* Fig. 7.8).
b. The blood pressure is universally recorded by auscultating the brachial artery in front of the elbow (Fig. 8.11).

- The anatomy of the cubital fossa is useful while dealing with the fracture around the elbow, like the supracondylar fracture of the humerus.

POSTERIOR COMPARTMENT

DISSECTION

Reflect the skin of back of arm to view the triceps brachii muscle. Define its attachments and separate the long head of the muscle from its lateral head.

Radial nerve will be seen passing between the long head of triceps and medial border of the humerus. Note the continuity of radial nerve up to axilla. Carefully cut through the lateral head of triceps to expose radial nerve along with profunda brachii vessels. Note that the radial nerve lies in the radial groove, on the back of humerus, passing between the lateral head of triceps above and its medial head below. In the lower part of arm, the radial nerve lies on the front of elbow just lateral to the brachialis, dividing into two terminal branches in the cubital fossa.

The ulnar nerve (which was seen in the anterior compartment of arm till its middle) pierces the medial intermuscular septum with its accompanying vessels, reaches the back of elbow and may easily be palpated on the back of medial epicondyle of humerus.

Features

The region contains the triceps muscle, the radial nerve and the profunda brachii artery. The nerve and artery run through the muscle. The ulnar nerve runs through the lower part of this compartment.

TRICEPS BRACHII MUSCLE

Origin

Triceps brachii muscle arises by the following three heads (Figs 8.20 and 8.21):

1 The *long head* arises from the infraglenoid tubercle of the scapula; it is the longest of the three heads.
2 The *lateral head* arises from an oblique ridge on the upper part of the posterior surface of the humerus, corresponding to the lateral lip of the radial (spiral) groove (*see* Fig. 2.14b).
3 The *medial head* arises from a large triangular area on the posterior surface of the humerus below the radial groove, as well as from the medial and lateral intermuscular septa. At the level of the radial

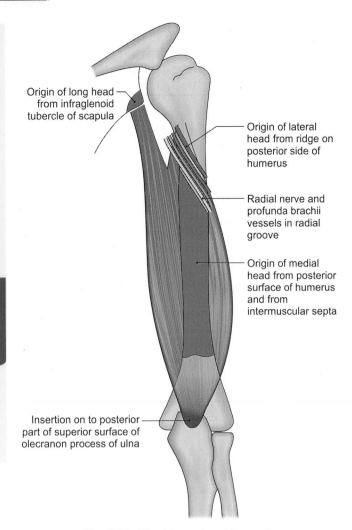

Origin of long head from infraglenoid tubercle of scapula

Origin of lateral head from ridge on posterior side of humerus

Radial nerve and profunda brachii vessels in radial groove

Origin of medial head from posterior surface of humerus and from intermuscular septa

Insertion on to posterior part of superior surface of olecranon process of ulna

Fig. 8.20: The triceps brachii muscle

groove, the medial head is medial to the lateral head (*see* Fig. 2.14b).

Insertion

The long and lateral heads converge and fuse to form a superficial flattened tendon which covers the medial head and are inserted into the posterior part of the superior surface of the *olecranon process* (*see* Fig. 2.23). The medial head is inserted partly into the superficial tendon, and partly into the olecranon. Although the medial head is separated from the capsule of the elbow joint by a small bursa, a few of its fibres are inserted into this part of the capsule: This prevents nipping of the capsule during extension of the arm. These fibres are referred to as the *articularis cubiti*, or as the *subanconeus*.

Nerve Supply

Each head receives a separate branch from the radial nerve (C7, C8). The branches arise in the axilla and in the radial groove.

CLINICAL ANATOMY

- In radial nerve injuries in the arm, the triceps brachii usually escapes complete paralysis because the two nerves supplying it, arise in the axilla.
- Physician holds the flexed forearm firmly. Patient is requested to extend his elbow against the resistance of the physicians hand. The contracting triceps brachii is felt (Fig. 8.22).

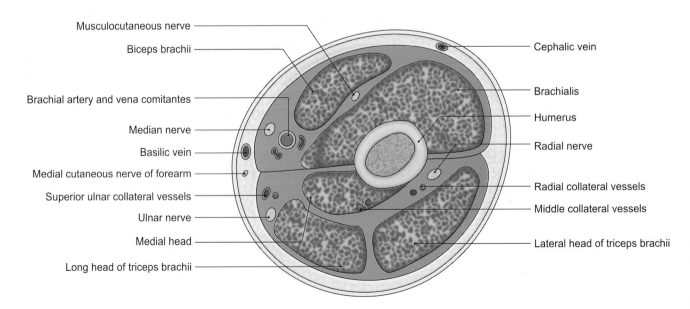

Musculocutaneous nerve

Biceps brachii

Brachial artery and vena comitantes

Median nerve

Basilic vein

Medial cutaneous nerve of forearm

Superior ulnar collateral vessels

Ulnar nerve

Medial head

Long head of triceps brachii

Cephalic vein

Brachialis

Humerus

Radial nerve

Radial collateral vessels

Middle collateral vessels

Lateral head of triceps brachii

Fig. 8.21: Transverse section through the arm a little below the insertion of the coracobrachialis and deltoid showing arrangement of three heads of the triceps, and the radial nerve in the radial groove

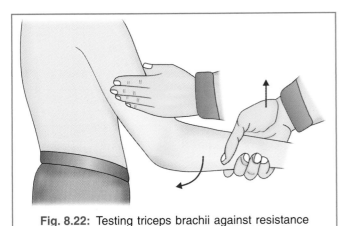

Fig. 8.22: Testing triceps brachii against resistance

Actions

The triceps is a powerful active extensor of the elbow. The long head supports the head of the humerus in the abducted position of the arm. Gravity extends the elbow passively.

Electromyography has shown that the medial head of the triceps is active in all forms of extension, and the actions of the long and lateral heads are minimal, except when acting against resistance.

RADIAL NERVE OR MUSCULOSPIRAL NERVE

Radial nerve is the largest branch of the posterior cord of the brachial plexus with a root value of C5–C8 and T1 (*see* Fig. 4.14).

Origin, Course and Termination

Radial nerve is given off from the posterior cord in the lower part of axilla.

1 It runs behind third part of axillary artery (*see* Figs 4.7c and d).
2 In the arm, it lies behind the brachial artery (*see* Fig. 4.9).
3 Leaves the brachial artery to enter the lower triangular space to reach the oblique radial sulcus on the back of humerus (Fig. 8.13).
4 The nerve reaches the lateral side of arm 5 cm below deltoid tuberosity, pierces lateral intermuscular septum to enter the anterior compartment of arm on its lateral aspect (Fig. 8.17).
5 It descends down across the lateral epicondyle into cubital fossa.
  Radial nerve terminates by dividing into a superficial and a deep branch just below the level of lateral epicondyle. These are seen in the cubital fossa (Fig. 8.18).

Relations

a. In the lower part of the axilla, radial nerve passes downwards and has the following relations.
  Anteriorly: Third part of the axillary artery (*see* Fig. 4.8).

Posteriorly: Subscapularis, latissimus dorsi and teres major.
Laterally: Axillary nerve and coracobrachialis.
Medially: Axillary vein (*see* Fig. 4.9).
b. In the upper part of the arm, it continues behind the brachial artery, and passes posterolaterally (with the profunda brachii vessels) through the lower triangular space, below the teres major, and between the long head of the triceps brachii and the humerus. It then enters the radial groove with the profunda vessels (*see* Fig. 6.11).
c. In the radial groove, the nerve runs downwards and laterally between the lateral and medial heads of the triceps brachii, in contact with the humerus (Fig. 8.13). At the lower end of the groove, 5 cm below the deltoid tuberosity, the nerve pierces the lateral intermuscular septum and passes into the anterior compartment of the arm (Fig. 8.23) to reach the cubital fossa where it ends by dividing into superficial and deep branches.

Branches and Distribution

Various branches of radial nerve are shown in Fig. 8.23.

Muscular

1 Before entering the spiral groove, radial nerve supplies the long and medial heads of the triceps brachii.
2 In the spiral groove, it supplies the lateral and medial heads of the triceps brachii and the anconeus.
3 Below the radial groove, on the front of the arm, it supplies the brachialis with proprioceptive fibres. The brachioradialis and extensor carpi radialis longus are supplied with motor fibres.

Cutaneous Branches

1 In the axilla, radial nerve gives off the posterior cutaneous nerve of the arm which supplies the skin on the back of the arm (*see* Fig. 7.1b).
2 In the radial groove, the radial nerve gives off the lower lateral cutaneous nerves of the arm and the posterior cutaneous nerve of the forearm.
  Articular branches: The articular branches near the elbow supply the elbow joint.

CLINICAL ANATOMY

• The radial nerve is very commonly damaged in the region of the radial (spiral) groove. The common causes of injury are as follows.
  a. Sleeping in an armchair with the limb hanging by the side of the chair (saturday night palsy), or even the pressure of the crutch (crutch paralysis) (Fig. 8.24a and b).
  b. Fractures of the shaft of the humerus. This results in the weakness and loss of power of

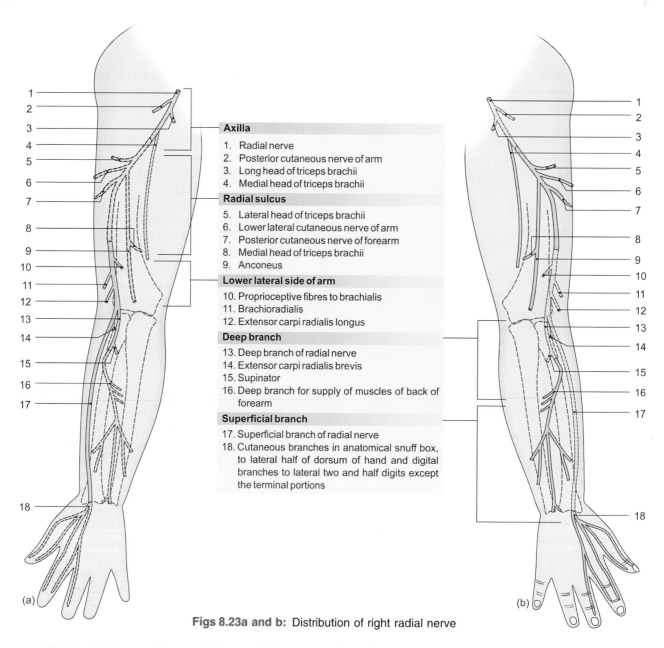

Axilla

1. Radial nerve
2. Posterior cutaneous nerve of arm
3. Long head of triceps brachii
4. Medial head of triceps brachii

Radial sulcus

5. Lateral head of triceps brachii
6. Lower lateral cutaneous nerve of arm
7. Posterior cutaneous nerve of forearm
8. Medial head of triceps brachii
9. Anconeus

Lower lateral side of arm

10. Proprioceptive fibres to brachialis
11. Brachioradialis
12. Extensor carpi radialis longus

Deep branch

13. Deep branch of radial nerve
14. Extensor carpi radialis brevis
15. Supinator
16. Deep branch for supply of muscles of back of forearm

Superficial branch

17. Superficial branch of radial nerve
18. Cutaneous branches in anatomical snuff box, to lateral half of dorsum of hand and digital branches to lateral two and half digits except the terminal portions

Figs 8.23a and b: Distribution of right radial nerve

extension at the wrist (wrist drop) (Fig. 8.25) and sensory loss over a narrow strip on the back of forearm, and on the lateral side of the dorsum of the hand (Fig. 8.26).

- Wrist drop is quite disabling, because the patient cannot grip any object firmly in the hand without the synergistic action of the extensors.

PROFUNDA BRACHII ARTERY

Profunda brachii artery is a large branch, arising just below the teres major. It accompanies the radial nerve through the radial groove, and before piercing the lateral intermuscular septum, it divides into the anterior and posterior descending branches which take part in the anastomoses around the elbow joint (Fig. 8.10).

Branches

1 The *radial collateral (anterior descending)* artery is one of the terminal branches, and represents the continuation of the profunda artery. It accompanies the radial nerve, and ends by anastomosing with the radial recurrent artery in front of the lateral epicondyle of the humerus (Fig. 8.10).

2 The *middle collateral (posterior descending)* artery is the largest terminal branch, which descends in the substance of the medial head of the triceps. It ends by anastomosing with the interosseous recurrent artery, behind the lateral epicondyle of the humerus (Fig. 8.10). It usually gives a branch which accompanies the nerve to the anconeus.

3 The *deltoid (ascending)* branch ascends between the long and lateral heads of the triceps, and

anastomoses with the descending branch of the posterior circumflex humeral artery.

4 The *nutrient artery to the humerus* is often present. It enters the bone in the radial groove just behind the deltoid tuberosity. However, it may be remembered that the main artery to the humerus is a branch of the brachial artery.

Mnemonics

Cubital fossa contents MBBR
From medial to lateral:
· Median nerve
· Brachial artery
· Tendon of biceps
· Radial nerve

Biceps brachii muscle: Origins
"You walk shorter to a street corner. You ride longer on a superhighway"
Short head originates from coracoid process.
Long head originates from the supraglenoid tubercle.

FACTS TO REMEMBER

• Medial root of median nerve crosses the axillary artery in front to join lateral root to form the median nerve.
• The order of structures from medial to lateral side in the cubital fossa is median nerve, brachial artery, tendon of biceps brachii and radial nerve.
• Triceps brachii is the only active extensor of elbow joint. Gravity extends the joint passively.
• Biceps brachii is a strong supinator of the flexed elbow, besides being its flexor.

CLINICOANATOMICAL PROBLEM

In a motorcycle accident, there was injury to the middle of back of arm
• What nerve is likely to be injured?
• What muscles are affected? Name five of them.
• What is the effect of injury?

Ans: Due to injury to the middle of back of arm, the radial nerve gets injured. The muscles of arm affected partially are lateral and medial heads of triceps brachii. A part of muscle escapes paralysis as it gets supplied in the axilla.

The other muscles affected are the extensors of forearm. These are brachioradialis, extensor carpi radialis longus and brevis, extensor digitorum and extensor pollicis longus.

The effect of injury is "wrist drop".

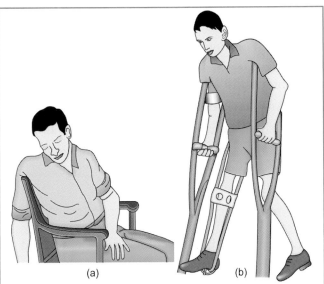

Figs 8.24a and b: Injury to radial nerve: (a) Saturday night palsy, and (b) crutch paralysis

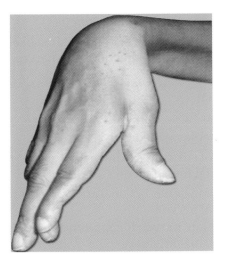

Fig. 8.25: Wrist drop

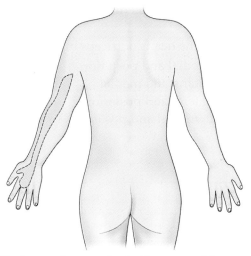

Fig. 8.26: Sensory loss over back of forearm and dorsum of hand

FREQUENTLY ASKED QUESTIONS

1. Describe musculocutaneous nerve under following headings:
   a. Root value   b. Course
   c. Branches   d. Relations
   e. Clinical anatomy

2. Enumerate all the boundaries and contents of cubital fossa. Give the clinical importance of the fossa.

3. Write short notes on:
   a. Changes at the level of insertion of coraco-brachialis
   b. Anastomoses around the elbow joint
   c. Origin and insertion of triceps brachii muscle
   d. Branches of deep branch of radial nerve. What is the effect of its injury?

MULTIPLE CHOICE QUESTIONS

1. Which event does not occur at the insertion of coracobrachialis?
   a. Median nerve crosses brachial artery from the lateral to the medial side
   b. Ulnar nerve pierces medial intermuscular septum
   c. Lateral cutaneous nerve of forearm pierces the deep fascia
   d. Radial nerve pierces lateral intermuscular septum

2. Interosseous recurrent artery is a branch of which artery?
   a. Ulnar
   b. Common interosseous
   c. Anterior interosseous
   d. Posterior interosseous

3. Which nerve is felt behind medial epicondyle of humerus?
   a. Radial
   b. Median
   c. Musculocutaneous
   d. Ulnar

4. Which of the following nerve injury leads to wrist drop?
   a. Ulnar
   b. Radial
   c. Median
   d. Axillary

5. Lateral boundary of cubital fossa is formed by which muscle?
   a. Biceps brachii
   b. Brachioradialis
   c. Brachialis
   d. Extensor carpi radialis longus

6. Fracture of humerus at mid-shaft is likely to cause injury to which of the following nerves?
   a. Median
   b. Radial
   c. Ulnar
   d. Musculocutaneous

7. Order of structures from medial side to lateral side in cubital fossa is:
   a. Median nerve, brachial artery, biceps tendon and radial nerve
   b. Median nerve, biceps tendon, radial nerve, branchial artery
   c. Median nerve, brachial artery, radial nerve and biceps tendon
   d. Brachial artery, median nerve, biceps tendon, radial nerve

8. Which are the heads of triceps brachii muscle:
   a. Long, medial and posterior
   b. Long, lateral and medial
   c. Long, lateral and posterior
   d. Lateral, medial and posterior

ANSWERS
1. c   2. d   3. d   4. b   5. b   6. b   7. a   8. b

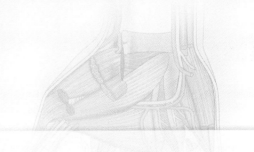

CHAPTER
9

Forearm and Hand

God gave you ears, eyes and hands. Use them on the patients in that order
—William Kelsey

INTRODUCTION

Forearm extends between the elbow and the wrist joints. Radius and ulna form its skeleton. These two bones articulate at both their ends to form superior and inferior radioulnar joints. Their shafts are kept at optimal distance by the interosseous membrane. Muscles accompanied by nerves and blood vessels are present both on the front and the back of the forearm. Hand is the most distal part of the upper limb, meant for carrying out diverse activities. Numerous muscles, tendons, bursae, blood vessels and nerves are artistically placed and protected in this region.

SURFACE LANDMARKS OF FRONT OF FOREARM

1 The *epicondyles* of the humerus have been examined. Note that medial epicondyle is more prominent than the lateral. The posterior surface of the medial epicondyle is crossed by the *ulnar nerve* which can be rolled under the palpating finger. Pressure on the nerve produces tingling sensations on the medial side of the hand (*see* Fig. 8.13).

2 The *tendon of the biceps brachii* can be felt in front of the elbow. It can be made prominent by flexing the elbow joint against resistance. Pulsations of the brachial artery can be felt just medial to the tendon (*see* Fig. 8.18).

3 The *head of the radius* can be palpated in a depression on the posterolateral aspect of the extended elbow, distal to the lateral epicondyle. Its rotation can be felt during pronation and supination of the forearm.

4 The *styloid process* of the radius projects 1 cm lower than the styloid process of the ulna (Fig. 9.1). It can be felt in the upper part of the anatomical snuff box. Its tip is concealed by the tendons of the *abductor pollicis longus* and the *extensor pollicis brevis,* which must be relaxed during palpation.

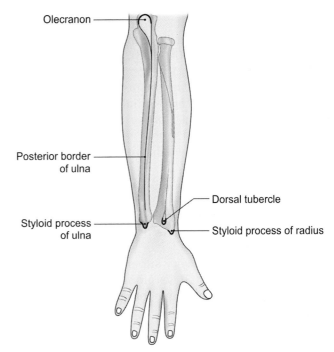

Fig. 9.1: Surface landmarks: Back of forearm

5 The *head of the ulna* forms a surface elevation on the medial part of the posterior surface of the wrist when the hand is pronated.

6 The *styloid process of the ulna* projects downwards from the posteromedial aspect of the lower end of the ulna. Its tip can be felt on the posteromedial aspect of the wrist, where it lies about 1 cm above the tip of the styloid process of the radius (Fig. 9.1).

7 The *pisiform bone* can be felt at the base of the hypothenar eminence (medially) where the tendon of the *flexor carpi ulnaris* terminates. It becomes visible and easily palpable at the medial end of the distal transverse crease (junction of forearm and hand) when the wrist is fully extended.

8 The *hook of the hamate* lies one finger breadth below the pisiform bone, in line with the ulnar border of the ring finger. It can be felt only on deep palpation through the hypothenar muscles.

9 The *tubercle of the scaphoid* lies beneath the lateral part of the distal transverse crease in an extended wrist. It can be felt at the base of the thenar eminence in a depression just lateral to the tendon of the flexor carpi radialis (Fig. 9.2).

10 The *tubercle (crest) of the trapezium* may be felt on deep palpation inferolateral to the tubercle of the scaphoid.

11 The *brachioradialis* becomes prominent along the lateral border of the forearm when the elbow is flexed against resistance in the midprone position of the hand.

12 The *tendons of the flexor carpi radialis, palmaris longus,* and *flexor carpi ulnaris* can be identified on the front of the wrist when the hand is flexed against resistance. The tendons lie in the order stated, from lateral to medial side (Fig. 9.3).

13 The pulsation of the *radial artery* can be felt in front of the lower end of the radius just lateral to the tendon of the flexor carpi radialis.

14 The pulsations of the *ulnar artery* can be felt by careful palpation just lateral to the tendon of the flexor carpi ulnaris. Here the ulnar nerve lies medial to the artery.

15 The *transverse creases* in front of the wrist are important landmarks. The proximal transverse crease lies at the level of the wrist joint, and distal crease corresponds to the proximal border of the flexor retinaculum.

16 The *median nerve* is very superficial in position at and above the wrist. It lies along the lateral edge of the tendon of the palmaris longus at the middle of the wrist.

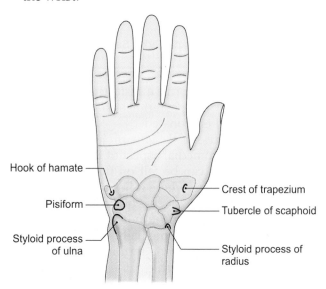

Fig. 9.2: Surface landmarks: Wrist and palm

Hook of hamate

Pisiform

Styloid process of ulna

Crest of trapezium

Tubercle of scaphoid

Styloid process of radius

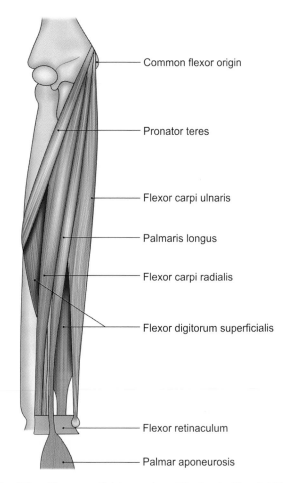

Common flexor origin

Pronator teres

Flexor carpi ulnaris

Palmaris longus

Flexor carpi radialis

Flexor digitorum superficialis

Flexor retinaculum

Palmar aponeurosis

Fig. 9.3a: The superficial muscles of the front of the right forearm

MUSCLES OF FRONT OF FOREARM

DISSECTION

The skin of the forearm has already been reflected on each side. Cut through the superficial and deep fasciae to expose the superficial muscles of the forearm.

Identify these five superficial muscles. These are from lateral to medial side, pronator teres getting inserted into middle of radius, flexor carpi radialis reaching till the wrist, palmaris longus continuing with palmar aponeurosis, flexor digitorum superficialis passing through the palm and most medially the flexor carpi ulnaris getting inserted into the pisiform bone (Fig. 9.3).

Deep muscles

Cut through the origin of superficial muscles of forearm at the level of medial epicondyle of humerus and reflect them distally. This will expose the three deep muscles, e.g. flexor pollicis longus, flexor digitorum profundus and pronator quadratus (*refer* the 🦴).

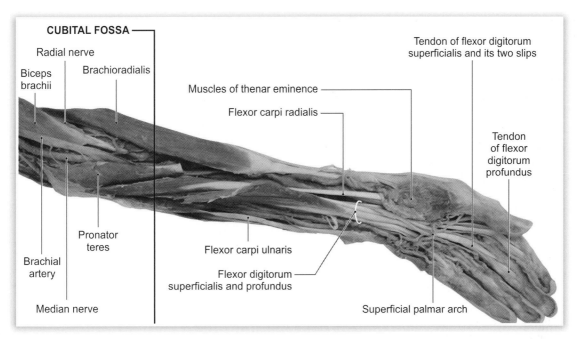

CUBITAL FOSSA

Radial nerve

Biceps brachii

Brachioradialis

Muscles of thenar eminence

Flexor carpi radialis

Tendon of flexor digitorum superficialis and its two slips

Tendon of flexor digitorum profundus

Pronator teres

Brachial artery

Median nerve

Flexor carpi ulnaris

Flexor digitorum superficialis and profundus

Superficial palmar arch

Fig. 9.3b: Dissection of cubital fossa, front of forearm and palm

The muscles of the front of the forearm may be divided into superficial and deep groups.

Components

The front of the forearm presents the following components for study.
1 Eight muscles, five superficial and three deep.
2 Two arteries, radial and ulnar.
3 Three nerves, median, ulnar and radial.

These structures can be better understood by reviewing the long bones of the upper limb and having an articulated hand by the side.

SUPERFICIAL MUSCLES

There are five muscles in the superficial group. These are the pronator teres, the flexor carpi radialis, the palmaris longus, the flexor carpi ulnaris and the flexor digitorum superficialis (Tables 9.1 and 9.2).

Common Flexor Origin

All the superficial flexors of the forearm have a common origin from the front of the medial epicondyle of the humerus. This is called the common flexor origin.

Additional Features of Superficial Muscles

1 *Pronator teres:* Pronator teres comprises a big humeral and a smaller ulnar head. Between the two heads,

Table 9.1: Attachment of the superficial muscles

Muscle	Origin	Insertion
1. **Pronator teres**	Medial epicondyle of humerus	Middle of lateral aspect of shaft of radius
2. **Flexor carpi radialis**	Medial epicondyle of humerus	Bases of second and third metacarpal bones
3. **Palmaris longus**	Medial epicondyle of humerus	Flexor retinaculum and palmar aponeurosis
4. **Flexor digitorum superficialis** (*see* Figs 2.22 and 9.8)		
• Humeroulnar head	Medial epicondyle of humerus; medial border of coronoid process of ulna	Muscle divides into 4 tendons. Each tendon divides into 2 slips which are inserted on sides of middle phalanx of 2nd to 5th digits (Fig. 9.3b)
Radial head	Anterior oblique line of shaft of radius	
5. **Flexor carpi ulnaris**		
• Humeral head	Medial epicondyle of humerus	Pisiform bone; insertion prolonged to hook of the hamate and base of fifth metacarpal bone (*see* Fig. 2.32a)
• Ulnar head	Medial aspect of olecranon process and posterior border of ulna	

Table 9.2: Nerve supply and actions of the superficial muscles

Muscle	Nerve supply	Actions
1. **Pronator teres**	Median nerve	Pronation of forearm
2. **Flexor carpi radialis**	Median nerve	Flexes and abducts hand at wrist joint
3. **Palmaris longus**	Median nerve	Flexes wrist joint
4. **Flexor digitorum superficialis** (Figs 9.4 and 9.5)	Median nerve	Flexes middle phalanx of fingers and assists in flexing proximal phalanx and wrist joint
5. **Flexor carpi ulnaris**	Ulnar nerve	Flexes and adducts the hand at the wrist joint

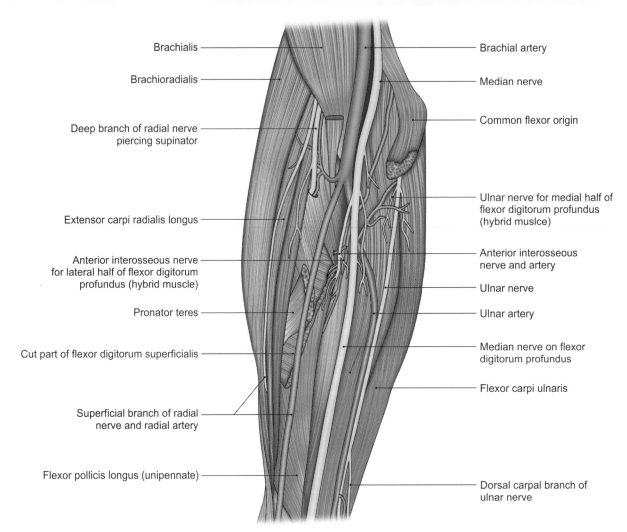

Fig. 9.4: Muscles, nerves and arteries seen in the forearm

median nerve leaves the cubital fossa. Deep to the two heads exits ulnar artery from cubital fossa into the front of forearm. It forms medial boundary of the cubital fossa. It is the pronator of forearm (*see* Figs 8.19 and 9.11).

2 *Flexor carpi radialis:* It passes through a separate deep compartment of the flexor retinaculum.

Flexor carpi radialis gets inserted into anterior aspects of bases of second and third metacarpal bones.

It is easily seen and is a guide to radial pulse which lies lateral to the tendon (Fig. 9.6).

3 *Palmaris longus:* Palmaris longus continues as palmar aponeurosis into the palm to protect the nerves and vessels there. Its tendon lies superficial to flexor retinaculum.

4 *Flexor carpi ulnaris:* It is inserted into pisiform bone. Pisiform is a sesamoid bone in this tendon.

5 *Flexor digitorum superficialis:* Flexor digitorum superficialis comprises the humeroulnar and radial

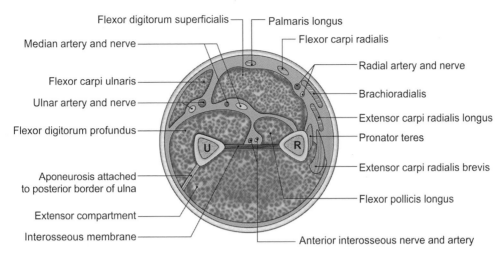

Fig. 9.5: Transverse section through the middle of forearm showing the compartments, nerves and arteries

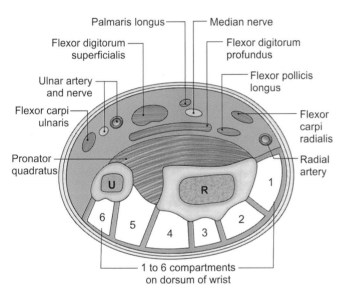

Fig. 9.6: Transverse section passing just above wrist showing arrangement of the structures in flexor (anterior) compartment

heads. The two heads of the muscle are joined by a fibrous arch. Median nerve and ulnar artery pass downwards deep to the fibrous arch (Fig. 9.4).

DEEP MUSCLES

Deep muscles of the front of the forearm are the flexor digitorum profundus, the flexor pollicis longus and the pronator quadratus and are described in Tables 9.3 and 9.4. Following are some other points of importance about these muscles.

Additional Points about the Flexor Digitorum Profundus

1 It is the most powerful, and most bulky muscle of the forearm. It forms the muscular elevation seen and felt on the posterior surface of the forearm medial to

the subcutaneous posterior border of the ulna (Fig. 9.5).
2 The main gripping power of the hand is provided by the flexor digitorum profundus.
3 The muscle is supplied by two different nerves. So it is a hybrid muscle.

Additional Points about the Flexor Pollicis Longus

1 The anterior interosseous nerve and vessels descend on the anterior surface of the interosseous membrane between the flexor digitorum profundus and the flexor pollicis longus (Fig. 9.5).
2 The tendon passes deep to the flexor retinaculum between the opponens pollicis and the oblique head of the adductor pollicis, to enter the fibrous flexor sheath of the thumb. It lies in radial bursa (Fig. 9.6).

Synovial Sheaths of Flexor Tendons

1 *Common flexor synovial sheath (ulnar bursa):* The long flexor tendons of the fingers (flexor digitorum superficialis and profundus) are enclosed in a common synovial sheath while passing deep to the flexor retinaculum (carpal tunnel). The sheath has a parietal layer lining the walls of the carpal tunnel, and a visceral layer closely applied to the tendons (Fig. 9.7). From the arrangement of the sheath, it appears that the synovial sac has been invaginated by the tendons from its lateral side. The synovial sheath extends upwards for 5.0 or 7.5 cm into the forearm and downwards into the palm up to the middle of the shafts of the metacarpal bones. It is important to note that the lower medial end is continuous with the digital synovial sheath of the little finger.
2 *Synovial sheath of the tendon of flexor pollicis longus (radial bursa):* This sheath is separate. Superiorly, it is coextensive with the common sheath and

Table 9.3: Attachments of the deep muscles

Muscle	Origin	Insertion
1. **Flexor digitorum profundus** (composite or hybrid muscle) (Figs 9.5 and 9.7)	• Upper three-fourths of the anterior and medial surface of the shaft of ulna • Upper three-fourths of the posterior border of ulna • Medial surface of the olecranon and coronoid processes of ulna • Adjoining part of the anterior surface of the interosseous membrane	• The muscle forms 4 tendons for the medial 4 digits which enter the palm by passing deep to the flexor retinaculum in ulnar bursa and digital synovial sheaths • Opposite the proximal phalanx of the corresponding digit, the tendon perforates the tendon of the flexor digitorum superficialis (Fig. 9.8) • Each tendon is inserted on the palmar surface of the base of the distal phalanx (Fig. 9.3b)
2. **Flexor pollicis longus**	• Upper three-fourths of the anterior surface of the shaft of radius (*see* Fig. 2.22) • Adjoining part of the anterior surface of the interosseous membrane	• The tendon enters the palm by passing deep to the flexor retinaculum • It is inserted into the palmar surface of the distal phalanx of the thumb
3. **Pronator quadratus**	Oblique ridge on the lower one-fourth of anterior surface of the shaft of ulna, and the area medial to it (*see* Fig. 2.22)	• Superficial fibres into the lower one-fourth of the anterior surface and the anterior border of the radius • Deep fibres into the triangular area above the ulnar notch

Table 9.4: Nerve supply and actions of the deep muscles

Muscle	Nerve supply	Actions
1. **Flexor digitorum profundus** (Fig. 9.4)	• Medial half by ulnar nerve • Lateral half by anterior interosseous nerve (C8, T1) (branch of median nerve)	• Flexor of distal phalanges after the flexor digitorum superficialis has flexed the middle phalanges • Secondarily, it flexes the other joints of the digits, fingers, and the wrist • It is the chief gripping muscle. It acts best when the wrist is extended
2. **Flexor pollicis longus**	Anterior interosseous nerve	• Flexes the distal phalanx of the thumb. Continued action may also flex the proximal joints crossed by the tendon
3. **Pronator quadratus**	Anterior interosseous nerve	• Superficial fibres pronate the forearm • Deep fibres bind the lower ends of radius and ulna

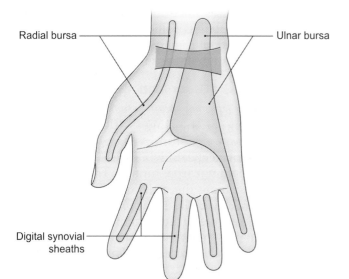

Fig. 9.7: The synovial sheaths of the flexor tendons, i.e. ulnar bursa, radial bursa and digital synovial sheaths

inferiorly it extends up to the distal phalanx of the thumb (Fig. 9.7).

3. *Digital synovial sheaths:* The sheaths enclose the flexor tendons in the fingers and line the fibrous flexor

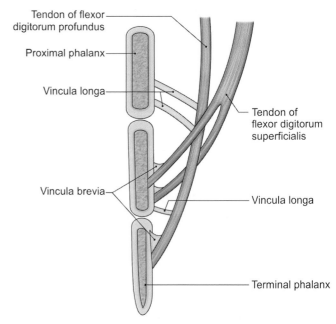

Fig. 9.8: The flexor tendons of a finger showing the vincula longa and brevia

sheaths. The digital sheath of the little finger is continuous with the ulnar bursa, and that of the thumb with the radial bursa. However, the digital sheaths of the index, middle and ring fingers are separate and independent (Fig. 9.7).

Vincula Longa and Brevia

The vincula longa and brevia are synovial folds, similar to the mesentery, which connect the tendons to the phalanges. They transmit vessels to the tendons (Fig. 9.8). These are the remnants of mesotendon.

ARTERIES OF FRONT OF FOREARM

DISSECTION

Having dissected the superficial and deep group of muscles of the forearm, identify the terminal branches of the brachial artery, e.g. ulnar and radial arteries and their branches.

Radial artery follows the direction of the brachial artery (Fig. 9.9).

Ulnar artery passes obliquely deep to heads of pronator teres and then runs vertically till the wrist. Carefully look for common interosseous branch of ulnar artery and its anterior and posterior branches (*see* Fig. 8.10).

Features

The most conspicuous arteries of the forearm are the radial and ulnar arteries. However, they mainly supply the hand through the deep and superficial palmar arches. The arterial supply of the forearm is chiefly derived from the common interosseous branch of the ulnar artery, which divides into anterior and posterior interosseous arteries. The posterior interosseous artery is reinforced in the upper part and replaced in the lower part by the anterior interosseous artery.

RADIAL ARTERY

Beginning, Course and Termination

Radial artery (Fig. 9.9) is the smaller terminal branch of the brachial artery in the cubital fossa. It runs downwards to the wrist with a lateral convexity. It leaves the forearm by turning posteriorly and entering the anatomical snuff box. As compared to the ulnar artery, it is quite superficial throughout its whole course. Its distribution in the hand is described later.

Relations

1 *Anteriorly:* It is overlapped by the brachioradialis in its upper part, but in the lower half it is covered only by skin, superficial and deep fasciae.

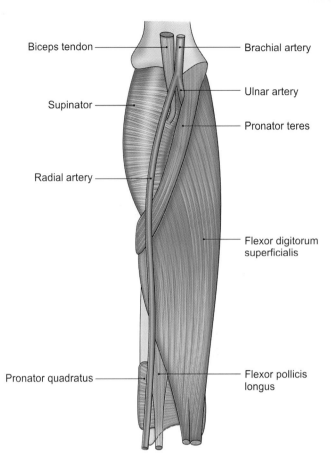

Fig. 9.9: Muscles lying deep to the radial artery

Labels: Biceps tendon, Brachial artery, Supinator, Ulnar artery, Pronator teres, Radial artery, Flexor digitorum superficialis, Pronator quadratus, Flexor pollicis longus

2 *Posteriorly:* It is related to the muscles attached to anterior surface of radius, i.e. biceps brachii, flexor pollicis longus, flexor digitorum superficialis and pronator quadratus.

3 *Medially:* It is related to the pronator teres in the upper one-third and the tendon of the flexor carpi radialis in the lower two-thirds of its course (Figs 9.9 and 9.10).

4 *Laterally:* Brachioradialis in the whole extent and the radial nerve in the middle one-third.

5 The artery is accompanied by venae comitantes.

Branches in the Forearm

1 The *radial recurrent artery* arises just below the elbow, runs upwards deep to the brachioradialis, and ends by anastomosing with the radial collateral artery (anterior branch of profunda brachii artery) in front of the lateral epicondyle of the humerus (*see* Fig. 8.10).

2 *Muscular branches* are given to the lateral muscles of the forearm.

3 The *palmar carpal branch* arises near the lower border of the pronator quadratus, runs medially deep to the flexor tendons, and ends by anastomosing with the palmar carpal branch of the ulnar artery, in front of the middle of the recurrent branch of the deep palmar

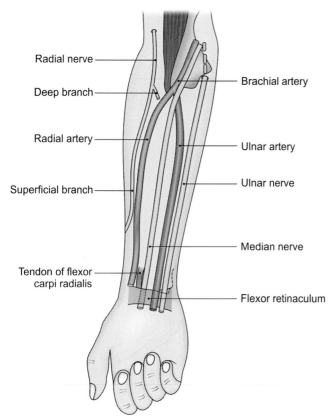

Fig. 9.10: The radial, median and ulnar nerves and vessels in the forearm

arch, to form a cruciform anastomosis. The palmar carpal arch supplies bones and joints at the wrist.

4 Dorsal carpal branch. It forms dorsal carpal arch with branch of ulnar artery.

5 The *superficial palmar branch* arises just before the radial artery leaves the forearm by winding backwards. The branch passes through the thenar muscles, and ends by joining the terminal part of the ulnar artery to complete the superficial palmar arch.

ULNAR ARTERY

Beginning, Course and Termination

Ulnar artery is the larger terminal branch of the brachial artery, and begins in the cubital fossa (Fig. 9.10). The artery runs obliquely downwards and medially in the upper one-third of the forearm; but in the lower two-thirds of the forearm its course is vertical (Fig. 9.4). It enters the palm by passing superficial to the flexor retinaculum. Its distribution in the hand is described later.

Relations

1 *Anteriorly:* In its upper half, the artery is deep and is covered by muscles arising from common flexor origin and median nerve. The lower half of the artery

is superficial and is covered only by skin and fascia (Fig. 9.4).

2 *Posteriorly:* It lies on brachialis and on the flexor digitorum profundus.

3 *Medially:* It is related to the ulnar nerve, and to the flexor carpi ulnaris (Fig. 9.11).

4 *Laterally:* It is related to the flexor digitorum superficialis (Fig. 9.4).

5 The artery is accompanied by venae comitantes.

Branches

1 The *anterior* and *posterior ulnar recurrent arteries* anastomose around the elbow. The smaller anterior ulnar recurrent artery runs up and ends by anastomosing with the inferior ulnar collateral artery in front of the medial epicondyle. The larger posterior ulnar recurrent artery arises lower than the anterior and ends by anastomosing with the superior ulnar collateral artery behind the medial epicondyle (*see* Fig. 8.11).

2 The *common interosseous artery* (about 1 cm long) arises just below the radial tuberosity. It passes backwards to reach the upper border of the interosseous membrane, and end by dividing into the anterior and posterior interosseous arteries.

The anterior interosseous artery is the deepest artery on the front of the forearm. It accompanies the anterior interosseous nerve.

It descends on the surface of the interosseous membrane between the flexor digitorum profundus and the flexor pollicis longus (Fig. 9.5).

It pierces the interosseous membrane at the upper border of the pronator quadratus to enter the extensor compartment.

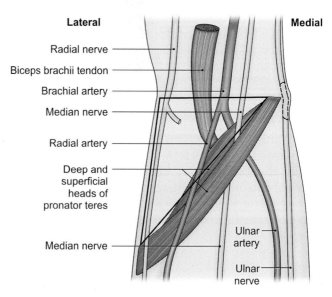

Fig. 9.11: Relations of the median nerve in right cubital fossa, and its entry into the forearm

The artery gives muscular branches to the deep muscles of the front of the forearm, nutrient branches to the radius and ulna and a *median artery* which accompanies the median nerve.

Near its origin, the *posterior interosseous artery* gives off the interosseous recurrent artery which runs upwards, and ends by anastomosing with middle collateral artery (posterior branch of profunda brachii artery) behind the lateral epicondyle. The posterior interosseous artery passes through a gap above the interosseous membrane to the back of forearm.

3 *Muscular branches* supply the medial muscles of the forearm.

4, 5 *Palmar* and *dorsal carpal branches* take part in the anastomoses round the wrist joint. The palmar carpal branch helps to form the palmar carpal arch.

The dorsal carpal branch arises just above the pisiform bone, winds backwards deep to the tendons, and ends in the dorsal carpal arch.

This arch is formed medially by the dorsal carpal branch of the ulnar artery, and laterally by the dorsal carpal branch of the radial artery.

NERVES OF FRONT OF FOREARM

DISSECTION

Median nerve is the chief nerve of the forearm. It enters the forearm by passing between two heads of pronator teres muscle. Its anterior interosseous branch is given off as it is leaving the cubital fossa. Identify median nerve stuck to the fascia on the deep surface of flexor digitorum superficialis muscle. Thus, the nerve lies superficial to the flexor digitorum profundus (Fig. 9.4).

Dissect the anterior interosseous nerve as it lies on the interosseous membrane between flexor pollicis longus and flexor digitorum profundus muscles (Fig. 9.4).

Identify the ulnar nerve situated behind the medial epicondyle. Trace it vertically down till the flexor retinaculum (Figs 9.10 and 9.11).

Trace the radial nerve and its two branches in the lateral part of the cubital fossa. Its deep branch is muscular and superficial branch is cutaneous (Fig. 9.4).

Nerves of the front of the forearm are the median, ulnar and radial nerves. The radial and ulnar nerves run along the margins of the forearm, and are never crossed by the corresponding vessels which gradually approach them. The ulnar artery, while approaching the ulnar nerve, gets crossed by the median nerve (Fig. 9.10).

MEDIAN NERVE

Median nerve is the main nerve of the front of the forearm. It also supplies the muscles of thenar eminence (Fig. 9.10).

The median nerve controls coarse movements of the hand, as it supplies most of the long muscles of the front of the forearm. It is, therefore, called the 'labourer's nerve'.

Course

Median nerve lies medial to brachial artery and enters the cubital fossa. It is the most medial content of cubital fossa (Fig. 9.11). Then it enters the forearm to lie between flexor digitorum superficialis and flexor digitorum profundus. It lies adherent to the back of superficialis muscle (Fig. 9.5). Then it reaches down the region of wrist where it lies deep and lateral to palmaris longus tendon (Fig. 9.10). Lastly, it passes deep to flexor retinaculum through carpal tunnel to enter the palm (Fig. 9.12).

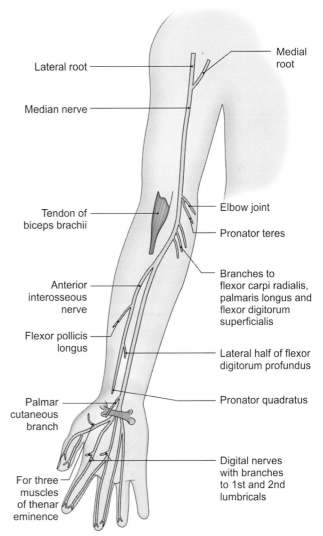

Fig. 9.12: Distribution of median nerve

Relations

1 In the cubital fossa, median nerve lies medial to the brachial artery, behind the bicipital aponeurosis, and in front of the brachialis (*see* Fig. 8.18).

2 The median nerve enters the forearm by passing between the two heads of the pronator teres. Here it crosses the ulnar artery from which it is separated by the deep head of the pronator teres (Fig. 9.11).

3 Along with the ulnar artery, the median nerve passes beneath the fibrous arch of the flexor digitorum superficialis, and runs deep to this muscle on the surface of the flexor digitorum profundus. It is accompanied by the median artery, a branch of the anterior interosseous artery. About 5 cm above the flexor retinaculum (wrist), it becomes superficial and lies between the tendons of the flexor carpi radialis (laterally) and the flexor digitorum superficialis (medially). It is overlapped by the tendon of the palmaris longus (Fig. 9.6).

4 The median nerve enters the palm by passing deep to the flexor retinaculum through the carpal tunnel.

Branches

1 *Muscular branches* are given off in the cubital fossa to flexor carpi radialis, palmaris longus and flexor digitorum superficialis (Fig. 9.12).

2 The *anterior interosseous branch* is given off in the upper part of the forearm. It supplies the flexor pollicis longus, the lateral half of the flexor digitorum profundus (giving rise to tendons for the index and middle fingers) and the pronator quadratus. The nerve also supplies the distal radioulnar and wrist joints (Fig. 9.12).

3 The *palmar cutaneous branch* arises a short distance above the flexor retinaculum, lies superficial to it and supplies the skin over the thenar eminence and the central part of the palm (*see* Fig. 7.1a).

4 *Articular branches* are given to the elbow joint and to the proximal radioulnar joint.

5 *Vascular branches* supply the radial and ulnar arteries.

6 A *communicating branch* is given to the ulnar nerve.

ULNAR NERVE

The ulnar nerve is also known as the 'musician's nerve' because it controls fine movements of the fingers. Its course in the palm will be considered in the later part of this chapter.

Course

Ulnar nerve is palpable as it lies behind medial epicondyle of humerus and is *not* a content of cubital fossa (Fig. 9.13a). It enters the forearm by passing between two heads of flexor carpi ulnaris, i.e. cubital tunnel, to lie along the lateral border of flexor carpi ulnaris in the forearm. In the last phase, it courses *superficial* to the flexor retinaculum, covered by its superficial slip or volar carpal ligament to enter the region of palm.

Relations

1 At the elbow, the ulnar nerve lies behind the medial epicondyle of the humerus. It enters the forearm by passing between the two heads of the flexor carpi ulnaris (Fig. 9.13a).

2 In the forearm, the ulnar nerve runs between the flexor digitorum profundus medially and the flexor digitorum superficialis laterally.

3 At the wrist, the ulnar neurovascular bundle lies between the flexor carpi ulnaris and the flexor digitorum superficialis. The bundle enters the palm by passing superficial to the flexor retinaculum, lateral to the pisiform bone.

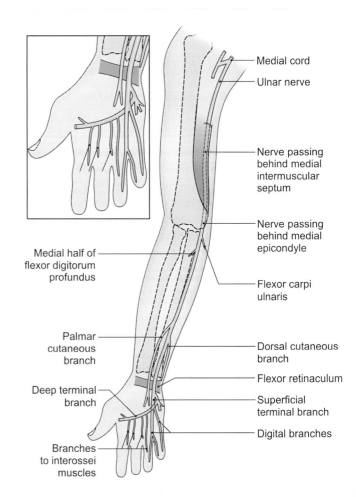

Fig. 9.13a: Course and branches of ulnar nerve

Labels: Medial cord; Ulnar nerve; Nerve passing behind medial intermuscular septum; Nerve passing behind medial epicondyle; Flexor carpi ulnaris; Dorsal cutaneous branch; Flexor retinaculum; Superficial terminal branch; Digital branches; Branches to interossei muscles; Deep terminal branch; Palmar cutaneous branch; Medial half of flexor digitorum profundus

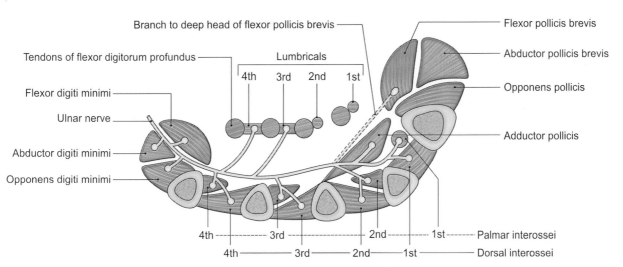

Fig. 9.13b: Distribution of deep branch of ulnar nerve

Branches

1 Muscular, to the flexor carpi ulnaris and the medial half of the flexor digitorum profundus.
2 Palmar cutaneous branch arises in the middle of the forearm and supplies the skin over the hypothenar eminence (*see* Fig. 7.1a).
3 Dorsal cutaneous branch arises 7.5 cm above the wrist, winds backwards and supplies the proximal parts of the medial 2½ fingers and the adjoining area of the dorsum of the hand (*see* Fig. 7.1b).
4 Articular branches are given off to the elbow joint.
5 Its branches in the palm are shown in Fig. 9.13b.

RADIAL NERVE

Course

The radial nerve divides into its two terminal branches in the cubital fossa just below the level of the lateral epicondyle of the humerus (Fig. 9.4).

Branches

The deep terminal branch (posterior interosseous) soon enters the back of the forearm by passing through the supinator muscle. It will be studied further in back of forearm as posterior interosseous nerve.

The superficial terminal branch (the main continuation of the nerve) runs down in front of the forearm.

The superficial terminal branch of the radial nerve is closely related to the radial artery only in the middle one-third of the forearm (Fig. 9.10).

In the upper one-third, it is widely separated from the artery, and in the lower one-third it passes backwards under the tendon of the brachioradialis.

The superficial terminal branch is purely cutaneous and is distributed to the lateral half of the dorsum of the hand, and to the proximal parts of the dorsal

surfaces of the thumb, the index finger, and lateral half of the middle finger (*see* Fig. 7.1b).

Injury to this branch results in small area of sensory loss over the root of the thumb.

PALMAR ASPECT OF WRIST AND HAND

DISSECTION

1. A horizontal incision at the distal crease of front of the wrist has already been made.
2. Make a vertical incision from the centre of the above incision through the palm to the centre of the middle finger (Fig. 9.14).
3. Make one horizontal incision along the distal palmar crease.

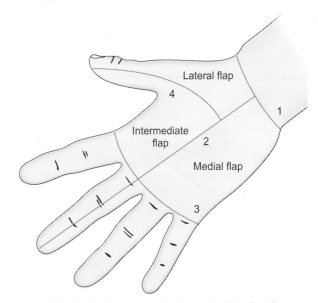

Fig. 9.14: Incisions of palm and digits (1–4)

4. Make an oblique incision starting 3 cm distal to incision no. 2 and extend it till the tip of the distal phalanx of the thumb.

Thus the skin of the palm gets divided into three areas. Reflect the skin of lateral and medial flaps on their respective sides. The skin of the intermediate flap is reflected distally towards the distal palmar crease. Further the skin of middle finger is to be reflected on either side.

Superficial fascia and deep fascia

Remove the superficial fascia to clean the underlying deep fascia.

Deep fascia is modified to form the flexor retinaculum at wrist, palmar aponeurosis in the palm, and fibrous flexor sheaths in the digits. Identify the structures on its superficial surface. Divide the flexor retinaculum between the thenar and hypothenar eminences, carefully preserving the underlying median nerve and long flexor tendons.

Identify long flexor tendons enveloped in their synovial sheaths including the digital synovial sheaths.

Features

The human hand is designed:
  i. For grasping,
 ii. For precise movements, and
iii. For serving as a tactile organ.
  There is a big area in the motor cortex of brain for muscles of hand.

The skin of the palm is:
  i. Thick for protection of underlying tissues.
 ii. Immobile because of its firm attachment to the underlying palmar aponeurosis.
iii. Creased. All of these characters increase the efficiency of the grip.
  The skin is supplied by spinal nerves C6–C8 (*see* Fig. 7.1a) through the median and ulnar nerves.

The superficial fascia of the palm is made up of dense fibrous bands which bind the skin to the deep fascia (palmar aponeurosis) and divide the subcutaneous fat into small tight compartments which serve as water-cushions during firm gripping. The fascia contains a subcutaneous muscle, the *palmaris brevis*, which helps in improving the grip by steadying the skin on the ulnar side of the hand. The superficial metacarpal ligament which stretches across the roots of the fingers over the digital vessels and nerves, is a part of this fascia.

The deep fascia is specialised to form:
  i. The flexor retinaculum at the wrist.
 ii. The palmar aponeurosis in the palm.
iii. The fibrous flexor sheaths in the fingers. All three form a continuous structure which holds the

tendons in position and thus increase the efficiency of the grip.

Flexor Retinaculum

Flexor retinaculum (Latin *to hold back*) is a strong fibrous band which bridges the anterior concavity of the carpus and converts it into a tunnel, the *carpal tunnel* (Fig. 9.15).

Attachments

Medially, to
1 The pisiform bone.
2 The hook of the hamate.

Laterally, to
1 The tubercle of the scaphoid, and
2 The crest of the trapezium.

On either side, the retinaculum has a slip:
1 The lateral *deep slip* is attached to the medial lip of the groove on the trapezium which is thus converted into a tunnel for the tendon of the flexor carpi radialis.
2 The medial *superficial slip (volar carpal ligament)* is also attached to the pisiform bone. The ulnar vessels and nerves pass deep to this slip (Figs 9.15 and 9.16).

Relations

The structures passing superficial to the flexor retinaculum are:
  i. The palmar cutaneous branch of the median nerve (Fig. 9.15).
 ii. The tendon of the palmaris longus.
iii. The palmar cutaneous branch of the ulnar nerve.
 iv. The ulnar vessels.
  v. The ulnar nerve.
  The thenar and hypothenar muscles arise from the retinaculum (Fig. 9.15).

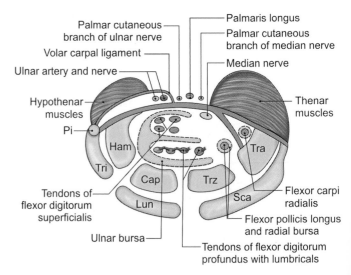

Fig. 9.15: Flexor retinaculum with its relations (schematic). Sca: scaphoid; Lun: lunate; Tri: triquetral; Pi: pisiform; Tra: trapezium; Trz: trapezoid; Cap: Capitate; Ham: hamate

The structures passing deep to the flexor retinaculum are:

i. The median nerve (Fig. 9.15).
ii. Four tendons of the flexor digitorum superficialis.
iii. Four tendons of the flexor digitorum profundus.
iv. The tendon of the flexor pollicis longus.
v. The ulnar bursa.
vi. The radial bursa.
vii. The tendon of the flexor carpi radialis lies between the retinaculum and its deep slip, in the groove on the trapezium (Fig. 9.15).

Palmar Aponeurosis

This term is often used for the entire deep fascia of the palm. However, it is better to restrict this term to the central part of the deep fascia of the palm which covers the superficial palmar arch, the long flexor tendons, the terminal part of the median nerve, and the superficial branch of the ulnar nerve (Fig. 9.16).

Features

Palmar aponeurosis is triangular in shape. The *apex* which is proximal, blends with the flexor retinaculum and is continuous with the tendon of the palmaris longus. The base is directed distally. It divides into superficial and deep strata, superficial is attached to dermis. Deep strata divides into four slips opposite the heads of the metacarpals of the medial four digits. Each slip divides into two parts which are continuous with the fibrous flexor sheaths. Extensions pass to the deep transverse metacarpal ligament, the capsule of the metacarpophalangeal joints and the sides of the base of the proximal phalanx. The digital vessels and nerves, and the tendons of the lumbricals emerge through the intervals between the slips. From the lateral and medial margins of the palmar aponeurosis, the lateral and medial *palmar septa* pass backwards and divide the palm into compartments.

Functions

Palmar aponeurosis fixes the skin of the palm and thus improves the grip. It also protects the underlying tendons, vessels and nerves.

Fibrous Flexor Sheaths of the Fingers

The fibrous flexor sheaths are made up of the deep fascia of the fingers. The fascia is thick and arched. It is attached to the sides of the phalanges and across the base of the distal phalanx. Proximally, it is continuous with a slip of the palmar aponeurosis.

In this way, a blind osseofascial tunnel is formed which contains the long flexor tendons enclosed in the digital synovial sheath (Figs 9.17a to c). The fibrous sheath is thick opposite the phalanges and thin opposite the joints to permit flexion.

The sheath holds the tendons in position during flexion of the digits.

CLINICAL ANATOMY

Dupuytren's contracture: This condition is due to inflammation involving the ulnar side of the palmar aponeurosis. There is thickening and contraction of the aponeurosis. As a result, the proximal phalanx and later the middle phalanx become flexed and cannot be straightened. The terminal phalanx remains unaffected. The ring finger is most commonly involved (Fig. 9.18).

INTRINSIC MUSCLES OF HAND

DISSECTION

Clean the thenar and hypothenar muscles. Carefully preserve the median nerve and superficial and deep branches of ulnar nerve which supply these muscles.

Abductor pollicis is the lateral muscle; flexor pollicis brevis is the medial one. Both these form the superficial lamina. The deeper lamina is constituted by opponens pollicis (Figs 9.19 to 9.22).

Cut through the abductor pollicis to expose the opponens pollicis. These three muscles constitute the muscles of thenar eminence.

Incise flexor pollicis brevis in its centre and reflect its two parts. This will reveal the tendon of flexor pollicis

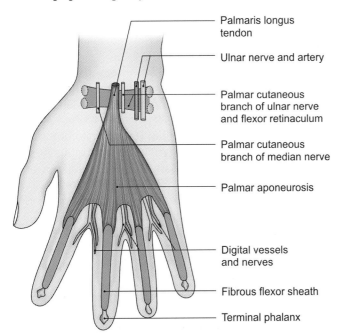

Fig. 9.16: The deep fascia of the hand forming the flexor retinaculum, palmar aponeurosis and fibrous flexor sheaths

Labels:
- Palmaris longus tendon
- Ulnar nerve and artery
- Palmar cutaneous branch of ulnar nerve and flexor retinaculum
- Palmar cutaneous branch of median nerve
- Palmar aponeurosis
- Digital vessels and nerves
- Fibrous flexor sheath
- Terminal phalanx

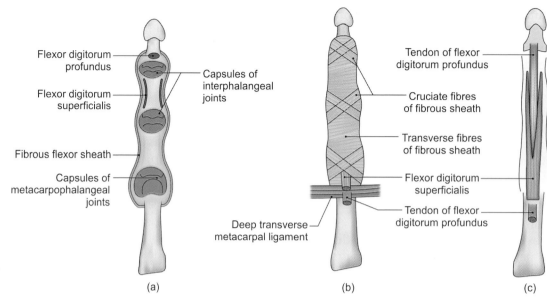

Figs 9.17a to c: The fibrous flexor sheath and its contents: (a) Bony attachments of the sheath and of the flexor tendons, (b) the fibrous sheath showing transverse fibres in front of the bones and cruciate fibres in front of joints, and (c) the flexor tendons after removal of the sheath

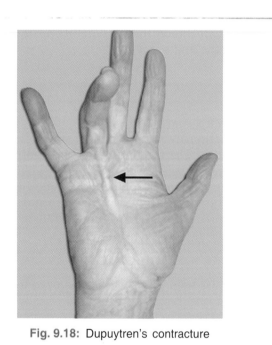

Fig. 9.18: Dupuytren's contracture

three muscles and trace their nerve supply from deep branch of ulnar nerve.

Between the two eminences of the palm, deep to palmar aponeurosis, identify the superficial palmar arch formed mainly by superficial branch of ulnar and superficial palmar branch of radial artery. Identify its common and proper digital branches.

Clean, dissect and preserve the branches of the median nerve and superficial division of ulnar nerve in the palm lying between the superficial palmar arch and long flexor tendons (Fig. 9.20).

Lying on a deeper plane are the tendons of flexor digitorum superficialis muscle. Dissect the peculiar mode of its insertion in relation to that of tendon of flexor digitorum profundus (Fig. 9.21).

Cut through the tendons of flexor digitorum superficialis 5 cm above the wrist. Divide both ends of superficial palmar arch. Reflect them distally towards the metacarpophalangeal joints.

Identify four tendons of flexor digitorum profundus diverging in the palm with four delicate muscles, the lumbricals, arising from them. Dissect the nerve supply to these lumbricals. The first and second are supplied from median and third and fourth from the deep branch of ulnar nerve (Fig. 9.21).

Divide the flexor digitorum profundus 5 cm above the wrist and reflect it towards the metacarpophalangeal joints. Trace one of its tendons to its insertion into the base of distal phalanx of one finger.

longus and adductor pollicis on a deeper plane. The three muscles of thenar eminence are supplied by thick recurrent branch of median nerve (Figs 9.20 and 9.22).

On the medial side of hand, identify thin palmaris brevis muscle in the superficial fascia. It receives a twig from the superficial branch of ulnar nerve.

Hypothenar eminence is comprised by abductor digiti minimi medially, flexor digiti minimi just lateral to it. Deep to both these lies opponens digiti minimi. Identify these

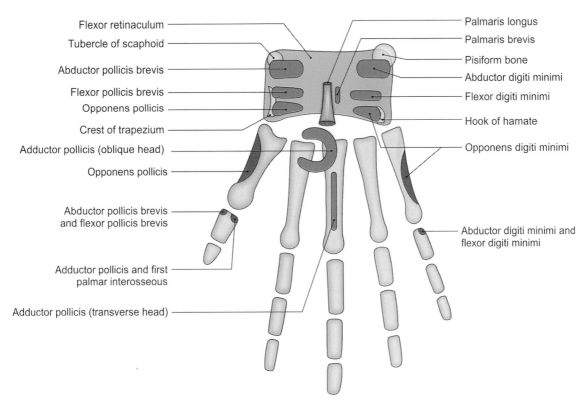

Fig. 9.19: The origin and insertion of the thenar and hypothenar muscles

Features

The intrinsic muscles of the hand serve the function of adjusting the hand during gripping and also for carrying out fine skilled movements. The origin and insertion of these muscles is within the territory of the hand.

There are 20 muscles in the hand. These are:

1 a. *Three muscles of thenar eminence*
    i. Abductor pollicis brevis (Fig. 9.19).
    ii. Flexor pollicis brevis.
    iii. Opponens pollicis.
   b. *One adductor of thumb:* Adductor pollicis.
2 *Four hypothenar muscles*
    i. Palmaris brevis.
    ii. Abductor digiti minimi.
    iii. Flexor digiti minimi (Fig. 9.20).
    iv. Opponens digiti minimi (Fig. 9.22).
   Muscles (ii) to (iv) are muscles of hypothenar eminence.
3 *Four lumbricals* (Fig. 9.21).
4 *Four palmar interossei* (Figs 9.23 and 9.24b).
5 *Four dorsal interossei* (Figs 9.23 and 9.24a).
   These muscles are described in Tables 9.5 and 9.6.

Actions of Thenar Muscles

In studying the actions of the thenar muscles, it must be remembered that the movements of the thumb take place in planes at right angles to those of the other digits because the thumb (first metacarpal) is rotated medially through 90 degrees. Flexion and extension of the thumb take place in the plane of the palm; while abduction and adduction at right angles to the plane of palm. Movement of the thumb across the palm to touch the other digits is known as "opposition". This movement is a combination of flexion and medial rotation.

Actions of Dorsal Interossei

All dorsal interossei cause abduction of the digits away from the line of the middle finger. This movement occurs in the plane of palm (Fig. 9.25) in contrast to the movement of thumb where abduction occurs at right angles to the plane of palm (Fig. 9.26). Note that movement of the middle finger to either medial or lateral side constitutes abduction. Also note that the first and fifth digits do not require dorsal interossei as they have their own abductors.

Testing of Some Intrinsic Muscles

a. *Pen/pencil test for abductor pollicis brevis:* Lay the hand flat on a table with the palm directed upwards. The patient is unable to touch with his thumb a pen/pencil held in front of the palm (Fig. 9.27).
b. *Test for opponens pollicis:* Request the patient to touch the proximal phalanx of 2nd to 5th digits with the tip of thumb.

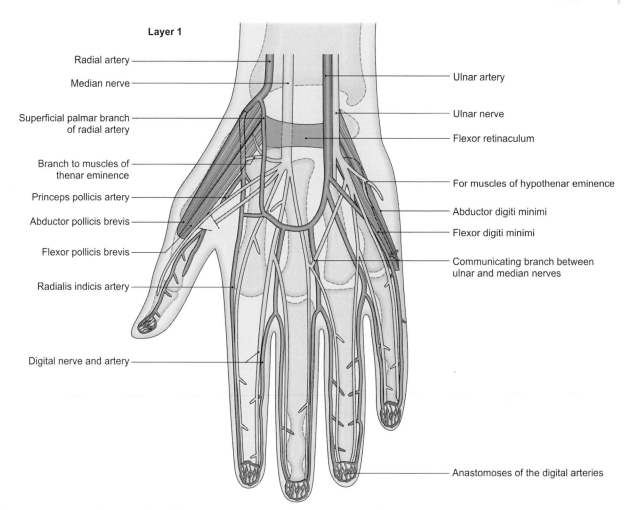

Fig. 9.20: Anterior view of right palm. Palmar aponeurosis and greater part of flexor retinaculum have been removed to display superficial palmar arch, ulnar nerve and median nerve, two muscles each of thenar and hypothenar eminences: Layer 1

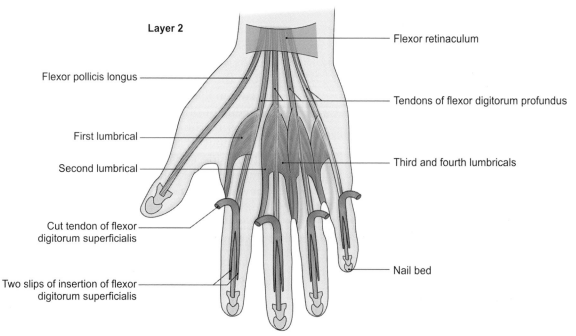

Fig. 9.21: The origin of the lumbrical muscles from tendons of flexor digitorum profundus: Layer 2

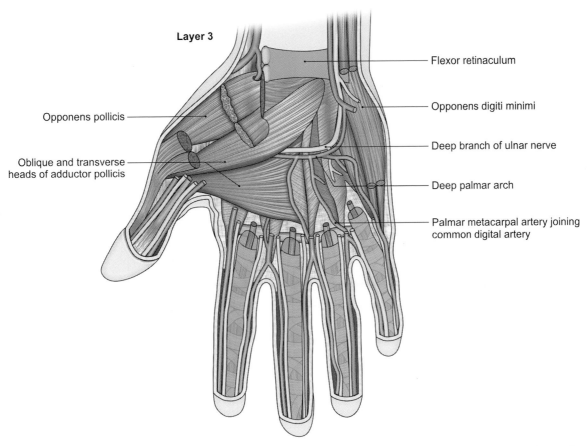

Layer 3

Opponens pollicis

Oblique and transverse heads of adductor pollicis

Flexor retinaculum

Opponens digiti minimi

Deep branch of ulnar nerve

Deep palmar arch

Palmar metacarpal artery joining common digital artery

Fig. 9.22: Deep palmar arch, deep branch of ulnar nerve, adductor pollicis and opponens muscles: Layer 3

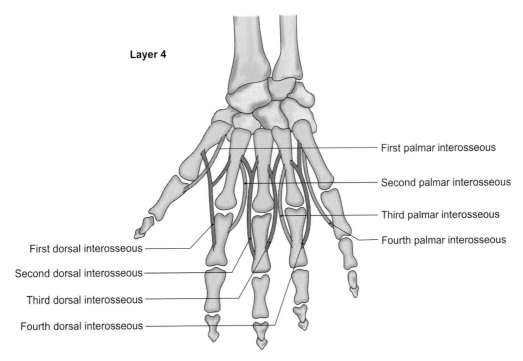

Layer 4

First palmar interosseous

Second palmar interosseous

Third palmar interosseous

Fourth palmar interosseous

First dorsal interosseous

Second dorsal interosseous

Third dorsal interosseous

Fourth dorsal interosseous

Fig. 9.23: Palmar and dorsal interossei muscles: Layer 4

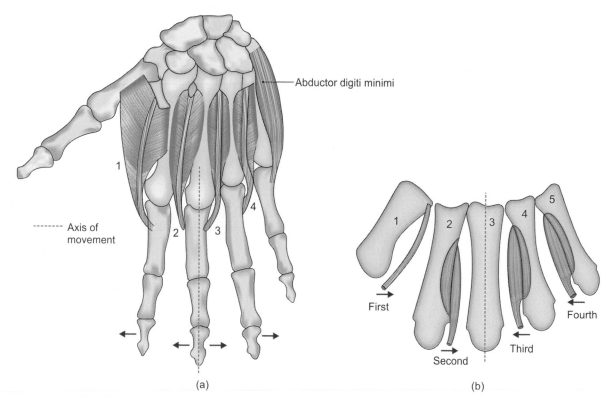

Figs 9.24a and b: (a) The dorsal interossei muscles, and (b) palmar interossei muscles

c. The *dorsal interossei* are tested by asking the subject to spread out the fingers against resistance. As index finger is abducted one feels 1st dorsal interosseous (Fig. 9.28).

d. The *palmar interossei* and *adductor pollicis* are tested by placing a piece of paper between the fingers (Fig. 9.29), between thumb and index finger and seeing how firmly it can be held (Fig. 9.30).

e. Froment's sign, or the book test which tests the *adductor pollicis* muscle. When the patient is asked to grasp a book firmly between the thumbs and other fingers of both the hands, the terminal phalanx of the thumb on the paralysed side becomes flexed at the interphalangeal joint (by the flexor pollicis longus which is supplied by the median nerve) (Fig. 9.31).

f. The lumbricals and interossei are tested by asking the subject to flex the fingers at the metacarpophalangeal joints against resistance.

ARTERIES OF HAND

DISSECTION

Deep to the lateral two tendons of flexor digitorum profundus muscle, note an obliquely placed muscle extending from two origins, i.e. from the shaft of the third metacarpal bone and the bases of 2nd and 3rd metacarpal bones and adjacent carpal bones to the base of proximal phalanx of the thumb. This is *adductor*

pollicis. Reflect the adductor pollicis muscle from its origin towards its insertion (Fig. 9.22).

Identify the deeply placed interossei muscles. Identify the radial artery entering the palm between two heads of first dorsal interosseous muscle and then between two heads of adductor pollicis muscle turning medially to join the deep branch of ulnar artery to complete the deep palmar arch (Fig. 9.32). Identify the deep branch of ulnar nerve lying in its concavity. Carefully preserve it, including its multiple branches. Deep branch of ulnar nerve ends by supplying the adductor pollicis muscle. It may supply deep head of flexor pollicis brevis also.

Lastly, define four small palmar interossei and four relatively bigger dorsal interossei muscles (Figs 9.23 and 9.24a and b).

Features

Arteries of the hand are the terminal parts of the ulnar and radial arteries. Branches of these arteries unite and form anastomotic channels called the superficial and deep palmar arches.

ULNAR ARTERY

The course of this artery in the forearm has been described earlier. It enters the palm by passing superficial to the flexor retinaculum but deep to volar carpal ligament (Fig. 9.15). It ends by dividing into the superficial palmar branch, which is the main continuation of the artery, and

Upper Limb

Section 1

Table 9.5: Attachments of small muscles of the hand

Name		Origin		Insertion
Muscles of thenar eminence				
Abductor pollicis brevis (Fig. 9.20)	1st layer	Tubercle of scaphoid, trapezium, flexor retinaculum		Base of proximal phalanx of thumb
Flexor pollicis brevis		Flexor retinaculum, trapezoid and capitate bones		Base of proximal phalanx of thumb
Opponens pollicis	3rd layer	Flexor retinaculum		Lateral half of palmar surface of the shaft of metacarpal bone of thumb
Adductor of thumb				
Adductor pollicis	3rd layer	Oblique head: Bases of 2nd–3rd metacarpals; transverse head: Shaft of 3rd metacarpal		Base of proximal phalanx of thumb on its medial aspect
Muscle of medial side of palm				
Palmaris brevis		Flexor retinaculum		Skin of palm on medial side
Muscles of hypothenar eminence				
Abductor digiti minimi	1st layer	Pisiform bone		Base of proximal phalanx of little finger
Flexor digiti minimi		Flexor retinaculum		Base of proximal phalanx of little finger
Opponens digiti minimi	3rd layer	Flexor retinaculum		Medial border of fifth metacarpal bone
Lumbricals (Fig. 9.21)				
Lumbricals (4) Arise from 4 tendons of flexor digitorum profundus	2nd layer 2nd layer	1st	Lateral side of tendon of flexor digitorum profundus of 2nd digit	Via extensor expansion into dorsum of bases of distal phalanges
		2nd	Lateral side of same tendon of 3rd digit	
		3rd	Adjacent sides of same tendons of 3rd and 4th digits	
		4th	Adjacent sides of same tendons of 4th and 5th digits	
Palmar interossei				
Palmar (4) (Fig. 9.24b)	4th layer	1st	Medial side of base of 1st metacarpal	Medial side of base of proximal phalanx of thumb or 1st digit
		2nd	Medial side of shaft of 2nd metacarpal	Via extensor expansion into dorsum of bases of distal phalanges of 2nd, 4th and 5th digits (Fig. 9.54)
		3rd	Lateral side of shaft of 4th metacarpal	
		4th	Lateral side of shaft of 5th metacarpal	
Dorsal interossei				
Dorsal (4) (Fig. 9.24a)	4th layer	1st	Adjacent sides of shafts of 1st and 2nd MC	Via extensor expansion into dorsum of bases of distal phalanges of 2nd, 3rd, 3rd and 4th digits
		2nd	Adjacent sides of shafts of 2nd and 3rd MC	
		3rd	Adjacent sides of shafts of 3rd and 4th MC	
		4th	Adjacent sides of shafts of 4th and 5th MC	

MC: Metacarpal

the deep palmar branch. These branches take part in the formation of the superficial palmar arch and deep palmar arch, respectively.

Superficial Palmar Arch

The arch represents an important anastomosis between the ulnar and radial arteries.

The convexity of the arch is directed towards the fingers, and its most distal point is situated at the level of the distal border of the fully extended thumb.

Formation

The superficial palmar arch is formed as the direct continuation of the ulnar artery beyond the flexor retinaculum, i.e. by the superficial palmar branch. On the lateral side, the arch is completed by superficial palmar branch of radial artery (Fig. 9.32).

Relations

The superficial palmar arch lies deep to the palmaris brevis and the palmar aponeurosis. It crosses the palm over the flexor digiti minimi, the flexor tendons of the fingers, the lumbricals, and the digital branches of the median nerve.

Branches

Superficial palmar arch gives off three common digital and one proper digital branches which supply the

Table 9.6: Nerve supply and actions of small muscles of the hand

Muscle	Nerve supply	Actions
Muscles of thenar eminence		
Abductor pollicis brevis (Fig. 9.20)	Median nerve	Abduction of thumb
Flexor pollicis brevis	Median nerve	Flexes metacarpophalangeal joint of thumb
Opponens pollicis	Median nerve	Pulls thumb medially and forward across palm (opposes thumb towards the fingers)
Adductor of thumb		
Adductor pollicis	Deep branch of ulnar nerve which ends in this muscle	Adduction of thumb
Muscle of medial side of palm		
Palmaris brevis	Superficial branch of ulnar nerve	Wrinkles skin to improve grip of palm
Muscles of hypothenar eminence		
Abductor digiti minimi	Deep branch of ulnar nerve	Abducts little finger
Flexor digiti minimi	Deep branch of ulnar nerve	Flexes little finger
Opponens digiti minimi	Deep branch of ulnar nerve	Pulls fifth metacarpal forward as in cupping the palm
Lumbricals (Fig. 9.21)		
Lumbricals (4)	First and second, i.e. lateral two by median nerve; third and fourth by deep branch of ulnar nerve	Flex metacarpophalangeal joints, extend interphalangeal joints of 2nd–5th digits
Palmar interossei		
Palmar (4) (Fig. 9.24b)	Deep branch of ulnar nerve	Palmar interossei adduct fingers towards centre of third digit or middle finger
Dorsal interossei		
Dorsal (4) (Figs 9.23 and 9.24a)	Deep branch of ulnar nerve	Dorsal interossei abduct fingers from centre of third digit. Both palmar and dorsal interossei flex the metacarpophalangeal joints and extend the interphalangeal joints

medial 3½ fingers. The lateral three common digital branches are joined by the corresponding palmar metacarpal arteries from the deep palmar arch.

The deep branch of the ulnar artery arises in front of the flexor retinaculum immediately beyond the pisiform bone. Soon it passes between the flexor and abductor digiti minimi to join and complete the deep palmar arch.

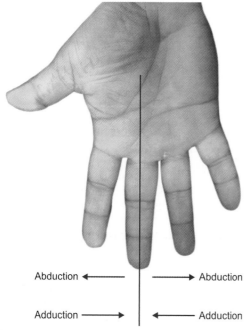

Fig. 9.25: The planes of movements of the fingers

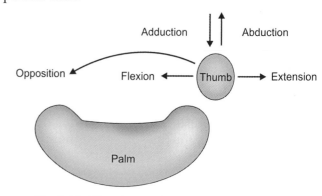

Fig. 9.26: The planes of movements of the thumb

Fig. 9.27: Pen test for abductor pollicis brevis

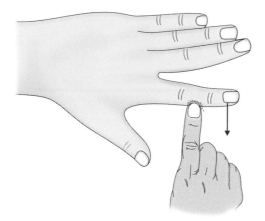

Fig. 9.28: Testing first dorsal interosseous muscle of hand

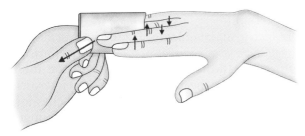

Fig. 9.29: Test for palmar interossei

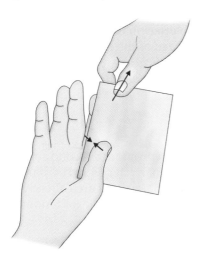

Fig. 9.30: Testing adductor pollicis

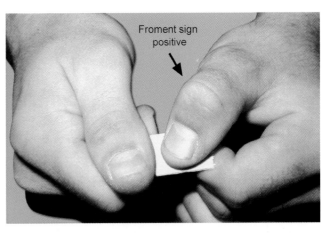

Fig. 9.31: Froment's test

CLINICAL ANATOMY

The radial artery is used for feeling the (arterial) pulse at the wrist. The pulsations can be felt well in this situation because of the presence of the flat radius behind the artery (Fig. 9.10).

RADIAL ARTERY

In this part of its course, the radial artery runs obliquely downwards, and backwards deep to the tendons of the abductor pollicis longus, the extensor pollicis brevis, and the extensor pollicis longus, and superficial to the lateral ligament of the wrist joint. Thus it passes through the *anatomical snuff box* to reach the proximal end of the first interosseous space (Fig. 9.33). Further, it passes between the two heads of the first dorsal interosseous muscle and between the two heads of adductor pollicis to form the deep palmar arch in the palm.

Course

Radial artery runs obliquely from the site of "radial pulse" to reach the anatomical snuff box. From there, it passes forwards to reach first interosseous space and then into the palm.

Relations

1 It leaves the forearm by winding backwards round the wrist.
2 It passes through the anatomical snuff box where it lies deep to the tendons of the abductor pollicis longus, the extensor pollicis brevis and the extensor pollicis longus.

   It is also crossed by the digital branches of the radial nerve.

   The artery is superficial to the lateral ligament of the wrist joint, the scaphoid and the trapezium.
3 It reaches the proximal end of the first interosseous space and passes between the two heads of the first dorsal interosseous muscle to reach the palm.

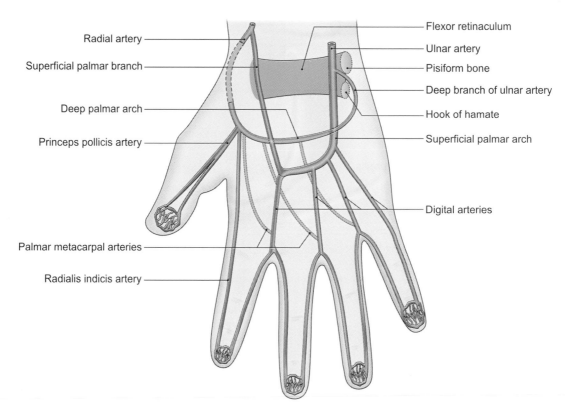

Fig. 9.32: The superficial and deep palmar arches

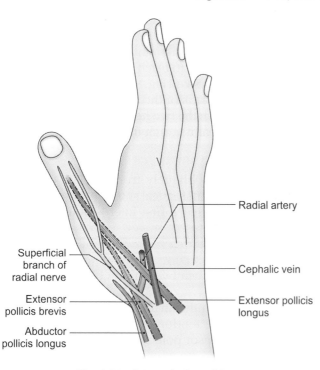

Fig. 9.33: Anatomical snuff box

4 In the palm, the radial artery runs medially. At first it lies deep to the oblique head of the adductor pollicis, and then passes between the two heads of this muscle to form deep palmar arch. Therefore, it is known as the deep palmar arch (Fig. 9.32).

Branches

Dorsum of hand: On the dorsum of the hand, the radial artery gives off:

1 A branch to the lateral side of the dorsum of the thumb.
2 The *first dorsal metacarpal artery.* This artery arises just before the radial artery passes into the interval between the two heads of the first dorsal interosseous muscle. It at once divides into two branches for the adjacent sides of the thumb and the index finger.

Palm: In the palm (deep to the oblique head of the adductor pollicis), the radial artery gives off:

1 The *princeps pollicis artery* which divides at the base of the proximal phalanx into two branches for the palmar surface of the thumb (Fig. 9.32).
2 The *radialis indicis artery* descends between the first dorsal interosseous muscle and the transverse head of the adductor pollicis to supply the lateral side of the index finger.

Deep Palmar Arch

Deep palmar arch provides a second channel connecting the radial and ulnar arteries in the palm (the first one being the superficial palmar arch already considered). It is situated deep to the long flexor tendons.

Formation

The deep palmar arch is formed mainly by the terminal part of the radial artery, and is completed medially at the base of the fifth metacarpal bone by the deep palmar branch of the ulnar artery (Fig. 9.32).

Relations

The arch lies on the proximal parts of the shafts of the metacarpals, and on the interossei; under the cover of the oblique head of the adductor pollicis, the flexor tendons of the fingers, and the lumbricals.

The deep branch of the ulnar nerve lies within the concavity of the arch.

Branches

1 From its convexity, i.e. from its distal side, the arch gives off three *palmar metacarpal arteries,* which run distally in the 2nd, 3rd and 4th spaces, supply the medial four metacarpals, and terminate at the finger clefts by joining the common digital branches of the superficial palmar arch (Fig. 9.32).

2 Dorsally, the arch gives off three (proximal) *perforating digital arteries* which pass through the medial three interosseous spaces to anastomose with the dorsal metacarpal arteries.

The digital perforating arteries connect the palmar digital branches of the superficial palmar arch with the dorsal metacarpal arteries.

3 *Recurrent branch* arises from the concavity of the arch and pass proximally to supply the carpal bones and joints, and ends in the palmar carpal arch.

NERVES OF HAND

ULNAR NERVE

Ulnar nerve is the main nerve of the hand (like the lateral plantar nerve in the foot).

Course

Ulnar nerve lies superficial to flexor retinaculum, covered only by the superficial slip of the retinaculum (volar carpal ligament—Fig. 9.15). It terminates by dividing into a superficial and a deep branch.

Superficial branch is cutaneous. The deep branch passes through the muscles of the hypothenar eminence to lie in the concavity of the deep palmar arch to end in the adductor pollicis (Fig. 9.22).

Relations

1 The ulnar nerve enters the palm by passing superficial to the flexor retinaculum where it lies between the pisiform bone and the ulnar vessels. Here the nerve divides into its superficial and deep terminal branches (Figs 9.13a and b).

2 The superficial terminal branch supplies the palmaris brevis and divides into two digital branches for the medial 1½ fingers (Fig. 9.34).

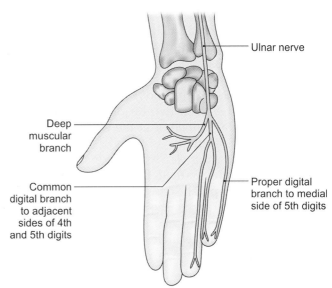

Fig. 9.34: Distribution of the branches of the ulnar nerve

3 The deep terminal branch accompanies the deep branch of the ulnar artery. It passes backwards between the abductor and flexor digiti minimi, and then between the opponens digiti minimi and the fifth metacarpal bone, lying on the hook of the hamate.

Finally, it turns laterally within the concavity of the deep palmar arch. It ends by supplying the adductor pollicis muscle (Fig. 9.22).

Branches

From Superficial Terminal Branch

1 Muscular branch: To palmaris brevis.
2 Cutaneous branches: Two palmar digital nerves supply the medial 1½ fingers with their nail beds (Fig. 9.34).

The medial branch supplies the medial side of the little finger.

The lateral branch is a common palmar digital nerve. It divides into two proper palmar digital nerves for the adjoining sides of the ring and little fingers.

The common palmar digital nerve communicates with the median nerve.

From Deep Terminal Branch

1 Muscular branches:
   a. At its origin, the deep branch supplies three muscles of hypothenar eminence (Fig. 9.13b).
   b. As the nerve crosses the palm, it supplies the medial two lumbricals and eight interossei.
   c. The deep branch terminates by supplying the adductor pollicis, and occasionally the deep head of the flexor pollicis brevis.

2 An articular branch supplies the wrist joint.

CLINICAL ANATOMY

- The ulnar nerve is also known as the 'musician's nerve' because it controls fine movements of the fingers (Fig. 9.34).
- The ulnar nerve is commonly injured at the elbow, behind the medial epicondyle or distal to elbow as it passes between two heads of flexor carpi ulnaris (cubital tunnel) or at the wrist in front of the flexor retinaculum.

  Ulnar nerve injury at the elbow: Flexor carpi ulnaris and the medial half of the flexor digitorum profundus are paralysed.
- Due to this paralysis, the medial border of the forearm becomes flattened. An attempt to produce flexion at the wrist result in abduction of the hand. The tendon of the flexor carpi ulnaris does not tighten on making a fist. Flexion of the terminal phalanges of the ring and little fingers is lost.
- The ulnar nerve controls fine movements of the fingers through its extensive motor distribution to the short muscles of the hand.
- *Ulnar nerve lesion at the wrist:* Produces 'ulnar claw-hand'.
- *Ulnar clawhand* is characterised by the following signs.

  a. Hyperextension at the metacarpophalangeal joints and flexion at the interphalangeal joints, involving the ring and little fingers—more than the index and middle fingers (Fig. 9.35). The little finger is held in extension by extensor muscles. The intermetacarpal spaces are hollowed out due to wasting of the interosseous muscles. Clawhand deformity is more obvious in wrist lesions as the profundus muscle is spared: This causes marked flexion of the terminal phalanges (action of paradox).

  b. Sensory loss is confined to the medial one-third of the palm and the medial 1½ fingers including their nail beds (Figs 9.36a and b). Medial half of dorsum of hand also shows sensory loss.

  c. *Vasomotor changes:* The skin areas with sensory loss is warmer due to arteriolar dilatation; it is also drier due to absence of sweating because of loss of sympathetic supply.

  d. *Trophic changes:* Long-standing cases of paralysis lead to dry and scaly skin. The nails crack easily with atrophy of the pulp of fingers.

  e. The patient is unable to spread out the fingers due to paralysis of the dorsal interossei. The power of adduction of the thumb, and flexion of the ring and little fingers are lost. It should be noted that median nerve lesions are more disabling. In contrast, ulnar nerve lesions leave a relatively efficient hand.

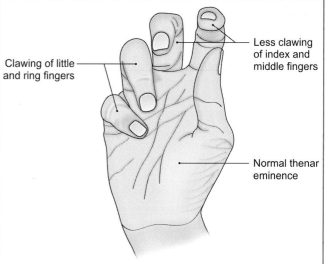

Fig. 9.35: Clawing of ring and little fingers

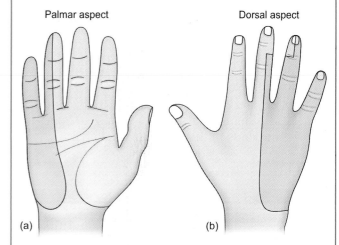

Figs 9.36a and b: Sensory loss on: (a) Palmar aspect, and (b) dorsal aspect of hand in ulnar nerve injury

MEDIAN NERVE

The median nerve is important because of its role in controlling the movements of the thumb which are crucial in the mechanism of gripping by the hand.

Course

Median nerve lies deep to flexor retinaculum in the carpal tunnel and enters the palm (Fig. 9.20). Soon it terminates by dividing into muscular and cutaneous branches.

Relations

1 The median nerve enters the palm by passing deep to the flexor retinaculum where it lies in the narrow space of the carpal tunnel in front of the ulnar bursa enclosing the flexor tendons.

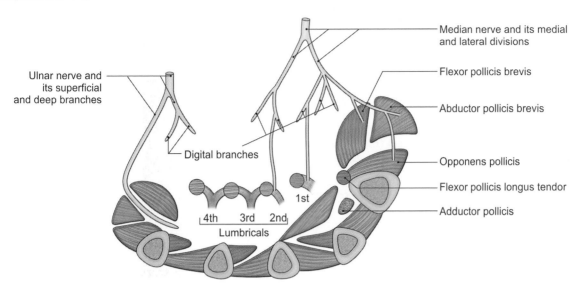

Fig. 9.37: Distribution of the median nerve in the hand. The main divisions of the ulnar nerve are also shown

Immediately, below the retinaculum, the nerve divides into lateral and medial divisions (Fig. 9.20).

2 The lateral division gives off a muscular branch to the thenar muscles, and three digital branches for the lateral 1½ digits including the thumb.

The muscular branch curls upwards round the distal border of the retinaculum and supplies the thenar muscles.

Out of the three digital branches, two supply the thumb and one the lateral side of the index finger.

The digital branch to the index finger also supplies the first lumbrical (Fig. 9.37).

3 The medial division divides into two common digital branches for the second and third interdigital clefts, supplying the adjoining sides of the index, middle and ring fingers.

The lateral common digital branch also supplies the second lumbrical.

Branches

In the hand, the median nerve supplies:

a. Five muscles, namely the abductor pollicis brevis, the flexor pollicis brevis, the opponens pollicis and the first and second lumbrical muscles.

b. Palmar skin over the lateral 3½ digits with their nail beds.

CLINICAL ANATOMY

- The median nerve controls coarse movements of the hand, as it supplies most of the long muscles of the front of the forearm. It is, therefore, called the *labourer's nerve*. It is also called "eye of the hand" as it is sensory to most of the hand.

- When the median nerve is injured above the level of the elbow, as might happen in *supracondylar fracture of the humerus*, the following features are seen.

  a. The flexor pollicis longus and lateral half of flexor digitorum profundus are paralysed. The patient is unable to bend the terminal phalanx of the thumb and index finger when the proximal phalanx is held firmly by the clinician (to eliminate the action of the short flexors) (Fig. 9.38). Similarly, the terminal phalanx of the middle finger can be tested.

  b. The forearm is kept in a supine position due to paralysis of the pronators.

  c. The hand is adducted due to paralysis of the flexor carpi radialis, and flexion at the wrist is weak.

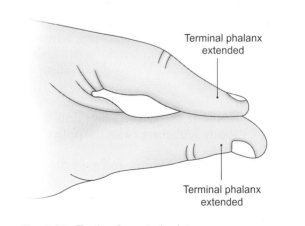

Fig. 9.38: Testing for anterior interosseous nerve

d. Flexion at the interphalangeal joints of the index and middle fingers is lost so that the index and the middle (to a lesser extent) fingers tend to remain straight while making a fist. This is called *pointing index finger* occurs due to paralysis of long flexors of the digit (Fig. 9.39).

e. Ape or monkey thumb deformity is present due to paralysis of the thenar muscles (Fig. 9.40).

f. The area of sensory loss corresponds to its distribution (Fig. 9.41) in the hand.

g. Vasomotor and trophic changes: The skin on lateral 3½ digits is warm, dry and scaly. The nails get cracked easily (Fig. 9.42).

• *Carpal tunnel syndrome (CTS):* Involvement of the median nerve in carpal tunnel at wrist has become a very common entity (Fig. 9.15).

a. This syndrome consists of motor, sensory, vasomotor and trophic symptoms in the hand caused by compression of the median nerve in the carpal tunnel. Examination reveals wasting of thenar eminence (ape-like hand), hypo-aesthesia to light touch on the palmar aspect of lateral 3½ digits. However, the skin over the thenar eminence is *not affected* as the branch of median nerve supplying it arises in the forearm.

b. Froment's sign/book holding test: The patient is unable to hold the book with thumb and other fingers.

c. Paper holding test: The patient is unable to hold paper between thumb and fingers.
Both these tests are positive because of paralysis of thenar muscles.

d. *Motor changes:* Ape-/monkey-like thumb deformity (Fig. 9.40), loss of opposition of thumb. Index and middle fingers lag behind while making the fist due to paralysis of 1st and 2nd lumbrical muscles (Fig. 9.43).

e. *Sensory changes:* Loss of sensations on lateral 3½ digits including the nail beds and distal phalanges on dorsum of hand (Fig. 9.41).

f. *Vasomotor changes:* The skin areas with sensory loss is warmer due to arteriolar dilatation; it is also drier due to absence of sweating due to loss of sympathetic supply.

g. *Trophic changes:* Long-standing cases of paralysis lead to dry and scaly skin. The nails crack easily with atrophy of the pulp of fingers (Fig. 9.42).

h. It occurs both in males and females between the age of 25 and 70. They complain of intermittent attacks of pain in the distribution of the median nerve on one or both sides. The attacks frequently occur at night. Pain may be

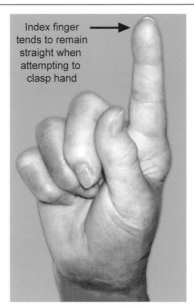

Fig. 9.39: Pointing index finger

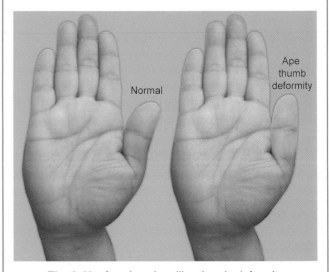

Fig. 9.40: Ape-/monkey-like thumb deformity

referred proximally to the forearm and arm. It is more common because of excessive working on the computer. Phalen's test (Fig. 9.44) is attempted for CTS.

• *Complete claw hand:* If both median and ulnar nerves are paralysed, the result is complete claw hand (Fig. 9.45).

RADIAL NERVE

The part of the radial nerve seen in the hand is a continuation of the superficial terminal branch. It reaches the dorsum of the hand (after winding round the lateral side of the radius) and divides into 4 dorsal

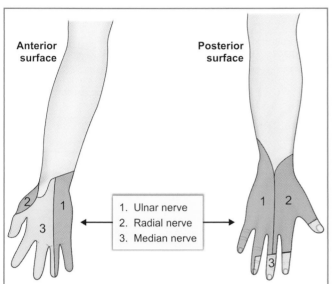

Fig. 9.41: Sensory loss in median, ulnar and radial nerves paralysis

1. Ulnar nerve
2. Radial nerve
3. Median nerve

Anterior surface

Posterior surface

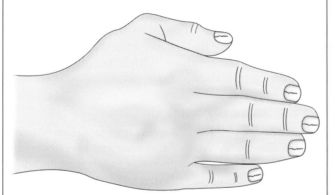

Fig. 9.42: Vasomotor and trophic changes in right hand

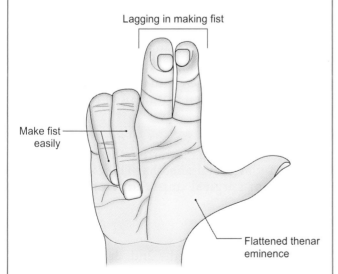

Lagging in making fist

Make fist easily

Flattened thenar eminence

Fig. 9.43: Lagging behind of index and middle fingers in making the fist due to paralysis of first and second lumbrical muscles in median nerve paralysis

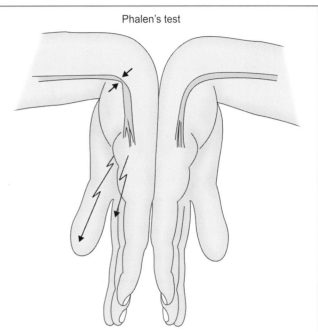

Phalen's test

Fig. 9.44: Phalen's test: Acutely flexed wrist causes pain in carpal tunnel syndrome

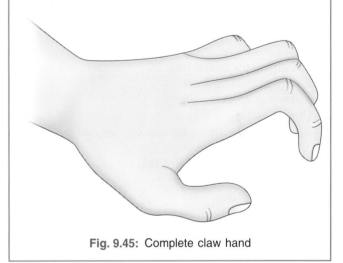

Fig. 9.45: Complete claw hand

digital branches which supply the skin of the digits as follows (*see* Fig. 7.1).

1st : Lateral side of thumb
2nd : Medial side of thumb
3rd : Lateral side of index finger
4th : Contiguous sides of index and middle fingers

Note that skin over the dorsum of the distal phalanges, is supplied by the median nerve (not radial) (Fig. 9.46). Sensory loss is less because of overlapping of nerves.

SPACES OF THE HAND

Having learnt the anatomy of the whole hand, the clinically significant spaces of the hand need to be

Palmar aspect   Dorsal aspect

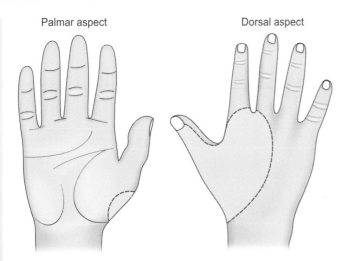

Fig. 9.46: Sensory loss in injury to superficial branch of radial nerve

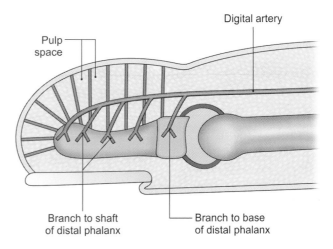

Fig. 9.47: The digital pulp space

understood and their boundaries to be identified from the following text.

The arrangement of fasciae and the fascial septa in the hand is such that many spaces are formed. These spaces are of surgical importance because they may become infected and distended with pus. The important spaces are as follows.

A. *Palmar spaces*
   1. Pulp space of the fingers
   2. Midpalmar space
   3. Thenar space
B. *Dorsal spaces*
   1. Dorsal subcutaneous space
   2. Dorsal subaponeurotic space
C. *The forearm space of Parona.*

Palmar Spaces

Pulp Space of the Fingers

The tips of the fingers and thumb contain subcutaneous fat arranged in tight compartments formed by fibrous septa which pass from the skin to the periosteum of the terminal phalanx. Infection of this space is known as *whitlow*. The rising tension in the space gives rise to severe throbbing pain.

Infections in the pulp space (whitlow) can be drained by a lateral incision which opens all compartments and avoids damage to the tactile tissue in front of the finger.

If neglected, a whitlow may lead to necrosis of the distal four-fifths of the terminal phalanx due to occlusion of the vessels by the tension. The proximal one-fifth (epiphysis) escapes because its artery does not traverse the fibrous septa (Fig. 9.47).

Midpalmar Space and Thenar Space

Midpalmar and thenar spaces are shown in Table 9.7 and Figs 9.52 and 9.53.

Dorsal Spaces

The *dorsal subcutaneous space* lies immediately deep to the loose skin of the dorsum of the hand. The *dorsal subaponeurotic space* lies between the metacarpal bones and the extensor tendons which are united to one another by a thin aponeurosis.

Forearm Space of Parona

Forearm space of Parona is a rectangular space situated deep in the lower part of the forearm just above the wrist. It lies in front of the pronator quadratus, and deep to the long flexor tendons. Superiorly, the space extends up to the oblique origin of the flexor digitorum superficialis. Inferiorly, it extends up to the flexor retinaculum, and communicates with the midpalmar space. The proximal part of the flexor synovial sheaths protrudes into the forearm space.

The forearm space may be infected through infections in the related synovial sheaths, especially of the ulnar bursa. Pus points at the margins of the distal part of the forearm where it may be drained by giving incision along the lateral margin of forearm.

SYNOVIAL SHEATHS

Many of the tendons entering the hand are surrounded by synovial sheaths. The extent of these sheaths is of surgical importance as they can be infected (Fig. 9.7).

Digital Synovial Sheaths

The synovial sheaths of the 2nd, 3rd and 4th digits are independent and terminate proximally at the levels of the heads of the metacarpals. The synovial sheath of the little finger is continuous proximally with the ulnar bursa, and that of the thumb with the

Table 9.7: Midpalmar and thenar spaces (Figs 9.48 and 9.49)

Features	Midpalmar space	Thenar space
1. Shape	Triangular	Triangular
2. Situation	Under the inner half of the hollow of the palm	Under the outer half of the hollow of the palm
3. Extent:		
Proximal	Distal margin of the flexor retinaculum	Distal margin of the flexor retinaculum
Distal	Distal palmar crease	Proximal transverse palmar crease
4. Communications:		
Proximal	Forearm space of Parona	Forearm space
Distal	Fascial sheaths of the 3rd and 4th lumbricals	Fascial sheath of the first lumbrical
5. Boundaries:		
Anterior	• Flexor tendons of 3rd, 4th and 5th fingers • 2nd, 3rd and 4th lumbricals • Palmar aponeurosis	• Short muscles of thumb • Flexor tendons of the index finger • First lumbrical • Palmar aponeurosis
Posterior	Fascia covering interossei and metacarpals	Transverse head of adductor pollicis
Lateral	Intermediate palmar septum	• Tendon of flexor pollicis longus with radial bursa • Lateral palmar septum
Medial	Medial palmar septum	Intermediate palmar septum
6. Drainage	Incision in either the 3rd or 4th web space	Incision in the first web, posteriorly

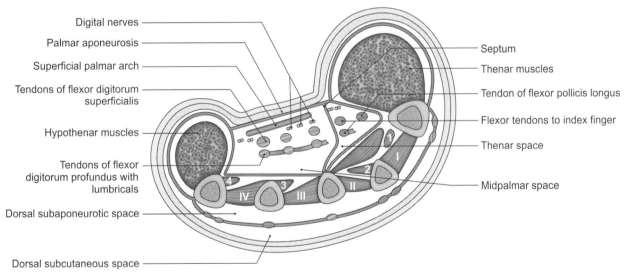

Fig. 9.48: Thenar, midpalmar, dorsal subcutaneous and dorsal subaponeurotic spaces. I, II, III, IV — dorsal interossei and 1, 2, 3, 4 — palmar interossei

radial bursa. Therefore, infections of the little finger and thumb are more dangerous because they can spread into the palm and even up to 2.5 cm above the wrist.

Ulnar Bursa

Infection of this bursa is usually secondary to the infection of the little finger, and this in turn may spread to the forearm space of the Parona. It results in an *hour-glass swelling* (so called because there is one swelling in the palm and another in the distal part of the forearm, the two being joined by a constriction in the region of the flexor retinaculum). It is also called compound palmar ganglion.

Radial Bursa

Infection of the thumb may spread to the radial bursa.

CLINICAL ANATOMY

Surgical Incisions

The surgical incisions of the hand are shown in Fig. 9.50.

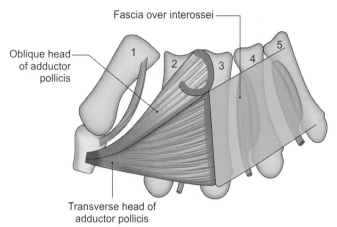

Fig. 9.49: Muscles forming floor of the thenar and midpalmar spaces

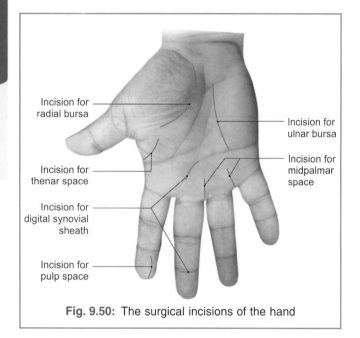

Fig. 9.50: The surgical incisions of the hand

BACK OF FOREARM AND HAND

This section deals mainly with the extensor retinaculum of the wrist, muscles of the back of the forearm, the deep terminal branch of the radial nerve, and the posterior interosseous artery.

SURFACE LANDMARKS

1 The *olecranon process* of the ulna is the most prominent bony point on the back of a flexed elbow (Fig. 9.1). Normally, it forms a straight horizontal line with the two epicondyles of the humerus when the elbow is extended, and an equilateral triangle when the elbow is flexed to a right angle (*see* Fig. 2.17). The relative position of the three bony points is disturbed when the elbow is dislocated.

2 The *head of the radius* can be palpated in a depression on the posterolateral aspect of an extended elbow just below the lateral epicondyle of the humerus. Its rotation can be felt during pronation and supination of the forearm.

3 The *posterior border of the ulna* is subcutaneous in its entire length. It can be felt in a longitudinal groove on the back of the forearm when the elbow is flexed and the hand is supinated. The border ends distally in the styloid process of the ulna. It separates the flexors from the extensors of the forearm. Being superficial, it allows the entire length of the ulna to be examined for fractures.

4 The *head of the ulna* forms a surface elevation on the posteromedial aspect of the wrist in a pronated forearm.

5 The *styloid processes of the radius and ulna* are important landmarks of the wrist. The styloid process of the radius can be felt in the upper part of the anatomical snuff box. It projects down 1 cm lower than the styloid process of the ulna. The latter descends from the posteromedial aspect of the ulnar head. The relative position of the two styloid processes is disturbed in fractures at the wrist, and is a clue to the proper realignment of fractured bones.

6 The *dorsal tubercle of the radius* (Lister's tubercle) can be palpated on the dorsal surface of the lower end of the radius in line with the cleft between the index and middle fingers. It is grooved on its medial side by the tendon of the extensor pollicis longus.

7 The heads of the metacarpals form the knuckles.

DORSUM OF HAND AND SUPERFICIAL MUSCLES

DISSECTION

Make the incision in the centre of dorsum of hand. Reflect the skin of dorsum of hand till the respective borders. Reflect the skin of dorsum of middle finger on each side. Look for nerves on the back of forearm and hand. These are superficial branch of radial nerve and dorsal branch of ulnar nerve.

The dorsal venous network is the most prominent component of the superficial fascia of dorsum of hand. (Identify the beginning of cephalic and basilic veins by tying a tourniquet on the forearm and exercising the closed fist on oneself.)

The deep fascia at the back of wrist is thickened to form extensor retinaculum. Define its margins and attachments. Identify the structures traversing its six compartments.

Clear the deep fascia over the back of forearm. Define the attachment of triceps brachii muscle on the olecranon process of ulna. Define the attachments of the seven superficial muscles of the back of the forearm.

Separate the anterolateral muscles, i.e. brachioradialis, extensor carpi radialis longus and brevis from the extensor digitorum lying in the centre and extensor digiti minimi and extensor carpi ulnaris situated on the medial aspect of the wrist. Anconeus is situated on the posterolateral aspect of the elbow joint. Dissect all these muscles and trace their nerve supply (Fig. 9.51a).

DORSUM OF HAND

1 *Skin:* It is loose on the dorsum of hand. It can be pinched off from the underlying structures.
2 *Superficial fascia:* The fascia contains dorsal venous plexus, cutaneous nerves, and dorsal carpal arch.
 a. *Dorsal venous plexus:* The digital veins from adjacent sides of index, middle; ring and little fingers form 3 dorsal metacarpal veins (*see* Fig. 7.7). These join with each other on dorsum of hand. The lateral end of this arch is joined by one digital vein from index finger and two digital veins from thumb to form cephalic vein. It runs proximally in the *anatomical snuff box*, curves, round the lateral border of wrist to come to front of forearm. In a similar manner, the medial end of the arch joins with one digital vein only from medial side of little finger to form basilic vein. It also curves round the medial side of wrist to reach front of forearm. These metacarpal veins may unite in different ways to form a dorsal venous plexus.
 b. *Cutaneous nerves:* These are superficial branch of radial nerve and dorsal branch of ulnar nerve. The nail beds and skin of distal phalanges of 3½ lateral nails is supplied by median nerve and 1½ medial nails by ulnar nerve. The superficial branch of radial nerve supplies lateral half of dorsum of hand with two digital branches to thumb and one to lateral side of index and another common digital branch to adjacent sides of index and middle fingers (*see* Fig. 7.1b).
 Dorsal branch of ulnar supplies medial half of dorsum of hand with proper digital branches to medial side of little finger; two common digital branches for adjacent sides of little and ring fingers and adjacent sides of ring and middle fingers.
 c. *Dorsal carpal arch:* It is formed by dorsal carpal branches of radial and ulnar arteries and lies close to the wrist joint. The arch gives three dorsal metacarpal arteries which supply adjacent sides of index, middle; ring and little fingers. One digital artery goes to medial side of little finger. The arch also gives branches to the dorsum of hand.

3 Spaces on dorsum of hand:
 There are two spaces on the dorsum of hand:
 a. Dorsal subcutaneous space, lying just subjacent to skin. Skin of dorsum of hand is loose can be pinched and lifted off.
 b. Dorsal subtendinous space lies deep to the extensor tendons, between the tendons and the metacarpal bones (Fig. 9.52).
4 *Deep fascia:* The deep fascia is modified at the back of hand to form extensor retinaculum.

Extensor Retinaculum

The deep fascia on the back of the wrist is thickened to form the extensor retinaculum which holds the extensor tendons in place. It is an oblique band, directed downwards and medially. It is about 2 cm broad vertically (Fig. 9.52).

Attachments

Laterally: Lower part of the sharp *anterior* border of the radius.
Medially:
 i. Styloid process of the ulna.
 ii. Triquetral.
 iii. Pisiform.

Compartments

The retinaculum sends down septa which are attached to the longitudinal ridges on the posterior surface of the lower end of radius. In this way, 6 osseofascial compartments are formed on the back of the wrist (*see* Fig. 2.21b). The structures passing through each compartment, from lateral to the medial side, are listed in Table 9.8 and Fig. 9.52.

Table 9.8: Structures in various compartments under extensor retinaculum

Compartment	Structure
I	• Abductor pollicis longus
	• Extensor pollicis brevis
II	• Extensor carpi radialis longus
	• Extensor carpi radialis brevis
III	• Extensor pollicis longus
IV	• Extensor digitorum
	• Extensor indicis
	• Posterior interosseous nerve
	• Anterior interosseous artery
V	• Extensor digiti minimi
VI	• Extensor carpi ulnaris

Each compartment is lined by a synovial sheath, which is reflected onto the contained tendons.

Anatomical Snuff Box

The *anatomical snuff box* (Fig. 9.33) is a triangular depression on the lateral side of the wrist. It is seen best when the thumb is extended.

Boundaries

It is bounded anteriorly by tendons of the abductor pollicis longus and extensor pollicis brevis, and posteriorly by the tendon of the extensor pollicis longus. It is limited above by the styloid process of the radius. The floor of the snuff box is formed by the scaphoid and the trapezium.

Contents

The radial artery, superficial branch of radial nerve and cephalic vein.

SUPERFICIAL MUSCLES

There are seven superficial muscles on the back of the forearm:

1 Anconeus
2 Brachioradialis (Fig. 9.51a)
3 Extensor carpi radialis longus (Fig. 9.53)
4 Extensor carpi radialis brevis
5 Extensor digitorum.
6 Extensor digiti minimi (Fig. 9.51b)
7 Extensor carpi ulnaris.

All the seven muscles cross the elbow joint. Most of them take origin (entirely or in part) from the tip of the lateral epicondyle of the humerus.

These muscles with their nerve supply and actions are described in Tables 9.9 and 9.10.

Additional Points

1 The extensor digitorum and extensor indicis pass through the same compartment of the extensor retinaculum, and have a common synovial sheath.
2 The four tendons of the extensor digitorum emerge from undercover of the extensor retinaculum and fan out over the dorsum of the hand. The tendon to the index finger is joined on its medial side by the tendon of the extensor indicis, and the tendon to the little finger is joined on its medial side by the two tendons of the extensor digiti minimi.
3 On the dorsum of the hand, adjacent tendons are variably connected together by three intertendinous connections directed obliquely downwards and laterally. The medial connection is strong; the lateral connection is weakest and may be absent.

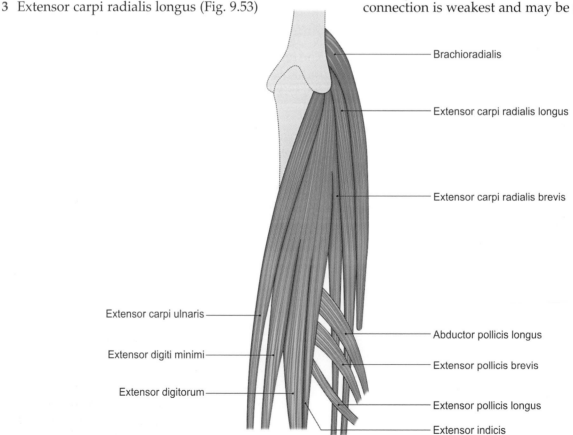

Fig. 9.51a: Muscles of the back of forearm. Tendons in I–VI compartments are shown

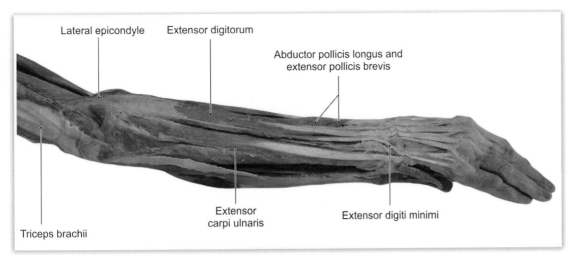

Fig. 9.51b: Dissection of back of forearm

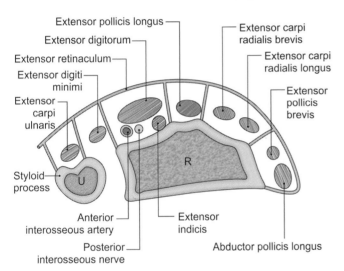

Fig. 9.52: Transverse section passing just above the wrist showing structures passing deep to the extensor retinaculum

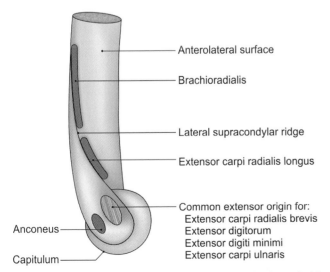

Fig. 9.53: Right humerus, lower end, seen from the lateral side, to show the origins of the seven superficial muscles of the forearm

The four tendons and three intertendinous connections are embedded in deep fascia, and together form the roof of the subtendinous (subaponeurotic) space on the dorsum of the hand.

DEEP MUSCLES

DISSECTION

Separate extensor carpi radials brevis from extensor digitorum and identify deeply placed supinator muscle.

Just distal to supinator is abductor pollicis longus. Other three muscles: extensor pollicis longus, extensor pollicis brevis and extensor indicis are present distal to abductor pollicis longus. Identify them all.

Features

These are as follows:
1 Supinator
2 Abductor pollicis longus
3 Extensor pollicis brevis
4 Extensor pollicis longus (*see* Fig. 2.23)
5 Extensor indicis

In contrast to the superficial muscles, none of the deep muscles crosses the elbow joint. These have been tabulated in Tables 9.11 and 9.12.

Dorsal Digital Expansion

The dorsal digital expansion (extensor expansion) is a small triangular aponeurosis (related to each tendon of the extensor digitorum) covering the dorsum of the proximal phalanx. Its base, which is proximal, covers the metacarpophalangeal (MP) joint. The main tendon of the extensor digitorum occupies the central part of the extension, and is separated from the MP joint by a bursa.

Table 9.9: Attachments of superficial muscles of back of forearm

Muscle	Origin	Insertion
1. **Anconeus**	Lateral epicondyle of humerus	Lateral surface of olecranon process of ulna
2. **Brachioradialis**	Upper 2/3rd of lateral supracondylar ridge of humerus	Base of styloid process of radius
3. **Extensor carpi radialis longus**	Lower 1/3rd of lateral supracondylar ridge of humerus	Posterior surface of base of second metacarpal bone
4. **Extensor carpi radialis brevis**	Lateral epicondyle of humerus	Posterior surface of base of third metacarpal
5. **Extensor digitorum**	Lateral epicondyle of humerus	Bases of middle phalanges of the 2nd–5th digits
6. **Extensor digiti minimi**	Lateral epicondyle of humerus	Extensor expansion of little finger
7. **Extensor carpi ulnaris**	Lateral epicondyle of humerus	Base of fifth metacarpal bone (Fig. 9.51b)

Table 9.10: Nerve supply and actions of superficial muscles of back of forearm

Muscle	Nerve supply	Actions
1. **Anconeus**	Radial nerve	Extends elbow joint
2. **Brachioradialis**	Radial nerve	Flexes forearm at elbow joint; rotates forearm to the midprone position from supine or prone positions
3. **Extensor carpi radialis longus**	Radial nerve	Extends and abducts hand at wrist joint
4. **Extensor carpi radialis brevis**	Deep branch of radial nerve	Extends and abducts hand at wrist joint
5. **Extensor digitorum**	Deep branch of radial nerve	Extends fingers of hand
6. **Extensor digiti minimi**	Deep branch of radial nerve	Extends metacarpophalangeal joint of little finger
7. **Extensor carpi ulnaris**	Deep branch of radial nerve	Extends and adducts hand at wrist joint

Table 9.11: Attachments of deep muscles of back of forearm

Muscle	Origin	Insertion
1. **Supinator** (Fig. 8.19)	Lateral epicondyle of humerus, annular ligament of superior radioulnar joint, supinator crest of ulna and depression anterior to it	Neck and whole shaft of upper one-third of radius
2. **Abductor pollicis longus** (*see* Fig. 2.23)	Posterior surface of shafts of radius and ulna	Base of first metacarpal bone
3. **Extensor pollicis brevis**	Posterior surface of shaft of radius	Base of proximal phalanx of thumb
4. **Extensor pollicis longus**	Posterior surface of shaft of ulna	Base of distal phalanx of thumb
5. **Extensor indicis**	Posterior surface of shaft of ulna	Extensor expansion of index finger

Table 9.12: Nerve supply and actions of deep muscles of back of forearm

Muscle	Nerve supply	Actions
1. **Supinator** (Fig. 9.9)	Deep branch of radial nerve	Supination of forearm when elbow is extended
2. **Abductor pollicis longus**	Deep branch of radial nerve	Abducts and extends thumb
3. **Extensor pollicis brevis**	Deep branch of radial nerve	Extends metacarpophalangeal joint of thumb
4. **Extensor pollicis longus**	Deep branch of radial nerve	Extends distal phalanx of thumb
5. **Extensor indicis**	Deep branch of radial nerve	Extends metacarpophalangeal joint of index finger

The posterolateral corners of the extensor expansion are joined by tendons of the interossei and of lumbrical muscles. The corners are attached to the deep transverse metacarpal ligament. The points of attachment of the interossei (proximal) and lumbrical (distal) are often called 'wing tendons' (Fig. 9.54).

Near the proximal interphalangeal joint, the extensor tendon divides into a central slip and two collateral slips. The central slip is joined by some fibres from the margins of the expansion, crosses the proximal interphalangeal joint, and is inserted on the dorsum of the base of the middle phalanx. The two collateral slips are joined by the remaining thick margin of the extensor expansion. They then join each other and are inserted on the dorsum of the base of the distal phalanx.

At the metacarpophalangeal and interphalangeal joints, the extensor expansion forms the dorsal part of the fibrous capsule of the joints.

The retinacular ligaments (link ligaments) extend from the side of the proximal phalanx, and form its fibrous flexor sheath, to the margins of the extensor expansion to reach the base of the distal phalanx (Fig. 9.54).

The muscles inserted into the dorsal digital expansions of:

Index finger: First dorsal interosseous, second palmar interosseous, first lumbrical, extensor digitorum slip, and extensor indicis (Fig. 9.54).

Middle finger: Second and third dorsal interossei, second lumbrical, extensor digitorum slip.

Ring finger: Fourth dorsal interosseous, third palmar interosseous, third lumbrical and extensor digitorum slip.

Little finger: Fourth palmar interosseous, fourth lumbrical, extensor digitorum slip and extensor digiti minimi.

POSTERIOR INTEROSSEOUS NERVE

DISSECTION

Deep terminal branch of radial nerve/posterior interosseous nerve and posterior interosseous artery:

Identify the posterior interosseous nerve at the distal border of exposed supinator muscle. Trace its branches to the various muscles.

Look for the radial nerve in the lower lateral part of front of arm between the brachioradialis, extensor carpi radialis longus laterally and brachialis muscle medially. Trace the two divisions of this nerve in the lateral part of the cubital fossa. The deep branch (posterior interosseous nerve) traverses between the two planes of supinator muscle and reaches the back of the forearm where it is already identified.

The nerve runs amongst the muscles of the back of the forearm, and ends at the level of the wrist in a pseudoganglion (Fig. 9.55).

This nerve is accompanied by posterior interosseous artery distal to the supinator muscle. This artery is supplemented by anterior interosseous artery in lower one-fourth of the forearm.

Features

It is the chief nerve of the back of the forearm. It is a branch of the radial nerve given off in the cubital fossa, just below the level of the lateral epicondyle of the humerus.

Course

It begins in cubital fossa. Passes through supinator muscle to reach back of forearm, where it descends downwards. It ends in a pseudoganglion in the 4th compartment of extensor retinaculum.

Relations

1 Posterior interosseous nerve leaves the cubital fossa and enters the back of the forearm by passing between the two planes of fibres of the supinator.

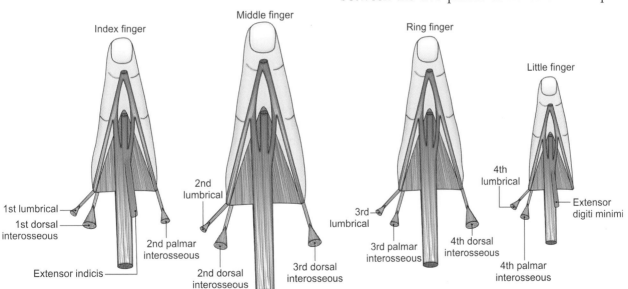

Fig. 9.54: The dorsal digital expansion of right index, middle, ring and little fingers. Note the insertions of the lumbricals and interossei into it

Within the muscle it winds backwards round the lateral side of the radius (Fig. 9.55).

2 It emerges from the supinator on the back of the forearm. Here it lies between the superficial and deep muscles. At the lower border of the extensor pollicis brevis, it passes deep to the extensor pollicis longus. It then runs on the posterior surface of the interosseous membrane up to the wrist where it enlarges into a *pseudoganglion* and ends by supplying the wrist and intercarpal joints.

Branches

Posterior interosseous nerve gives muscular, articular and sensory branches (Fig. 9.56).

A. *Muscular branches*
   a. Before piercing the supinator, branches are given to the extensor carpi radialis brevis and to the supinator.
   b. While passing through the supinator, another branch is given to the supinator.
   c. After emerging from the supinator, the nerve gives three short branches to:
      i. The extensor digitorum (Fig. 9.51a).
      ii. The extensor digiti minimi.
      iii. The extensor carpi ulnaris.

It also gives two long branches:
   i. A lateral branch supplies the abductor longus and the extensor pollicis brevis.
   ii. A medial branch supplies the extensor pollicis longus and the extensor indicis.

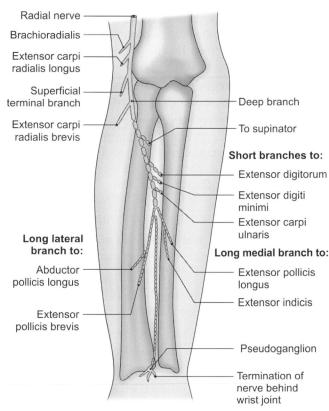

Fig. 9.56: Branches of the posterior interosseous nerve

B. *Articular branches*
   Articular branches are given to:
   i. The wrist joint.
   ii. The distal radioulnar joint.
   iii. Intercarpal and intermetacarpal joints.
C. *Sensory branches*
   Sensory branches are given to the interosseous membrane, the radius and the ulna.

POSTERIOR INTEROSSEOUS ARTERY

Course

Posterior interosseous artery is the smaller terminal branch of the common interosseous, given off in the cubital fossa. It enters the back of the forearm and lies in between the muscles there.

It terminates by anastomosing with the anterior interosseous artery.

Relations

1 It is the smaller terminal branch of the common interosseous artery in the cubital fossa.

2 It enters the back of the forearm by passing between the oblique cord and the upper margin of the interosseous membrane (Fig. 9.55).

3 It appears on the back of the forearm in the interval between the supinator and the abductor pollicis

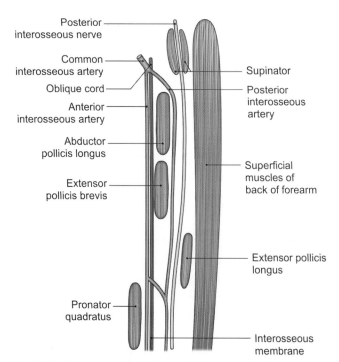

Fig. 9.55: Course and relations of the posterior interosseous nerve and the interosseous arteries

longus and thereafter accompanies the posterior interosseous nerve. At the lower border of the extensor indicis, the artery becomes markedly reduced and ends by anastomosing with the anterior interosseous artery which reaches the posterior compartment by piercing the interosseous membrane at the upper border of the pronator quadratus. Thus in its lower one-fourth, the back of the forearm is supplied by the anterior interosseous artery.

4 The posterior interosseous artery gives off an interosseous recurrent branch which runs upwards and takes part in the anastomosis on the back of the lateral epicondyle of the humerus (*see* Fig. 8.10).

Mnemonics

Anterior forearm muscles: Superficial group "Pretti Found Pamela for Fight"

Pronator teres

Flexor carpi radialis

Palmaris longus

Flexor carpi ulnaris

Flexor digitorum superficialis

Interossei muscles: Actions of dorsal vs. palmar in hand "PAd and DAb"

The **P**almar **Ad**duct and the **D**orsal **Ab**duct.

– Use your hand to dab with a pad.

Median nerve: Hand muscles innervated "The LOAF muscles"

Lumbricals 1 and 2

Opponens pollicis

Abductor pollicis brevis

Flexor pollicis brevis

🔑 FACTS TO REMEMBER

- Median nerve exits the cubital fossa by passing between two heads of pronator teres while ulnar artery passes deep to both the heads of pronator teres.
- Anterior interosseous branch of median nerve supplies 2½ muscles of front of the forearm, i.e. flexor pollicis longus, pronator quadratus and lateral half of flexor digitorum profundus.
- Flexor retinaculum has a superficial slip medially and a deep slip laterally. Deep to superficial slip course ulnar nerve and vessels and superficial to the deep slip passes the tendon of flexor carpi radialis.

- Thenar eminence *does not* include the adductor pollicis muscle. It comprises abductor pollicis brevis, flexor pollicis brevis and opponens pollicis.
- Median nerve supplies 5 muscles in the palm, three muscles of thenar eminence and 1st and 2nd lumbricals. It is called "Labourer's nerve". Median nerve is also the "Eye of the hand".
- Ulnar nerve is called "Musician's nerve". It supplies 15 intrinsic muscles of the hand.
- There are 12 muscles on the back of forearm, two are smaller lying in upper 1/4th of the forearm, five are inserted close to the wrist; five get inserted into the phalanges. All are supplied by posterior interosseous nerve. Injury to the nerve causes "wrist drop".
- Lateral 3½ nail beds are supplied by median nerve and medial 1½ nail beds by ulnar nerve.

CLINICOANATOMICAL PROBLEMS

Case 1

A young man practising tennis complained of severe pain over lateral part of his right elbow. The pain was pin-pointed over his lateral epicondyle.

- Why does pain occur over lateral epicondyle during tennis games?
- Which other games can cause similar pain?

Ans: The pain is due to lateral epicondylitis, also called *tennis elbow*. This is due to repeated microtrauma to the common extensor origin of extensor muscles of the forearm. It can also occur in swimming, gymnastics, basketball, table tennis, i.e. any sport which involves strenuous use of the extensors of the forearm. It may be a degenerative condition.

Case 2

A 55-year-old woman complained of abnormal sensations in her right thumb, index, middle and part of ring fingers. Her pain increased during night. There was weakness of her thumb movements.

- Which nerve was affected and where? Name the syndrome.

Ans: Median nerve is affected while it travels deep to the flexor retinaculum. The syndrome is *'carpal tunnel syndrome'*. There are abnormal sensation in lateral 3½ digits, but there is no loss of sensation over lateral two-thirds of palm. The nerve supply of this area is from palmar cutaneous branch of median nerve which passes superficial to the flexor retinaculum.

FREQUENTLY ASKED QUESTIONS

1. Describe flexor digitorum profundus muscle under following headings: Origin, insertion, nerve supply, actions and special features
2. Discuss the formation, course and branches of superficial and deep palmar arches
3. Write short notes on:
   a. Flexor retinaculum of wrist
   b. Layers of palm with their components
   c. Midpalmar and thenar spaces
   d. Extensor retinaculum of wrist and structures passing in various compartments under the retinaculum
   e. Carpal tunnel syndrome
   f. Wrist drop
   g. Complete claw hand

MULTIPLE CHOICE QUESTIONS

1. Which of the following nerves leads to wrist drop?
   a. Ulnar
   b. Radial
   c. Median
   d. Musculocutaneous
2. Which nerve supplies adductor pollicis?
   a. Median
   b. Superficial branch of ulnar
   c. Deep branch of ulnar
   d. Radial
3. Which of the following is the action of dorsal interosseous?
   a. Abduction of fingers
   b. Flexion of thumb
   c. Adduction of fingers
   d. Extension of metacarpophalangeal joints
4. Which of the following muscles is not supplied by median nerve?
   a. Abductor pollicis brevis
   b. Flexor pollicis brevis
   c. Opponens pollicis
   d. Adductor pollicis
5. Which of the following nerves is involved in carpal tunnel syndrome?
   a. Ulnar   b. Median
   c. Radial   d. Musculocutaneous
6. Which of the following structures does not pass through the carpal tunnel?
   a. Palmar cutaneous branch of median nerve
   b. Median nerve
   c. Tendons of flexor digitorum profundus
   d. Tendon of flexor pollicis longus
7. Superficial cut only on the flexor retinaculum of wrist would damage all structures, *except:*
   a. Median nerve
   b. Palmar cutaneous branch of median nerve
   c. Palmar cutaneous branch of ulnar nerve
   d. Ulnar nerve
8. All the following structures are present in the carpal tunnel, *except:*
   a. Tendon of palmaris longus
   b. Tendon of flexor pollicis longus
   c. Tendons of flexor digitorum profundus
   d. Median nerve
9. Compression of median nerve within carpal tunnel causes inability to:
   a. Flex the interphalangeal joint of thumb
   b. Extend the interphalangeal joint of thumb
   c. Adduct the thumb
   d. Abduct the thumb
10. de Quervain's disease affects:
    a. Tendons of abductor pollicis longus and abductor pollicis brevis
    b. Tendons of abductor pollicis longus and extensor pollicis brevis
    c. Tendons of extensor carpi radialis longus and extensor carpi radialis brevis
    d. Tendons of flexor pollicis longus and flexor pollicis brevis

ANSWERS

1. b   **2.** c   **3.** a   **4.** d   **5.** b   **6.** a   **7.** a   **8.** a   **9.** d   **10.** b

Joints of Upper Limb

Pronation is giving and supination is getting. There is no less joy in giving than in getting
If I have seen farther, it is by standing on the shoulder of giants

INTRODUCTION

Joints are sites where two or more bones or cartilages articulate. Free movements occur at the synovial joints. Shoulder joint is the most freely mobile joint. Shoulder joint gets excessive mobility at the cost of its own stability, since both are not feasible to the same degree. The carrying angle in relation to elbow joint is to facilitate carrying objects like buckets without hitting the pelvis.

Supination and pronation are basic movements for the survival of human being. During pronation, the food is picked and by supination it is put at the right place—the mouth. While 'giving', one pronates, while 'getting' one supinates.

The first carpometacarpal joint allows movements of opposition of thumb with the fingers for picking up or holding things. Thumb is the most important digit. Remember Muni Dronacharya asked Eklavya to give his right thumb as *Guru-Dakshina*, so that he is not able to outsmart Arjuna in archery.

SHOULDER GIRDLE

The shoulder girdle connects the upper limb to the axial skeleton. It consists of the clavicle and the scapula. Anteriorly, the clavicle reaches the sternum and articulates with it at the sternoclavicular joint. The clavicle and the scapula are united to each other at the acromioclavicular joint. The scapula is not connected to the axial skeleton directly, but is attached to it through muscles. The clavicle and the scapula have been studied in Chapter 2. The joints of the shoulder girdle are described below.

STERNOCLAVICULAR JOINT

DISSECTION

Remove the subclavius muscle from first rib at its attachment with its costal cartilage. Identify the costo-clavicular ligament.

Define the sternoclavicular joint and clean the anterior and superior surfaces of the capsule of this joint. Cut carefully through the joint to expose the intra-articular disc positioned between the clavicle and the sternum. The fibrocartilaginous disc divides the joint cavity into a superomedial and an inferolateral compartments.

Features

The sternoclavicular joint is a synovial joint. It is a compound joint as there are three elements taking part in it; namely the medial end of the clavicle, the clavicular notch of the manubrium sterni, and the upper surface of the first costal cartilage. It is a complex joint as its cavity is subdivided into two compartments, superomedial and inferolateral by an intra-articular disc (Fig. 10.1).

The *articular surface* of the clavicle is covered with fibrocartilage (as the clavicle is a membrane bone). The surface is convex from above downwards and slightly concave from front to back. The sternal surface is smaller than the clavicular surface. It has a reciprocal convexity and concavity. Because of the concavoconvex shape of the articular surfaces, the joint can be classified as a saddle joint.

The *capsular ligament* is attached laterally to the margins of the clavicular articular surface; and medially to the margins of the articular areas on the sternum and on the first costal cartilage. It is strong anteriorly and posteriorly where it constitutes the anterior and posterior sternoclavicular ligaments.

However, the main bond of union at this joint is the *articular disc*. The disc is attached laterally to the clavicle on a rough area above and posterior to the articular area for the sternum. Inferiorly, the disc is attached to the sternum and to the first costal cartilage at their junction. Anteriorly and posteriorly, the disc fuses with the capsule.

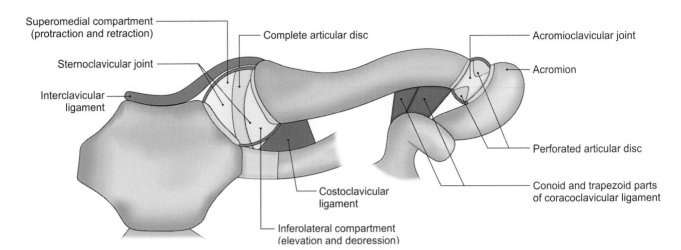

Fig. 10.1: The sternoclavicular and acromioclavicular joints

There are two other ligaments associated with this joint. The *interclavicular* ligament passes between the sternal ends of the right and left clavicles, some of its fibres being attached to the upper border of the manubrium sterni (Fig. 10.1).

The *costoclavicular ligament* is attached above to the rough area on the inferior aspect of the medial end of the clavicle. Inferiorly, it is attached to the first costal cartilage and to the first rib. It consists of anterior and posterior laminae.

Blood supply: Internal thoracic and suprascapular arteries.

Nerve supply: Medial supraclavicular nerve.

Movements: Movements of the sternoclavicular joint can be best understood by visualizing the movement at the lateral end of clavicle. These movements are elevation/ depression, protraction/retraction and anterior and posterior rotation of the clavicle. The anterior and posterior rotation of clavicle is utilized in overhead movements of the shoulder girdle.

ACROMIOCLAVICULAR JOINT

DISSECTION

Remove the muscles attached to the lateral end of clavicle and acromial process of scapula. Define the articular capsule surrounding the joint. Cut through the capsule to identify the intra-articular disc. Look for the strong coracoclavicular ligament.

Features

The acromioclavicular joint is a plane synovial joint. It is formed by articulation of small facets present:
  i. At the lateral end of the clavicle.
 ii. On the medial margin of the acromion process of the scapula.

The facets are covered with fibrocartilage. The cavity of the joint is subdivided by an articular disc which may have perforation in it (Fig. 10.1).

The bones are held together by a fibrous capsule and by the articular disc. However, the main bond of union between the scapula and the clavicle is the coracoclavicular ligament described below (Fig. 10.1).

Blood supply: Suprascapular and thoracoacromial arteries.

Nerve supply: Lateral supraclavicular nerve.

Movements: See movements of shoulder girdle.

Coracoclavicular Ligament

The ligament consists of two parts—conoid and trapezoid. The trapezoid part is attached, below to the upper surface of the coracoid process; and above to the trapezoid line on the inferior surface of the lateral part of the clavicle. The conoid part is attached, below to the root of the coracoid process just lateral to the scapular notch. It is attached above to the inferior surface of the clavicle on the conoid tubercle.

Movements of the Shoulder Girdle

Movements at the two joints of the girdle are always associated with the movements of the scapula (Figs 10.2a to f). The movements of the scapula may or may not be associated with the movements of the shoulder joint. The various movements of shoulder girdle are described below.

a. *Elevation* of the scapula (as in shrugging the shoulders). The movement is brought about by the upper fibres of the trapezius and by the levator scapulae.

It is associated with the elevation of the lateral end, and depression of the medial end of the clavicle. The clavicle moves round an anteroposterior axis formed by the costoclavicular ligament (Fig. 10.2a).

b. *Depression* of the scapula (drooping of the shoulder). It is brought about by gravity, and actively by the lower fibres of the serratus anterior and by the pectoralis minor.

It is associated with the depression of the lateral end, and elevation of the medial end of the clavicle (Fig. 10.2b).

Movements (a) and (b) occur in inferolateral compartment.

c. *Protraction* of the scapula (as in pushing and punching movements). It is brought about by the serratus anterior and by the pectoralis minor (*see* Fig. 3.24).

It is associated with forward movements of the lateral end and backward movement of the medial end of the clavicle (Fig. 10.2c).

d. *Retraction* of the scapula (squaring the shoulders) is brought about by the rhomboids and by the middle fibres of the trapezius.

It is associated with backward movement of the lateral end and forward movement of the medial end of the clavicle (Fig. 10.2d). Movements (c) and (d) occur in superomedial compartment.

e. *Lateral or forward rotation* of the scapula round the chest wall takes place during overhead abduction of the arm. The scapula rotates around the coraco-clavicular ligaments. The movement is brought about by the upper fibres of the trapezius and the lower fibres of the serratus anterior. This movement is associated with rotation of the clavicle around its long axis (Fig. 10.2e).

f. *Medial or backward rotation* of the scapula occurs under the influence of gravity, although it can be brought about actively by the levator scapulae and the rhomboids (Fig. 10.2f).

Movements (e) and (f) occur in inferolateral compartment.

Ligaments of the Scapula

The *coracoacromial ligament* (*see* Fig. 6.7): It is a triangular ligament, the apex of which is attached to the tip of the acromion, and the base to the lateral border of the coracoid process.

The acromion, the coracoacromial ligament and the coracoid process, together form the *coracoacromial arch*, which is known as the secondary socket for the head of the humerus. It adds to the stability of the joint and protects the head of the humerus.

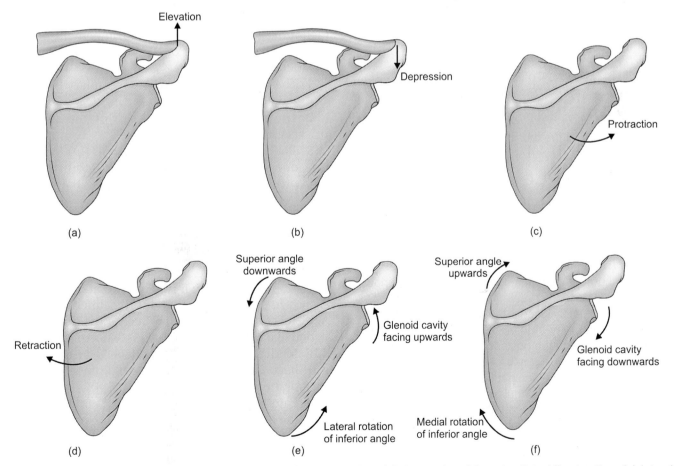

Figs 10.2a to f: Movements of the right shoulder girdle: (a) Elevation, (b) depression, (c) protraction, (d) retraction, (e) lateral rotation of inferior angle, and (f) medial rotation of inferior angle

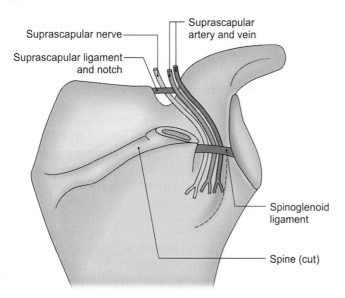

Suprascapular nerve

Suprascapular ligament and notch

Suprascapular artery and vein

Spinoglenoid ligament

Spine (cut)

Fig. 10.3: The suprascapular and spinoglenoid ligaments

The suprascapular ligament: It converts the scapular notch into a foramen. The suprascapular nerve passes below the ligament, and the suprascapular artery and vein above the ligament (Fig. 10.3).

The spinoglenoid ligament: It is a weak band which bridges the spinoglenoid notch. The suprascapular nerve and vessels pass beneath the arch to enter the infraspinous fossa.

SHOULDER JOINT

DISSECTION

Having studied all the muscles at the upper end of the scapula, it is wise to open and peep into the most mobile shoulder joint.

Identify the muscles attached to the greater and lesser tubercles of humerus. Deep to the acromion look for the subacromial bursa.

Identify coracoid process, acromion process and triangular coracoacromial arch binding these two bones together (*see* Fig. 6.7).

Trace the supraspinatus muscle from supraspinous fossa of scapula to the greater tubercle of humerus. On its way, it is intimately fused to the capsule of the shoulder joint. In the same way, tendons of infraspinatus and teres minor also fuse with the posterior part of the capsule.

Inferiorly, trace the tendon of long head of triceps brachii from the infraglenoid tubercle of scapula.

Cut through the subscapularis muscle at the neck of scapula. It also gets fused with the anterior part of capsule of the shoulder joint as it passes to the lesser tubercle of humerus.

Having studied the structures related to shoulder joint, the capsule of the joint is to be opened.

A vertical incision is given in the posterior part of the capsule of the shoulder joint. The arm is rotated medially and laterally. This helps in head of humerus getting separated from the shallow glenoid cavity.

Inside the capsule, the shining tendon of long head of biceps brachii is visible as it traverses the intertubercular sulcus to reach the supraglenoid tubercle of scapula. This tendon also gets continuous with the labrum glenoidale attached to the rim of glenoid cavity.

Type

The shoulder joint is a synovial joint of ball and socket variety.

The articular surface, ligaments, and bursae related to this important joint are explained below.

Articular Surface

The joint is formed by articulation of the glenoid cavity of scapula and the head of the humerus. Therefore, it is also known as the glenohumeral articulation.

Structurally, it is a weak joint because the glenoid cavity is too small and shallow to hold the head of the humerus in place (the head is four times the size of the glenoid cavity). However, this arrangement permits great mobility. Stability of the joint is maintained by the following factors.

1. The coracoacromial arch or secondary socket for the head of the humerus (*see* Fig. 6.8).
2. The musculotendinous cuff of the shoulder (*see* Fig. 6.7).
3. The glenoidal labrum (Latin *lip*) helps in deepening the glenoid fossa. Stability is also provided by the muscles attaching the humerus to the pectoral girdle, the long head of the biceps brachii, and the long head of the triceps brachii. Atmospheric pressure also stabilises the joint.

Ligaments

1. *The capsular ligament:* It is very loose and permits free movements. It is least supported inferiorly where dislocations are common. Such a dislocation may damage the closely related axillary nerve (*see* Fig. 6.8).
   - Medially, the capsule is attached to the scapula beyond the supraglenoid tubercle and the margins of the labrum.
   - Laterally, it is attached to the anatomical neck of the humerus with the following exceptions:
     Inferiorly, the attachment extends down to the surgical neck (*see* Figs 2.14a and b).
     Superiorly, it is deficient for passage of the tendon of the long head of the biceps brachii (Fig. 10.4a).

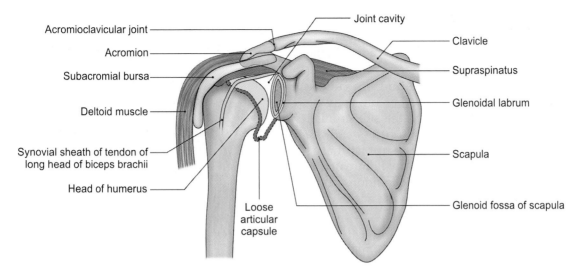

Fig. 10.4a: The shoulder joint

- Anteriorly, the capsule is reinforced by supplemental bands called the superior, middle and inferior glenohumeral ligaments.

  The area between the superior and middle glenohumeral ligament is a point of weakness in the capsule (foramen of Weitbrecht) which is a common site of anterior dislocation of humeral head.

  The capsule is lined with synovial membrane. An extension of this membrane forms a tubular sheath for the tendon of the long head of the biceps brachii.

2 *The coracohumeral ligament:* It extends from the root of the coracoid process to the neck of the humerus

opposite the greater tubercle. It gives strength to the capsule.

3 *Transverse humeral ligament:* It bridges the upper part of the bicipital groove of the humerus (between the greater and lesser tubercles). The tendon of the long head of the biceps brachii passes deep to the ligament.

4 *The glenoidal labrum:* It is a fibrocartilaginous rim which covers the margins of the glenoid cavity, thus increasing the depth of the cavity.

Bursae Related to the Joint

1 The subacromial (subdeltoid) bursa (*see* Figs 6.7 and 6.8).

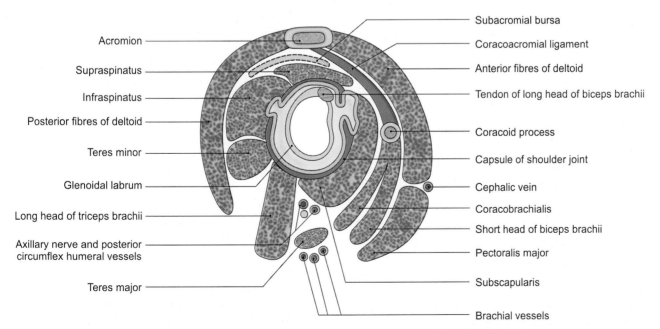

Fig. 10.4b: Schematic sagittal section showing relations of the shoulder joint

2 The subscapularis bursa, communicates with the joint cavity.

3 The infraspinatus bursa, may communicate with the joint cavity.

The subacromial and the subdeltoid bursae are commonly continuous with each other but may be separate. Collectively they are called the subacromial bursa, which separates the acromion process and the coracoacromial ligaments from the supraspinatus tendon and permits smooth motion. Any failure of this mechanism can lead to inflammatory conditions of the supraspinatus tendon.

Relations

- *Superiorly:* Coracoacromial arch, subacromial bursa, supraspinatus and deltoid (Fig. 10.4).
- *Inferiorly:* Long head of the triceps brachii, axillary nerves and posterior circumflex humeral artery.
- *Anteriorly:* Subscapularis, coracobrachialis, short head of biceps brachii and deltoid.
- *Posteriorly:* Infraspinatus, teres minor and deltoid.
- *Within the joint:* Tendon of the long head of the biceps brachii.

Blood Supply

1 Anterior circumflex humeral vessels.
2 Posterior circumflex humeral vessels.
3 Suprascapular vessels.
4 Subscapular vessels.

Nerve Supply

1 Axillary nerve.
2 Musculocutaneous nerve.
3 Suprascapular nerve.

Movements of Shoulder Joint

The shoulder joint enjoys great freedom of mobility at the cost of stability. There is no other joint in the body which is more mobile than the shoulder joint. This wide range of mobility is due to laxity of its fibrous capsule, and the four times large size of the head of the humerus as compared with the shallow glenoid cavity. The range of movements is further increased by concurrent movements of the shoulder girdle (Figs 10.5 and 10.6).

However, this large range of motion makes glenohumeral joint more susceptible to dislocations, instability, degenerative changes and other painful conditions specially in individuals who perform repetitive overhead motions (cricketers).

Movements of the shoulder joint are considered in relation to the scapula rather than in relation to the sagittal and coronal planes. When the arm is by the side (in the

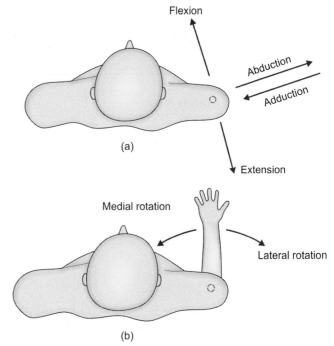

Figs 10.5a and b: Planes of movements of the shoulder joint: (a) Flexion, extension, abduction, adduction, and (b) medial and lateral rotations

resting position) the glenoid cavity faces almost equally forwards and laterally; and the head of the humerus faces medially and backwards. Keeping these directions in mind, the movements are analysed as follows.

1 *Flexion and extension:* During flexion, the arm moves forwards and medially, and during extension, the arm moves backwards and laterally. Thus flexion and extension take place in a plane parallel to the surface of the glenoid cavity (Figs 10.6a and b).

2 *Abduction and adduction* take place at right angles to the plane of flexion and extension, i.e. approximately midway between the sagittal and coronal planes. In abduction, the arm moves anterolaterally away from the trunk. This movement is in the same plane as that of the body of the scapula (Figs 10.6c and d).

3 *Medial and lateral rotations* are best demonstrated with a midflexed elbow. In this position, the hand is moved medially across the chest in medial rotation, and laterally in lateral rotation of the shoulder joint (Figs 10.6e and f).

4 *Circumduction* is a combination of different movements as a result of which the hand moves along a circle. The range of any movement depends on the availability of an area of free articular surface on the head of the humerus.

Muscles bringing about movements at shoulder joint are shown in Table 10.1. Abduction has been analysed.

Figs 10.6a to f: Movements of the shoulder joint: (a) Flexion, (b) extension, (c) abduction, (d) adduction, (e) medial rotation, (f) lateral rotation

	Table 10.1: Muscles bringing about movements at the shoulder joint	
Movements	*Main muscles*	*Accessory muscles*
1. Flexion	• Clavicular head of the pectoralis major • Anterior fibres of deltoid	• Coracobrachialis • Short head of biceps brachii
2. Extension	• Posterior fibres of deltoid • Latissimus dorsi	• Teres major • Long head of triceps brachii • Sternocostal head of the pectoralis major
3. Adduction	• Pectoralis major • Latissimus dorsi • Short head of biceps brachii • Long head of triceps brachii	• Teres major • Coracobrachialis
4. Abduction	• Both supraspinatus and deltoid muscles initiate abduction and are involved throughout the range of abduction from 0°–90°. • Serratus anterior 90°–180° • Upper and lower fibres of trapezius 90°–180°	—
5. Medial rotation	• Pectoralis major • Anterior fibres of deltoid • Latissimus dorsi • Teres major	• Subscapularis
6. Lateral rotation	• Posterior fibres of deltoid • Infraspinatus • Teres minor	—

Analysis of the Overhead Movement of the Shoulder

The overhead movements of flexion and abduction of the shoulder are brought about by smooth and coordinate motion at all joints of the shoulder complex: glenohumeral, sternoclavicular, acromioclavicular, and scapulothoracic. Only glenohumeral joint motion cannot bring about the 180 degrees of movement that takes place in overhead shoulder movements. The scapula contributes to overhead flexion and abduction by rotating upwardly by 50–60 degrees. The glenohumeral joint contributes 100–120 degrees of flexion and 90–120 degrees of abduction to the total 170–180 degrees of overhead movements. This makes the overall ratio of 2 degrees of motion of shoulder to 1 degree of scapulothoracic motion and is often referred to as "scapulo-humeral rhythm". Thus for every 15 degrees of elevation, 10 degrees occur at shoulder joint and 5 degrees are due to movement of the scapula.

The humeral head undergoes lateral rotation at around 90 degrees of abduction to help clear the greater tubercle under the acromion. Although deltoid is the main abductor of the shoulder, the rotator muscles, namely the supraspinatus, infraspinatus, teres minor and the subscapularis play a very important role in providing static and dynamic stability to the head of the humerus. Thus the deltoid and these four muscles constitute a "couple" which permits true abduction in the plane of the body of the scapula.

In addition, the scapular muscles such as trapezius, serratus anterior, levator scapulae and rhomboids provide stability and mobility to the scapula in the coordinated overhead motion.

Serratus anterior is chiefly inserted into the inferior angle of scapula. It rotates this angle laterally. At the same time, trapezius rotates the medial border at root of spine of scapula downwards. The synergic action of these two muscles turns the glenoid cavity upwards increasing the range of abduction at the shoulder joint.

CLINICAL ANATOMY

- The clavicle may be dislocated at either of its ends. At the medial end, it is usually dislocated forwards. Backward dislocation is rare as it is prevented by the costoclavicular ligament.
- The main bond of union between the clavicle and the manubrium is the articular disc. Apart from its attachment to the joint capsule, the disc is also attached above to the medial end of the clavicle, and below to the manubrium. This prevents the sternal end of the clavicle from tilting upwards when the weight of the arm depresses the acromial end (Fig. 10.1).

- The clavicle dislocates upwards at the acromioclavicular joint, because the clavicle overrides the acromion.
- The weight of the limb is transmitted from the scapula to the clavicle through the coracoclavicular ligament, and from the clavicle to the sternum through the sternoclavicular joint. Some of the weight also passes to the first rib by the costoclavicular ligament. The clavicle usually fractures between these two ligaments (Fig. 10.1).
- *Dislocation:* The shoulder joint is more prone to dislocation than any other joint. This is due to laxity of the capsule and the disproportionate area of the articular surfaces. Dislocation usually occurs when the arm is abducted. In this position, the head of the humerus presses against the lower unsupported part of the capsular ligament. Thus almost always the dislocation is primarily

---

DANCING SHOULDER

When one flexes the arm at shoulder joint,
there is one small point
which you must remember;
whether it is July or November
there is a gamble of two muscles
Pectoralis major and Anterior deltoid in the tussles.

To Teres major, Latissimus dorsi was happily married
but while extending, these got joined with Posterior deltoid.

In adduction of course,
the joint decided a better course.
It went off with two majors (Pectoralis major and Teres major),
On the way they stopped for some gazers,
The two majors danced with Subscapularis
during medial rotation,
Even Anterior deltoid and Latissimus dorsi,
soon joined the happy flirtation

If one wants the joint to laterally rotate,
then there is difference in the mate.
Posterior deltoid dances with Infraspinatus,
Even Teres minor comes and triangulates.

When just abduction is desired,
Supraspinatus and Mid-deltoid are required.
But if Kapil Dev has to do the bowling
come Trapezius and Serratus anterior following.

Small muscles provide stability
Large ones give it mobility
And shoulder joint dances,
dances and dances.

subglenoid. Dislocation endangers the axillary nerve which is closely related to the lower part of the joint capsule (*see* Fig. 6.12).

- *Optimum attitude:* In order to avoid ankylosis, many diseases of the shoulder joint are treated in an optimum position of the joint. In this position, the arm is abducted by 45–90 degrees.
- *Shoulder tip pain:* Irritation of the peritoneum underlying diaphragm from any surrounding pathology causes referred pain in the shoulder. This is so because the phrenic nerve carrying impulses from peritoneum and the supraclavicular nerves (supplying the skin over the shoulder) both arise from spinal segments C3, C4 (Figs 10.7a and b).
- The shoulder joint is most commonly approached (surgically) from the front. However, for aspiration, the needle may be introduced either anteriorly through the deltopectoral triangle (closer to the deltoid), or laterally just below the acromion (Fig. 10.8).
- *Frozen shoulder:* This is a common occurrence. Pathologically, the two layers of the synovial membrane become adherent to each other. Clinically, the patient (usually 40–60 years of age) complains of progressively increasing pain in the shoulder, stiffness in the joint and restriction of all movements particularly external rotation, abduction and medial rotation. As the contribution of the glenohumeral joint is reduced, the patient shows altered scapulohumeral rhythm due to excessive use of scapular motion while performing overhead flexion and abduction. The surrounding muscles show disuse atrophy. The disease is self-limiting and the patient may recover spontaneously in about two years and much earlier by physiotherapy.
- Shoulder joint disease can be excluded, if the patient can raise both his arms above the head and bring the two palms together (Fig. 10.9). Deltoid muscle and axillary nerve are likely to be intact.

ELBOW JOINT

DISSECTION

Cut through the muscles arising from the lateral and medial epicondyles of humerus and reflect them distally, if not already done.

Also cut through biceps brachii, brachialis and triceps brachii 3 cm proximal to the elbow joint and reflect them distally.

Remove all the muscles fused with the fibrous capsule of the elbow joint and define its attachments.

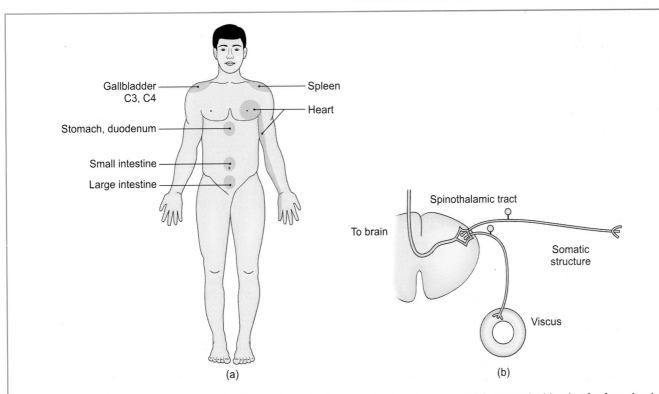

Figs 10.7a and b: (a) Shoulder tip pain. Other sites of referred pain also shown, and (b) anatomical basis of referred pain

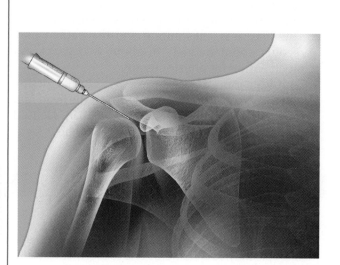

Fig. 10.8: Site of aspiration of shoulder joint

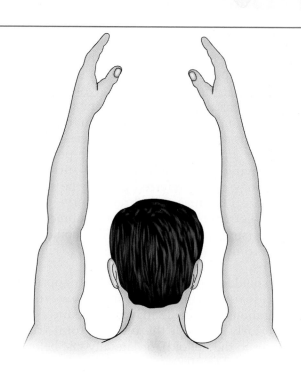

Fig. 10.9: Exclusion of shoulder joint disease

Features

The elbow joint is a hinge variety of synovial joint between the lower end of humerus and the upper ends of radius and ulna bones.

Elbow joint is the term used for humeroradial and humeroulnar joints. The term elbow complex also includes the superior radioulnar joint also.

Articular Surfaces

Upper

The capitulum and trochlea of the humerus.

The coronoid fossa lies just above the trochlea and is designed in a manner that the coronoid process of ulna fits into it in extreme flexion. Similarly, the radial fossa just above the capitulum allows for radial head fitting in the radial fossa in extreme flexion.

Lower

i. Upper surface of the head of the radius articulates with the capitulum.
ii. Trochlear notch of the ulna articulates with the trochlea of the humerus (Fig. 10.10).

The elbow joint is continuous with the superior radioulnar joint. The humeroradial, the humeroulnar and the superior radioulnar joints are together known as cubital articulations.

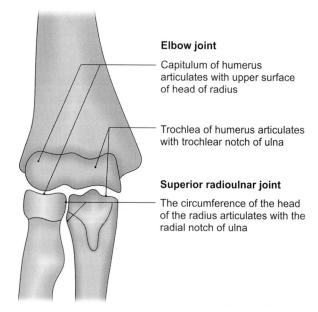

Elbow joint

Capitulum of humerus articulates with upper surface of head of radius

Trochlea of humerus articulates with trochlear notch of ulna

Superior radioulnar joint

The circumference of the head of the radius articulates with the radial notch of ulna

Fig. 10.10: The cubital articulations, including the elbow and superior radioulnar joints

Ligaments

1 *Capsular ligament: Superiorly,* it is attached to the lower end of the humerus in such a way that the capitulum, the trochlea, the radial fossa, the coronoid fossa and the olecranon fossa are intracapsular. *Inferomedially,* it is attached to the margin of the trochlear notch of

the ulna except laterally; *inferolaterally*, it is attached to the annular ligament of the superior radioulnar joint. The synovial membrane lines the capsule and the fossae, named above.

The *anterior ligament*, and the *posterior ligament* are thickening of the capsule.

2 The *ulnar collateral ligament* is triangular in shape (Fig. 10.11). Its apex is attached to the medial epicondyle of the humerus, and its base to the ulna. The ligament has thick anterior and posterior bands: These are attached below to the coronoid process and the olecranon process, respectively. Their lower ends are joined to each other by an oblique band which gives attachment to the thinner intermediate fibres of the ligament. The ligament is crossed by the *ulnar nerve* and it gives origin to the flexor digitorum superficialis. It is closely related to the flexor carpi ulnaris and the triceps brachii.

3 The *radial collateral or lateral ligament:* It is a fan-shaped band extending from the lateral epicondyle to the annular ligament. It gives origin to the supinator and to the extensor carpi radialis brevis (Fig. 10.12).

Relations

- *Anteriorly:* Brachialis, median nerve, brachial artery and tendon of biceps brachii (*see* Fig. 9.4).
- *Posteriorly:* Triceps brachii and anconeus.
- *Medially:* Ulnar nerve, flexor carpi ulnaris and common flexors.
- *Laterally:* Supinator, extensor carpi radialis brevis and other common extensors.

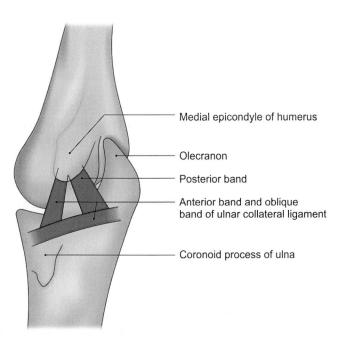

Fig. 10.11: The ulnar collateral ligament of the elbow joint showing anterior, posterior and oblique bands

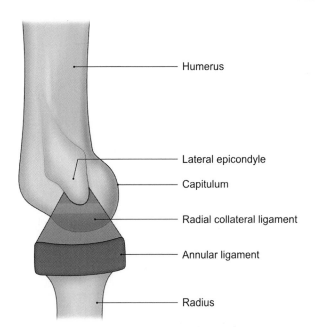

Fig. 10.12: The radial collateral ligament of the elbow joint

Blood Supply

From anastomoses around the elbow joint (*see* Fig. 8.10).

Nerve Supply

The joint receives branches from the following nerves.
 i. Ulnar nerve.
 ii. Median nerve.
 iii. Radial nerve.
 iv. Musculocutaneous nerve through its branch to the brachialis.

Movements

1 Flexion is brought about by:
    i. Brachialis.
    ii. Biceps brachii.
    iii. Brachioradialis.
2 Extension is produced by:
    i. Triceps brachii.
    ii. Anconeus.

Carrying Angle

The transverse axis of the elbow joint is directed medially and downwards. Because of this, the extended forearm is not in straight line with the arm, but makes an angle of about 13 degrees with it. This is known as the carrying angle. The factors responsible for formation of the carrying angle are as follows.

a. The medial flange of the trochlea is 6 mm deeper than the lateral flange.
b. The superior articular surface of the coronoid process of the ulna is placed oblique to the long axis of the bone.

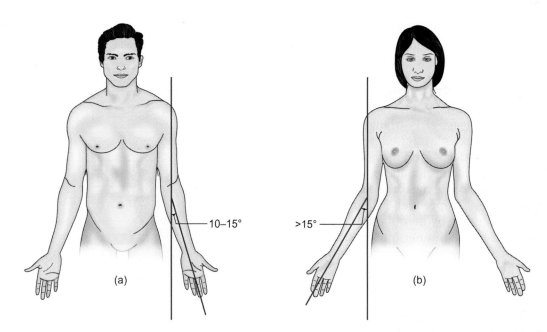

Figs 10.13a and b: Carrying angle: (a) 10–15° in males, and (b) more than 15° in females

The carrying angle disappears in full flexion of the elbow, and also during pronation of the forearm. The forearm comes into line with the arm in the midprone position, and this is the position in which the hand is mostly used. This arrangement of gradually increasing carrying angle during extension of the elbow increases the precision with which the hand (and objects held in it) can be controlled. The angle is 10–15° in males (Fig. 10.13a) and more than 15° in females (Fig. 10.13b)

CLINICAL ANATOMY

- *Distension* of the elbow joint by an effusion occurs posteriorly because here the capsule is weak and the covering deep fascia is thin. Aspiration is done posteriorly on any side of the olecranon (Fig. 10.14).
- *Dislocation* of the elbow is usually posterior, and is often associated with fracture of the coronoid process. The triangular relationship between the olecranon and the two humeral epicondyles is lost (*see* Fig. 2.17).
- *Subluxation* of the head of the radius (pulled elbow) occurs in children when the forearm is suddenly pulled in pronation. The head of the radius slips out from the annular ligament (*see* Fig. 2.25).
- *Tennis elbow* occurs in tennis players. Abrupt pronation with fully extended elbow may lead to pain and tenderness over the lateral epicondyle which gives attachment to common extensor origin (Fig. 10.15). This is possibly due to:
a. Sprain of radial collateral ligament.

b. Tearing of fibres of the extensor carpi radialis brevis.
c. Recent researches have pointed out that it is more of a degenerative condition rather than inflammatory condition.
- *Student's* (*Miner's*) *elbow* is characterised by effusion into the bursa over the subcutaneous posterior surface of the olecranon process. Students during lectures support their head (for sleeping) with their hands with flexed elbows. The bursa on the olecranon process gets inflamed (Fig. 10.16).
- Golfer's elbow is the microtrauma of medial epicondyle of humerus, occurs commonly in golf players. The common flexor origin undergoes repetitive strain and results in a painful condition on the medial side of the elbow (Fig. 10.17).
- If carrying angle (normal is 13°) is more, the condition is cubitus valgus, ulnar nerve may get stretched leading to weakness of intrinsic muscles of hand. If the angle is less, it is called cubitus varus (Fig. 10.18).
- Under optimal position of the elbow: Generally elbow flexion between 30 and 40 degrees is sufficient to perform common activities of daily living such as eating, combing, dressing, etc. Because of this reason even people who have lost terminal flexion or extension after a fracture/trauma are able to accomplish these personal tasks without much problems.

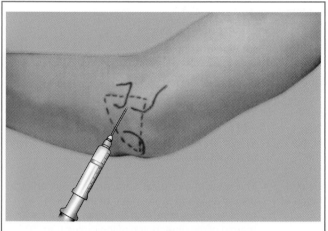

Fig. 10.14: Aspiration of elbow joint

Fig. 10.15: Tennis elbow

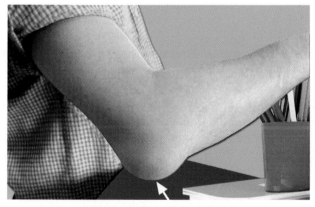

Fig. 10.16: Student's elbow

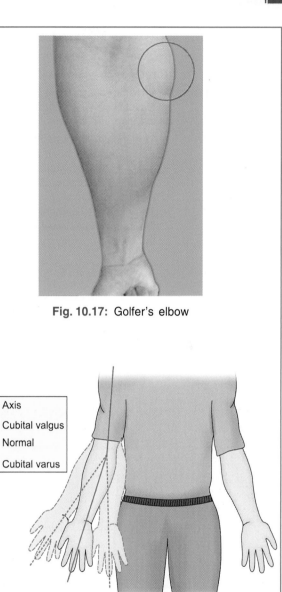

Fig. 10.17: Golfer's elbow

Axis
Cubital valgus
Normal
Cubital varus

Fig. 10.18: Normal, cubitus valgus, and cubitus varus

RADIOULNAR JOINTS

DISSECTION

Remove all the muscles covering the adjacent sides of radius, ulna and the intervening interosseous membrane. This will expose the superior and inferior radioulnar joints including the interosseous membrane.

Cut through the annular ligament to see the superior radioulnar joint.

Clean and define the interosseous membrane. Lastly cut through the capsule of inferior radioulnar joint to locate the intra-articular fibrocartilaginous disc of the joint.

Learn the movements of supination and pronation on dry bones and on yourself.

Features

The radius and the ulna are joined to each other at the superior and inferior radioulnar joints. These are described in Table 10.2. The radius and ulna are also connected by the interosseous membrane which constitutes middle radioulnar joint (Fig. 10.19).

Table 10.2: Radioulnar joints (Fig. 10.19)

Features	Superior radioulnar joint	Inferior radioulnar joint
Type	Pivot type of synovial joint	Pivot type of synovial joint
Articular surfaces	• Circumference of head of radius • Osseofibrous ring, formed by the radial notch of the ulna and the annular ligament	• Head of ulna • Ulnar notch of radius
Ligaments	• The annular ligament forms four-fifths of the ring within which the head of the radius rotates. It is attached to the margins of the radial notch of the ulna, and is continuous with the capsule of the elbow joint above • The quadrate ligament extends from the neck of the radius to the lower margin of the radial notch of the ulna	• The capsule surrounds the joint. The weak upper part is evaginated by the synovial membrane to form a recess (recessus sacciformis) in front of the interosseous membrane • The apex of triangular fibrocartilaginous articular disc is attached to the base of the styloid process of the ulna, and the base to the lower margin of the ulnar notch of the radius (Fig. 10.20)
Blood supply	Anastomoses around the lateral side of the elbow joint	Anterior and posterior interosseous arteries
Nerve supply	Musculocutaneous, median, and radial nerves	Anterior and posterior interosseous nerves
Movements	Supination and pronation	Supination and pronation

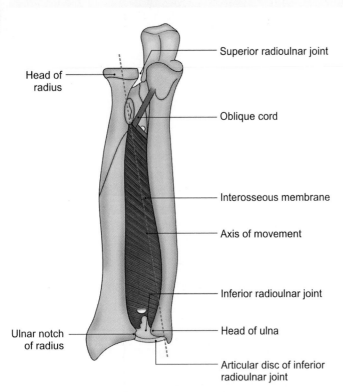

Fig. 10.19: Radioulnar joints

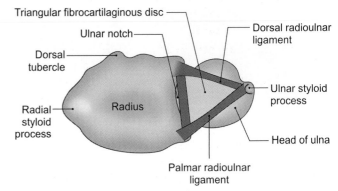

Fig. 10.20: Triangular fibrocartilaginous disc of inferior radioulnar joint

1 Superiorly, the interosseous membrane begins 2–3 cm below the radial tuberosity. Between the oblique cord and the interosseous membrane, there is a gap for passage of the posterior interosseous vessels to the back of the forearm.

2 Inferiorly, a little above its lower margin, there is an aperture for the passage of the anterior interosseous vessels to the back of the forearm.

3 The anterior surface is related to the flexor pollicis longus, the flexor digitorum profundus, the pronator quadratus, and to the anterior interosseous vessels and nerve (*see* Fig. 2.22).

4 The posterior surface (*see* Fig. 9.55) is related to the supinator, the abductor pollicis longus, the extensor pollicis brevis, the extensor pollicis longus, the extensor indicis, the anterior interosseous artery and the posterior interosseous nerve.

INTEROSSEOUS MEMBRANE

The interosseous membrane connects the shafts of the radius and ulna. It is attached to the interosseous borders of these bones. The fibres of the membrane run downwards and medially from the radius to ulna (Fig. 10.19). The two bones are also connected by the oblique cord which extends from the tuberosity of the radius to the tuberosity of the ulna. The direction of its fibres is opposite to that in the interosseous membrane.

The interosseous membrane performs the following functions.

a. It binds the radius and ulna to each other.

b. It provides attachments to many muscles.

c. It transmits forces (including weight) applied to the radius (through the hand) to the ulna. This transmission is necessary as radius is the main bone taking part in the wrist joint, while the ulna is the main bone taking part in the elbow joint (*see* Fig. 1.2 and Flowchart 1.1).

SUPINATION AND PRONATION

Supination and pronation are rotatory movements of the forearm/hand around a vertical axis. In a semiflexed elbow, the palm is turned upwards in supination, and downwards in pronation (kings pronate, beggars supinate). The movements are permitted at the superior and inferior radioulnar joints.

During pronation, head of radius spins within annular ligament. As radius with the hand comes medially across the lower part of ulna, the interosseous membrane is spiralised. During supination, the membrane is despiralised.

The vertical axis of movement of the radius passes through the centre of the head of the radius above, and through the ulnar attachment of the articular disc below (Fig. 10.19). However, this axis is not stationary because the lower end of the ulna is not fixed: It moves backwards and laterally during pronation, and forwards and medially during supination. As a result of this movement, the axis (defined above) is displaced laterally in pronation, and medially in supination.

Supination is more powerful than pronation because it is an antigravity movement. Supination movements are responsible for all screwing movements of the hand, e.g. as in tightening nuts and bolts. Morphologically, pronation and supination were evolved for picking up food and taking it to the mouth.

Around 50 degrees of supination and 50 degrees of pronation are generally required to perform many of the routine activities.

Pronation is brought about chiefly by the pronator quadratus. It is aided by the pronator teres when the movement is rapid and against resistance. Gravity also helps (Fig. 10.21).

Supination is brought about by the supinator muscle and the biceps brachii. Slow supination, with elbow extended, is done by the supinator. Rapid supination with the elbow flexed, and when performed against resistance, is done mainly by the biceps brachii (Fig. 10.22).

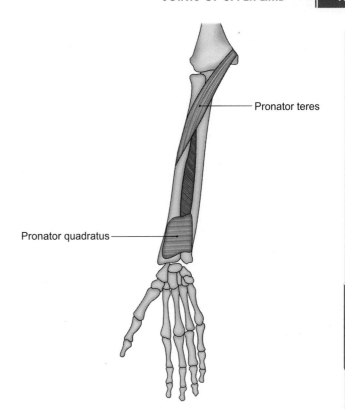

Fig. 10.21: Pronators of the forearm

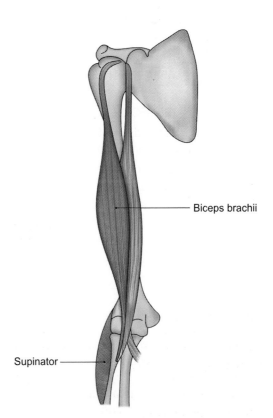

Fig. 10.22: Supinators of the forearm

Upper Limb

Section 1

CLINICAL ANATOMY

Supination and pronation: During supination, the radius and ulna are parallel to each other. During pronation, radius crosses over the ulna (Figs 10.23a and b). In synostosis (fusion) of upper end of radius and ulna, pronation is not possible.

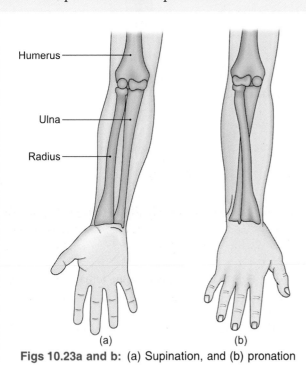

Figs 10.23a and b: (a) Supination, and (b) pronation

WRIST (RADIOCARPAL) JOINT

DISSECTION

Cut through the thenar and hypothenar muscles from their origins and reflect them distally.

Separate the flexor and extensor retinacula of the wrist from the bones.

Cut through flexor and extensor tendons (if not already done) and reflect them distally.

Define the capsular attachments and ligaments and relations of the wrist joint.

Type

Wrist joint is a synovial joint of the ellipsoid variety between lower end of radius and articular disc of inferior radioulnar joint proximally and three lateral bones of proximal row of carpus, i.e. scaphoid, lunate and triquetral distally.

The pisiform does not play a role in the radiocarpal articulation. It is a sesamoid bone acting as a pulley for flexor carpi ulnaris.

Articular Surfaces

Upper

1 Inferior surface of the lower end of the radius (*see* Fig. 2.24a).
2 Articular disc of the inferior radioulnar joint (Fig. 10.24b).

Lower

1 Scaphoid
2 Lunate
3 Triquetral bones.

Ligaments

1 The *articular capsule* surrounds the joint. It is attached above to the lower ends of the radius and ulna, and below to the proximal row of carpal bones. A protrusion of synovial membrane, called the recessus sacciformis, lies in front of the styloid process of the ulna and in front of the articular disc. It is bounded inferiorly by a small meniscus projecting inwards from the ulnar collateral ligament between the styloid process and the triquetral bone. The fibrous capsule is strengthened by the following ligaments.

2 On the palmar aspect, there are two palmar carpal ligaments.

The *palmar radiocarpal ligament* is a broad band. It begins above from the anterior margin of the lower end of the radius and its styloid process, runs downwards and medially, and is attached below to the anterior surfaces of the scaphoid, the lunate and triquetral bones.

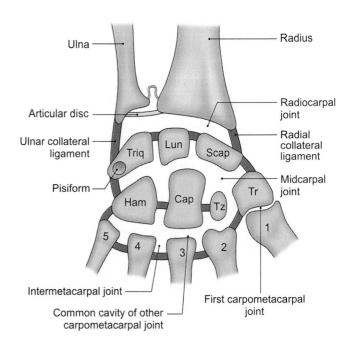

Fig. 10.24a: Joints in the region of the wrist

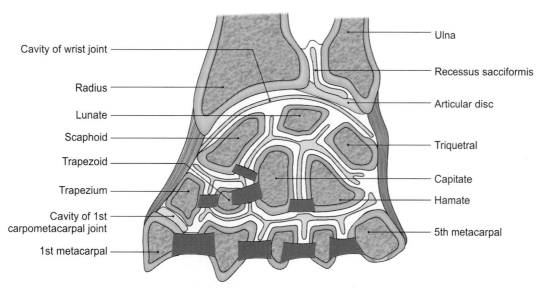

Fig. 10.24b: Cavity of wrist, inferior radioulnar, intercarpal and 1st carpometacarpal joints

The *palmar ulnocarpal ligament* is a rounded fasciculus. It begins above from the base of the styloid process of the ulna and the anterior margin of the articular disc, runs downwards and laterally, and is attached to the lunate and triquetral bones.

Both the palmar carpal ligaments are considered to be intracapsular.

3 On the dorsal aspect of the joint, there is one *dorsal radiocarpal ligament*. It is weaker than the palmar ligaments. It begins above from the posterior margin of the lower end of the radius, runs downwards and medially, and is attached below to the dorsal surfaces of the scaphoid, lunate and triquetral bones (Fig. 10.25).

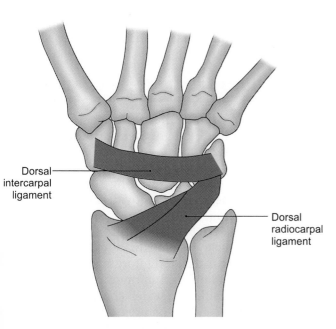

Fig. 10.25: Some ligaments of the wrist

4 The *radial collateral ligament* extends from the tip of the styloid process of the radius to the lateral side of the scaphoid bone (Fig. 10.24a). It is related to the radial artery.

5 The *ulnar collateral ligament* extends from the tip of the styloid process of the ulna to the triquetral and pisiform bones.

Both the collateral ligaments are poorly developed.

Relations

- *Anterior:* Long flexor tendons with their synovial sheaths, and median nerve (*see* Fig. 9.6).
- *Posterior:* Extensor tendons of the wrist and fingers with their synovial sheaths (*see* Fig. 9.52).
- *Lateral:* Radial artery (*see* Fig. 9.33).

Blood Supply

Anterior and posterior carpal arches.

Nerve Supply

Anterior and posterior interosseous nerves.

Movements

Movements at the radiocarpal joints are accompanied by movements at the midcarpal joint. The midcarpal joint is anatomically separate from radiocarpal joint. The joint between the two rows of carpal bones does not have smooth joint line because of multiple small joints. However, it still behaves as a functional unit in all movements of the wrist joint.

In addition to the congruency and the shape of the articular surfaces of radius and carpal bones, the length of the ulna can also affect the amount of motion available at the wrist joint. In the ulnar negative variance, the distal end of ulna is shorter than the radius and vice versa in ulnar positive variance. The wrist joint has the following movements.

1 *Flexion:* It takes place more at the midcarpal than at the wrist joint. The main flexors are:
   i. Flexor carpi radialis (Figs 10.26a and b).
   ii. Flexor carpi ulnaris.
   iii. Palmaris longus.

The movement is assisted by long flexors of the fingers and thumb (Fig. 10.34), and abductor pollicis longus.

2 *Extension:* It takes place mainly at the wrist joint. The main extensors are:
   i. Extensor carpi radialis longus.
   ii. Extensor carpi radialis brevis.
   iii. Extensor carpi ulnaris.

It is assisted by the extensors of the fingers and thumb (Figs 10.27a and b).

3 *Abduction (radial deviation):* It occurs mainly at the midcarpal joint. The main abductors are:
   i. Flexor carpi radialis.
   ii. Extensor carpi radialis longus and extensor carpi radialis brevis.
   iii. Abductor pollicis longus and extensor pollicis brevis.

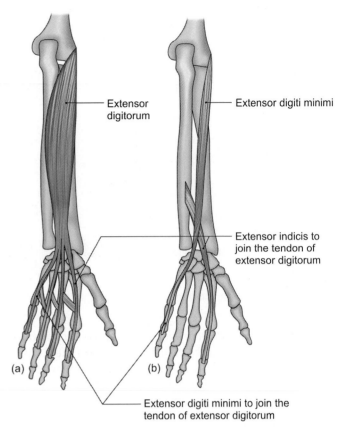

Figs 10.27a and b: (a) Extensor digitorum, and (b) extensor digiti minimi

4 *Adduction (ulnar deviation):* It occurs mainly at the wrist joint. The main adductors are:
   i. Flexor carpi ulnaris.
   ii. Extensor carpi ulnaris.

5 *Circumduction:* The range of flexion is more than that of extension. Similarly, the range of adduction is greater than abduction (due to the shorter styloid process of ulna).

CLINICAL ANATOMY

- The wrist joint and interphalangeal joints are commonly involved in rheumatoid arthritis (Figs 10.28a and b).
- The back of the wrist is the common site for a ganglion. It is a cystic swelling resulting from mucoid degeneration of synovial sheaths around the tendons (Fig. 10.29).
- The wrist joint can be aspirated from the posterior surface between the tendons of the extensor pollicis longus and the extensor digitorum (Fig. 10.30).
- The joint is immobilised in optimum position of 30 degrees dorsiflexion (extension).
- Because of the complex nature of the joint and the multiple articulations, any injury to the ligaments

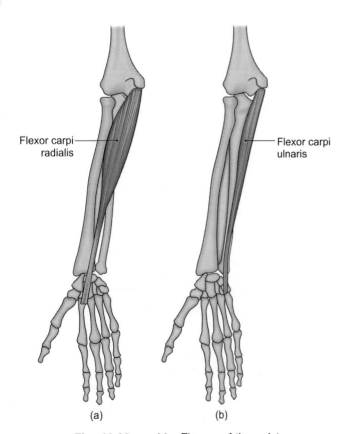

Figs 10.26a and b: Flexors of the wrist

attached to the proximal or the distal row of carpal bones may cause subluxation of the carpals ventrally or dorsally leading to painful condition of the wrist.

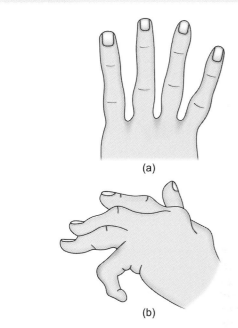

(a)

(b)

Figs 10.28a and b: Rheumatoid arthritis leading to deformities

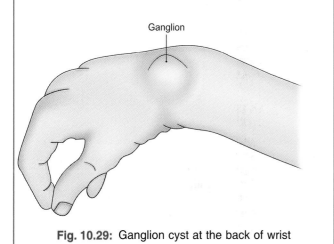

Ganglion

Fig. 10.29: Ganglion cyst at the back of wrist

JOINTS OF HAND

DISSECTION

Out of these, the most important joint with a separate joint cavity is the first carpometacarpal joint. This is the joint of the thumb and a wide variety of functionally useful movements take place here. Identify the distal surface of trapezium and base of first metacarpal bone.

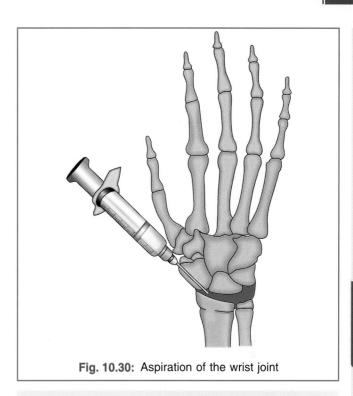

Fig. 10.30: Aspiration of the wrist joint

Define the metacarpophalangeal and interphalangeal joints.

For their dissection, remove all the muscles and tendons from the anterior and posterior aspects of any two metacarpophalangeal joints. Define the articular capsule and ligaments. Do the same for proximal and distal interphalangeal joints of one of the fingers and define the ligaments.

INTERCARPAL, CARPOMETACARPAL AND INTERMETACARPAL JOINTS

There are three joint cavities among the intercarpal, carpometacarpal and intermetacarpal joints, which are:
1 Pisotriquetral,
2 First carpometacarpal, and
3 A common cavity for the rest of the joints. The common cavity may be described as the *midcarpal* (transverse intercarpal) joint between the proximal and distal rows of the carpus, which communicates with intercarpal joints superiorly, and with intercarpal, carpometacarpal and intermetacarpal joints inferiorly (Figs 10.24a and b).

The midcarpal joint permits movements between the two rows of the carpus as already described with the wrist joint.

FIRST CARPOMETACARPAL JOINT

First carpometacarpal joint is only carpometacarpal joint which has a separate joint cavity. Movements at this joint are, therefore, much more free than at any other corresponding joint.

Type

Saddle variety of synovial joint (because the articular surfaces are concavoconvex).

Articular Surfaces

i. The distal surface of the trapezium
ii. The proximal surface of the base of the first metacarpal bone.

The articulating surface of trapezium is concave in the sagittal plane and convex in the frontal plane.

The concavoconvex nature of the articular surfaces permits a wide range of movements (Figs 10.24a and b).

Ligaments

1 Capsular ligament surrounds the joint. In general, it is thick but loose, and is thickest dorsally and laterally.
2 Lateral ligament is broad band which strengthens the capsule laterally.
3 The anterior ligament
4 The posterior ligaments are oblique bands running downwards and medially.

Relations

Anteriorly: The joint is covered by the muscles of the thenar eminence (*see* Figs 9.22).

Posteriorly: Long and short extensors of the thumb (Figs 10.32a and b).

Medially: First dorsal interosseous muscle, and the radial artery (passing from the dorsal to the palmar aspect of the hand through the interosseous space).

Laterally: Tendon of the abductor pollicis longus.

Blood Supply

Radial vessels supply blood to the synovial membrane and capsule of the joint.

Nerve Supply

First digital branch of median nerve supplies the capsule of the joint.

Movements

Flexion and extension of the thumb take place in the plane of the palm, and abduction and adduction at right angles to the plane of the palm. In opposition, the thumb crosses the palm and touches other fingers. Flexion is associated with medial rotation, and extension with lateral rotation at the joint.

Circumduction is a combination of different movements mentioned. The following muscles bring about the movements (Figs 10.31a to e).

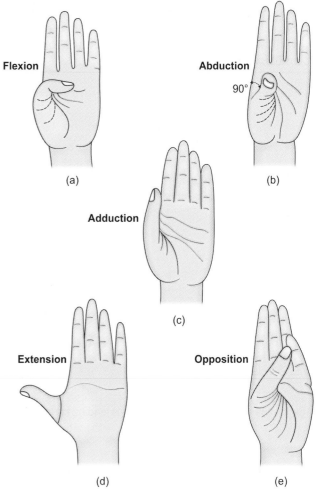

Figs 10.31a to e: Movements of the thumb

1 Flexion	• Flexor pollicis brevis (*see* Fig. 9.20)
	• Opponens pollicis
2 Extension	• Extensor pollicis brevis
	• Extensor pollicis longus (Figs 10.32a and b)
3 Abduction	• Abductor pollicis brevis (*see* Fig. 9.20)
	• Abductor pollicis longus
4 Adduction	Adductor pollicis (*see* Fig. 9.22)
5 Opposition	• Opponens pollicis (*see* Fig. 9.22)
	• Flexor pollicis brevis

The opposition is a sequential movement of abduction, flexion, adduction of the 1st metacarpal with simultaneous rotation. Opposition is unique to human beings and is one of the most important movements of the hand considering that this motion is used in almost all types of gripping actions.

The adductor pollicis and the flexor pollicis longus exert pressure on the opposed fingers.

CLINICAL ANATOMY

- The 1st carpometacarpal joint can undergo degenerative changes with age which is a painful condition of the base of the thumb.
- The synovial lining of the tendons of extensor pollicis brevis and abductor pollicis longus can get inflamed due to repetitive strain and can lead to a painful condition called de Quervains tenosynovitis. Movement of the thumb can aggravate pain in this condition.

METACARPOPHALANGEAL JOINTS

Type

Metacarpophalangeal joints are synovial joints of the ellipsoid variety.

Ligaments

Each joint has the following ligaments.
1 *Capsular ligament:* This is thick in front and thin behind.
2 *Palmar ligament:* This is a strong fibrocartilaginous plate which replaces the anterior part of the capsule. It is more firmly attached to the phalanx than to the metacarpal. The various palmar ligaments of the metacarpophalangeal joints are joined to one another by the deep transverse metacarpal ligament.
3 *Medial and lateral collateral ligaments:* These are oblique bands placed at the sides of the joint. Each runs downwards and forwards from the head of the metacarpal bone to the base of the phalanx. These are taut in flexion and relaxed in extension.

Movements at First Joint and Muscles Producing them

1 *Flexion:* Flexor pollicis longus and flexor pollicis brevis.
2 *Extension:* Extensor pollicis longus and extensor pollicis brevis (Figs 10.32a and b).
3 *Abduction:* Abductor pollicis brevis (*see* Fig. 9.20).
4 *Adduction:* Adductor pollicis (*see* Fig. 9.22).

Movements at Second to Fifth
Joints and Muscles Producing them

1 *Flexion:* Interossei and lumbricals (*see* Figs 9.21 and 9.23).
2 *Extension:* Extensors of the fingers (Fig. 10.27).
3 *Abduction:* Dorsal interossei (*see* Fig. 9.23).
4 *Adduction:* Palmar interossei (*see* Fig. 9.23).
5 *Circumduction:* Above muscles in sequence.

INTERPHALANGEAL JOINTS (PROXIMAL AND DISTAL)

Type

Hinge variety of synovial joints (Fig. 10.33).

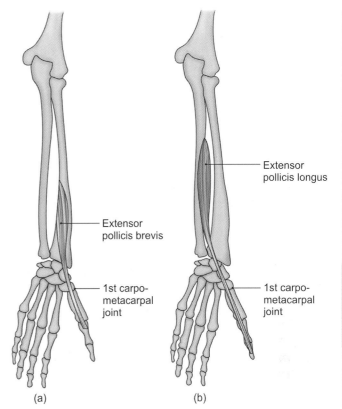

Figs 10.32a and b: Extensors of the joints of thumb

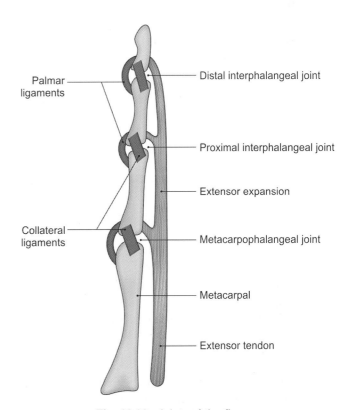

Fig. 10.33: Joints of the fingers

Ligaments

Similar to the metacarpophalangeal joints, that is one palmar fibrocartilaginous ligament and two collateral bands running downwards and forwards.

Movements at Interphalangeal Joint of Thumb

Flexion: Flexor pollicis longus.

Extension: Extensor pollicis longus.

Movements at Second to Fifth Digits

1 *Flexion:* Flexor digitorum superficialis at the proximal interphalangeal joint, and the flexor digitorum profundus at the distal joint (Fig. 10.34).
2 *Extension:* Interossei and lumbricals (*see* Figs 9.21 and 9.23).

Segmental Innervation of Movements of Upper Limb

Figures 10.35a to f show the segments of the spinal cord responsible for movements of the various joints of the upper limb.

The proximal muscles of upper limb are supplied by proximal nerve roots forming brachial plexus and distal muscles by the distal or lower nerve roots. In shoulder, abduction is done by muscles supplied by C5 spinal segment and adduction by muscles innervated by C6, C7 spinal segments.

Elbow joint is flexed by C5, C6 and extended by C7, C8 innervated muscles. Supination is caused by muscle

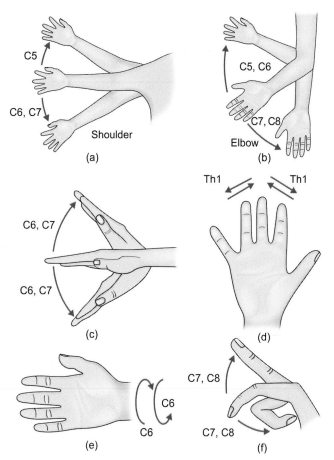

Figs 10.35a to f: Segmental innervation of movements of the upper limb

innervated by C6 spinal segment even pronation is done through C6 spinal segment.

Extension and flexion of wrist is done through C6, C7 spinal segments. Both the palmar and dorsal interossei are innervated by T 1 spinal segment.

The interphalangeal joints also are flexed and extended by same spinal segments, i.e. C7, C8.

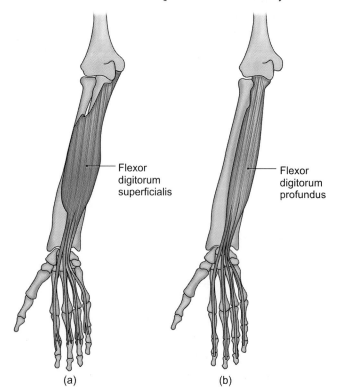

Figs 10.34a and b: (a) Flexor digitorum superficialis, and (b) flexor digitorum profundus

> 🔑 **FACTS TO REMEMBER**
>
> • Sternoclavicular joint is a saddle variety of synovial joint. Its cavity is divided into two parts by an articular disc.
> • Movements of shoulder girdle help the movements of shoulder joint during 90°–180° abduction
> • Shoulder joint is freely mobile and is vulnerable to dislocation.
> • Ulnar nerve lies behind medial epicondyle. It is not a content of the cubital fossa.
> • Carrying angle separates the wrist from the hip joint while carrying buckets, etc.
> • Biceps brachii is an important supinator of forearm when the elbow is flexed.

- Kings pronate, while beggars supinate.
- Movements of pronation and supination are not occurring at the elbow or wrist joints.
- First carpometacarpal joint is the most important joint as it permits the thumb to oppose the palm/fingers for holding things.
- Shoulder joint commonly dislocates inferiorly.
- Ulnar nerve lies behind medial epicondyle, pressing the nerve cause tingling sensation. That is why the bone is named "humerus".
- Giving is pronation, receiving is supination. Picking up food with digits is pronation, putting it in the mouth is supination.
- Axis of movements of abduction and adduction of fingers is through the centre of the middle finger.

CLINICOANATOMICAL PROBLEM

A 70-year-old lady fell on her left forearm. She heard a crack in the wrist. There was swelling and a bend just proximal to wrist with lateral deviation of the hand.
- Which forearm bone is fractured?
- Reason of bend just proximal to wrist.
- What joints can be subluxated?

Ans: There is fracture of the distal end of radius. The backward bend just proximal to the wrist is due to the pull of extensor muscles on the distal segment of radius. The inferior radioulnar joint is usually subluxated.

FREQUENTLY ASKED QUESTIONS

1. Describe the shoulder joint under the following headings:
   a. Type
   b. Articular surface
   c. Ligaments
   d. Movements with their muscles
   e. Clinical anatomy
2. Tabulate the features of superior and inferior radio-ulnar joints

3. Write short notes on:
   a. Carrying angle
   b. Movements of the thumb with muscles responsible for these movements
   c. Movements of wrist. Enumerate the muscles causing these movements
   d. Movements occurring at the shoulder girdle
   e. Movements at metacarpophalangeal joint of middle finger with the muscles responsible for them.

MULTIPLE CHOICE QUESTIONS

1. One of the following muscles is not a medial rotator of the shoulder joint:
   a. Pectoralis major
   b. Teres major
   c. Teres minor
   d. Latissimus dorsi
2. What type of joint is superior radioulnar joint?
   a. Pivot
   b. Saddle
   c. Plane
   d. Hinge
3. First carpometacarpal joint is:
   a. Saddle
   b. Ellipsoid

   c. Hinge
   d. Pivot
4. Articular surface of sternal end of clavicle is covered by:
   a. Fibrocartilage
   b. Hyaline cartilage
   c. Elastic cartilage
   d. None of the above
5. Which of the following joints contains an articular disc?
   a. Sternoclavicular
   b. Superior radioulnar
   c. Shoulder
   d. Elbow

6. Which of the following muscles causes protraction of scapula?
   a. Serratus anterior
   b. Levator scapulae
   c. Trapezius
   d. Latissimus dorsi

7. Which of the following muscles is supplied by two nerves with different root values?
   a. Flexor pollicis longus
   b. Pronator teres
   c. Flexor digitorum superficialis
   d. Flexor digitorum profundus

8. Trapezius retracts the scapula along with which of the following muscles:
   a. Rhomboids
   b. Latissimus dorsi
   c. Serratus anterior
   d. Levator scapulae

9. Which of the following muscles is flexor, adductor and medial rotator of shoulder joint?
   a. Pectoralis minor
   b. Pectoralis major
   c. Teres minor
   d. Infraspinatus

ANSWERS

| 1. c | 2. a | 3. a | 4. a | 5. a | 6. a | 7. d | 8. a | 9. b |

Surface Marking, Radiological Anatomy and Comparison of Upper and Lower Limbs

Happiness doesn't result from what we get, but from what we give
Do your best and let God do the rest
—Ben carson

INTRODUCTION

Surface marking is the projection of the deeper structures on the surface. Its importance lies in various medical and surgical procedures.

SURFACE MARKING

The bony landmarks seen in different regions of the upper limb have been described in appropriate sections.

The surface marking of important structures is given in this chapter.

ARTERIES

Axillary Artery

Hold the arm at right angles to the trunk with the palm directed upwards. The artery is then marked as a straight line by joining the following two points.
- *Point 1:* Midpoint of the clavicle.
- *Point 2:* At the lower limit of the lateral wall of axilla where the arterial pulsations can be felt in living person (Fig. 11.1).

At its termination, the axillary artery, along with the accompanying nerves, forms a prominence which lies behind another projection caused by the biceps and coracobrachialis.

Brachial Artery

Brachial artery is marked by joining the following two points.

- *Point 1:* At the lower limit of the lateral wall of the axilla. Here the axillary artery ends and the brachial artery begins (Fig. 11.2).
- *Point 2:* At the level of the neck of the radius medial to the tendon of the biceps brachii (Fig. 11.2).

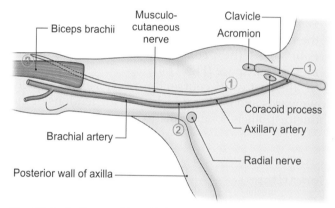

Fig. 11.1: Axillary and brachial arteries with musculocutaneous nerve

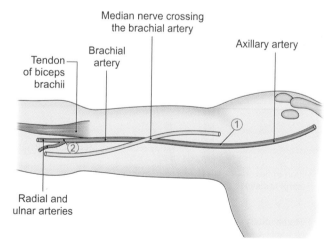

Fig. 11.2: Median nerve in front of arm related to axillary and brachial arteries

Thus the artery begins on the medial side of the upper part of the arm, and runs downwards and slightly laterally to end in front of the elbow. At its termination, it bifurcates into the radial and ulnar arteries.

Radial Artery

In the Forearm

Radial artery is marked by joining the following points.
- *Point 1:* In front of the elbow at the level of the neck of the radius medial to the tendon of the biceps brachii (Fig. 11.3).
- *Point 2:* At the wrist between the anterior border of the radius laterally and the tendon of the flexor carpi radialis medially, where the radial pulse is commonly felt (Fig. 11.3).

Its course is curved with a gentle convexity to the lateral side.

In the Hand

Radial artery is marked by joining the following points.
- *Point 1:* Just below the tip of the styloid process of the radius (Fig. 11.4).
- *Point 2:* At the proximal end of the first intermetacarpal space (Fig. 11.4).

In this part of its course, the artery runs obliquely downwards and backwards deep to the tendons of the abductor pollicis longus, the extensor pollicis brevis,

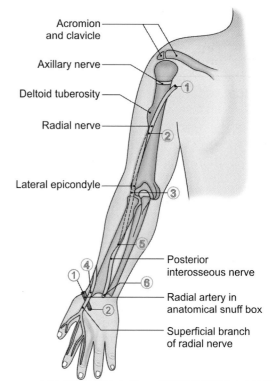

Fig. 11.4: Surface projection of axillary, radial, posterior interosseous nerves and radial artery in anatomical snuff box (posterior view of left limb)

and superficial to the lateral ligament of the wrist joint. Thus it passes through the *anatomical snuff box* to reach the proximal end of the first intermetacarpal space.

Deep Palmar Arch

Deep palmar arch is formed as the direct continuation of the radial artery. It has a slight convexity towards the fingers.
- *Point 3:* At proximal part of 1st dorsal intermetacarpal space (Fig. 11.3).
- *Point 4:* Just distal to hook of hamate (Fig. 11.3).

It is marked by a slightly convex line, 4 cm long, just distal to the hook of the hamate bone (Fig. 11.3).

The deep palmar arch lies 1.2 cm proximal to the superficial palmar arch across the metacarpals, immediately distal to their bases. The deep branch of ulnar nerve lies in its concavity (*see* Fig. 9.22).

Ulnar Artery

Ulnar artery is marked by joining the following three points.
- *Point 1:* In front of the elbow at the level of the neck of the radius medial to the tendon of the biceps brachii (Fig. 11.3).
- *Point 5:* At the junction of the upper one-third and lower two-thirds of the medial border of the forearm (lateral to the ulnar nerve) (Fig. 11.3).
- *Point 6:* Lateral to the pisiform bone (Fig. 11.3).

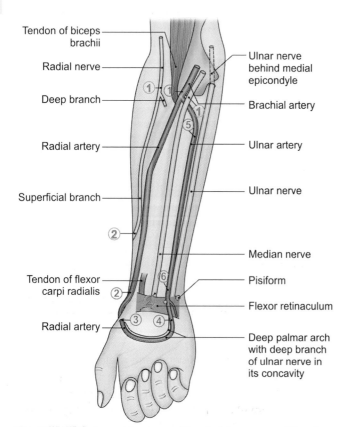

Fig. 11.3: Arteries and nerves of front of forearm and the deep palmar arch

Thus the course of the ulnar artery is oblique in its upper one-third, and vertical in its lower two-thirds. The ulnar nerve lies just medial to the ulnar artery in the lower two-thirds of its course. The ulnar artery continues in the palm as the superficial palmar arch.

Superficial Palmar Arch

Superficial palmar arch is formed by the direct continuation of the ulnar artery, and is marked as a curved line by joining the following points:
- *Point 1:* Just lateral and distal to the pisiform bone (Fig. 11.5).
- *Point 2:* Medial to the hook of the hamate bone (Fig. 11.5).
- *Point 3:* On the distal border of the thenar eminence in line with the cleft between the index and middle fingers (*see* Figs 9.32 and 11.5).

The convexity of the arch is directed towards the fingers, and its most distal point is situated at the level of the distal border of the fully extended thumb.

NERVES

Axillary Nerve with its Divisions

Axillary nerve is marked as a horizontal line on the deltoid muscle, 2 cm above the midpoint between the tip of the acromion process and the insertion of the deltoid (Fig. 11.4).

Intramuscular injections in the deltoid are given below the middle part of the muscle to avoid injury to the axillary nerve and its accompanying vessels.

Musculocutaneous Nerve

Musculocutaneous nerve is marked by joining the following two points.
- *Point 1:* Just lateral to the axillary artery 3 cm proximal to its termination (Fig. 11.1).
- *Point 2:* Lateral to the tendon of the biceps brachii muscle 2 cm above the bend of the elbow. Here it pierces the deep fascia and continues as the lateral cutaneous nerve of the forearm (*see* Fig. A1.1).

Median Nerve

In the Arm

Mark the brachial artery. The nerve is then marked lateral to the artery in the upper half, and medial to the artery in the lower half of the arm. The nerve crosses the artery anteriorly in the middle of the arm (Fig. 11.2).

In the Forearm

Median nerve is marked by joining the following two points.
- *Point 1:* Medial to the brachial artery at the bend of the elbow (Fig. 11.3).

- *Point 2:* In front of the wrist, over the tendon of the palmaris longus or 1 cm medial to the tendon of the flexor carpi radialis (Fig. 11.3).

In the Hand

Median nerve enters the palm by passing deep to flexor retinaculum, immediately below which it divides into lateral and medial branches. Lateral branch supplies the three muscles of thenar eminence and gives two branches to the thumb, and one to lateral side of index finger. Medial branch gives branches for the adjacent sides of index, middle and ring fingers. The lateral three and a half nail beds are also supplied (Figs 11.5, 11.6 and A1.4).

Radial Nerve

In the Arm

Radial nerve is marked by joining the following points.
- *Point 1:* At the lateral wall of the axilla at its lower limit (Figs 11.1 and 11.4).
- *Point 2:* At the junction of the upper one-third and lower two-thirds of a line joining the lateral epicondyle with the insertion of the deltoid (Fig. 11.4).
- *Point 3:* On the front of the elbow just below the level of the lateral epicondyle 1 cm lateral to the tendon of the biceps brachii (Fig. 11.4).

The first and second points are joined across the back of the arm to mark the oblique course of the radial nerve in the radial (spiral) groove (posterior compartment). The second and third points are joined on the front of the arm to mark the vertical course of the nerve in the anterior compartment (*see* Fig. A1.3).

In the Forearm

Superficial branch of radial nerve is marked by joining the following three points.
- *Point 1:* 1 cm lateral to the biceps tendon just below the level of the lateral epicondyle (Fig. 11.3).
- *Point 2:* At the junction of the upper two-thirds and lower one-third of the lateral border of the forearm just lateral to the radial artery (Fig. 11.3).
- *Point 4:* At the anatomical snuff box (Fig. 11.4).

The nerve is vertical in its course between points one and two. At the second point, it inclines backwards to reach the snuff box.

The nerve is closely related to the lateral side of the radial artery only in the middle one-third of the forearm.

Posterior Interosseous Nerve/ Deep Branch of Radial Nerve

It is marked by joining the following three points.
- *Point 3:* 1 cm lateral to the biceps brachii tendon just below the level of the lateral epicondyle (Fig. 11.4).
- *Point 5:* At the junction of the upper one-third and lower two-thirds of a line joining the middle of the

Upper Limb

Section 1

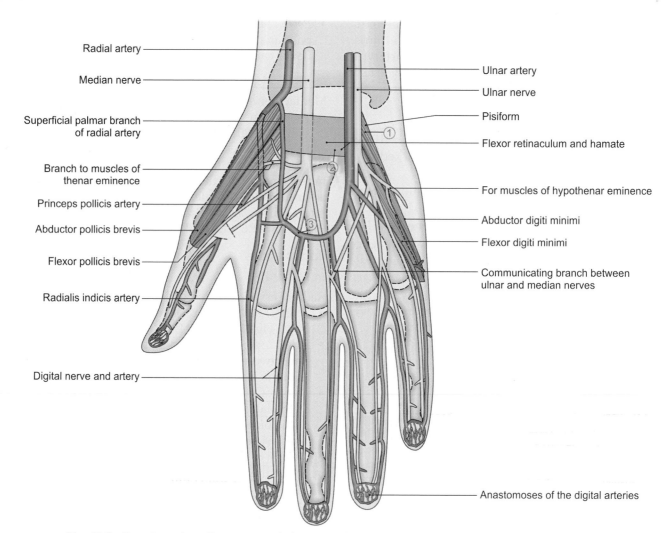

Fig. 11.5: Branches of median nerve and ulnar nerve in the palm. Superficial palmar arch is also shown

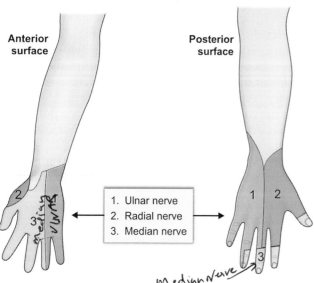

Anterior surface

Posterior surface

1. Ulnar nerve
2. Radial nerve
3. Median nerve

Fig. 11.6: Cutaneous nerve supply of palm and dorsum of hand

posterior aspect of the head of the radius to the dorsal tubercle at the lower end of the radius or Lister's tubercle (Fig. 11.4).

• *Point 6:* On the back of the wrist 1 cm medial to the dorsal tubercle (Fig. 11.4).

Posterior interosseous nerve supplies the muscles of posterior aspect of the forearm

Ulnar Nerve

In the Arm

Ulnar nerve is marked by joining the following points.

• *Point 1:* On the lateral wall of the axilla at its lower limit (lower border of the teres major muscle) (Fig. 11.7).

• *Point 2:* At the middle of the medial border of the arm.

• *Point 3:* Behind the base of the medial epicondyle of the humerus.

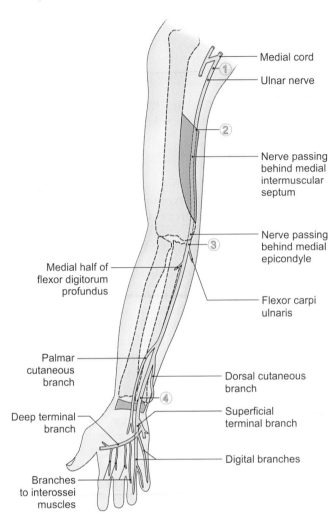

Fig. 11.7: Course of ulnar nerve

JOINTS

Shoulder Joint

The anterior margin of the glenoid cavity corresponds to the lower half of the shoulder joint. It is marked by a line 3 cm long drawn downwards from a point just lateral to the tip of the coracoid process. The line is slightly concave laterally.

Elbow Joint

The joint line is situated 2 cm below the line joining the two epicondyles, and slopes downwards and medially. This slope is responsible for the carrying angle.

Wrist Joint

The joint line is concave downwards, and is marked by joining the styloid processes of the radius and ulna.

RETINACULA

Flexor Retinaculum

Flexor retinaculum is marked by joining the following four points.

  i. Pisiform bone.
 ii. Tubercle of the scaphoid bone.
iii. Hook of the hamate bone (Fig. 11.8).
 iv. Crest of the trapezium.

   The upper border is obtained by joining the first and second points, and the lower border by joining the third and fourth points. The upper border is concave upwards, and the lower border is concave downwards (*see* Figs 9.15 and 9.16).

In the Forearm

Ulnar nerve is marked by joining the following two points.

• *Point 3:* On the back of the base of the medial epicondyle of the humerus (Fig. 11.7).

• *Point 4:* Lateral to the pisiform bone.

   In the lower two-thirds of the forearm, the ulnar nerve lies medial to the ulnar artery (Fig. 11.3).

In the Hand

Ulnar nerve lies superficial to the medial part of flexor retinaculum and medial to ulnar vessels where it divides into superficial and deep branches. The superficial branch supplies medial 1½ digits including their nail beds (Fig. 11.7). The deep branch passes backwards between pisiform and hook of hamate to lie in the concavity of the deep palmar arch (Fig. 11.3).

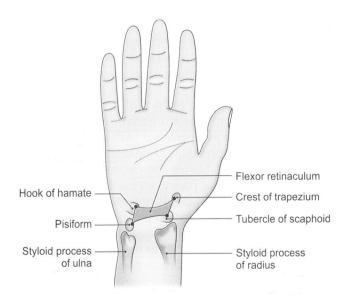

Fig. 11.8: Flexor retinaculum

Extensor Retinaculum

Extensor retinaculum is an oblique band directed downwards and medially, and is about 2 cm broad (vertically). Laterally, it is attached to the lower salient part of the anterior border of the radius, and medially to the medial side of the carpus (pisiform and triquetral bones) and to the styloid process of the ulna (*see* Fig. 9.52).

SYNOVIAL SHEATHS OF THE FLEXOR TENDONS

Common Flexor Synovial Sheath (Ulnar Bursa)

Above the flexor retinaculum (or lower transverse crease of the wrist), it extends into the forearm for about 2.5 cm. Here its medial border corresponds to the lateral edge of the tendon of the flexor carpi ulnaris, and its lateral border corresponds roughly to the tendon of the palmaris longus.

Ulnar bursa becomes narrower behind the flexor retinaculum, and broadens out below it.

Most of it terminates at the level of the upper transverse creases of the palm, but the medial part is continued up to the distal transverse crease of the little finger.

Synovial Sheaths for the Tendon of Flexor Pollicis Longus (Radial Bursa)

Radial bursa is a narrow tube which is coextensive with the ulnar bursa in the forearm and wrist. Below the flexor retinaculum, it is continued into the thumb up to its distal crease (*see* Fig. 9.7).

Digital Synovial Sheaths

The synovial sheaths of the flexor tendons of the index, middle and ring fingers extend from the necks of the metacarpal bones (corresponding roughly to the lower transverse crease of the palm) to the bases of the terminal phalanges (*see* Fig. 9.7).

RADIOLOGICAL ANATOMY OF UPPER LIMB

General Remarks

In the case of the limbs, plain radiography is mainly required. For complete information, it is always advisable to have anteroposterior (AP) as well as lateral views; and as far as possible radiographs of the opposite limb should be available for comparison. The skeleton, owing to its high radiopacity, forms the most striking feature in plain skiagrams. In general, the following information can be obtained from plain skiagrams of the limbs.

1 *Fractures* are seen as breaks in the surface continuity of the bone. A fracture line is usually irregular and asymmetrical. An epiphyseal line of an incompletely ossified bone, seen as a gap, should not be mistaken for a fracture. It has regular margins, and is bilaterally

symmetrical. Supernumerary or accessory bones are also symmetrical.
2 *Dislocations* are seen as deranged or distorted relations between the articular bony surfaces forming a joint.
3 Below the age of 25 years, the age of a person can be determined from the knowledge of ossification of the bones.
4 Certain *deficiency diseases* like rickets and scurvy can be diagnosed.
5 *Infections* (osteomyelitis) and growths (osteoma, osteoclastoma, osteosarcoma, etc.) can be diagnosed. A localised rarefaction of a bone may indicate an infection.
6 *Congenital absence or fusion* of bones can be seen.

Reading Plain Skiagrams of Limbs

1 Identify the view of the picture, anteroposterior or lateral. Each view shows a specific shape and arrangement of the bones.
2 Identify all the bones and their different parts visible in the given radiogram. Normal overlapping and 'end-on' appearances of bones in different views should be carefully studied.
3 Study the normal relations of the bones forming joints. The articular cartilage is radiolucent and does not cast any shadow. The radiological 'joint space' indicates the size of the articular cartilages. Normally, the joint space is about 2–5 mm in adults.
4 Study the various epiphyses visible in young bones and try to determine the age of the person concerned.

Shoulder

A. The following are seen in an AP view of the shoulder (Figs 11.9a and b).
  1 The upper end of the humerus, including the head, greater and lesser tubercles and intertubercular sulcus.
  2 The scapula, including the glenoid cavity, coracoid (seen end-on), acromion, its lateral, medial and superior borders, and the superior and inferior angles. The suprascapular notch may be seen.
  3 The clavicle, except for its medial end.
  4 Upper part of the thoracic cage, including the upper ribs.
B. Study the normal appearance of the following joints.
  1 *Shoulder joint:* The glenoid cavity articulates only with the lower half of the head of the humerus (when the arm is in the anatomical position). The upper part of the head lies beneath the acromion process. The greater tuberosity forms the lateral most bony point in the shoulder region.
  2 Acromioclavicular joint.
C. Note the epiphyses if any, and determine the age with the help of ossifications described with individual bones.

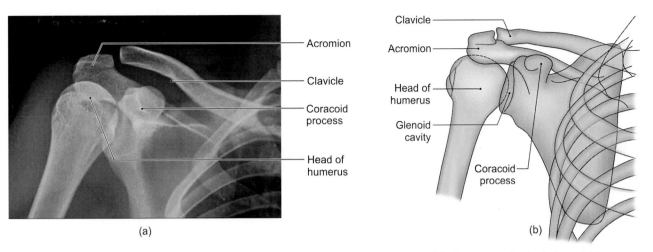

Figs 11.9a and b: (a) Anteroposterior view of the shoulder joint, and (b) diagrammatic depiction of (a)

Elbow

A. Identify the following bones in an AP and lateral views of the elbow (Figs 11.10a and b).
  1 The lower end of humerus, including the medial and lateral epicondyles, the medial and lateral supracondylar ridges, trochlea, the capitulum and the olecranon fossa.
  2 The upper end of the ulna, including the olecranon and coronoid processes.
  3 The upper end of the radius including its head, neck and tuberosity.
B. Study the normal appearance of the following joints in AP view.

1 Elbow joint.
2 Superior radioulnar joint.
C. Note the olecranon and coronoid processes in a lateral view of the elbow (Figs 11.11a and b).
D. Note the epiphyses (if any) and determine the age with the help of ossifications described with individual bones.

Hand

A. Identify the following bones in an AP skiagram (Figs 11.12a and b).
  1 The lower end of the radius with its styloid process.
  2 The lower end of the ulna with its styloid process.

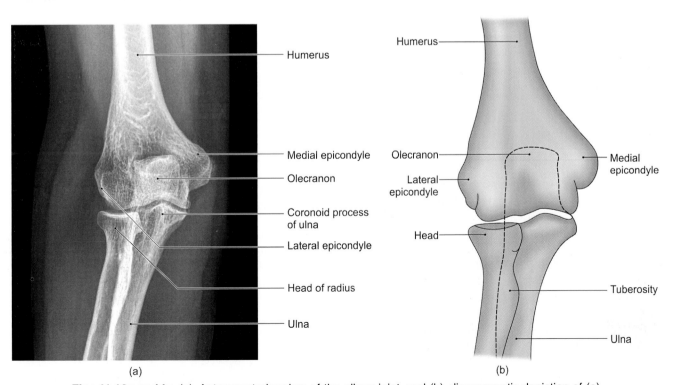

Figs 11.10a and b: (a) Anteroposterior view of the elbow joint, and (b) diagrammatic depiction of (a)

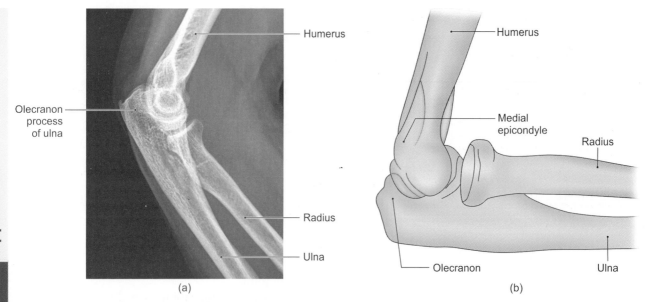

Figs 11.11a and b: (a) Lateral view of the elbow joint, and (b) diagrammatic depiction of (a)

3 The eight carpal bones. Note the overlapping of the triquetral and pisiform bones; and of the trapezium with the trapezoid. Also identify the tubercle of the scaphoid and the hook of the hamate.
4 The five metacarpal bones.
5 The fourteen phalanges.
6 The sesamoid bones present in relation to the thumb, and occasionally in relation to the other fingers.
B. Study the normal appearance of these joints.
1 The wrist joint.

2 The inferior radioulnar joint.
3 The intercarpal, carpometacarpal, metacarpo-phalangeal and interphalangeal joints.
C. Note the following bones in a lateral skiagram.
1 Lunate.
2 Scaphoid.
3 Capitate.
4 Trapezium.
D. Note the epiphyses and other incomplete ossifications, and determine the age with the help of ossifications described with individual bones.

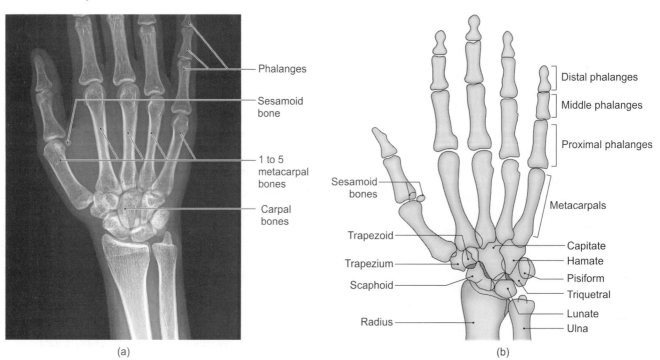

Figs 11.12a and b: (a) Anteroposterior view of the hand, and (b) diagrammatic depiction of (a)

Comparison of upper and lower limbs

	Upper limb	Lower limb
General	The upper limb is for range and variety of movements. Thumb assisted by palm and fingers has the power of holding articles. Upper limb bud rotates laterally, so that the thumb points laterally. Nerve supply: Ventral rami of cervical 5–8 and thoracic 1 segments of spinal cord. Musculocutaneous, median and ulnar nerves supply the flexor aspects of the limb, while the axillary nerve supplies deltoid and radial nerve supplies the triceps brachii (extensor of elbow) and its branch the posterior interosseous supplies the extensors of wrist	Lower limb with long and heavy bones supports and stabilises the body. Lower limb bud rotates medially, so that big toe points medially. Nerve supply: Ventral rami of lumbar 2–5 and sacral 1–3 segments of spinal cord. The two gluteal nerves supply glutei. Sciatic and one of its terminal branches, the tibial nerve supplies the flexor aspect of the limb. The other terminal branch of sciatic nerve, i.e. common peroneal, supplies the extensors of ankle joint (dorsiflexors) through its deep peroneal branch. Its superficial branch supplies the peroneal muscles of the leg. Femoral supplies the quadriceps femoris (extensor of knee) while obturator nerve supplies the adductors.

	Arm	*Thigh*
Bones	Humerus is the longest bone of upper limb	Femur is the longest bone of lower limb and of the body
Joints	Shoulder joint is a multiaxial joint	Hip joint is a multiaxial joint
Muscles	Anteriorly: Biceps, brachialis and coraco-brachialis supplied by musculocutaneous nerve Posteriorly: Triceps brachii supplied by radial nerve	Posteriorly: Hamstrings supplied by sciatic Anteriorly: Quadriceps by femoral Medially: Adductors by obturator nerve
Nerves	Musculocutaneous for anterior compartment of arm. Radial for posterior compartment. Coraco-brachialis equivalent to medial compartment of arm also supplied by musculocutaneous nerve	Sciatic for posterior compartment of thigh, femoral for anterior compartment of thigh, obturator for adductor muscles of medial compartment of thigh
Branches	Muscular, cutaneous, articular/genicular, vascular and terminal branches	Muscular, cutaneous, articular/genicular, vascular and terminal branches
Arteries	Axillary, brachial, profunda (deep) brachii	Femoral, popliteal and profunda femoris (deep)

	Forearm	*Leg*
Bones	Radius: Preaxial bone Ulna: Postaxial bone	Tibia: Preaxial bone Fibula: Postaxial bone
Joints	Elbow joint formed by humerus, radius and ulna, communicates with superior radioulnar joint. Forearm is characterised by superior and inferior radioulnar joints. These are both pivot variety of synovial joints permitting rotatory movements of pronation and supination, e.g. meant for picking up food and putting it in the mouth	Knee joint formed by femur, tibia and patella. Fibula does not participate in knee joint. An additional bone (sesamoid) patella makes its appearance. This is an important weight-bearing joint
Muscles	Palmaris longus Flexor digitorum profundus Flexor pollicis longus Flexor digitorum superficialis Flexor carpi ulnaris Flexor carpi radialis Abductor pollicis longus Extensor digitorum Extensor pollicis longus	Plantaris Flexor digitorum longus Flexor hallucis longus Soleus and flexor digitorum brevis Gastrocnemius (medial head) Gastrocnemius (lateral head) Tibialis anterior Extensor digitorum longus Extensor hallucis longus
General	Anterior aspect: Flexors of wrist and pronators of forearm Posterior aspect: Extensors of wrist, and supinator	Anterior aspect: Dorsiflexors of ankle joint Posterior aspect: Plantar flexors (flexors) of ankle joint Lateral aspect: Evertors of subtalar joint

(Contd.)

Section 1 | Upper Limb

Comparison of upper and lower limbs *(Contd.)*

	Upper limb	Lower limb
	Forearm	*Leg*
Nerves	Median nerve for 6½ muscles and ulnar nerve for 1½ muscles of anterior aspect of forearm. These are flexors of wrist and pronators of forearm. Posterior interosseous nerve or deep branch of radial supplies the extensors of the wrist and the supinator muscle of forearm. It winds around radius (preaxial bone) and corresponds to deep peroneal nerve. The superficial branch of radial nerve corresponds to the superficial peroneal nerve	Tibial nerve for all the plantar flexors of the ankle joint. Common peroneal winds around neck of fibula (postaxial bone) and divides into superficial and deep branches. The deep peroneal supplies dorsiflexors (extensors) of the ankle joint. The superficial peroneal nerve supplies a separate lateral compartment of leg
Arteries	Brachial divides into radial and ulnar branches in the cubital fossa. Radial corresponds to anterior tibial artery	Popliteal divides into anterior tibial and posterior tibial in the popliteal fossa. Posterior tibial corresponds to ulnar artery
	Hand	*Foot*
Bones and joints	There are eight small carpal bones occupying very small area of the hand. First carpometacarpal joint, i.e. joint between trapezium and base of 1st metacarpal is a unique joint. It is of saddle variety and permits a versatile movement of opposition in addition to other movements. This permits the hand to hold things, e.g. doll, pencil, food, bat, etc. Opponens pollicis is specially for opposition	Seven big tarsal bones occupying almost half of the foot. There are special joints between talus, calcaneus and navicular, i.e. subtalar and talocalcaneonavicular joints. They permit the movements of inversion and eversion (raising the medial border/lateral border of the foot) for walking on the uneven surfaces. This movement of inversion is similar to supination and of eversion to pronation of forearm. Flexor digitorum accessorius is a distinct muscle to straighten the action of flexor digitorum longus tendons in line with the toes on which these act. Tibialis anterior, tibialis posterior and peroneus longus reach the foot and sole for the movements of inversion (first two) and eversion (last one) respectively
Nerves	Median nerve supplies 5 muscles of hand including 1st and 2nd lumbricals (abductor pollicis brevis, flexor pollicis brevis, opponens pollicis, 1st and 2nd lumbricals)	Medial plantar supplies four muscles of the sole including 1st lumbrical (abductor hallucis, flexor hallucis brevis, flexor digitorum brevis, 1st lumbrical)
	Ulnar nerve corresponds to lateral plantar nerve and supplies 15 intrinsic muscles of the hand	Lateral plantar corresponds to ulnar nerve and supplies 14 intrinsic muscles of the sole
Muscles	Muscles which enter the palm from forearm, e.g. flexor digitorum superficialis, flexor digitorum profundus, flexor pollicis longus are supplied by the nerves of the forearm. 1st and 2nd lumbricals are unipennate and are supplied by median nerve. 3rd and 4th are bipennate being supplied by deep branch of ulnar nerve. No muscle on dorsum of hand	Muscles which enter the sole from the leg, e.g. flexor digitorum longus, flexor hallucis longus, tibialis posterior, peroneus longus, are supplied by the nerves of the leg. 1st lumbrical is unipennate and is supplied by medial plantar, 2nd–4th are bipennate being supplied by deep branch of lateral plantar nerve. Extensor digitorum brevis present on dorsum of foot
Blood vessels	Radial artery corresponds to anterior tibial while ulnar artery corresponds to posterior tibial artery. Ulnar artery divides into superficial and deep branches. There are two palmar arches, superficial and deep. The superficial arch mainly is formed by ulnar artery and deep arch is formed mainly by the radial artery. Cephalic vein is along the preaxial border. Basilic vein runs along the postaxial border of the limb and terminates in the middle of the arm	Posterior tibial artery divides into medial plantar and lateral plantar branches. There is only one arch, the plantar arch formed by lateral plantar and dorsalis pedis (continuation of anterior tibial) arteries
		The great saphenous vein with perforators lies along the preaxial border. The short saphenous vein lies along the postaxial border but it terminates in the popliteal fossa

	Comparison of upper and lower limbs *(Contd.)*	
	Upper limb	**Lower limb**
	Hand	*Foot*
Axis	The axis of movement of adduction and abduction is through the third digit or middle finger. So the middle finger has two dorsal interossei muscles	The axis of movement of adduction and abduction passes through the 2nd digit. So 2nd toe possesses two dorsal interossei muscles
	Palm	*Sole*
I Layer	Abductor pollicis brevis Flexor pollicis brevis Flexor digiti minimi Abductor digiti minimi	Abductor hallucis brevis Flexor digitorum brevis Abductor digiti minimi
Between I and II layers	Superficial palmar arch Branches of median nerve Branches of superficial branch of ulnar nerve	No such arch Branches of medial plantar nerve and artery Branches of superficial branch of lateral plantar nerve
II Layer	Tendons of flexor digitorum superficialis Tendons of flexor digitorum profundus and lumbricals Tendon of flexor pollicis longus	Tendon of flexor digitorum longus, lumbricals and flexor digitorum accessorius Tendon of flexor hallucis longus
III Layer	Opponens pollicis Adductor pollicis Opponens digiti minimi	Flexor hallucis brevis Adductor hallucis Flexor digiti minimi brevis
Between III and IV layers	Deep palmar arch and deep branch of ulnar nerve	Plantar arch with deep branch of lateral plantar nerve
IV Layer	1–4 palmar interossei 1–4 dorsal interossei	1–3 plantar interossei 1–4 dorsal interossei Tendons of tibialis posterior and peroneus longus

FREQUENTLY ASKED QUESTIONS

1. Trace the beginning and course of radial and ulnar arteries in the forearm
2. Trace the beginning, course of radial, median and ulnar nerves in the forearm
3. Write short notes on:
   a. Anatomical snuff box
   b. Synovial sheaths of the flexor tendons
   c. Surface marking of flexor retinaculum of wrist
   d. Surface marking and attachments of extensor retinaculum

Appendix 1

INTRODUCTION

The **nerves** are very important and precious component of our body. This appendix deals with the main nerves of the upper limb. Most of the nerves course through different regions of the upper limb and have been described in parts in the respective regions. In this appendix, the course of the entire nerve from origin to its termination including the branches and clinical aspects has been described briefly (Fig. A1.1a). **Arteries** of upper limb have been tabulated in Table A1.5. Important **clinical terms** related to upper limb have been defined and **multiple choice questions** are given.

MUSCULOCUTANEOUS NERVE

Musculocutaneous nerve is so named as it supplies muscles of front of arm and skin of lateral side of forearm.

Root Value

Ventral rami of C5–C7 segments of spinal cord.

Course

Axilla and Arm

Musculocutaneous nerve is a branch of the lateral cord of brachial plexus, lies lateral to axillary and upper part of brachial artery. It supplies coracobrachialis, pierces the muscle to lie in the intermuscular septum between biceps brachii and brachialis muscles, both of which are supplied by this nerve (*see* Fig. 8.6 and A1.1).

Forearm

About 2.5 cm above the crease of elbow, it becomes cutaneous by piercing the deep fascia. The nerve is called the lateral cutaneous nerve of forearm which supplies skin of lateral side of forearm both on the front and back.

Branches

Muscular	Coracobrachialis, long head of biceps brachii, short head of biceps brachii, and brachialis (Fig. A1.1).
Cutaneous	Lateral side of forearm (both on the front and the back).
Articular	Elbow joint.

This nerve rarely gets injured.

AXILLARY OR CIRCUMFLEX NERVE

Axillary nerve is called axillary as it runs through the upper part of axilla though it does not supply any structure there. It is called circumflex as it courses around the surgical neck of humerus (*see* Fig. 8.13) to supply the prominent deltoid muscle.

Root Value

Ventral rami of C5, C6 segments of spinal cord.

Course

Axilla

Axillary or circumflex nerve is the smaller terminal branch of posterior cord seen in the axilla (*see* Fig. 4.14).

Quadrangular Space

The nerve passes backwards through the quadrangular space (bounded by subscapularis above, teres major below, long head of triceps brachii medially and surgical neck of humerus laterally) (*see* Fig. 6.11). Here it lies below the capsule of the shoulder joint.

Surgical Neck of Humerus

Then it passes behind the surgical neck of humerus where it divides into anterior and posterior divisions (Fig. A1.1).

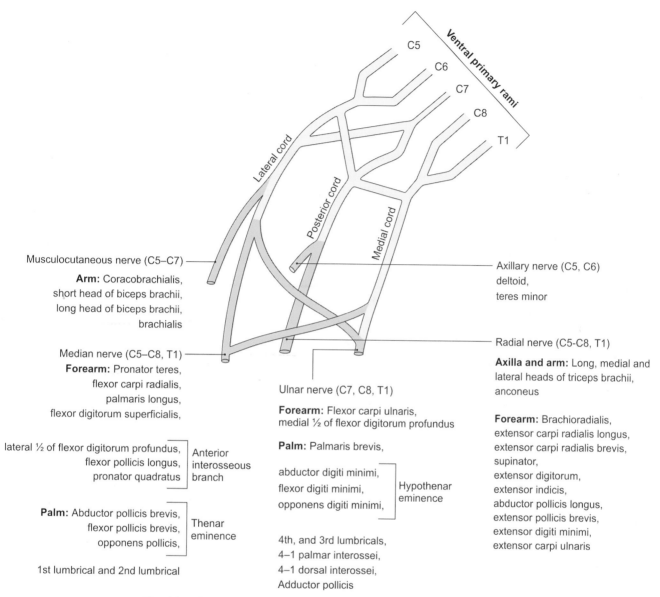

Musculocutaneous nerve (C5–C7)
Arm: Coracobrachialis,
short head of biceps brachii,
long head of biceps brachii,
brachialis

Median nerve (C5–C8, T1)
Forearm: Pronator teres,
flexor carpi radialis,
palmaris longus,
flexor digitorum superficialis,

lateral ½ of flexor digitorum profundus,   ⎤ Anterior
flexor pollicis longus,   ⎟ interosseous
pronator quadratus   ⎦ branch

Palm: Abductor pollicis brevis, ⎤ Thenar
flexor pollicis brevis,   ⎟ eminence
opponens pollicis,   ⎦

1st lumbrical and 2nd lumbrical

Ulnar nerve (C7, C8, T1)

Forearm: Flexor carpi ulnaris,
medial ½ of flexor digitorum profundus

Palm: Palmaris brevis,

abductor digiti minimi,   ⎤ Hypothenar
flexor digiti minimi,   ⎟ eminence
opponens digiti minimi,   ⎦

4th, and 3rd lumbricals,
4–1 palmar interossei,
4–1 dorsal interossei,
Adductor pollicis

Axillary nerve (C5, C6)
deltoid,
teres minor

Radial nerve (C5-C8, T1)
Axilla and arm: Long, medial and
lateral heads of triceps brachii,
anconeus

Forearm: Brachioradialis,
extensor carpi radialis longus,
extensor carpi radialis brevis,
supinator,
extensor digitorum,
extensor indicis,
abductor pollicis longus,
extensor pollicis brevis,
extensor digiti minimi,
extensor carpi ulnaris

Fig. A1.1: Brachial plexus and muscular branches of the main nerves

Branches

The branches of axillary nerve are presented in Table A1.1.

RADIAL NERVE

Radial nerve is the thickest branch of brachial plexus.

Root value

Ventral rami of C5–C8, T1 segments of spinal cord (*see* Fig. 4.14).

Course

Axilla

Radial nerve lies against the muscles forming the posterior wall of axilla, i.e. subscapularis, teres major

and latissimus dorsi. It then lies for a short distance in arm behind brachial artery. Then it enters in the lower triangular space between teres major, long head of triceps brachii and shaft of humerus. It gives two muscular and one cutaneous branch in the axilla (Fig. A1.1).

Radial Sulcus

Radial nerve enters through the lower triangular space into the radial sulcus, where it lies between the long and medial heads of triceps brachii along with profunda brachii vessels (*see* Fig. 6.11). Long and lateral heads form the roof of the radial sulcus. It leaves the sulcus by piercing the lateral intermuscular septum. In the sulcus, it gives three muscular and two cutaneous branches.

Table A1.1: Branches of axillary nerve

	Trunk	Anterior division	Posterior division
Muscular	—	Deltoid (most part)	Deltoid (posterior part) and teres minor. The nerve to teres minor is characterised by the presence of a pseudoganglion
Cutaneous	—	—	Upper lateral cutaneous nerve of arm
Articular and vascular	Shoulder joint	—	To posterior circumflex humeral artery

Front of Arm

The radial nerve descends on the lower and lateral side of front of arm deep in the interval between brachialis on medial side and brachioradialis with extensor carpi radialis longus on the lateral side to reach capitulum of humerus (*see* Fig. 8.17).

Cubital Fossa

The nerve enters the lateral side of cubital fossa. There the radial nerve terminates by dividing into superficial and deep branches.

The deep branch supplies extensor carpi radialis brevis and supinator. Then it courses between two heads of supinator to reach back of forearm (*see* Fig. 8.17).

Front of Forearm

The superficial branch leaves the cubital fossa to enter lateral side of front of forearm, accompanied by the radial vessels in its upper two-thirds (*see* Fig. 9.10). At the junction of upper two-thirds and lower one-third, the superficial branch turns laterally to reach the posterolateral aspect of forearm.

Wrist and Dorsum of Hand

The superficial branch descends till the anatomical snuff box to reach dorsum of hand, where it supplies skin of lateral half of dorsum of hand and lateral 2½ digits till distal interphalangeal joints (*see* Figs 7.1b and 9.33).

Back of Forearm and Wrist

The deep branch of radial nerve enters the back of forearm, where it supplies the muscles mentioned in Table A1.2b. Lower down it passes through the 4th compartment under the extensor retinaculum to reach the back of wrist where it ends in a pseudoganglion, branches of which supply the neighbouring joint (*see* Fig. 9.56).

Branches of Radial Nerve

The branches of radial nerve are presented in Table A1.2a.

Branches of deep division of radial nerve are shown in Table A1.2b.

Branches of superficial division of radial nerve are shown in Table A1.2c.

MEDIAN NERVE

Median nerve is called median as it runs in the median plane of the forearm.

Root Value

Ventral rami of C5–C8, T1 segments of spinal cord.

Course

Axilla

Median nerve is formed by two roots, lateral root from lateral cord and medial root from medial cord of brachial plexus. Medial root crosses the axillary artery to join the lateral root. The median nerve runs on the lateral side of axillary artery (*see* Fig. 8.9).

Arm

Median nerve continues to run on the lateral side of brachial artery till the middle of arm, where it crosses in front of the artery, passes anterior to elbow joint into the cubital fossa (*see* Figs 8.9 and 8.17 and A1.1).

Cubital Fossa

Median nerve lies most medial in the cubital fossa. It gives three branches to flexor muscles of the forearm. It leaves the fossa by passing between two heads of pronator teres (*see* Figs 9.11 and 9.12).

Forearm

Median nerve enters the forearm and lies in the centre of forearm. It lies deep to fibrous arch of flexor digitorum superficialis on the flexor digitorum profundus. Adheres to deep surface of flexor digitorum superficialis, leaves the muscle, along its lateral border. Lastly, it is placed deep and lateral to palmaris longus.

Flexor Retinaculum

Median nerve lies deep to flexor retinaculum to enter palm (*see* Fig. 9.10).

Palm

Median nerve lies medial to the muscles of thenar eminence, which it supplies. It also gives cutaneous branches to lateral 3½ digits and their nail beds including skin of distal phalanges on their dorsal aspect (*see* Figs 7.1, 9.12 and 9.41).

Table A1.2a: Branches of radial nerve

	Axilla	Radial sulcus	Lateral side of arm
Muscular	Long head of triceps brachii Medial head of triceps brachii	Lateral head of triceps brachii Medial head of triceps brachii Anconeus	Brachioradialis Extensor carpi radialis longus Lateral part of brachialis (proprioceptive)
Cutaneous	Posterior cutaneous nerve of arm	Posterior cutaneous nerve of forearm Lower lateral cutaneous nerve of arm	–
Vascular		To profunda brachii artery	–
Terminal	–	–	Superficial and deep or posterior interosseous branches

Table A1.2b: Branches of deep division of radial nerve

	Cubital fossa	Back of forearm	Wrist
Muscular	Extensor carpi radialis brevis and supinator	Abductor pollicis longus, extensor pollicis brevis, extensor pollicis longus, extensor digitorum, extensor indicis, extensor digiti minimi and extensor carpi ulnaris	—
Articular	—	—	To inferior radioulnar, wrist and intercarpal joints

Table A1.2c: Branches of superficial division of radial nerve

	Forearm	Anatomical snuff box and dorsum of hand
Cutaneous and vascular	Lateral side of forearm and radial vessels	Skin over anatomical snuff box, lateral half of dorsum of hand and lateral 2½ digits till their distal interphalangeal joints
Articular	—	To wrist joint, 1st carpometacarpal joint, metacarpophalangeal and interphalangeal joints of the thumb, index and middle fingers

Branches of Median Nerve

The branches of median nerve are presented in Table A1.3.

ULNAR NERVE

Ulnar nerve is named so as it runs along the medial or ulnar side of the upper limb.

Root Value

Ventral rami of C8 and T1. It also gets fibres of C7 from the lateral root of median nerve (*see* Fig. 4.14).

Course

Axilla

Ulnar nerve lies in the axilla between the axillary vein and axillary artery on a deeper plane.

Arm

Ulnar nerve lies medial to brachial artery. Runs downwards with the brachial artery in its proximal part

(*see* Fig. 8.9). At the middle of arm, it pierces the medial intermuscular septum to lie on its back and descends on the back of medial epicondyle of humerus where it can be palpated. Palpation causes tingling sensations (*see* Fig. 8.13). That is why humerus is called "funny bone".

Forearm

Ulnar nerve enters the forearm by passing between two heads of flexor carpi ulnaris. There it lies on medial part of flexor digitorum profundus.
Ulnar nerve is not a content of cubital fossa.
It is accompanied by the ulnar artery in lower two-thirds of forearm (*see* Fig. 9.10).

It gives two muscular and two cutaneous branches (Table A1.4 and Fig. A1.1).

Flexor Retinaculum

Finally, it lies on the medial part of flexor retinaculum to enter palm. At the distal border of retinaculum, the nerve divides into its superficial and deep branches (*see* Figs 9.13a and 9.15).

Table A1.3: Branches of median nerve

	Axilla and arm	Cubital fossa	Forearm	Palm
Muscular	Pronator teres in lower part of arm	Flexor carpi radialis, flexor digitorum superficialis, palmaris longus	Anterior interosseous which supplies: lateral half of flexor digitorum profundus, pronator quadratus, and flexor pollicis longus	Recurrent branch for abductor pollicis brevis, flexor pollicis brevis, opponens pollicis. 1st and 2nd lumbricals (see Fig. 9.12) from the digital nerves
Cutaneous	—	—	Palmar cutaneous branch for lateral two-thirds of palm	• Two digital branches to lateral and medial sides of thumb • One to lateral side of index finger • Two to adjacent sides of index and middle fingers • Two to adjacent sides of middle and ring fingers. These branches also supply dorsal aspects of distal phalanges of lateral 3½ digits
Articular and vascular	Brachial artery	Elbow joint	—	Give vascular and articular branches to joints of hand

Palm

Superficial branch supplies palmaris brevis and gives digital branches to medial 1½ digits including medial 1½ nail beds till the distal interphalangeal joints.

Deep branch supplies most of the intrinsic muscles of the hand. At first it supplies three muscles of hypothenar eminence, running in the concavity of deep palmar arch it gives branches to 4th and 3rd lumbricals from deep aspect; 4,3,2,1 dorsal interossei and 4,3,2,1 palmar interossei to end in adductor pollicis.

Since it supplies intrinsic muscles of hand responsible for finer movements, this nerve is called 'musician's nerve' (see Figs 9.13b and 9.22).

Branches

The branches of ulnar nerve are presented in Table A1.4 and Fig. A1.1.

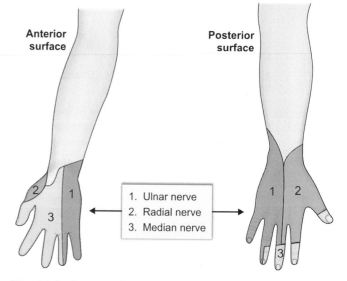

Fig. A1.2: Sensory loss in median, ulnar and radial nerves paralyses

Table A1.4: Branches of ulnar nerve

	Forearm	Hand (see Figs 9.13a and b)
Muscular	Medial half of flexor digitorum profundus, flexor carpi ulnaris	Superficial branch; palmaris brevis. Deep branch—Muscles of hypothenar eminence, medial two lumbricals, 4–1 dorsal interossei and 4–1 palmar interossei and adductor pollicis
Cutaneous/digital	Dorsal cutaneous branch for medial half of dorsum of hand. Palmar cutaneous branch for medial one-third of palm. Digital branches to medial 1½ fingers, nail beds and dorsal aspects of distal phalanges	
Vascular/articular	Also supplies digital vessels and joints of medial side of hand	

CLINICAL ANATOMY

Musculocutaneous nerve injury

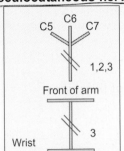

1 and 2: Paralysis of biceps and brachialis
3. Sensory loss on lateral side of forearm

Axillary nerve injury

Loss of abduction from beginning to 90°
Sensory loss over lower half of deltoid—regimental/badge sign.

Radial nerve injury

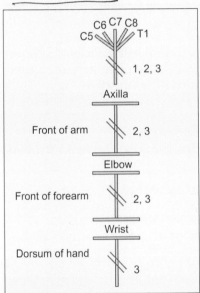

1. No extension of elbow
2. Wrist drop
3. Sensory loss (Fig. A1.2)

Median nerve injury

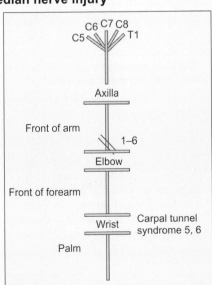

1. Weak flexion of wrist
2. Loss of pronation of forearm
3. Loss of flexion of proximal interphalangeal and distal interphalangeal joints of index and middle fingers
4. Loss of flexion at interphalangeal joint of thumb
5. Loss of thenar eminence
6. Sensory, trophic and vasomotor changes (*see* Figs 9.40 to 9.44 and A1.2)

Ulnar nerve injury

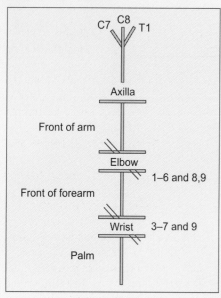

1. Flattening of medial border of forearm
2. Loss of flexion at distal interphalangeal joints of 4th and 5th digits
3. Loss of hypothenar eminence
4. Loss of adduction of thumb
5. Loss of abduction of all fingers except little finger
6. Loss of adduction of all fingers
7. Slight clawing of 2nd and 3rd digits
8. Marked clawing of 4th and 5th digits
9. Sensory, trophic and vasomotor changes (Fig. A1.2)

- If ulnar nerve is injured at the elbow, the clawing of the fingers is less, because medial half of flexor digitorum profundus (flexor of proximal and distal interphalangeal joints) also gets paralysed. If ulnar nerve is injured at wrist, the clawing of the fingers is more as intact flexor digitorum profundus flexes the digits more. Thus if lesion is proximal (near elbow), clawing is less. On the contrary, if lesion is distal (near wrist), clawing is more. This is called "action of paradox"/ulnar paradox.
- If both ulnar and median nerves get paralysed, there is complete claw hand (see Fig. 9.49).
  Table A1.5 gives the arteries of upper limb with their branches and area of distribution. Table A1.6 shows the comparison between injuries of median and ulnar nerves at the wrist.

Table A1.5: Arteries of upper limb		
Artery	*Origin, course and termination*	*Area of distribution*
AXILLARY ARTERY (*see* Fig. 4.6 and Fig. A1.3)	Starts at the outer border of first rib as continuation of subclavian artery, runs through axilla and continues as brachial artery at the lower border of teres major muscle	Supplies all walls of axilla, pectoral region including mammary gland
Superior thoracic (*see* Fig. 4.10)	From 1st part of axillary artery	Supplies upper part of thoracic wall and the pectoral muscles
Thoracoacromial	From 2nd part of axillary artery, pierces clavipectoral fascia and divides into deltoid, acromial and clavicular and pectoral branches	Supplies pectoral and deltoid muscles
Lateral thoracic	From 2nd part of axillary artery runs along inferolateral border of pectoralis minor	Supplies the muscles of thoracic wall including the mammary gland
Anterior circumflex humeral	From third part of axillary artery runs on the anterior aspect of intertubercular sulcus and anastomoses with large posterior humerus circumflex humeral artery	Supplies the neighbouring shoulder joint and the muscles
Posterior circumflex humeral	From third part of axillary artery lies along the surgical neck of humerus with axillary nerve	Supplies huge deltoid muscle, skin overlying it and the shoulder joint
Subscapular (*see* Figs 4.10 and 6.12)	Largest branch of axillary artery runs along the muscles of posterior wall of axilla	Supplies muscles of posterior wall of axilla, i.e. teres major, latissimus dorsi, subscapularis. Takes part in anastomoses around scapula
BRACHIAL ARTERY	Starts at the lower border of teres major as continu-	Supplies muscles of the arm, humerus

(Contd...)

Table A1.5: Arteries of upper limb (Contd...)

Artery	Origin, course and termination	Area of distribution
(see Fig. 8.9)	ation of axillary artery. Runs on anterior aspect of arm and ends by dividing into radial and ulnar arteries at neck of radius in the cubital fossa	bone and skin of whole of arm. Takes part in anastomoses around elbow joint
Profunda brachii artery (see Fig. 8.10)	Largest branch of brachial artery. Runs with radial nerve in the radial sulcus of humerus. Reaching the lateral side of arm ends by dividing into anterior and posterior branches	Supplies muscles of back of arm and its branches anastomose with branches of radial artery and ulnar artery on lateral epicondyle of humerus
Superior ulnar collateral artery (see Fig. 8.10)	Branch of brachial artery. Accompanies ulnar nerve. Takes part in anastomoses around elbow joint	Supplies muscles of arm and elbow joint on its medial aspect
Muscular branches	Branches arise from brachial artery	Supplies biceps and triceps brachii muscles
Nutrient artery	Branch of brachial and enters the nutrient foramen of humerus	Supplies blood to red bone narrow
Inferior ulnar collateral artery	Branch of brachial	Takes part in the anastomoses around elbow joint from medial side
RADIAL ARTERY (see Figs 8.17 and 9.20)	Starts as smaller branch of brachial artery, lies on the lateral side of forearm, then in the anatomical snuff box to reach the palm, where it continues as deep palmar arch	Muscles of lateral side of forearm, including the overlying skin. Gives a branch for completion of superficial palmar arch. Digital branches to thumb and lateral side of index finger
Radial recurrent artery (see Fig. 8.10)	Branch of radial artery	Supplies elbow joint. Takes part in anastomoses around elbow joint
Muscular branches	Branches of radial artery	Muscles attached to radius, e.g. biceps brachii, pronator teres, pronator quadratus, flexor pollicis longus, flexor digitorum superficialis
Superficial palmar branch (see Fig. 9.20)	Branch of radial artery in lower part of forearm, before radial artery winds posteriorly	Crosses front of thenar muscles and joins the superficial branch of ulnar artery to complete superficial palmar arch
Dorsal carpal branch	Branch of radial artery as it lies in the anatomical snuff box	Supplies wrist joint
Princeps pollicis artery (see Fig. 9.20)	Branch of radial artery in palm, runs along thumb	Supplies muscles, tendons, skin and joints in relation to thumb
Radialis indicis artery (see Fig. 9.20)	Branch of radial artery in palm, runs along radial side of index finger	Supplies tendons, joints and skin of index finger
ULNAR ARTERY (see Fig. 9.10)	Originates as the larger terminal branch of brachial artery at neck of radius. Courses first obliquely in upper one-third and then vertically in lower two-thirds of forearm. Lies superficial to flexor retinaculum and ends by dividing into superficial and deep branches	Gives branches to take part in the anastomoses around elbow joint. Branches supply muscles of front of forearm, back of forearm and nutrient arteries to forearm bones
Anterior and posterior ulnar recurrent arteries (see Fig. 8.10)	Branches of ulnar artery curve upwards and reach elbow joint	Take part in anastomoses around elbow joint
Common interosseous	Large branch of ulnar artery	Supplies all the muscles of forearm
Branches		
a. Anterior interosseous artery	Branch of common interosseous artery runs on interosseous membrane	Supplies both the bones of forearm and muscles attached to these bones
b. Posterior interosseous artery	Branch of common interosseous artery reaches back of forearm	Supplies muscles of back of forearm. Also take part in anastomoses around elbow joint
Superficial branch	Larger terminal branch of ulnar artery joins	Gives branches to tendon in the palm,

(Contd...)

Table A1.5: Arteries of upper limb (*Contd...*)

Artery	Origin, course and termination	Area of distribution
(*see* Fig. 9.20)	superficial palmar branch of radial artery to form superficial palmar arch	digital branches along fingers. Also supply joints and overlying skin
Deep branch (*see* Fig. 9.22)	Smaller terminal branch of ulnar artery that joins with the terminal part of radial artery to form the deep palmar arch which lies deep to the long flexor tendons of the palm. It is also proximal to the superficial palmar arch	Branches of deep palmar arch join the digital branches of superficial palmar arch, supplementing the blood supply to the digits or fingers

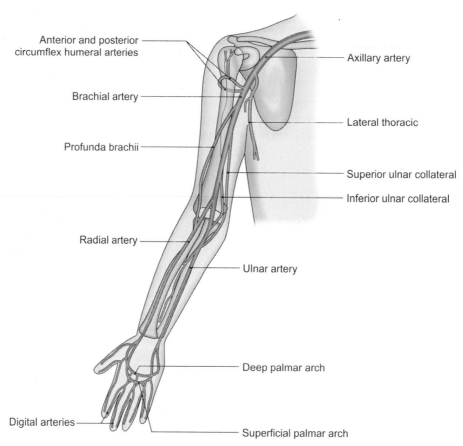

Anterior and posterior circumflex humeral arteries

Brachial artery

Profunda brachii

Radial artery

Digital arteries

Axillary artery

Lateral thoracic

Superior ulnar collateral

Inferior ulnar collateral

Ulnar artery

Deep palmar arch

Superficial palmar arch

Fig. A1.3: Arteries of the upper limb

Table A1.6: Comparison of injury of median and ulnar nerves at wrist

Injury to median nerve at wrist	Injury to ulnar nerve at wrist
Loss of thenar eminence	Loss of hypothenar eminence
Normal fist making by 4th, 5th digits	Clawing of 4th and 5th digits
Lagging behing of 2nd and 3rd digits in fist making	Slight clawing of 2nd and 3rd digits
	Gutters seen in palm
Sensory loss over lateral 3½ digits	Sensory loss over medial 1½ digits
Loss of pronation of forearm	Loss of adduction of 2nd–5th digits
Loss of opposition of thumb	Loss of abduction of 2nd–4th digits

CLINICAL TERMS

Shoulder joint may be dislocated anteroinferiorly: The shoulder joint is surrounded by short muscles on all aspects except inferiorly. Since the joint is quite mobile, it dislocates at the unprotected site, i.e. inferiorly (*see* Fig. 2.18).

Student's elbow: Inflammation of the bursa over the insertion of triceps brachii is called student's elbow. It is common in students as they use the flexed elbow to support the head while attempting hard to listen to the lectures in between their 'naps' (*see* Fig. 10.16).

Tennis elbow: Lateral epicondylitis occurs in players of lawn tennis or table tennis. The extensor muscles of forearm are used to hit the ball sharply, causing repeated *microtrauma* to the lateral epicondyle and its subsequent inflammation (*see* Fig. 10.15). It may be a degenerative condition.

Pulled elbow: While pulling the children by their hands (getting them off the bus) the head of radius may slip out of the annular ligament. Annular ligament is not tight in children as in adults, so the head of radius slips out (*see* Fig. 2.26).

Boxer's palsy or swimmer's palsy: Serratus anterior causes the movement of protraction. If the long thoracic nerve is injured, the muscle gets paralysed, seen as "winging of scapula" (*see* Fig. 2.12). Such a person cannot hit his opponent by that hand. Neither can he make strokes while swimming.

Golfer's elbow/medial epicondylitis: Occurs in golf players. Repeated microtrauma to medial epicondyles causes inflammation of common flexor origin and pain in flexing the wrist (*see* Fig. 10.17).

Waiter's tip or policeman's tip: "Taking the tip quietly" Erb–Duchenne paralysis occurs due to involvement of Erb's point. At Erb's point, C5, C6 roots join to form upper trunk, two divisions of the trunk arise and two branches, the suprascapular and nerve to subclavius also arise (*see* Fig. 4.16).

Wrist drop: Paralysis of radial nerve in axilla or radial sulcus or anterolateral side of lower part of arm or paralysis of its deep branch in cubital fossa leads to wrist drop (*see* Fig. 8.25).

Carpal tunnel syndrome: Median nerve gets compressed under the flexor retinaculum, leading to paralysis of muscles of thenar eminence. It is called 'ape-like or monkey-like hand'. There is loss of sensation in lateral 3½ digits including nail beds. Median nerve is the 'eye of the hand'. There is little clawing of index and middle fingers also (*see* Figs 9.40 to 9.44).

Cubital tunnel syndrome: Ulnar nerve gets entrapped between two heads of flexor carpi ulnaris muscle, leading to paralysis of medial half of flexor digitorum profundus and muscles of hypothenar eminence, all interossei and adductor pollicis and 3rd and 4th lumbricals. There is clawing of medial two digits, gutters in the hand and loss of hypothenar eminence (*see* Figs 9.35 and 9.36).

Volkmann's ischaemic contracture: This condition occurs due to fibrosis of the muscles of the forearm, chiefly the flexors. It usually occurs with injury to the brachial artery in supracondylar fractures of humerus (*see* Fig. 2.16b).

Dupuytren's contracture: This clinical condition is due to fibrosis of medial part of palmar aponeurosis especially the part reaching the ring and little fingers. The fibrous bands are attached to proximal and middle phalanges and not to distal phalanges. So proximal and middle phalanges are flexed, while distal phalanges remain extended (*see* Fig. 9.18).

Funny bone: Ulnar nerve is palpable in flexed elbow behind the medial epicondyle. Palpating the nerve gives rise to funny sensations in the medial side of forearm. Since medial epicondyle is part of humerus, it is called humerus or funny bone (*see* Fig. 2.15).

Pointing finger: Branch of anterior interosseus nerve to lateral half of flexor digitorum profundus is injured in the middle of the forearm. The index finger is affected the most. It remains extended and keeps pointing forwards (despite the fact that remaining three fingers are pointing towards self) (*see* Fig. 9.39).

Complete claw hand: Complete claw hand is due to injury of lower trunk of brachial plexus especially the root, which supplies intrinsic muscles of hand. The injury is called 'Klumpke's paralysis'. The metacarpophalangeal joints are extended while both the interphalangeal joints of all fingers are actually flexed (*see* Fig. 9.45).

Breast: The breast is a frequent site of carcinoma (cancer). Several anatomical facts are of importance in diagnosis and treatment of this condition. Abscesses may also form in the breast and may require drainage. The following facts are worthy of note.

Incisions into the breast are usually made radially to avoid cutting the lactiferous ducts (*see* Fig. 3.9).

Cancer cells may infiltrate the suspensory ligaments. The breast then becomes fixed. Contraction of the ligaments can cause retraction or puckering (folding) of the skin.

Infiltration of lactiferous ducts and their consequent fibrosis can cause retraction of the skin.

Obstruction of superficial lymph vessels by cancer cells may produce oedema of the skin giving rise to an appearance like that of the skin of an orange (*peau d'orange* appearance) (*see* Fig. 3.16).

Because of bilateral communications of the lymphatics of the breast across the midline, cancer may spread from one breast to the other (*see* Fig. 3.17).

Because of communications of the lymph vessels with those in the abdomen, cancer of the breast may spread to the liver. Cancer cells may 'drop' into the pelvis especially ovary (Krukenberg's tumour) producing secondaries there (*see* Fig. 3.17).

Apart from the lymphatics, cancer may spread through the veins. In this connection, it is important to know that the veins draining the breast communicate with the vertebral venous plexus of veins. Through these communications, cancer can spread to the vertebrae and to the brain (*see* Fig. 3.17).

Blood pressure: The blood pressure is universally recorded by auscultating the brachial artery on the anteromedial aspect of the elbow joint (*see* Fig. 8.11).

Intravenous injection: The median cubital vein is the vein of choice for intravenous injections, for withdrawing blood from donors, and for cardiac catheterisation, because it is fixed by the perforator and does not slip away during piercing (*see* Fig. 7.8).

Intramuscular injection: Intramuscular injections are often given into the deltoid. They should be given in the middle of the muscle to avoid injury to the axillary nerve (*see* Fig. 6.9).

Radial pulse: The radial artery is used for feeling the (arterial) pulse at the wrist. The pulsation can be felt well in this situation because of the presence of the flat radius behind the artery (*see* Fig. 9.10).

Ligaments of Cooper: Fibrous strands extending between skin overlying the breast to the underlying pectoral muscles. These support the gland.

Montgomery's glands: Glands beneath the areola of mammary gland.

Subareolar plexus of Sappey: Lymphatic plexus beneath the areola of the breast.

Lister's tubercle: Dorsal tubercle on lower end of posterior surface of radius. This acts as a pulley for the tendon of extensor pollicis longus.

de Quervain's disease is a thickening of sheath around tendons of abductor pollicis longus and extensor pollicis brevis giving rise to pain on lateral side of wrist.

FREQUENTLY ASKED QUESTIONS

1. Enumerate branches of:
   - Radial nerve in axilla and in radial sulcus
   - Branches of median nerve in forearm
   - Branches of median nerve in palm
   - Branches of ulnar nerve in palm
   - Branches of musculocutaneous nerve
   - Branches of brachial artery
   - Branches of ulnar artery in forearm
   - Branches of radial artery in forearm
   - Enumerate the palpable arteries in upper limb
   - Branches of superficial palmar arch

MULTIPLE CHOICE QUESTIONS

A. Match the following on the left side with their appropriate answers on the right side:

1. The nerve injury and the clinical signs:
   a. Radial nerve   i. Partial claw hand
   b. Median nerve   ii. Wrist drop
   c. Long thoracic nerve   iii. Ape thumb
   d. Ulnar nerve   iv. Winging of scapula

2. Tendon reflexes and segmental innervation:
   a. Triceps   i. C5, C6, C7
   b. Biceps brachii   ii. C5, C6
   c. Brachioradialis   iii. C6, C7, C8

3. Muscles and the movements at shoulder joints:
   a. Deltoid   i. Medial rotation
   b. Subscapularis   ii. Lateral rotation
   c. Latissimus dorsi   iii. Abduction
   d. Teres minor   iv. Extension

4. Muscles and their nerve supply:
   a. Deltoid   i. Ulnar
   b. Supinator   ii. Median
   c. 1st lumbrical   iii. Axillary
   d. Adductor pollicis   iv. Radial

5. Sensory innervation of skin:

a. Palmar surface of ring and little fingers	i. C3, C4
b. Palmar surface of thumb and index finger	ii. C8
c. Medial aspect of arm	iii. T1, T2
d. Tip of the shoulder	iv. C6

B. For each of the incomplete statements or questions below, one or more completions or answers given is/are correct. Select.

A. If only a, b and c are correct

B. If only a and c are correct

C. If only b and d are correct

D. If only d is correct

E. If all are correct

6. Injury to the median nerve in the arm would affect:

a. Pronation of the forearm

b. Flexion of the wrist

c. Flexion of the thumb

d. Supination of the forearm

7. Which of the following is/are true regarding humerus?

a. The head of the humerus commonly dislocates posteriorly.

b. Common sites of fracture are surgical neck, shaft and supracondylar region

c. Lower end is the growing end.

d. Axillary, radial and ulnar nerves are directly related to the bone

8. Clavicle:

a. Is a long bone

b. Develops by intramembranous ossification

c. Is the first bone to ossify

d. Has a well-developed medullary cavity

9. In Erb's paralysis:

a. Abduction and lateral rotation of the arm are lost.

b. Flexion and pronation of the forearm are lost

c. Biceps and supinator jerks are lost

d. Sensations are lost over the medial side of the arm

10. Which of the following statements is/are true regarding 'mammary gland'?

a. It is modified sweat gland

b. Lies in superficial fascia

c. 75% of the lymph from mammary gland drains into axillary lymph nodes

d. Some lymphatic vessels communicate with the lymph vessels of opposite side

ANSWERS
1. a. – ii, b. – iii,   c. – iv,   d – i.   2. a. – iii,   b. – ii, c. – i,
3. a.–iii., b. – i.,   c. – iv.,   d. – ii.   4. a. – iii.,   b. – iv, c. – ii, d. – i
5. a. – ii., b. – iv,   c. – iii,   d. – i,   6. A   7. C   8. A   9. B   10. E.

FURTHER READING

1. An, KN, Berger RA, Cooney WP (eds). *Biomechanics of the wrist joint*. New York, Springer-Verlag, 1991.

2. Arora J, Suri RK and Rath G. Unusual insertion pattern of pectoralis minimus muscle-A Case Report. *Int. Med Jr.* 2008; 15:315–317.

3. Burkart AC, Debski RE. Anatomy and function of the glenohumeral ligaments in anterior shoulder instability. *Clin Orthopaed Related Res* 2002; 400:32.

4. Ellis H, Colborn GL, Skandalakis JE. Surgical, embryology and anatomy of the breast and its related anatomic structures. *Surg Clin North Am* 1993; 73:611–32.

5. Groen G, Baljet B, Drukker J. The nerve and nerve plexuses of the human vertebral column. *Amer J. Anat* 1990; 188:282–96.

6. Haider SJ, Obuoforibo AA. Analysis of the muscular activity during abduction at shoulder in the plane of scapula. *J Anat Soc* India 1987; 36:2, 90–93

7. Jayakumari S, Rath G, Arora J. Unilateral double axillary and double brachial arteries: Embryological basis and clinical implications. *Int. J. Morph.* 2006; 24(3): 463–68.

8. Leiber RL, Jacobson MD, Fazeli BM, Abrams RA, Botte MJ, Architecture of selected muscles of the arm and forearm; anatomy and implications for tendon transfer. *J Hand Surg* 1992; 17A:787–98.

9. Paul S, Sehgal R, Khatri K. Anatomical variations in the labral attachment of long head of biceps brachii. *J Anat. Soc.* India 53(2), Dec 2004, 49–51.

10. Serletti JM, Moran SL. Microvascular reconstruction of the breast. *Semin Surg Oncol* 2000; 19:264–71.

11. Soni S, Rath G, Suri RK and Loh H. Anomalous pectoral musculature: a case report. *Anatomical Science International* 2008; 83:310–313.

12. Spinner MJB. *Kaplan's Functional and Surgical Anatomy of the Hand*, 3rd edn. Philadelphia: Lippincott, William & Wilkins 1984.

13. Tan ST, Smith PJ, Anomalous extensor muscles of the hand; a review. *J Hand Surg* 1999; 24A:449–55.

1. a. Identify the muscle.
    b. Name its nerve supply.

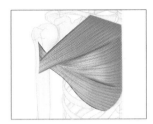

2. a. Identify the cord of brachial plexus.
    b. Enumerate its branches.

3. a. Identify the muscle.
    b. Name its heads.

4. a. Identify the area.
    b. Name its contents in order.

5. a. Identify the nerve.
    b. Name its muscular branches in the palm.

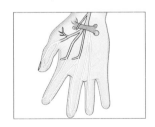

6. a. Identify the joint.
    b. Name its movements.

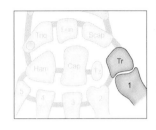

7. a. Identify the structure on right middle finger
    b. Name the muscles inserted.

8. a. Identify the structure.
    b. Name the structures lying on its superficial aspect.

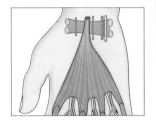

9. a. Identify the structure.
    b. Name the contents of its 4th compartment.

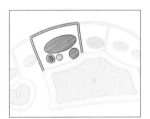

10. a. Identify the muscle.
    b. Name the nerves supplying it.

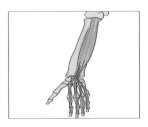

ANSWERS: SPOTS ON UPPER LIMB

1. a. Pectoralis major
    b. Medial pectoral and lateral pectoral nerves

2. a. Medial cord of brachial plexus
    b. • Medial pectoral
       • Medial cutaneous nerve of arm
       • Medial cutaneous nerve of forearm
       • Ulnar nerve
       • Medial root of median

3. a. Biceps brachii
    b. Long head and short head

4. a. Cubital fossa
    b. • Median nerve
       • Brachial artery
       • Tendon of biceps brachii
       • Radial nerve

5. a. Median nerve
    b. • Flexor pollicis brevis
       • Abductor pollicis brevis
       • Opponens pollicis
       • 1st and 2nd lumbricals

6. a. 1st carpometacarpal joint
    b. • Flexion with medial rotation
       • Extension with lateral rotation
       • Abduction
       • Adduction
       • Opposition

7. a. Extensor expansion of right middle finger
    b. • Tendon of extensor digitorum
       • 2nd lumbrical
       • 2nd and 3rd dorsal interossei

8. a. Flexor retinaculum
    b. • Palmar cutaneous branch of median nerve
       • Tendon of palmaris longus
       • Palmar cutaneous branch of ulnar nerve
       • Ulnar artery
       • Ulnar nerve

9. a. Extensor retinaculum
    b. • Tendon of extensor digitorum
       • Tendon of extensor indicis
       • Anterior interosseous artery
       • Posterior interosseous nerve

10. a. Flexor digitorum profundus
    b. Medial half by ulnar nerve and lateral half by anterior interosseous branch of median nerve

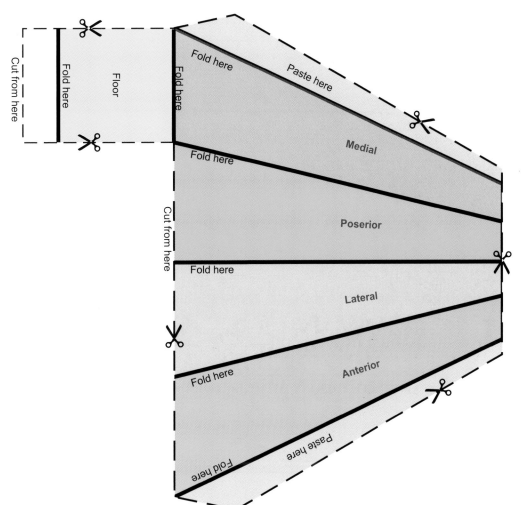

Right axilla

Fold here
Fold here
Fold here
Paste here
Medial
Poserior
Fold here
Lateral
Fold here
Anterior
Fold here
Paste here
Cut from here
Floor
Fold here
Cut from here
Fold here

Thorax

Anatomy Made Easy

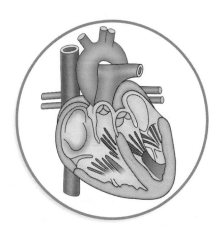

Ichchak dana, beechak dana, dane upar dana
Hands naache, feet naache, brain hai khushnama
Ichchak dana.
Closed cage mai baitha ek naajuk bechara
lub dub, lub dub hi karta hai ye aawara
Lekin iska bahut sensitive hai mijajana
agar tute to mushkil hai samjhana
is liye kisi ka "ye" na dukhana
Ichchak dana
Bolo kya—heart, bolo kya—heart

Introduction

Pray as if everything depended on God and work as if everything depended upon man

Thorax (Latin *chest*) forms the upper part of the trunk of the body. It not only permits boarding and lodging of the thoracic viscera, but also provides necessary shelter to some of the abdominal viscera.

The trunk of the body is divided by the *diaphragm* into an upper part, called the *thorax,* and a lower part, called the *abdomen.* The thorax is supported by a skeletal framework, *thoracic cage.* The thoracic cavity contains the principal organs of respiration—the lungs and of circulation—the heart, both of which are vital for life.

SURFACE LANDMARKS OF THORAX

Bony Landmarks

1 *Suprasternal or jugular notch* (Fig. 12.1): It is felt just above the superior border of the manubrium between the sternal ends of the clavicles. It lies at the level of the lower border of the body of the second thoracic vertebra. The trachea can be palpated in this notch.

2 *Sternal angle/angle of Louis:* It is felt as a transverse ridge about 5 cm below the suprasternal notch. It marks the manubriosternal joint, and lies at the level of the second costal cartilage anteriorly, and the disc between the fourth and fifth thoracic vertebrae posteriorly. *This is an important landmark for the following reasons.*

a. The ribs are counted from this level downwards. There is no other reliable point (anteriorly) from which the ribs may be counted. The second costal cartilage and second rib lie at the level of the sternal angle or angle of Louis (French physician 1787–1872). The ribs are counted from here by tracing the finger downwards and laterally (because the lower costal cartilages are crowded and the anterior parts of the intercostal spaces are very narrow).

b. It marks the plane which separates the superior mediastinum from the inferior mediastinum.

c. The ascending aorta ends at this level.

d. The arch of the aorta begins and also ends at this level.

e. The descending aorta begins at this level.

f. The trachea divides into two principal bronchi.

g. The azygos vein arches over the root of the right lung and opens into the superior vena cava.

h. The pulmonary trunk divides into two pulmonary arteries just below this level.

i. The thoracic duct crosses from the right to the left side at the level of the fifth thoracic vertebra and reaches the left side at the level of the sternal angle.

j. It marks the upper limit of the base of the heart.

k. The cardiac plexuses are situated at the same level.

3 *Xiphisternal joint:* The costal margin on each side is formed by the seventh to tenth costal cartilages. Between the two costal margins, there lies the

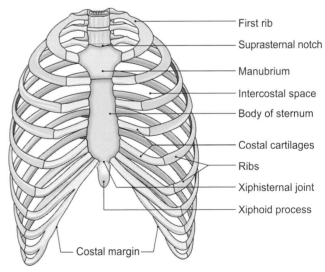

Fig. 12.1: Shape and construction of the thoracic cage as seen from the front

First rib
Suprasternal notch
Manubrium
Intercostal space
Body of sternum
Costal cartilages
Ribs
Xiphisternal joint
Xiphoid process
Costal margin

infrasternal or subcostal angle. The depression in the angle is also known as the epigastric fossa.

The xiphoid (Greek *sword*) process lies in the floor of the epigastric fossa. At the apex of the angle, the xiphisternal joint may be felt as a short transverse ridge. It lies at the level of the upper border of the ninth thoracic vertebra (Fig. 12.1).

4 *Costal cartilages:* The *second* costal (Latin *rib*) cartilage is attached to the sternal angle. The *seventh* cartilage bounds the upper part of the infrasternal angle. The lateral border of the rectus abdominis or the linea semilunaris joins the costal margin at the tip of the ninth costal cartilage. The tenth costal cartilage forms the lower part of the costal margin (Figs 12.1 and 12.2).

5 *Ribs:* The scapula overlies the second to seventh ribs on the posterolateral aspect of the chest wall. The tenth rib is the lowest point, lies at the level of the third lumbar vertebra. Though the eleventh rib is longer than the twelfth, both of them are confined to the back and are not seen from the front (Fig. 12.2).

6 *Thoracic vertebral spines:* The first prominent spine felt at the lower part of the back of the neck is that of the *seventh cervical vertebra* or *vertebra prominens*. Below this spine, all the thoracic spines can be palpated along the posterior median line (Fig. 12.3). The third thoracic spine lies at the level of the roots of the spines of the scapulae. The seventh thoracic spine lies at the level of the inferior angles of the scapulae.

Soft Tissue Landmarks

1 *The nipple:* The position of the nipple varies considerably in females, but in males it usually lies in the fourth intercostal space about 10 cm from the midsternal line (Fig. 12.4).

2 *Apex beat:* It is a visible and palpable cardiac impulse in the left fifth intercostal space 9 cm from the midsternal line, or medial to the midclavicular line.

3 *Trachea:* It is palpable in the suprasternal notch midway between the two clavicles.

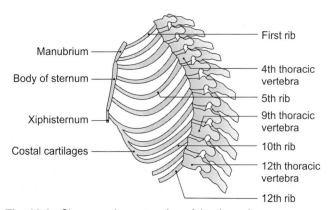

Fig. 12.2: Shape and construction of the thoracic cage as seen from the lateral side

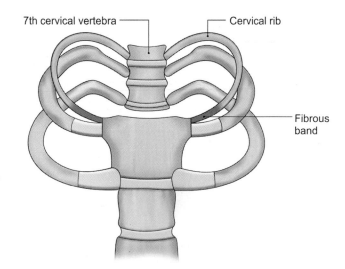

Fig. 12.3: Shape and construction of the thoracic cage as seen from behind

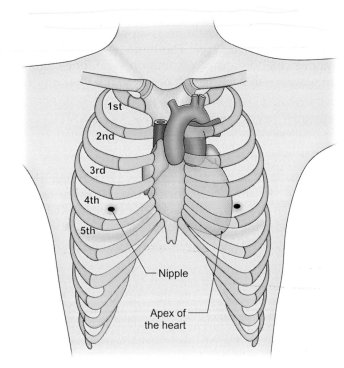

Fig. 12.4: Soft tissue landmarks

4 *Midclavicular or mammary plane:* It is a vertical plane passing through the midinguinal point, the tip of the ninth costal cartilage and middle of clavicle (Fig. 12.5).

5 *Midaxillary line:* It passes vertically between the two folds of the axilla (Fig. 12.5).

6 *Scapular line:* It passes vertically along the inferior angle of the scapula.

Section 2 **Thorax**

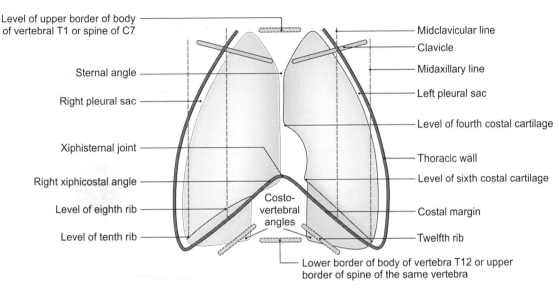

Level of upper border of body of vertebral T1 or spine of C7

Sternal angle

Right pleural sac

Xiphisternal joint

Right xiphicostal angle

Level of eighth rib

Level of tenth rib

Costo-vertebral angles

Midclavicular line

Clavicle

Midaxillary line

Left pleural sac

Level of fourth costal cartilage

Thoracic wall

Level of sixth costal cartilage

Costal margin

Twelfth rib

Lower border of body of vertebra T12 or upper border of spine of the same vertebra

Fig. 12.5: Surface marking of midclavicular and midaxillary lines

SKELETON OF THORAX

The skeleton of thorax is also known as the thoracic cage. It is an osseocartilaginous elastic cage which is primarily designed for increasing and decreasing the intrathoracic pressure, so that air is sucked into the lungs during inspiration and expelled during expiration.

FORMATION

Anteriorly, by the sternum (Greek *chest*) (Figs 12.1 and 12.2).

Posteriorly, by the 12 thoracic vertebrae and the intervening intervertebral discs (Fig. 12.3).

On each side, by 12 ribs with their cartilages.

Each rib articulates posteriorly with the vertebral column. Anteriorly, only the upper seven ribs articulate with the sternum through their cartilages and these are called *true or vertebrosternal ribs.*

The costal cartilages of the next three ribs, i.e. the eighth, ninth and tenth end by joining the next higher costal cartilage. These ribs are, therefore, known as *vertebrochondral ribs.* The costal cartilages of the seventh, eighth, ninth and tenth ribs form the sloping costal margin.

The anterior ends of the eleventh and twelfth ribs are free. These are called *floating or vertebral ribs.* The vertebrochondral and vertebral ribs, i.e. the last five ribs, are also called false ribs because they do not articulate with the sternum.

The costovertebral, costotransverse, manubriosternal and chondrosternal joints permit movements of the thoracic cage during breathing.

CLINICAL ANATOMY

The chest wall of the child is highly elastic, and fractures of the ribs are, therefore, rare. In adults, the ribs may be fractured by direct or indirect violence (Fig. 12.6). In indirect violence, like crush injury, the rib fractures at its weakest point located at the angle. The upper two ribs which are protected by the clavicle, and the lower two ribs which are free to swing are least commonly injured.

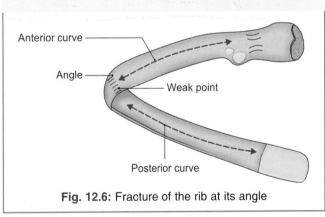

Anterior curve

Angle

Weak point

Posterior curve

Fig. 12.6: Fracture of the rib at its angle

SHAPE

The thorax resembles a truncated cone which is narrow above and broad below (Fig. 12.7). The narrow upper end is continuous with the root of the neck from which it is partly separated by the suprapleural membrane or Sibson's fascia. The broad or lower end is almost completely separated from the abdomen by the diaphragm which is deeply concave downwards. The thoracic cavity is actually much smaller than what it

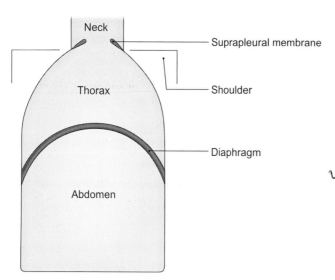

Fig. 12.7: Scheme to show how the size of the thoracic cavity is reduced by the upward projection of the diaphragm, and by the inward projection of the shoulders

appears to be because the narrow upper part appears broad due to the shoulders, and the lower part is greatly encroached upon by the abdominal cavity due to the upward convexity of the diaphragm.

In transverse section, the thorax is reniform (bean-shaped, or kidney-shaped). The transverse diameter is greater than the anteroposterior diameter. However, in infants below the age of two years, it is circular. In quadrupeds, the anteroposterior diameter is greater than the transverse, as shown in Fig. 12.8.

In infants, the ribs are horizontal and as a result the respiration is purely abdominal by the action of the diaphragm.

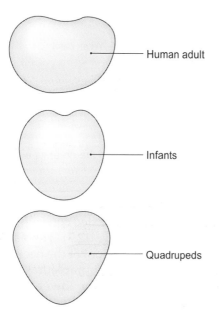

Fig. 12.8: The shape of the thorax as seen in transverse section in: Human adult, infants, and quadrupeds

In adults, the thorax is oval. The ribs are oblique and their movements alternately increase and decrease the diameters of the thorax. This results in the drawing in of air into the thorax called *inspiration* and its expulsion is called *expiration*. This is called *thoracic respiration*. In the adult, we, therefore, have both abdominal and thoracic respirations.

CLINICAL ANATOMY

- Diaphragm descends during inspiration to increase the vertical diameter of thoracic cage.
- *Hiccups:* These occur due to spasmodic involuntary contractions of the diaphragm accompanied by closed glottis. These usually occur due to gastric irritation. Hiccups may also be due to phrenic nerve irritation, uraemia or hysteria.

SUPERIOR APERTURE/INLET OF THORAX

The narrow upper end of the thorax, which is continuous with the neck, is called the inlet of the thorax (Fig. 12.9). It is kidney-shaped. Its transverse diameter is 10–12.5 cm. The anteroposterior diameter is about 5 cm.

Boundaries

Anteriorly: Upper border of the manubrium sterni.

Posteriorly: Superior surface of the body of the first thoracic vertebra.

On each side: First rib with its cartilage.

The plane of the inlet is directed downwards and forwards with an obliquity of about 45 degrees. The anterior part of the inlet lies 3.7 cm below the posterior

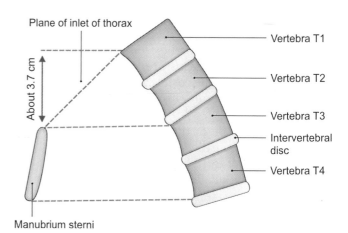

Fig. 12.9: The plane of the inlet of the thorax

part, so that the upper border of the manubrium sterni lies at the level of the upper border of the third thoracic vertebra.

Partition at the Inlet of Thorax

The partition is in two halves, right and left, with a cleft in between. Each half is covered by a fascia, known as *Sibson's fascia or suprapleural membrane*. It partly separates the thorax from the neck. The membrane is triangular in shape. Its apex is attached to the tip of the transverse process of the seventh cervical vertebra and the base to the inner border of the first rib and its cartilage.

Morphologically, Sibson's fascia is regarded as the flattened tendon of the scalenus minimus (pleuralis) muscle. It is thus formed by scalenus minimus and endothoracic fascia. Functionally, it provides rigidity to the thoracic inlet, so that the root of the neck is not puffed up and down during respiration. The inferior surface of the membrane is fused to the cervical pleura, beneath which lies the apex of the lung. Its superior surface is related to the subclavian vessels and other structures at the root of the neck (Figs 12.10 and 12.11a and b).

Structures Passing through the Inlet of Thorax

Viscera

Trachea, oesophagus, apices of the lungs with pleura, remains of the thymus. Figure 12.12 depicts the structures passing through the inlet of the thorax.

Large Vessels

Brachiocephalic artery on right side.

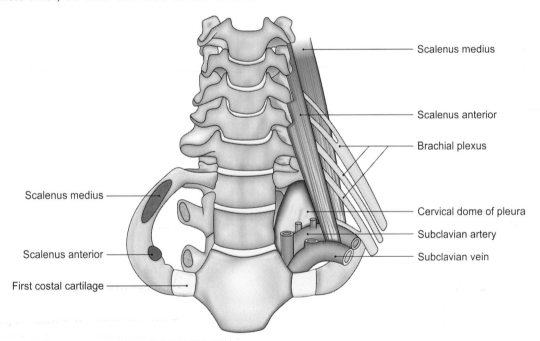

Fig. 12.10: Thoracic inlet showing cervical dome of the pleura on left side of body and its relationship to inner border of first rib

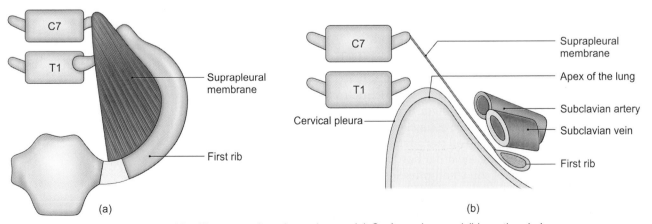

Figs 12.11a and b: The suprapleural membrane: (a) Surface view, and (b) sectional view

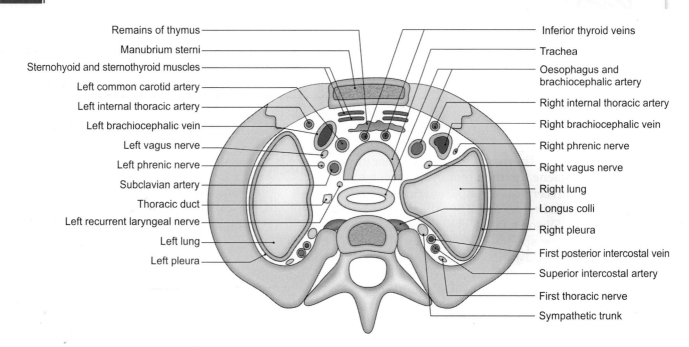

Fig. 12.12: Structures passing through the inlet of the thorax

Left common carotid artery and the left subclavian artery on the left side. Right and left brachiocephalic veins.

Smaller Vessels

1 Right and left internal thoracic arteries.
2 Right and left superior intercostal arteries.
3 Right and left first posterior intercostal veins.
4 Inferior thyroid veins.

Nerves

1 Right and left phrenic nerves.
2 Right and left vagus nerves.
3 Right and left sympathetic trunks.
4 Right and left first thoracic nerves as they ascend across the first rib to join the brachial plexus.

Muscles

Sternohyoid, sternothyroid and longus colli.

CLINICAL ANATOMY

- A cervical rib is a rib attached to vertebra C7. It occurs in about 0.5% of subjects (Fig. 12.13). Such a rib may exert traction on the lower trunk of the brachial plexus which arches over a cervical rib. Such a person complains of paraesthesia or abnormal sensations along the ulnar border of the forearm, and wasting of the small muscles of the hand supplied by segment T1 (Fig. 12.14). Vascular changes may also occur.

- In coarctation or narrowing of the aorta, the posterior intercostal arteries get enlarged greatly to provide a collateral circulation. Pressure of the enlarged arteries produces characteristic notching on the ribs (Fig. 12.15) especially in their posterior parts.

- *Thoracic inlet syndrome:* Two structures arch over the first rib—the subclavian artery and first thoracic nerve. These structures may be pulled or pressed by a cervical rib or by variations in the insertion of the scalenus anterior. The symptoms may, therefore, be vascular, neural, or both.

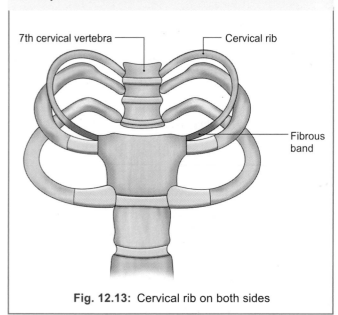

Fig. 12.13: Cervical rib on both sides

Boundaries

Anteriorly: Infrasternal angle between the two costal margins.

Posteriorly: Inferior surface of the body of the twelfth thoracic vertebra.

On each side: Costal margin formed by the cartilages of seventh to twelfth ribs.

Diaphragm at the Outlet of Thorax

The outlet is closed by a large musculotendinous partition, called the diaphragm—the *thoracoabdominal diaphragm*—which separates the thorax from the abdomen.

Structures Passing through the Diaphragm

There are three large and several small openings in the diaphragm which allow passage to structures from thorax to abdomen or *vice versa* (Fig. 12.16).

Large openings: These are vena caval opening in the central tendon, oesophageal opening in the right crus of diaphragm and aortic opening behind the median arcuate ligament.

The structures passing through large openings are put in Table 12.1.

Small openings: Superior epigastric artery passes in space of Larrey present between slip of xiphoid process and 7th costal cartilaginous slip of the diaphragm. When foramen is enlarged it is known as foramen of Morgagni.

Musculophrenic artery perforates diaphragm at the level of 9th costal cartilage.

Lower 5 intercostal vessels and nerves pass between costal origins of diaphragm and transversus abdominis.

Subcostal vessels and nerves pass behind lateral arcuate ligament. Sympathetic trunk passes behind medial arcuate ligament. Greater and lesser splanchnic nerves pierce each crus. Left phrenic nerve pierces left cupola.

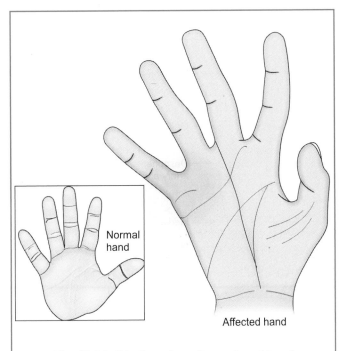

Fig. 12.14: Wasting of small muscles of hand

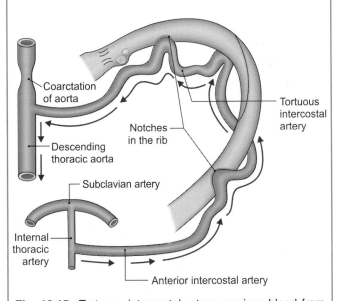

Fig. 12.15: Tortuous intercostal artery receives blood from anterior intercostal artery, transfers it to descending aorta beyond coarctation. Tortuous intercostal artery produces notches in the rib

INFERIOR APERTURE/OUTLET OF THORAX

The inferior aperture is the broad end of the thorax which surrounds the upper part of the abdominal cavity, but is separated from it by the diaphragm (Greek *across fence*).

FACTS TO REMEMBER

- Thoracic cavity houses a single heart with pericardium, two lungs with pleurae, blood vessels, nerves and lymphatics.
- Rib may be present in relation to cervical seven and lumbar one vertebrae. The cervical rib may give symptoms.
- Ribs are weak at their angles and are vulnerable to injury at that area.
- Apex beat lies below and medial to the normally placed left nipple.

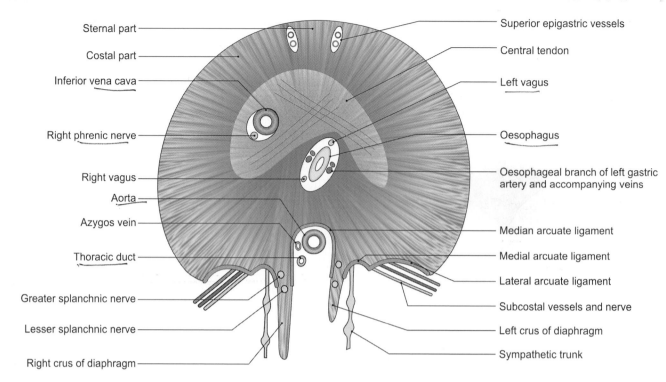

Fig. 12.16: Structures passing through the diaphragm

Labels (left side, top to bottom): Sternal part, Costal part, Inferior vena cava, Right phrenic nerve, Right vagus, Aorta, Azygos vein, Thoracic duct, Greater splanchnic nerve, Lesser splanchnic nerve, Right crus of diaphragm

Labels (right side, top to bottom): Superior epigastric vessels, Central tendon, Left vagus, Oesophagus, Oesophageal branch of left gastric artery and accompanying veins, Median arcuate ligament, Medial arcuate ligament, Lateral arcuate ligament, Subcostal vessels and nerve, Left crus of diaphragm, Sympathetic trunk

Table 12.1: Large openings in thoracoabdominal diaphragm

Opening	Situation	Shape	Structures passing	Effect on contraction
Vena cava *(vein)*	T8, junction of right and median leaflet of central tendon	Quadrilateral	IVC Right phrenic nerve Lymphatic of liver	Dilation
Oesophageal	T10, splitting of right crus	Elliptical	Oesophagus Both vagal trunks Left gastric vessels	Constriction
Aortic *(Artery)*	T12, behind median arcuate ligament	Rounded	Aorta Thoracic duct Azygos vein	No change

- 2nd costal cartilage at the manubriosternal angle is extremely important landmark. The 2nd intercostal space lies below this cartilage and is used for counting the intercostal spaces for the position of heart, lungs and liver.
- 1–7 ribs with costal cartilages reach the sternum, costal cartilages of 8–10 ribs form the costal margin, while 11th and 12th ribs do not reach the front at all.

CLINICOANATOMICAL PROBLEM

A young adult suffering from chronic anaemia was asked to get sternal puncture done to find out the reason for anaemia

- What is sternal puncture/bone marrow biopsy?
- Classify bones according to shape.

Ans: The sternum is single median line bone in the anterior part of the thoracic cage. It is a flat bone. Its upper part, manubrium is wider and comprises two plates of compact bone with intervening cancellous bone. During sternal puncture, a thick needle is pierced through the skin, fascia and anterior plate of compact bone till it reaches the bone marrow in the cancellous bone. About 0.3 c.c of bone marrow is aspirated and slides are prepared immediately to be stained and studied to find out, if the defect is in maturation of RBC or WBC.

Bones are classified as long bone, e.g. humerus; short bone, e.g. tarsal bones; flat bone, e.g. sternum; irregular bone, e.g. vertebra; sesamoid bone, e.g. patella; pneumatic bone, e.g. maxilla.

FREQUENTLY ASKED QUESTIONS

1. Enumerate the landmarks at the level of sternal angle
2. Enumerate various structures passing through the inlet of thorax
3. Write short notes on:
   a. Boundaries of thorax
   b. Cervical rib
   c. Main openings in the thoracoabdominal diaphragm, including their levels and contents
   d. Sternal puncture/bone marrow biopsy
   e. Coarctation of aorta
   f. Enumerate the parts of rib and the joints formed by a typical rib

MULTIPLE CHOICE QUESTIONS

1. Three large openings in the diaphragm are at levels of following thoracic vertebrae:
   a. T8, T9, T10   b. T7, T8, T9
   c. T8, T10, T12   d. T9, T10 T12
2. All the following structures course through the inlet of thorax in the median plane, *except*:
   a. Trachea
   b. Oesophagus
   c. Thymus
   d. Left recurrent laryngeal nerve
3. Suprapleural membrane is attached to:
   a. Anterior aspect of clavicle
   b. Upper border of scapula
   c. Inner margin of 1st rib and its cartilage
   d. Transverse process of 6th cervical vertebra
4. The outlet of thorax is highest in which of the following lines:
   a. Posterior median   b. Anterior median
   c. Midaxillary   d. Scapular line
5. Which spinal nerve is affected in thoracic inlet syndrome?
   a. Seventh cervical
   b. Eighth cervical
   c. First thoracic
   d. Second thoracic

ANSWERS

1. c   2. d   3. c   4. b   5. c

Bones and Joints of Thorax

Vegetarianism, nonviolence and compassion for all beings are fundamental to health, healing and social order
—Rig Veda

INTRODUCTION

The thorax is an osseocartilaginous cavity or cage for various viscera, providing them due support and protection. This cage is not static, but dynamic, as it moves at its various joints, increasing or decreasing the various diameters of the cavity for an extremely important process of respiration, which is life for all of us.

BONES OF THORAX

RIBS OR COSTAE

1 There are 12 ribs on each side forming the greater part of the thoracic skeleton.
   The number may be increased by development of a cervical or a lumbar rib; or the number may be reduced to 11 by the absence of the twelfth rib.

2 The ribs are bony arches arranged one below the other (Fig. 13.1). The gaps between the ribs are called intercostal spaces (*see* Fig. 12.1).
   The spaces are deeper in front than behind, and deeper between the upper than between the lower ribs.

3 The ribs are placed obliquely, the upper ribs being less oblique than the lower. The obliquity reaches its maximum at the ninth rib, and thereafter it gradually decreases to the twelfth rib.

4 The length of the ribs increases from the first to the seventh ribs, and then gradually decreases from the eighth to twelfth ribs.

5 The breadth of the ribs decreases from above downwards. In the upper ten ribs, the anterior ends are broader than the posterior ends.

6 The first 7 ribs which are connected through their cartilages to the sternum are called true ribs, or *vertebrosternal ribs*. The remaining five are false ribs. Out of these the cartilages of the eighth, ninth and tenth ribs are joined to the next higher cartilage and

are known as *vertebrochondral ribs*. The anterior ends of the eleventh and twelfth ribs are free and are called floating ribs or *vertebral ribs*.

7 The first two and last three ribs have special features, and are atypical ribs. The third to ninth ribs are typical ribs.

Typical Ribs

Side Determination

1 The anterior end bears a concave depression. The posterior end bears a head, a neck and a tubercle.

2 The shaft is convex outwards and there is a costal groove situated along the lower part of its inner surface, so that the lower border is thin and the upper border rounded.

Features

Each rib has two ends, anterior and posterior. Its shaft comprises upper and lower borders and outer and inner surfaces.

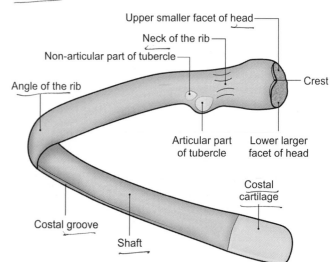

Fig. 13.1: A typical rib of the left side

The *anterior sternal end* is oval and concave for articulation with its costal cartilage.

The *posterior* or *vertebral end* is made up of the following parts.

1 The *head* has two facets that are separated by a crest. The lower larger facet articulates with the body of the numerically corresponding vertebra while the upper smaller facet articulates with the next higher vertebra (Figs 13.2 and 13.20).

2 The *neck* lies in front of the transverse process of its own vertebra, and has two surfaces; anterior and posterior and two borders; superior and inferior. The anterior surface of the neck is smooth. The posterior surface is rough. The superior border or *crest of the neck* is thin. The inferior border is rounded.

3 The *tubercle* is placed on the outer surface of the rib at the junction of the neck and shaft. Its medial part is articular and forms the costotransverse joint with the transverse process of the corresponding vertebra. The lateral part is non-articular (Fig. 13.1).

The *shaft* is flattened so it has two surfaces—outer and inner; and two borders, upper and lower. The shaft is curved with its convexity outwards (Fig. 13.3). It is bent at the *angle* which is situated about 5 cm lateral to the tubercle. It is also twisted at the angle.

1 The *outer surface:* The angle is marked by an oblique line on the outer surface, directed downwards and laterally.

2 The *inner surface* is smooth and covered by the pleura. This surface is marked by a ridge which is continuous behind with the lower border of the neck. The costal groove lies between this ridge and the inferior border. The costal groove contains the posterior intercostal vessels and intercostal nerve (Fig. 13.4).

3 The *upper border* is thick and has outer and inner lips.

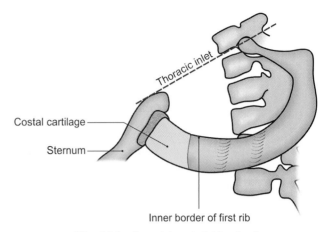

Fig. 13.3: A costal arch (side view)

Attachments and Relations of a Typical Rib

1 Anteriorly, the head provides attachment to the radiate ligament (Fig. 13.5) and is related to the sympathetic chain and to the costal pleura.

2 The crest of the head provides attachment to the intra-articular ligament of the costovertebral joint.

3 Attachments to the neck:
   a. The anterior surface is covered by costal pleura.
   b. The inferior costotransverse ligament is attached to the rough posterior surface (Fig. 13.5).
   c. The two laminae of the superior costotransverse ligament are attached to the crest of the neck (Fig. 13.6).

4 The lateral non-articular part of the *tubercle* gives attachment to the lateral costotransverse ligament (Fig. 13.5).

5 Attachments on the shaft:
   a. The thoracolumbar fascia and the lateral fibres of the sacrospinalis muscle are attached to the angle. Medial to the angle, the *levator costae* and the sacrospinalis (longissimus) are attached (Fig. 13.8). About 5 cm from the anterior end, there is an indistinct oblique line, known as the *anterior angle*, which separates the origins of the *external oblique* from *serratus anterior* in case of fifth to eighth ribs.

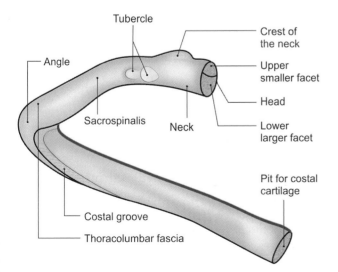

Fig. 13.2: A typical rib viewed obliquely from behind

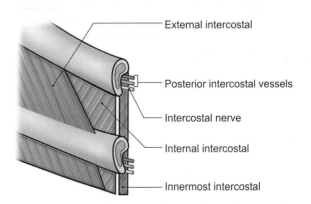

Fig. 13.4: Contents of costal groove and intercostal muscles

Section 2   Thorax

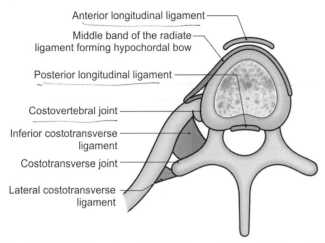

Fig. 13.5: Attachments and articulations of the posterior end of a typical rib

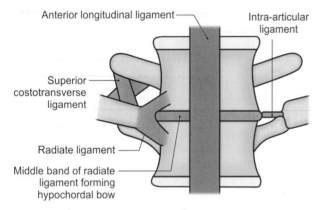

Fig. 13.6: The superior costotransverse, radiate and intra-articular ligaments

The anterior angle also separates the origin of external oblique from that of latissimus dorsi in case of ninth and tenth ribs (Fig. 13.8b).

b. The *internal intercostal* muscle arises from the floor of the costal groove. The *intercostalis intimus* arises from the middle two-fourths of the ridge above the groove (Fig. 13.4). The *subcostalis* is attached to the inner surfaces of the lower ribs.

c. The external intercostal muscle is attached on the outer lip of the upper border, while the internal intercostal and intercostalis intimi are attached on the inner lip of the upper border (Fig. 13.4).

OSSIFICATION OF A TYPICAL RIB

A typical rib ossifies in cartilage from:

a One primary centre (for the shaft) which appears, near the angle, at about the eighth week of intrauterine life.

b Three secondary centres, one for the head and two for the tubercle, which appear at puberty and unite with the rest of the bone after 20 years.

First Rib

Identification

1 It is the shortest, broadest and most curved rib.

2 The shaft is not twisted. There is no costal groove.

3 It is flattened from above downwards so that it has superior and inferior surfaces; outer and inner borders.

Side Determination

1 The anterior end is larger, thicker and pitted. The posterior end is small and rounded.

2 The outer border is convex with no costal groove.

3 The upper surface of the shaft is crossed obliquely by two shallow grooves separated by a ridge. The ridge is enlarged at the inner border of the rib to form the *scalene tubercle* (Fig. 13.7).

When the rib is placed on a horizontal plane, i.e. with the superior surface facing upwards, both the ends of the rib touch the surface.

Features of First Rib

1 The *anterior end* is larger and thicker than that in the other ribs. It is continuous with the first costal cartilage.

2 The *posterior end* comprises the following.
   a. The *head* is small and rounded. It articulates with the body of first thoracic vertebra.
   b. The *neck* is rounded directed laterally, upwards and backwards.
   c. The *tubercle* is large. It coincides with the angle of the rib. It articulates with the transverse process of first thoracic vertebra to form the costotransverse joint.

3 The *shaft (body)* has two surfaces, upper and lower and two borders, outer and inner.
   a. The *upper surface* is marked by two shallow grooves, separated near the inner border by the scalene tubercle.
   b. The *lower surface* is smooth and has no costal groove.
   c. The *outer border* is convex, thick behind and thin in front.
   d. The *inner border* is concave.

Attachments and Relations

1 Anteriorly, the neck is related from medial to lateral side to:
   a. Sympathetic **chain**.
   b. Posterior intercostal **vein**.
   c. Superior intercostal **artery**.
   d. Ventral ramus of first thoracic **nerve** (Fig. 13.7).
   (Mnemonic—**chain** pulling a V**A**N)

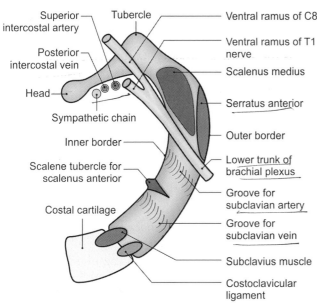

Fig. 13.7: Superior view of the first rib (left side)

2 Superiorly, the neck is related to:
   a. The deep cervical vessels.
   b. The eighth cervical nerve.

3 The anterior groove on the superior surface of the shaft lodges the subclavian vein, and the posterior groove lodges the subclavian artery and the lower trunk of the brachial plexus.

4 The structures attached to the upper surface of the shaft are:
   a. The origin of the subclavius muscle at the anterior end.
   b. The attachment of the costoclavicular ligament at the anterior end behind the subclavius.
   c. The insertion of the scalenus anterior on the scalene tubercle.
   d. The insertion of the scalenus medius on the elongated rough area behind the groove for the subclavian artery.

5 The lower surface of the shaft is covered by costal pleura and is related near its outer border to the small first intercostal nerve which is very small.

6 The outer border gives origin to:
   a. The external intercostal muscle, and
   b. The upper part of the first digitation of the serratus anterior, just behind the groove for the subclavian artery. The thick portion of the outer border is covered by the scalenus posterior.

7 The inner border gives attachment to the suprapleural membrane.

8 The tubercle gives attachment to the lateral costotransverse ligament.

OSSIFICATION

The first rib ossifies from one primary centre for the shaft and only two secondary centres, one for the head and the other for the tubercle. Otherwise its ossification is similar to that of a typical rib.

Second Rib

Features

The features of the second rib are:
1 The length is twice that of the first rib.
2 The shaft is sharply curved, like that of the first rib.
3 The non-articular part of the tubercle is small.
4 The angle is slight and is situated close to the tubercle.
5 The shaft has no twist. The outer surface is convex and faces more upwards than outwards. Near its middle, it is marked by a large rough tubercle. This tubercle is a unique feature of the second rib. The inner surface of the shaft is smooth and concave. It faces more downwards than inwards. There is a short costal groove on the posterior part of this surface.

The posterior part of the upper border has distinct outer and inner lips. The part of the outer lip just in front of the angle is rough.

Attachments

1 The rough tubercle on the outer surface gives origin to 1½ digitations of the serratus anterior muscle.
2 The rough part of the upper border receives the insertion of the scalenus posterior.

Tenth Rib

The tenth rib closely resembles a typical rib, but is:
1 Shorter.
2 Has only a single facet on the head, for the body of the tenth thoracic vertebra.

Eleventh and Twelfth Ribs

Eleventh and twelfth ribs are short. They have pointed ends. The necks and tubercles are absent. The angle and costal groove are poorly marked in the eleventh rib and are absent in the twelfth rib.

Attachment and Relations of the Twelfth Rib

1 The capsular and radiate ligaments are attached to the head of the rib (Fig. 13.6).
2 The following are attached on the inner surface.
   a. The quadratus lumborum is inserted on the lower part of the medial half to two-thirds of this surface (Fig. 13.8a).

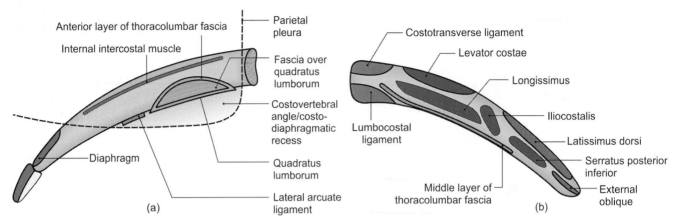

Figs 13.8a and b: The right twelfth rib: (a) Inner surface, and (b) outer surface

b. The fascia covering the quadratus lumborum is also attached to this part of the rib.

c. The internal intercostal muscle is inserted near the upper border.

d. The costodiaphragmatic recess of the pleura is related to the medial three-fourths of the costal surface.

e. The diaphragm takes origin from the anterior end of this surface.

3 The following are attached to the outer surface.

   a. *Attachments on the medial half*

     i. Costotransverse ligament (Fig. 13.8b).

     ii. Lumbocostal ligament

     iii. Lowest levator costae

     iv. Iliocostalis and longissimus parts of sacrospinalis.

   b. *Attachments on the lateral half*

     i. Insertion of serratus posterior inferior

     ii. Origin of latissimus dorsi

     iii. Origin of external oblique muscle of abdomen.

4 The intercostal muscles are attached to the upper border.

5 The structures attached to the lower border are:

   a. Middle layer of thoracolumbar fascia.

   b. Lateral arcuate ligament, at the lateral border of the quadratus lumborum.

   c. Lumbocostal ligament near the head, extending to the transverse process of first lumbar vertebra.

OSSIFICATION

The eleventh and twelfth ribs ossify from one primary centre for the shaft and one secondary centre for the head.

COSTAL CARTILAGES

The costal cartilages represent the unossified anterior parts of the ribs. They are made up of hyaline cartilage.

They contribute materially to the elasticity of the thoracic wall.

The medial ends of the costal cartilages of the first seven ribs are attached directly to the sternum. The eighth, ninth and tenth cartilages articulate with one another and form the costal margin. The cartilages of the eleventh and twelfth ribs are small. Their ends are free and lie in the muscles of the abdominal wall.

The direction of the costal cartilages is variable. As the first costal cartilage approaches the sternum, it descends a little. The second cartilage is horizontal. The third ascends slightly. The remaining costal cartilages are angular. They continue the downward course of the rib for some distance, and then turn upwards to reach either the sternum or the next higher costal cartilage (*see* Fig. 12.1).

Each cartilage has two surfaces, anterior and posterior; two borders, superior and inferior; and two ends, lateral and medial.

Attachments

Anterior Surface

1 Anterior surface of the first costal cartilage articulates with the clavicle and takes part in forming the sternoclavicular joint. It gives attachment to:

   a. The sternoclavicular articular disc (*see* Chapter 10).

   b. The joint capsule of sternoclavicular joint.

   c. The sternoclavicular ligament.

   d. The subclavius muscle (Fig. 13.7).

2 The second to sixth costal cartilages give origin to the pectoralis major (Fig. 13.9).

3 The remaining cartilages are covered by and give partial attachment to some of the flat muscles of the anterior abdominal wall. The internal oblique muscle is attached to the, eighth, ninth and tenth cartilages; and the rectus abdominis to the fifth, sixth and seventh cartilages.

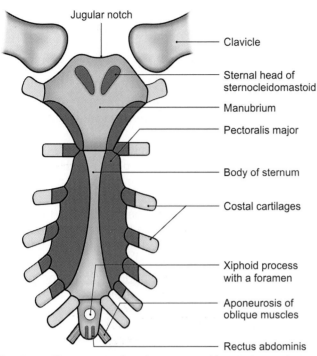

Fig. 13.9: The sternum: Anterior aspect, with muscle attachment

Posterior Surface

1 The first cartilage gives origin to the sternothyroid muscle.
2 The second to sixth cartilages receive the insertion of the sternocostalis (Fig. 13.12).
3 The seventh to twelfth cartilages give attachment to the transversus abdominis and to the diaphragm.

Superior and Inferior Borders

1 The borders give attachment to the internal intercostal muscles and the external intercostal membranes of the spaces concerned (*see* Fig. 14.1).
2 The seventh to tenth cartilages articulate with one another at the points of their maximum convexity, to form synovial joints.

Lateral End

The lateral end of each cartilage forms a primary cartilaginous joint with the rib concerned.

Medial End

1 The first cartilage forms a primary cartilaginous joint with the manubrium.
2 The second to seventh cartilages form synovial joints with the sternum.
3 The eighth, ninth and tenth cartilages are connected to the next higher cartilage by synovial joints.
4 The ends of the eleventh and twelfth cartilages are pointed and free.

CLINICAL ANATOMY

• Weakest area of rib is the region of its angle. This is the commonest site of fracture.
• Cervical rib occurs in 0.5% of persons. It may articulate with first rib or may have a free end. It may cause pressure on lower trunk of brachial plexus, resulting in paraesthesia along the medial border of forearm and wasting of intrinsic muscles of hand (*see* Fig. 12.14). It may also cause pressure on the subclavian artery.
• In rickets, there is inadequate mineralisation of bone matrix at the growth plates due to increased bone resorption. Due to deposition of unmineralised matrix there, is widening of the wrist and rachitic rosary, i.e. prominent costochondral junctions in thoracic cage.

STERNUM

The sternum is a flat bone, forming the anterior median part of the thoracic skeleton. In shape, it resembles a short sword. The upper part, corresponding to the handle, is called the *manubrium*. The middle part, resembling the blade is called the body. The lowest tapering part forming the point of the sword is the *xiphoid process* or xiphisternum.

The sternum is about 17 cm long. It is longer in males than in females (Figs 13.9 to 13.11).

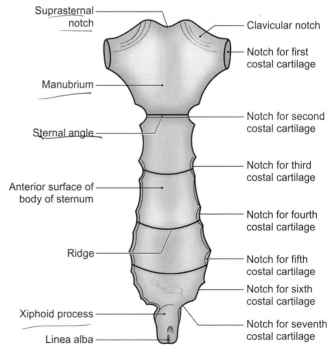

Fig. 13.10: The sternum: Anterior aspect

Thorax

Section 2

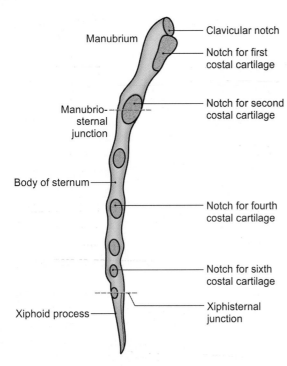

Fig. 13.11: The sternum: Lateral aspect

Manubrium

The manubrium is quadrilateral in shape. It is the thickest and strongest part of the sternum. It has two surfaces, anterior and posterior; and four borders, superior, inferior, and two lateral.

The *anterior surface* is convex from side to side and concave from above downwards (Fig. 13.10).

The *posterior surface* is concave and forms the anterior boundary of the superior mediastinum.

The *superior border* is thick, rounded and concave. It is marked by the suprasternal notch or jugular notch or interclavicular notch in the median part, and by the clavicular notch on each side. The clavicular notch articulates with the medial end of the clavicle to form the sternoclavicular joint (Fig. 13.11).

The *inferior border* forms a secondary cartilaginous joint with the body of the sternum. The manubrium makes a slight angle with the body, convex forwards, called the *sternal angle of Louis*. Events at the sternal angle:

 i. Formation of cardiac plexus
 ii. Upper limit of base of heart
 iii. Arch of aorta starts here as continuation of ascending aorta
 iv. Arch of aorta ends here to continue as descending thoracic aorta
 v. Trachea divides into 2 branches.

The *lateral border* forms a primary cartilaginous joint with the first costal cartilage, and present a demifacet

for synovial articulation with the upper part of the second costal cartilage.

Attachments

1 The anterior surface gives origin on either side to:
   a. The pectoralis major.
   b. The sternal head of the sternocleidomastoid (Fig. 13.9).
2 The posterior surface gives origin to:
   a. The sternohyoid in upper part (Fig. 13.12).
   b. The sternothyroid in lower part.
   c. The lower half of this surface is related to the arch of the aorta. The upper half is related to the left brachiocephalic vein, the brachiocephalic artery, the left common carotid artery and the left subclavian artery. The lateral portions of the surface are related to the corresponding lung and pleura.
3 The suprasternal notch gives attachment to the lower fibres of the interclavicular ligament, and to the two subdivisions of the investing layer of cervical fascia.
4 The margins of each clavicular notch give attachment to the capsule of the corresponding sternoclavicular joint (*see* Chapter 10).

Body of the Sternum

The body is longer, narrower and thinner than the manubrium. It is widest close to its lower end opposite the articulation with the fifth costal cartilage. It has two surfaces, anterior and posterior; two lateral borders; and two ends, upper and lower.

1 The *anterior surface* is nearly flat and directed forwards and slightly upwards. It is marked by three ill-defined transverse ridges, indicating the lines of fusion of the four small segments called *sternebrae*.
2 The *posterior surface* is slightly concave and is marked by less distinct transverse lines.

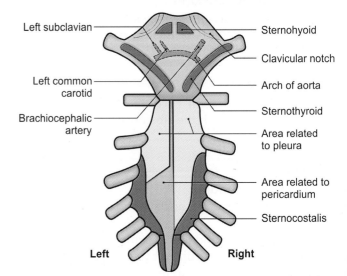

Fig. 13.12: Attachments on the posterior surface of the sternum

3 The lateral borders form synovial joints with the lower part of the second costal cartilage, the third to sixth costal cartilages, and the upper half of the seventh costal cartilage (Fig. 13.11).

4 The upper end forms a secondary cartilaginous joint with the manubrium at the sternal angle.

5 The lower end is narrow and forms a primary cartilaginous joint with the xiphisternum.

Attachments

1 The anterior surface gives origin on either side to the pectoralis major muscle (Fig. 13.9).

2 The lower part of the posterior surface gives origin on either side to the sternocostalis muscle.

3 On the right side of the median plane, the posterior surface is related to the anterior border of the right lung and pleura. On the left side, the upper two pieces of the body are related to the left lung and pleura, and the lower two pieces to the pericardium (Fig. 13.12).

4 Between the facets for articulation with the costal cartilages, the lateral borders provide attachment to the external intercostal membranes and to the internal intercostal muscles (*see* Fig. 14.1).

Xiphoid Process

The xiphoid process is the smallest part of the sternum. It is at first cartilaginous, but in the adult it becomes ossified near its upper end. It varies greatly in shape and may be bifid or perforated. It lies in the floor of the epigastric fossa (Fig. 13.10).

Attachments

1 The anterior surface provides insertion to the medial fibres of the rectus abdominis, and to the aponeuroses of the external and internal oblique muscles of the abdomen.

2 The posterior surface gives origin to the diaphragm. It is related to the anterior surface of the liver.

3 The lateral borders of the xiphoid process give attachment to the aponeuroses of the internal oblique and transversus abdominis muscles.

4 The upper end forms a primary cartilaginous joint with the body of the sternum.

5 The lower end affords attachment to the linea alba.

DEVELOPMENT AND OSSIFICATION

The sternum develops by fusion of two sternal plates formed on either side of the midline. The fusion of the two plates takes place in a craniocaudal direction.

Manubrium is ossified from 2 centers appearing in 5th month. First and second sternebrae ossify from one centre appearing in 5th month. Third and fourth

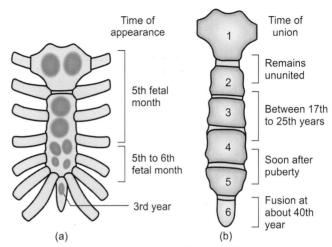

Figs 13.13a and b: Ossification of sternum

sternebrae ossify from paired centres which appear in 5th and 6th months. These fuse with each other from below upwards during puberty. Fusion is complete by 25 years of age. The manubriosternal joint is a secondary cartilaginous joint and usually persists throughout life.

The centre for the xiphoid process appears during the third year or later. It fuses with the body at about 40 years (Figs 13.13a and b).

CLINICAL ANATOMY

- Bone marrow for examination is usually obtained by manubriosternal puncture (Fig. 13.14). It is done in its upper half to prevent injury to arch of aorta which lies behind its lower half.

- The slight movements that take place at the manubriosternal joint are essential for movements of the ribs.

- In the anomaly called 'funnel chest', the sternum is depressed (Fig. 13.15a).

- In another anomaly called 'pigeon chest', there is forward projection of the sternum like the keel of a boat, and flattening of the chest wall on either side (Fig. 13.15b).

- For cardiac surgery, the manubrium and/or body of sternum need to be splitted in midline and the incision is closed with stainless steel wires.

- Sternum is protected from injury by attachment of elastic costal cartilages. Indirect violence may lead to fracture of sternum.

- Non-fusion of the sternal plates causes *ectopia cordis*, where the heart lies uncovered on the surface. Partial fusion of the plates may lead to the formation of *sternal foramina, bifid xiphoid* process, etc. (Fig. 13.9).

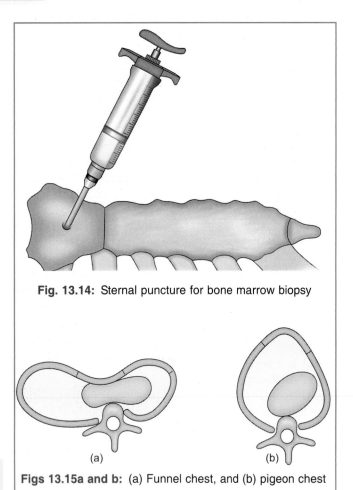

Fig. 13.14: Sternal puncture for bone marrow biopsy

(a)   (b)

Figs 13.15a and b: (a) Funnel chest, and (b) pigeon chest

The vertebral column is made up of 33 vertebrae; seven cervical, twelve thoracic, five lumbar, five sacral and four coccygeal. In the thoracic, lumbar and sacral regions, the number of vertebrae corresponds to the number of spinal nerves, each nerve lying below the corresponding vertebra. In the cervical region, there are eight nerves, the upper seven lying above the corresponding vertebrae and the eighth below the seventh vertebra. In the coccygeal region, there is only one coccygeal nerve.

Sometimes the vertebrae are also grouped according to their mobility. The movable or true vertebrae include the seven cervical, twelve thoracic and five lumbar vertebrae, making a total of 24. Twelve thoracic vertebrae have ribs attached to them. The fixed vertebrae include those of the sacrum and coccyx.

The length of the spine is about 70 cm in males and about 60 cm in females. The intervertebral discs contribute one-fifth of the length of the vertebral column.

As a result of variations in the width of the vertebrae, the vertebral column can be said to be made up of four pyramids (Fig. 13.16a). This arrangement has a functional bearing. The narrowing of the vertebral column at the level of the disc between fourth thoracic and fifth thoracic vertebrae is partly compensated for by the transmission of weight to the lower thoracic region through the sternum and ribs.

Curvatures

In Sagittal Plane

1 *Primary curves* are present at birth due to the shape of the vertebral bodies. The primary curves are thoracic and sacral, both of which are concave forwards.

2 *Secondary curves* are postural and are mainly due to the shape of the intervertebral disc. The secondary

VERTEBRAL COLUMN

Vertebral Column as a Whole

The vertebral column is also called the spine, the spinal column, or back bone. It is the central axis of the body. It supports the body weight and transmits it to the ground through the lower limbs.

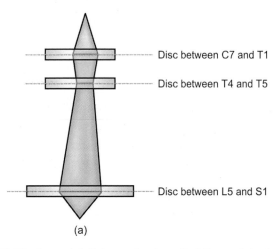

Disc between C7 and T1

Disc between T4 and T5

Disc between L5 and S1

(a)

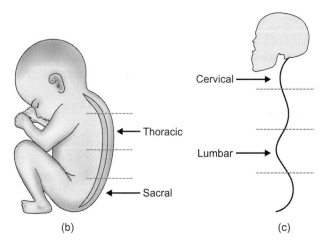

Cervical

Thoracic

Lumbar

Sacral

(b)   (c)

Figs 13.16a to c: (a) Scheme to show that the vertebral column is divisible into a number of pyramidal segments, (b) primary curves, and (c) secondary curves

or compensatory curves are cervical and lumbar, both of which are convex forwards. The cervical curve appears during four to five months after birth when the infant starts supporting its head: The lumbar curve appears during twelve to eighteen months when the child assumes the upright posture (Figs 13.16b and c).

In Coronal Plane *(Lateral Curve)*

There is slight lateral curve in the thoracic region with its concavity towards the left. It is possible due to the greater use of the right upper limb and the pressure of the aorta.

The curvatures add to the elasticity of the spine, and the number of curves gives it a higher resistance to weight than would be afforded by a single curve.

Parts of a Typical Vertebra

A typical vertebra is made up of the following parts:
1 The *body* lies anteriorly. It is shaped like a short cylinder, being rounded from side to side and having flat upper and lower surfaces that are attached to those of adjoining vertebrae by intervertebral discs (Fig. 13.17).
2 The *pedicles,* right and left, are short rounded bars that project backwards, and somewhat laterally, from the posterior aspect of the body.
3 Each pedicle is continuous, posteromedially, with a vertical plate of bone called the *lamina.* The laminae of the two sides pass backwards and medially to meet in the midline. The pedicles and laminae together constitute the *vertebral* or *neural arch.*
4 Bounded anteriorly by the posterior aspect of the body, on the sides by the pedicles, and behind by the lamina, there is a large *vertebral foramen.*
Each vertebral foramen forms a short segment of the vertebral canal that runs through the whole length of the vertebral column and lodges the spinal cord.

5 Passing backwards and usually downwards from the junction of the two laminae, there is the spine or *spinous process* (Fig. 13.18).
6 Passing laterally and usually somewhat downwards from the junction of each pedicle and the corresponding lamina, there is a *transverse process.* The spinous and transverse processes serve as levers for muscles acting on the vertebral column.
From a morphological point of view, the transverse processes are made up of two elements, the transverse element and the costal element. In the thoracic region, the two elements remain separate, and the costal elements form the ribs. In the rest of the vertebral column, the derivatives of costal element are different from those derived from transverse element. This is shown in Table 13.1.
7 Projecting upwards from the junction of the pedicle and the lamina, there is on either side, a *superior articular process;* and projecting downwards there is an *inferior articular process* (Fig. 13.19). Each process bears a smooth articular facet: The superior facet of one vertebra articulates with the inferior facet of the vertebra above it.
8 The pedicle is much narrower in vertical diameter than the body and is attached nearer its upper border.

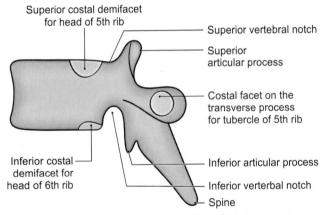

Fig. 13.18: Typical thoracic vertebra (5th), lateral view

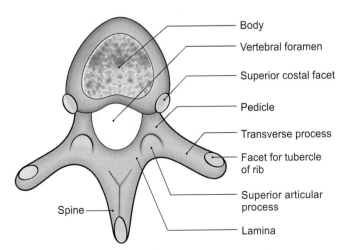

Fig. 13.17: Typical thoracic vertebra, superior aspect

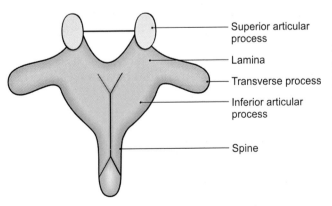

Fig. 13.19: Typical thoracic vertebra, posterior aspect

Section **2**   Thorax

Table 13.1: The transverse and costal elements of the vertebrae

Region	Transverse element	Costal element (Fig. 13.20)
1. Thoracic	Forms the descriptive transverse process	Forms the rib
2. Cervical	Fuses with the costal element and forms the medial part of the posterior wall of the foramen transversarium	1. Anterior wall of foramen transversarium, 2. Anterior tubercle, 3. Costotransverse bar, 4. Posterior tubercle, and 5. Lateral part of the posterior wall of the foramen
3. Lumbar	Forms the accessory process	Forms the real (descriptive) transverse process
4. Sacrum	Fuses with the costal element to form the posterior part of the lateral mass	Forms the anterior part of the lateral mass

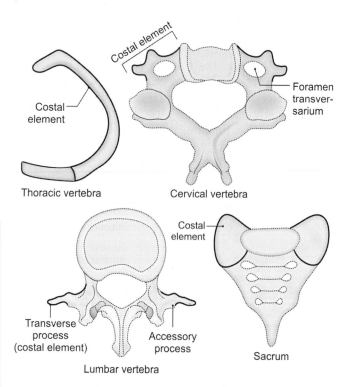

Fig. 13.20: Costal elements in various vertebrae

As a result, there is a large *inferior vertebral notch* below the pedicle. Above the pedicle, there is a much shallower *superior vertebral notch*. The superior and inferior notches of adjoining vertebrae join to form the *intervertebral foramina* which give passage to the dorsal and ventral rami of the spinal nerves emerging from the spinal cord.

Thoracic Vertebrae

Identification

The thoracic vertebrae are identified by the presence of costal facets on the sides of the vertebral bodies. The costal facets may be two or only one on each side (Fig. 13.18).

There are 12 thoracic vertebrae, out of which the second to eighth are typical, and the remaining five (first, ninth, tenth, eleventh and twelfth) are atypical.

Typical Thoracic Vertebrae

1 The body is heart-shaped with roughly the same measurements from side to side and anteroposteriorly. On each side, it bears two costal demifacets. The *superior costal demifacet* is larger and placed on the upper border of the body near the pedicle. It articulates with the head of the numerically corresponding rib. The *inferior costal demifacet* is smaller and placed on the lower border in front of the inferior vertebral notch. It articulates with the next lower rib (Fig. 13.18).

2 *The vertebral foramen* is comparatively small and circular.

3 *The vertebral arch shows:*

a. The *pedicles* are directed straight backwards. The superior vertebral notch is shallow, while the inferior vertebral notch is deep and conspicuous.

b. The *laminae* overlap each other from above.

c. The *superior articular processes* project upwards from the junction of the pedicles and laminae. The articular facets are flat and are directed backwards. This direction permits rotatory movements of the spine.

d. The *inferior articular processes* are fused to the laminae. Their articular facets are directed forwards.

e. The *transverse processes* are large, and are directed laterally and backwards from the junction of the pedicles and laminae. The anterior surface of each process bears a facet near its tip, for articulation with the tubercle of the corresponding rib. In the upper six vertebrae, the costal facets on the transverse processes are concave, and face forwards and laterally. In lower four, the facets are flat and face upwards, laterally and slightly forwards (Fig. 13.24). In the last two vertebrae, the articular facets are absent (*see* costotransverse joints below).

f. The *spine* is long, and is directed downwards and backwards. The fifth to ninth spines are the longest, more vertical and overlap each other. The upper and lower spines are less oblique in direction.

Attachments

1. The upper and lower borders of the body give attachment, in front and behind respectively to the *anterior and posterior longitudinal ligaments* (Fig. 13.5).
2. The upper borders and lower parts of the anterior surfaces of the laminae provide attachment to the *ligamenta flava*.
3. The transverse process gives attachment to:
   a. The *lateral costotransverse ligament* at the tip.
   b. The *superior costotransverse ligament* along the lower border.
   c. The *inferior costotransverse ligament* along the anterior surface.
   d. The *intertransverse ligaments* and muscles to upper and lower borders.
   e. The *levator costae* on the posterior surface.
4. The spines give attachment to the *supraspinous* and *interspinous ligaments*. They also give attachment to several muscles including the trapezius, the rhomboids, the latissimus dorsi, the serratus posterior superior and the serratus posterior inferior, and many deep muscles of the back.

First Thoracic Vertebra

1. The body of this vertebra resembles that of a cervical vertebra. It is broad and not heart-shaped. Its upper surface is lipped laterally and bevelled anteriorly. The superior costal facet on the body is complete (Fig. 13.21). It articulates with the head of the first rib. The inferior costal facet is a 'demifacet' for the second rib.
2. The spine is thick, long and nearly horizontal.
3. The superior vertebral notches are well marked, as in cervical vertebrae.
4. Facet on transverse process is concave on T1–T6 vertebrae.

Ninth Thoracic Vertebra

The ninth thoracic vertebra resembles a typical thoracic vertebra except that the body has only the superior costal demifacets. The inferior costal facets are absent (Fig. 13.21). Facet on transverse process is flat on T7–T10 vertebrae.

Tenth Thoracic Vertebra

The tenth thoracic vertebra resembles a typical thoracic vertebra except that the body has a single complete

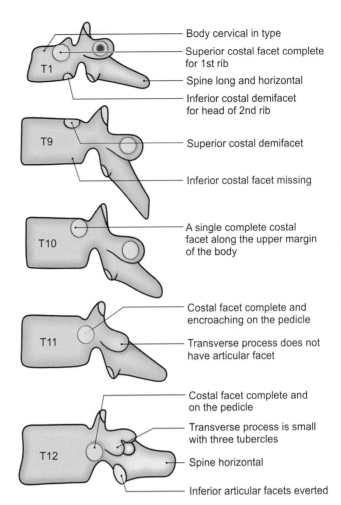

Body cervical in type

Superior costal facet complete for 1st rib

Spine long and horizontal

Inferior costal demifacet for head of 2nd rib

Superior costal demifacet

Inferior costal facet missing

A single complete costal facet along the upper margin of the body

Costal facet complete and encroaching on the pedicle

Transverse process does not have articular facet

Costal facet complete and on the pedicle

Transverse process is small with three tubercles

Spine horizontal

Inferior articular facets everted

Fig. 13.21: Features of atypical thoracic vertebrae

superior costal facet on each side, extending onto the root of the pedicle (Fig. 13.21).

Eleventh Thoracic Vertebra

1. The body has a single large costal facet on each side, extending onto the upper part of the pedicle (Fig. 13.21).
2. The transverse process is small, and has no articular facet.
   Sometimes it is difficult to differentiate between tenth and eleventh thoracic vertebrae.

Twelfth Thoracic Vertebra

1. The shapes of the body, pedicles, transverse processes and spine are similar to those of a lumbar vertebra. However, the body bears a single costal facet on each side, which lies more on the lower part of the pedicle than on the body.
2. The transverse process is small and has no facet, but has superior, inferior and lateral tubercles (Fig. 13.21).
3. The inferior articular facets are lumbar in type. These are everted and are directed laterally, but the superior articular facets are thoracic in type.

OSSIFICATION

The ossification of thoracic vertebra and typical vertebra is similar. It ossifies in cartilage from three primary and five secondary centres.

The three primary centres—one for the centrum and one for each half of the neural arch, appear during eighth to ninth week of fetal life. At birth, the vertebra consists of three parts, the centrum and two halves of the neural arch. The two halves of the neural arch fuse posteriorly during the first year of life. The neural arch is joined with the centrum by the *neurocentral synchondrosis*. Bony fusion occurs here during the third to sixth years of life.

Five secondary centres—one for the upper surface and one for the lower surface of the body, one for each transverse process, and one for the spine appear at about the 15th year and fuse with the rest of the vertebra at about the 25th year (Fig. 13.22).

CLINICAL ANATOMY

- Failure of fusion of the two halves of the neural arch results in 'spina bifida'. Sometimes the body ossifies from two primary centres, and if one centre fails to develop, one half, right or left of the body is missing. This results in a hemivertebra and lateral bend in the vertebral column or scoliosis.

- In young adults, the discs are very strong. However, after the second decade of life, degenerative changes set in resulting in weakness of the annulus fibrosus. When such a disc is subjected to strain, the annulus fibrosus may rupture leading to prolapse of the nucleus pulposus. This is commonly referred to as *disc prolapse*. It may occur even after a minor strain. In addition to prolapse of the nucleus pulposus,

internal derangements of the disc may also take place.

- Disc prolapse is usually posterolateral. The prolapsed nucleus pulposus presses upon adjacent nerve roots and gives rise to pain that radiates along the distribution of the nerve. Such pain along the course of the sciatic nerve is called *sciatica*. Motor effects, with loss of power and reflexes, may follow. Disc prolapse occurs most frequently in the lower lumbar region (Fig. 13.23). It is also common in the lower cervical region from fifth to seventh cervical vertebrae.

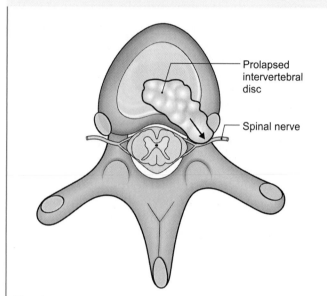

Prolapsed intervertebral disc

Spinal nerve

Fig. 13.23: Disc prolapse causing pressure on the spinal nerve

JOINTS OF THORAX

Manubriosternal Joint

Manubriosternal joint is a secondary cartilaginous joint. It permits slight movements of the body of the sternum on the manubrium during respiration.

Costovertebral Joints

The head of a typical rib articulates with its own vertebra, and also with the body of the next higher vertebra, to form two plane synovial joints separated by an intra-articular ligament (Fig. 13.6). This ligament is attached to the ridge on the head of the rib and to the intervertebral disc.

Other ligaments of the joint include a capsular ligament and a triradiate ligament. The middle band of the triradiate ligament forms the hypochordal bow (Fig. 13.5), uniting the joints of the two sides.

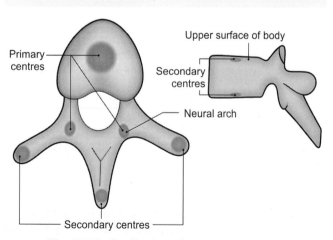

Primary centres

Upper surface of body

Secondary centres

Neural arch

Secondary centres

Fig. 13.22: Ossification of a thoracic vertebra

Costotransverse Joints

The tubercle of a typical rib articulates with the facet on anterior surface of transverse process of the corresponding vertebra to form a synovial joint.

The capsular ligament is strengthened by three costotransverse ligaments. The superior costotransverse ligament has two laminae which extend from the crest on the neck of the rib to the transverse process of the vertebra above. The inferior costotransverse ligament passes from the posterior surface of the neck to the transverse process of its own vertebra. The lateral costo-transverse ligament connects the lateral non-articular part of the tubercle to the tip of the transverse process of its own vertebra.

The articular facets on the tubercles of the upper six ribs are convex, and permit rotation of the neck of the rib for *pump-handle movements* (Fig. 13.24). Rotation of rib-neck backwards causes elevation of second to sixth ribs with moving forwards and upwards of the sternum. This increases the anteroposterior diameter of the thorax (Fig. 13.25).

The articular surfaces of the seventh to tenth ribs are flat, permitting up and down gliding movements or bucket-handle movements of the lower ribs. When the neck of seventh to tenth ribs moves upwards, backwards and medially, the result is increase in infrasternal angle. This causes increase in transverse diameter of thorax (Fig. 13.26).

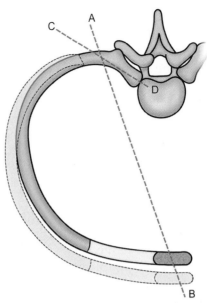

Fig. 13.25: The axes of movement (AB and CD) of a vertebrosternal rib. The interrupted lines indicate the position of the rib in inspiration

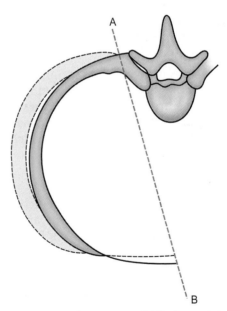

Fig. 13.26: The axes of movement (AB) of a vertebrochondral rib. The interrupted lines indicate the position of the rib in inspiration

For explanation of the terms 'pump-handle' and 'bucket-handle' movements, *see* 'Respiratory Movements'.

Costochondral Joints

Each rib is continuous anteriorly with its cartilage, to form a primary cartilaginous joint. No movements are permitted at these joints.

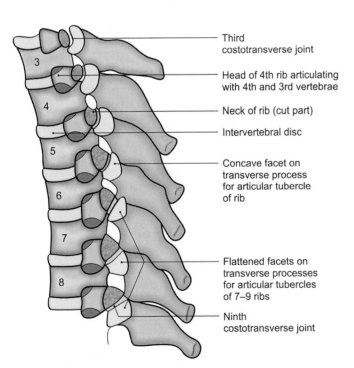

Third costotransverse joint

Head of 4th rib articulating with 4th and 3rd vertebrae

Neck of rib (cut part)

Intervertebral disc

Concave facet on transverse process for articular tubercle of rib

Flattened facets on transverse processes for articular tubercles of 7–9 ribs

Ninth costotransverse joint

Fig. 13.24: A section through the costotransverse joints from the third to the ninth inclusive. Contrast the concave facets on the upper with the flattened facets on the lower transverse processes

Chondrosternal Joints

The first chondrosternal joint is a primary cartilaginous joint, it does not permit any movement. This helps in the stability of the shoulder girdle and of the upper limb.

The second to seventh costal cartilages articulate with the sternum by synovial joints. Each joint has a single cavity except in the second joint where the cavity is divided in two parts. The joints are held together by the capsular and radiate ligaments.

Interchondral Joints

The fifth to ninth costal cartilages articulate with one another by synovial joints. The tenth cartilage is united to the ninth by fibrous tissue.

The movements taking place at the various joints described above are considered under 'Respiratory Movements'.

Intervertebral Joints

Adjoining vertebrae are connected to each other at five joints. There is a median joint between the vertebral bodies, and four joints—two on the right side and two on the left side—between the articular processes.

The joints between the articular processes are plane synovial joints.

The joint between the vertebral bodies is a symphysis (secondary cartilaginous joint). The surfaces of the vertebral bodies are lined by thin layers of hyaline cartilage. Between these layers of hyaline cartilage, there is a thick plate of fibrocartilage which is called the intervertebral disc.

Intervertebral Discs

These are fibrocartilaginous discs which intervene between the bodies of adjacent vertebrae, and bind them together. Their shape corresponds to that of the vertebral bodies between which they are placed. The thickness of the disc varies in different regions of the vertebral column, and in different parts of the same disc. In the cervical and lumbar regions, the discs are thicker in front than behind, while in the thoracic region they are of uniform thickness. The discs are thinnest in the upper thoracic region, and thickest in the lumbar region.

The discs contribute about one-fifth of the length of the vertebral column. The contribution is greater in the cervical and lumbar regions than in the thoracic region.

Each disc is made up of the following two parts.

1 The *nucleus pulposus* is the central part of the disc. It is soft and gelatinous at birth. It is kept under tension and acts as a hydraulic shock absorber. With advancing age, the elasticity of the disc is much reduced (Figs 13.27a and c).

2 The *annulus fibrosus* forms the peripheral part of the disc. It is made up of a narrower outer zone of collagenous fibres and a wider inner zone of fibrocartilage. The fibres form laminae that are arranged in the form of incomplete rings. The rings are connected by strong fibrous bands. The outer collagenous fibres blend with the anterior and posterior longitudinal ligaments (Figs 13.27a to c).

Functions

1 The intervertebral discs give shape to the vertebral column.
2 They act as a remarkable series of shock absorbers or buffers.
3 Because of their elasticity, they allow slight movement of vertebral bodies on each other, more so in the cervical and lumbar regions. When the slight movements at individual discs are added together, they become considerable.

Ligaments Connecting Adjacent Vertebrae

Apart from the intervertebral discs and the capsules around the joints between the articular processes, adjacent vertebrae are connected by several ligaments which are as follows.

1 The *anterior longitudinal ligament* passes from the anterior surface of the body of one vertebra to another. Its upper end reaches the basilar part of the occipital bone (Fig. 13.5).
2 The *posterior longitudinal ligament* is present on the posterior surface of the vertebral bodies within the

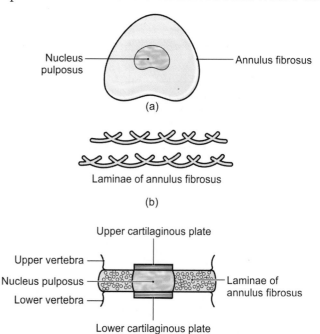

Figs 13.27a to c: Structure of an intervertebral disc. (a) Superior view, (b) arrangement of laminae, and (c) vertical section

vertebral canal. Its upper end reaches the body of the axis vertebra (C2) beyond which it is continuous with the *membrana tectoria* (Fig. 13.5).

3 The *intertransverse ligaments* connect adjacent transverse processes.

4 The *interspinous ligaments* connect adjacent spines.

5 The *supraspinous ligaments* connect the tips of the spines of vertebrae from the seventh cervical to the sacrum. In the cervical region, they are replaced by the ligamentum nuchae.

6 The *ligamenta flava* (singular = ligamentum flavum) connect the laminae of adjacent vertebrae. They are made up mainly of elastic tissue.

Movements of the Vertebral Column

Movements between adjacent vertebrae occur simultaneously at all the joints connecting them. Movement between any two vertebrae is slight. However, when the movements between several vertebrae are added together the total range of movement becomes considerable. The movements are those of flexion, extension, lateral flexion and a certain amount of rotation. The range of movement differs in different parts of the vertebral·column. This is influenced by the thickness and flexibility of the intervertebral discs and by the orientation of the articular facets.

Flexion and extension occur freely in the cervical and lumbar regions, but not in the thoracic region. Rotation is free in the thoracic region, and restricted in the lumbar and cervical regions.

RESPIRATORY MOVEMENTS

Introduction

The lungs expand during inspiration and retract during expiration. These movements are governed by the following two factors.

1 Alterations in the capacity of the thorax are brought about by movements of the thoracic wall. Increase in volume of the thoracic cavity creates a negative intrathoracic pressure which sucks air into the lungs. Movements of the thoracic wall occur chiefly at the costovertebral and manubriosternal joints.

2 Elastic recoil of the pulmonary alveoli and of the thoracic wall expels air from the lungs during expiration.

Principles of Movements

1 Each rib may be regarded as a lever, the fulcrum of which lies just lateral to the tubercle. Because of the disproportion in the length of the two arms of the lever, the slight movements at the vertebral end of the rib are greatly magnified at the anterior end (Fig. 13.28).

2 The anterior end of the rib is lower than the posterior end. Therefore, during elevation of the rib, the anterior end also moves forwards. This occurs mostly in the vertebrosternal ribs. Along with the up and down movements of the second to sixth ribs, the body of the sternum also moves up and down called *pump-handle movements* (Fig. 13.29). In this way, the anteroposterior diameter of the thorax is increased.

3 The middle of the shaft of the rib lies at a lower level than the plane passing through the two ends. Therefore, during elevation of the rib, the shaft also moves outwards. This causes increase in the transverse diameter of the thorax.

Such movements occur in the vertebrochondral ribs, and are called *bucket-handle movements*.

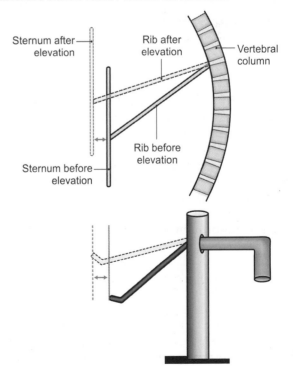

Fig. 13.29: Diagram showing how 'pump-handle' movements of the sternum bring about an increase in the anteroposterior diameter of the thorax

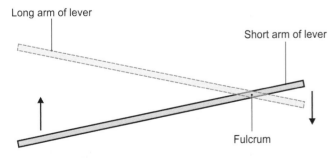

Fig. 13.28: Diagram comparing a rib to a lever

Section 2 Thorax

4 The thorax resembles a cone, tapering upwards. As a result, each rib is longer than the next higher rib. On elevation, the larger lower rib comes to occupy the position of the smaller upper rib which pushes sternum forwards. This also increases the transverse diameter of the thorax (Fig. 13.30).

5 Vertical diameter is increased by the "piston movements" of the thoracoabdominal diaphragm (Fig. 13.31).

Summary of the Factors Producing Increase in Diameters of the Thorax

The anteroposterior diameter is increased:

1 Mainly by the *pump-handle* movements of the sternum brought about by elevation of the vertebrosternal second to sixth ribs.

2 Partly by elevation of the seventh to tenth vertebrochondral ribs.

The transverse diameter is increased:

1 Mainly by the *bucket-handle* movements of the seventh to tenth vertebrochondral ribs.

2 Partly by elevation of the second to sixth vertebrosternal ribs.

The vertical diameter is increased by descent of the diaphragm as it contracts. This is called *piston mechanism*. During inspiration, the diaphragm contracts and it comes down by 2 cm. It is aided by relaxation of muscles of anterior abdominal wall. During expiration, abdominal muscles contract and diaphragm is pushed

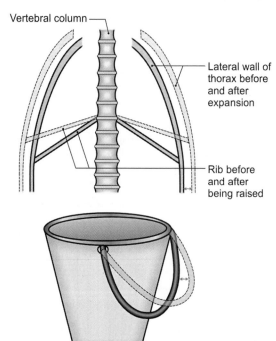

Fig. 13.30: Scheme showing how 'bucket-handle' movements of the vertebrochondral ribs bring about an increase in the transverse diameter of the thorax

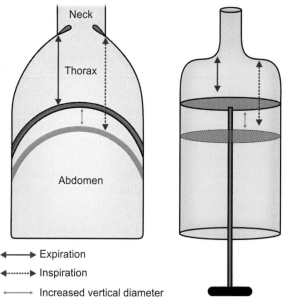

→ Expiration
◀┄┄┄▶ Inspiration
◀── Increased vertical diameter

Fig. 13.31: Scheme showing how piston movements of thoracoabdominal diaphragm bring about an increase in the vertical diameter of the thorax

upwards. It facilitates in inspiration of at least 400 ml of air during each contraction.

In females, respiration is thoracoabdominal and in males it is abdominothoracic type.

Respiratory Muscles

For inspiration—diaphragm, external intercostal muscle and interchondral part of internal intercostal of contralateral side.

Deep inspiration—erector spinae, scalene muscles, pectoral muscles.

For expiration—passive process.

Forced expiration—muscles of anterior abdominal wall.

Respiratory Movements during Different Types of Breathing

Inspiration

1 *Quiet inspiration*
   a. The anteroposterior diameter of the thorax is increased by elevation of the second to sixth ribs. The first rib remains fixed.
   b. The transverse diameter is increased by elevation of the seventh to tenth ribs.
   c. The vertical diameter is increased by descent of the diaphragm.

2 *Deep inspiration*
   a. Movements during quiet inspiration are increased.
   b. The first rib is elevated directly by the scaleni, and indirectly by the sternocleidomastoid.
   c. The concavity of the thoracic spine is reduced by the erector spinae.

3 *Forced inspiration*

  a. All the movements described are exaggerated.

  b. The scapulae are elevated and fixed by the trapezius, the levator scapulae and the rhomboids, so that the serratus anterior and the pectoralis minor muscles may act on the ribs.

  c. The action of the erector spinae is appreciably increased.

Expiration

1 *Quiet expiration:* The air is expelled mainly by the elastic recoil of the chest wall and pulmonary alveoli, and partly by the tone of the abdominal muscles.

2 *Deep and forced expiration:* Deep and forced expiration is brought about by strong contraction of the abdominal muscles and of the latissimus dorsi.

CLINICAL ANATOMY

- In dyspnoea or difficulty in breathing, the patients are most comfortable on sitting up, leaning forwards and fixing the arms. In the sitting posture, the position of diaphragm is the lowest allowing maximum ventilation. Fixation of the arms fixes the scapulae, so that the serratus anterior and pectoralis minor may act on the ribs to good advantage.

- The height of the diaphragm in the thorax is variable according to the position of the body and tone of the abdominal muscles. It is highest on lying supine, so the patient is extremely uncomfortable, as he/she needs to exert immensely for inspiration. The diaphragm is lowest while sitting. The patient is quite comfortable as the effort required for inspiration is the least.

The diaphragm is midway in position while standing, but the patient is too ill or exhausted to stand. So dyspnoeic patients feel comfortable while sitting (Figs 13.32a to c).

- Most prominent role in respiration is played by diaphragm.

- Respiration occurs in two phases:
  Inspiration—active phase of 1 second
  Expiration—passive phase of 3 second.

- In young children (up to 2 yrs of age), the thoracic cavity is almost circular in cross-section so the scope for anteroposterior or side to side expansion is limited. The type of respiration in children is abdominal.

- In women of advanced stage of pregnancy, descent of diaphragm is limited, so the type of respiration in them is mainly thoracic.

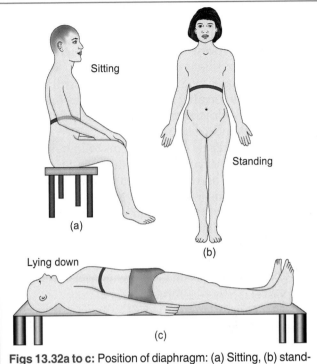

Sitting

Standing

Lying down

(a)

(b)

(c)

Figs 13.32a to c: Position of diaphragm: (a) Sitting, (b) standing, and (c) lying down

---

Mnemonics

Structures in costal groove VAN from above downwards

Posterior intercostal **v**ein
Posterior intercostal **a**rtery
Intercostal **n**erve

Structures on neck of 1st rib, sympathetic trunk and VAN from medial to lateral side

Posterior intercostal **v**ein
Superior intercostal **a**rtery
1st thoracic **n**erve

Vertebrae: Recognising a Thoracic from Lumbar

- Presence of costal facets on the sides of the body and transverse process
- Shape of the vertebral body
  – Thoracic is heart-shaped body (since your heart is in your thorax).
  – Lumbar is kidney-/bean-shaped body (since kidneys are in lumbar area)
- Spine is long and oblique

FACTS TO REMEMBER

- Sternum forms joints with its own parts:
  – One manubriosternal joint—secondary cartilaginous.
  – Three joints between sternebrae—primary cartilaginous.

Section 2 Thorax

- One joint between sternum and xiphoid process—primary cartilaginous.
- Sternum forms 2 joints with clavicles of the 2 sides, saddle type of synovial joint
- It articulates with 1st–7th costal cartilages on each side forming a total of 14 joints—all plane synovial joints except 1st chondrosternal which is synchondrosis.
- A typical thoracic vertebra forms following joints:
  - Body of one vertebrae with body of vertebra above and body of vertebra below—secondary cartilaginous joint (2 joints).
  - Lower larger part of head of corresponding rib for the demifacet along the upper border of the body on each side (2 joints).
  - Upper smaller part of head of a lower rib for the demifacet along the lower border of the body on each side (2 joints).
  - Superior articular processes on each side with the inferior articular processes of the vertebra above (2 joints).
  - Inferior articular processes on each side with the superior articular processes of the vertebra below (2 joints).
  - Transverse process of the vertebra with the articular part of the tubercle of the rib on each side (2 joints).
  - Body of the vertebra with the pedicle of the vertebra on each side. These are primary cartilaginous joints (2 joints).

  Thus there are 14 joints which a typical thoracic vertebra makes.

  2 secondary cartilaginous joints
  2 primary cartilaginous joints
  10 plane joints of synovial variety
- *The ribs are arched bones. Joints formed by a typical rib are:*
  - Posterior end or head of a typical rib articulates with two adjacent vertebrae, corresponding one and one above it and the intervening intervertebral disc.
  - The articular part of the tubercle articulates with transverse process of corresponding vertebra
  - The anterior part of the shaft of rib continues as the costal cartilage. It is primary cartilaginous joint.
  - A costal cartilage forms plane synovial joint with the side of sternum.
- Respiratory movements produced by movements of thoracoabdominal diaphragm are called "abdominal respiration".
- Respiratory movements produced by movements of intercostal muscles are called "thoracic respiration".

CLINICOANATOMICAL PROBLEM

During 'pranayama', deep regulated and smooth breathing occurs.
- Which diameters increase during deep breathing?

Ans: The anteroposterior diameter increases by "pump-handle movement" of the sternum.

The transverse diameter increases by the "bucket-handle movement" of the 7–10 ribs.

The vertical diameter increases by "piston movement" of the thoracoabdominal diaphragm. During inspiration, the vertical diameter is increases by 3–5 cm and during expiration, the vertical diameter decreases.

Principles of movements

1 Each rib may be regarded as a lever, the fulcrum of which lies just lateral to the tubercle. Because of the disproportion in the length of the two arms of the lever, the slight movements at the vertebral end of the rib are greatly magnified at the anterior end (Fig. 13.28).

2 The anterior end of the rib is lower than the posterior end. Therefore, during elevation of the rib, the anterior end also moves forwards. This occurs mostly in the vertebrosternal ribs.

  In this way, the anteroposterior diameter of the thorax is increased. Along with the up and down movements of the second to sixth ribs, the body of the sternum also moves up and down called 'pump-handle movements' (Fig. 13.29).

3 The middle of the shaft of the rib lies at a lower level than the plane passing through the two ends. Therefore, during elevation of the rib, the shaft also moves outwards. This causes increase in the transverse diameter of the thorax.

  Such movements occur in the vertebrochondral ribs, and are called 'bucket-handle movements'.

4 The thorax resembles a cone, tapering upwards. As a result, each rib is longer than the next higher rib. On elevation, the larger lower rib comes to occupy the position of the smaller upper rib. This also increases the transverse diameter of the thorax (Fig. 13.30).

5 Contraction of the diaphragm with relaxation of anterior abdominal wall muscles increases the vertical diameter. Up and down movements as a result of contraction and relaxation of thoracoabdominal diaphragm can alter the vertical diameter of the thoracic cavity. This movement is called "piston movement".

FREQUENTLY ASKED QUESTIONS

1. Enumerate the parts of a rib and the joints formed by a typical rib.
   a. Name the structures related to the neck of first rib
   b. Enumerate the joints formed by the manubrium, and by sternum with the costal cartilages
   c. Which area of sternum is related to the pericardium
   d. When do the secondary curvatures appear in the vertebral column
   e. Name the joints formed by typical thoracic vertebra

2. Give an account of the various respiratory movements. Name the muscles responsible for inspiratory and expiratory movements.

MULTIPLE CHOICE QUESTIONS

1. Transverse diameter of thoracic cage increases by:
   a. Pump-handle movement of ribs
   b. Bucket-handle movement of ribs
   c. Caliper movement of ribs
   d. Contraction of diaphragm

2. Anteroposterior diameter of thorax increases by:
   a. Pump-handle movement of ribs
   b. Bucket-handle movement of ribs
   c. Contraction of diaphragm
   d. Relaxation of diaphragm

3. Which one out of the following is a primary cartilaginous joint?
   a. Costovertebral
   b. Costotransverse
   c. First costochondral
   d. Manubriosternal

4. Which of the following ribs articulates with one vertebra only?
   a. First
   b. Second
   c. Third
   d. Fourth

5. The tubercle of a typical rib articulates with the facet on the transverse process of:
   a. Vertebra above
   b. Vertebra below
   c. Its own vertebra
   d. All of the above

6. Which of the following ribs articulates with transverse process of a thoracic vertebra?
   a. Eleventh
   b. Twelfth
   c. First
   d. None of the above

7. The most characteristic feature of the thoracic vertebrae is:
   a. The body is heart-shaped
   b. The spine is oblique
   c. The body has costal facets
   d. Vertebral foramen is small and circular

8. The lower larger facet on the head of a typical rib articulates with the demifacet on:
   a. Inferior part of corresponding vertebrae
   b. Superior part of corresponding vertebrae
   c. Inferior part of vertebra above the corresponding vertebrae
   d. Superior part of vertebra below the corresponding vertebrae

ANSWERS

1. b	2. a	3. c	4. a	5. c	6. c	7. c	8. b

Wall of Thorax

Internal thoracic arteries are being used for cardiac bypass.

INTRODUCTION

The thorax is covered by muscles of pectoral region of upper limb. In addition, the intercostal muscles and membranes fill up the gaps between adjacent ribs and cartilages. These muscles provide integrity to the thoracic wall. A right and left pair of thoracic nerves fulfil the exact definition of the dermatome.

The posterior intercostal vein, posterior intercostal artery and intercostal nerve (VAN) lie from above downwards in the costal groove of the ribs.

Sympathetic part of autonomic nervous system starts from the lateral horns of thoracic 1 to thoracic 12 segments of the spinal cord. It continues up to lumbar 2 segment.

Coverings of the Thoracic Wall

The thoracic wall is covered from outside to inside by the following structures—skin, superficial fascia, deep fascia, and extrinsic muscles. The extrinsic muscles covering the thorax are as follows.

Muscles of the Upper Limb

1 Pectoralis major
2 Trapezius
3 Serratus anterior
4 Pectoralis minor
5 Latissimus dorsi
6 Levator scapulae
7 Rhomboid major
8 Rhomboid minor
9 Serratus posterior superior
10 Serratus posterior inferior

Muscles of the Abdomen

1 Rectus abdominis.
2 External oblique.

Muscles of the Back

Erector spinae (sacrospinalis).

In addition to the muscles listed above, a number of other muscles of the abdomen and of the head and neck are attached to the margins of the two apertures of the thorax.

THORACIC WALL PROPER

DISSECTION

Detach the serratus anterior and the pectoralis major muscles from the upper ribs. Note the external intercostal muscle in the second and third intercostal spaces. Its fibres run anteroinferiorly. Follow it forwards to the external intercostal membrane which replaces it between the costal cartilages (Figs 14.1 and 14.2).

Cut the external intercostal membrane and muscle along the lower border of two spaces. Reflect them upwards to expose the internal intercostal muscle. The direction of its fibres is posteroinferior, at right angle to that of external oblique.

Follow the lateral cutaneous branch of one intercostal nerve to its trunk deep to internal intercostal muscle. Trace the nerve and accompanying vessels round the thoracic wall. Note their collateral branches lying along the upper margin of the rib below. Trace the muscular branches of the trunk of intercostal nerve and its collateral branch. Trace the anterior cutaneous nerve as well (Fig. 14.3).

Identify the deepest muscle in the intercostal space, the innermost intercostal muscle (Table 14.1). This muscle is deficient in the anterior and posterior ends of the intercostal spaces, where the neurovascular bundle rests directly on the parietal pleura.

Expose the internal thoracic artery 1 cm from the lateral margin of sternum by carefully removing the intercostal muscles and membranes from the upper three intercostal spaces (Fig. 14.11).

Trace the artery through the upper six intercostal spaces and identify its two terminal branches (*see* Fig. 21.7). Trace its venae comitantes upwards till third costal cartilage where these join to form internal thoracic vein, which drains into the brachiocephalic vein.

Follow the course and branches of both anterior and posterior intercostal arteries including the course and tributaries of azygos vein.

Features

The thoracic cage forms the skeletal framework of the wall of the thorax. The gaps between the ribs are called *intercostal spaces*. They are filled by the intercostal muscles and contain the intercostal nerves, vessels and lymphatics. There are nine intercostal spaces anteriorly and eleven intercostal spaces posteriorly.

Intercostal Muscles

These are:
1 The external intercostal muscle.
2 The internal intercostal muscle.
    Each comprises intercartilaginous in front and interosseous in posterolateral part.
3 The transversus thoracis muscle which is divisible into three parts, namely the subcostalis, the intercostalis intimi (innermost intercostal) and the sternocostalis. The attachments of these muscles are given in Table 14.1.

Extent

The *external intercostal muscle* extends from the tubercle of the rib posteriorly to the costochondral junction anteriorly. Between the costochondral junction and the sternum, it is replaced by the external or *anterior*

intercostal membrane. The posterior end of the muscle is continuous with the posterior fibres of the *superior costotransverse ligament* (Fig. 14.1).

The *internal intercostal muscle* extends from the lateral border of the sternum to the angle of the rib. Beyond the angle, it becomes continuous with the *internal or posterior intercostal membrane*, which is continuous with the anterior fibres of the *superior costotransverse ligament*.

The subcostalis is confined to the posterior part of the lower intercostal spaces only.

The intercostalis intimi is confined to the middle two-fourths of all the intercostal spaces (Fig. 14.4).

The sternocostalis is present in relation to the anterior parts of the upper intercostal spaces (*see* Fig. 13.2 and 14.4).

Direction of Fibres

In the anterior part of the intercostal space:
1 The fibres of the external intercostal muscle run downwards, forwards and medially in front.

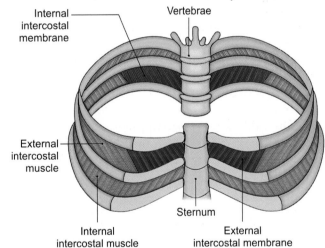

Fig. 14.1: External and internal intercostal muscles with external and internal intercostal membranes

Muscle	Origin	Insertion
1. External intercostal	Lower border of the rib above the space	Outer lip of the upper border of the rib below
2. Internal intercostal	Floor of the costal groove of the rib above	Inner lip of the upper border of the rib below
3. Transversus thoracis		
a. Subcostalis	Inner surface of the rib near the angle	Inner surface of two or three ribs below
b. Intercostalis intimi/ innermost intercostal	Middle two-fourths of the ridge above the costal groove	Inner lip of the upper border of the rib below
c. Sternocostalis	• Lower one-third of the posterior surface of the body of the sternum	Costal cartilages of the 2nd to 6th ribs
	• Posterior surface of the xiphoid	
	• Posterior surface of the costal cartilages of the lower 3 or 4 true ribs near the sternum	

Table 14.1: The attachments of the intercostal muscles (Figs 14.1 and 14.2)

Section 2 Thorax

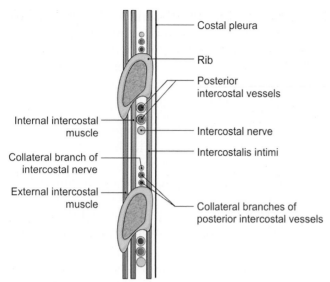

Fig. 14.2: Section through intercostal space showing neuro-vascular bundle and its collateral branches

2   The fibres of the internal intercostal run downwards, backwards and laterally, i.e. at right angle to those of the external intercostal.

3   The fibres of the transversus thoracis run in the same direction as those of the internal intercostal.

Nerve Supply

All intercostal muscles are supplied by the intercostal nerves of the spaces in which they lie.

Actions of the Intercostal Muscles

1   The main action of the intercostal muscles is to prevent intercostal spaces being drawn in during inspiration and bulging outwards during expiration.

2   The external intercostals, interchondral portions of the internal intercostals, and the levator costae may elevate the ribs during inspiration.

3   The internal intercostals except for the interchondral portions and the transversus thoracis may depress the ribs or cartilages during expiration.

Intercostal Nerves

The intercostal nerves are the anterior primary rami of thoracic one to thoracic eleven (Fig. 14.3) spinal nerves after the dorsal primary ramus has been given off. The anterior primary ramus of the twelfth thoracic nerve forms the subcostal nerve. In addition to supplying the intercostal spaces, the upper two intercostal nerves also supply the upper limb. The lower five intercostal nerves, seventh to eleventh thoracic nerves also supply abdominal wall. These are, therefore, said to be *thoraco-abdominal nerves*. The remaining nerves, third to sixth, supply only the thoracic wall; they are called *typical intercostal nerves*.

The *subcostal nerve* is distributed to the abdominal wall and to the skin of the buttock.

Course

Intercostal nerve runs in the costal groove and ends near the sternum.

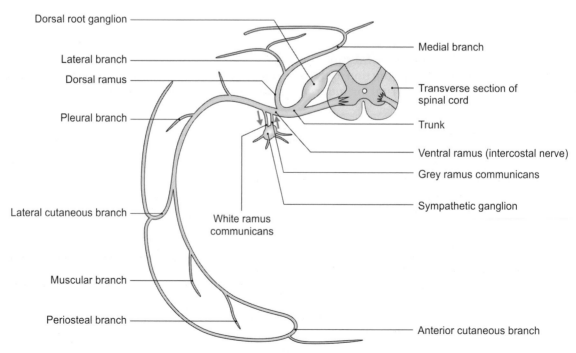

Fig. 14.3: Typical thoracic spinal nerve

Relations

1 Each nerve passes below the neck of the rib of the same number and enters the costal groove.
2 In the costal groove, the nerve lies below the posterior intercostal vessels. The relationship of structures in the costal groove from above downwards is posterior intercostal vein, posterior intercostal artery and intercostal nerve (VAN) (Fig. 14.2).

In the posterior part of the costal groove, the nerve lies between the pleura, with the endothoracic fascia and the internal intercostal membrane.

In the greater part of the space, the nerve lies between the intercostalis intimi and the internal intercostal muscle (Fig. 14.4).

3 Near the sternum, the nerve crosses in front of the internal thoracic vessels and the sternocostalis muscle. It then pierces the internal intercostal muscle, the external intercostal membrane and the pectoralis major muscle to terminate as the anterior cutaneous nerve of the thorax.

Branches

Muscular Branches

1 Numerous muscular branches supply the intercostal muscles, the transversus thoracis and the serratus posterior superior.

2 A collateral branch arises near the angle of the rib and runs in the lower part of the space in the same neurovascular plane. It supplies muscles of the space.

Sensory Branches

1 The main branch and the collateral branch also supply parietal pleura, periosteum of the ribs. The lower nerves in addition supply the parietal peritoneum.
2 The lateral cutaneous branch arises near the angle of the rib and accompanies the main trunk up to the lateral thoracic wall where it pierces the intercostal muscles and other muscles of the body wall along the midaxillary line. It is distributed to the skin after dividing into anterior and posterior branches.
3 The anterior cutaneous branch emerges on the side of the sternum to supply the overlying skin after dividing into medial and lateral branches.

Communicating Branches

1 Each nerve is connected to a thoracic sympathetic ganglion by a distally placed white and a proximally placed grey ramus communicans (Fig. 14.3).
2 The lateral cutaneous branch of the second intercostal nerve is known as the *intercostobrachial nerve*. It supplies the skin of the floor of the axilla and of the upper part of the medial side of the arm (*see* Fig. 7.1).

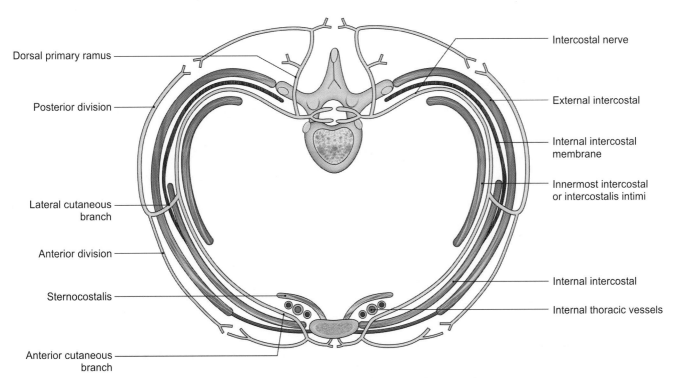

Dorsal primary ramus

Posterior division

Lateral cutaneous branch

Anterior division

Sternocostalis

Anterior cutaneous branch

Intercostal nerve

External intercostal

Internal intercostal membrane

Innermost intercostal or intercostalis intimi

Internal intercostal

Internal thoracic vessels

Fig. 14.4: The course and branches of a typical intercostal nerve

CLINICAL ANATOMY

- Irritation of the intercostal nerves causes severe pain which is referred to the front of the chest or abdomen, i.e. at the peripheral termination of the nerve. This is known as *root pain* or *girdle pain*.
- Herpes virus may cause infection of intercostal nerves. If herpes infection is in 2nd thoracic nerve, there is referred pain via intercostobrachial nerve to the medial side of arm.
- Internal thoracic artery is mobilised and its distal cut end is joined to the coronary artery distal to its narrowed segment.
- Pus from the vertebral column tends to track around the thorax along the course of the neurovascular bundle, and may point at any of the three sites of exit of the branches of a thoracic nerve; one dorsal primary ramus and two cutaneous branches (Fig. 14.5).
- In superior vena caval obstruction before the entry of vena azygos, the vena azygos is the main channel which transmits the blood from the upper half of the body to the inferior vena cava (*see* Fig. 19.4 and Flowchart 14.1). In its blockage after entry of vena azygos, flow of blood is shown in Flowchart 14.2 and Fig. 14.6.

Flowchart 14.1: Superior vena cava blockage before entry of vena azygos

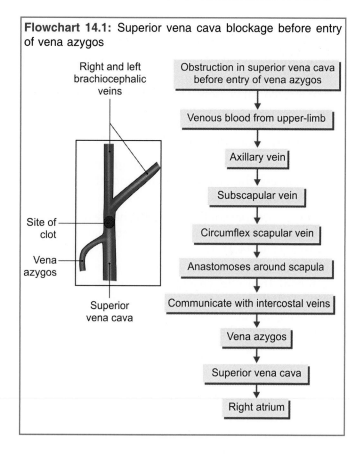

Intercostal Arteries

Each intercostal space contains one posterior intercostal artery with its collateral branch and two anterior intercostal arteries. The greater part of the space is supplied by the posterior intercostal artery (Fig. 14.7).

Posterior Intercostal Arteries

These are 11 in number on each side, one in each space.

1 The first and second posterior intercostal arteries arise from the superior intercostal artery which is a branch of costocervical trunk of the subclavian artery.

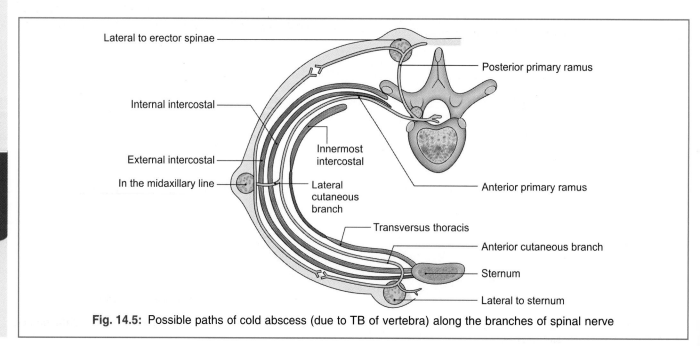

Fig. 14.5: Possible paths of cold abscess (due to TB of vertebra) along the branches of spinal nerve

Flowchart 14.2: Superior vena cava blockage after entry of vena azygos

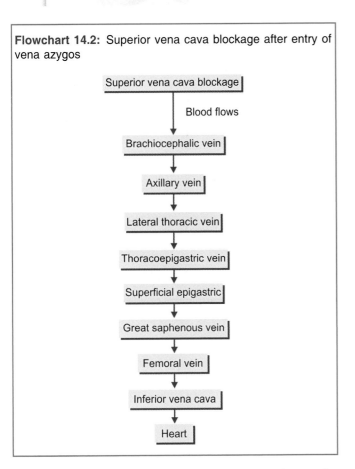

Fig. 14.6: Obstruction to superior vena cava after entry of vena azygos

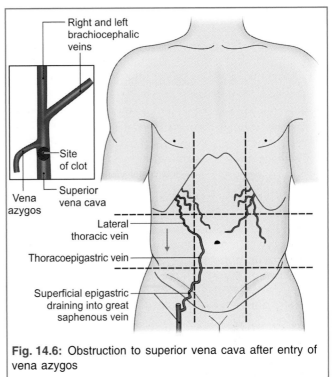

2   The third to eleventh arteries arise from the descending thoracic aorta (Fig. 14.8). The right-sided arteries are longer than those of the left side as aorta is to the left of median plane.

Course and Relations

In front of the vertebrae: The right posterior intercostal arteries are longer than the left, and pass behind the oesophagus, the thoracic duct, the azygos vein and the sympathetic chain (Fig. 14.9).

The left posterior intercostal arteries pass behind the hemiazygos vein and the sympathetic chain.

In the intercostal space: The artery is accompanied by the intercostal vein and nerve, the relationship from above downwards being vein-artery-nerve (VAN).

The neurovascular bundle runs forwards in the costal groove, first between the pleura and the internal intercostal membrane and then between the internal intercostal and intercostalis intimi muscles (Fig. 14.4).

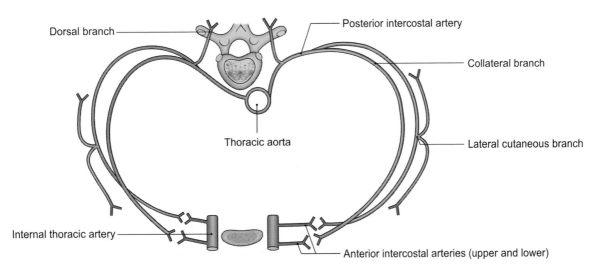

Fig. 14.7: Scheme showing the intercostal arteries. Each intercostal space contains one posterior intercostal, its collateral branch and two anterior intercostal arteries

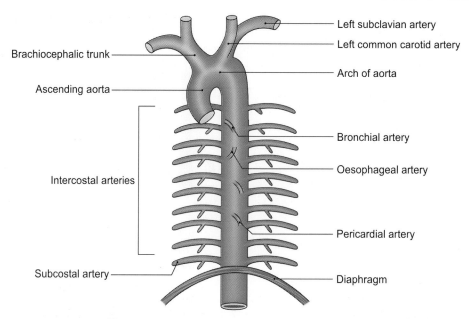

Fig. 14.8: Branches of descending thoracic aorta

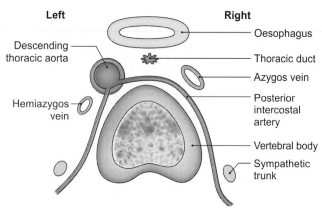

Fig. 14.9: The origin of the right and left posterior intercostal arteries from the aorta. Note that the arteries are longer on the right side

Termination

Each posterior intercostal artery ends at the level of the costochondral junction by anastomosing with the upper anterior intercostal artery of the space (Fig. 14.7).

Branches

1 A dorsal branch supplies the muscles and skin of the back, and gives off a spinal branch to the spinal cord and vertebrae (Fig. 14.7).
2 A collateral branch arises near the angle of the rib, descends to the upper border of the lower rib, and ends by anastomosing with the lower anterior intercostal artery of the space.
3 Muscular arteries are given off to the intercostal muscles, the pectoral muscles and the serratus anterior.

4 A lateral cutaneous branch accompanies the nerve of the same name.
5 Mammary branches arise from the second, third and fourth arteries and supply the mammary gland.
6 The right bronchial artery arises from the right third posterior intercostal artery.

Anterior Intercostal Arteries

There are nine intercostal spaces anteriorly as only ten ribs reach front of body. There are two anterior intercostal arteries in each space. In the upper six spaces, they arise from the internal thoracic artery (*see* Fig. 21.7). In seventh to ninth spaces, the arteries are branches of musculophrenic artery. The two anterior intercostal arteries end at the costochondral junction by anastomosing with the respective posterior intercostal arteries and with the collateral branches of the posterior intercostal arteries.

Intercostal Veins

There are two *anterior intercostal veins* in each of the upper nine spaces. They accompany the corresponding arteries. In the upper three spaces, the veins end in the internal thoracic vein. In 4–6 spaces, the veins end in venae comitantes accompanying internal thoracic artery. In the succeeding spaces, they end in the venae comitantes accompanying musculophrenic artery.

There is one *posterior intercostal vein* and one collateral vein in each intercostal space. Each vein accompanies the corresponding artery and lies superior to the artery. The tributaries of these veins correspond to the branches of the arteries. They include veins from the vertebral

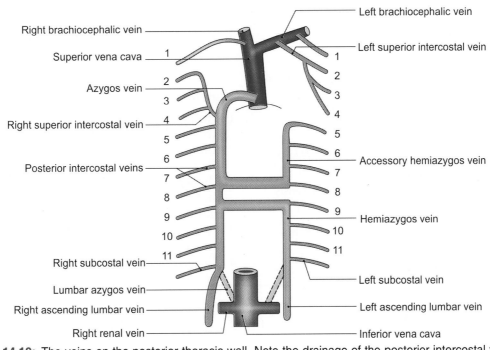

Fig. 14.10: The veins on the posterior thoracic wall. Note the drainage of the posterior intercostal veins

canal, the vertebral venous plexus, and the muscles and skin of the back. Vein accompanying the collateral branch of the artery drains into the posterior intercostal vein.

The mode of termination of the posterior intercostal veins is different on the right and left sides as given in Table 14.2, and shown in Fig. 14.10.

The azygos and hemiazygos veins are described later.

Lymphatics of an Intercostal Space

Lymphatics from the anterior part of the spaces pass to the anterior intercostal or *internal mammary nodes* which lie along the internal thoracic artery. Their efferents unite with those of the tracheobronchial and brachiocephalic nodes to form the *bronchomediastinal trunk*, which joins the *right lymphatic trunk on the right side* and the *thoracic duct on the left side*.

Lymphatics from the posterior part of the space pass to the posterior intercostal nodes which lie on the heads and necks of the ribs. Their efferents in the lower four spaces unite to form a trunk which descends and opens into the *cisterna chyli*. The efferents from the upper spaces drain into the *thoracic duct* on the left side and into *bronchomediastinal trunk* on the right side (*see* Fig. 20.7).

INTERNAL THORACIC ARTERY

Origin

Internal thoracic artery arises from the inferior aspect of the first part of the subclavian artery opposite the thyrocervical trunk. The origin lies 2 cm above the sternal end of the clavicle (Fig. 14.11).

Beginning, Course and Termination

Internal thoracic artery arises from lower border of 1st part of subclavian artery. It descends medially and downwards behind sternal end of clavicle, and 1st costal cartilage. Runs vertically downwards 2 cm from lateral border of sternum till 6th intercostal space.

The artery terminates in the sixth intercostal space by dividing into the superior epigastric and musculophrenic arteries (*see* Fig. 21.7).

The artery is accompanied by two venae comitantes which unite at the level of the fourth costal cartilage to form the internal thoracic or internal mammary vein.

Table 14.2: Termination of posterior intercostal veins		
Veins	*On right side they drain into*	*On left side they drain into*
1st	Right brachiocephalic vein	Left brachiocephalic vein
2nd, 3rd, 4th	Join to form right superior intercostal vein which drains into the azygos vein	Join to form left superior intercostal vein which drains into the left brachiocephalic vein
5th to 8th	Azygos vein	Accessory hemiazygos vein
9th to 11th and subcostal	Azygos vein	Hemiazygos vein

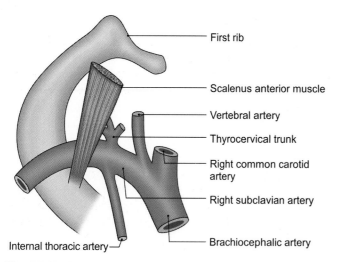

Fig. 14.11: The origin of the internal thoracic artery from the first part of the subclavian artery

The vein runs upwards along the medial side of the artery to end in the brachiocephalic vein at the inlet of the thorax.

A chain of lymph nodes lies along the artery.

Relations

Above the first costal cartilage, it runs downwards, forwards and medially, behind:
1 The sternal end of the clavicle.
2 The internal jugular vein.
3 The brachiocephalic vein
4 The first costal cartilage.
5 The phrenic nerve. It descends in front of the cervical pleura.

Below the first costal cartilage, the artery runs vertically downwards up to its termination in the 6th intercostal space. Its relations are as follows.

Anteriorly

1 Pectoralis major.
2 Upper six costal cartilages.
3 External intercostal membranes.
4 Internal intercostal muscles.
5 The first six intercostal nerves (Fig. 14.4).

Posteriorly

The endothoracic fascia and pleura up to the second or third costal cartilage. Below this level, the sternocostalis muscle separates the artery from the pleura (Fig. 14.12).

Branches

1 The *pericardiacophrenic artery* arises in the root of the neck and accompanies the phrenic nerve to reach the diaphragm. It supplies the pericardium and the pleura (*see* Fig. 15.1).
2 The *mediastinal arteries* are small irregular branches that supply the thymus, in front of the pericardium, and the fat in the mediastinum.
3 Two *anterior intercostal arteries* are given to each of the upper six intercostal spaces.
4 The *perforating branches* accompany the anterior cutaneous nerves. In the female, the perforating branches in the second, third and fourth spaces are large and supply the breast.
5 The *superior epigastric artery* runs downwards behind the seventh costal cartilage and enters the rectus sheath by passing between the sternal and costal slips of the diaphragm.
6 The *musculophrenic artery* runs downwards and laterally behind the seventh, eighth, and ninth costal cartilages. It gives two anterior intercostal branches to each of these three spaces. It perforates the diaphragm near the 9th costal cartilage and terminates by anastomosing with other arteries on the undersurface of the diaphragm.

Note that through its various branches, the internal thoracic artery supplies the anterior thoracic and abdominal walls from the clavicle to the umbilicus.

AZYGOS VEIN

The azygos vein drains the thoracic wall and the upper lumbar region (Figs 14.10 and *see* 20.6b and c). It forms an important channel connecting the superior and inferior venae cavae. The term 'azygos' means unpaired. The vein occupies the upper part of the posterior abdominal wall and the posterior mediastinum. It also

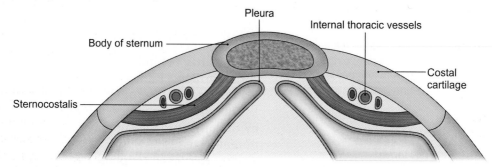

Fig. 14.12: Transverse section through the anterior thoracic wall to show the relations of the internal thoracic vessels. In the lower part of their course, the vessels are separated from the pleura by the sternocostalis muscle

connects portal venous system, caval venous system and vertebral venous system.

Formation

The azygos vein is formed by union of the lumbar azygos, right subcostal and right ascending lumbar veins.

1 The lumbar azygos vein may be regarded as the abdominal part of the azygos vein. It lies to the right of the lumbar vertebrae. Its lower end communicates with the inferior vena cava.
2 The right subcostal vein accompanies the corresponding artery.
3 The ascending lumbar vein is formed by vertical anastomoses that connect the lumbar veins. The azygos vein may be formed by union of the right subcostal and ascending lumbar veins.

Course

1 The azygos vein enters the thorax by passing through the aortic opening of the diaphragm (*see* Fig. 12.16).
2 The azygos vein then ascends up to fourth thoracic vertebra where it arches forwards over the root of the right lung and ends by joining the posterior aspect of the superior vena cava before it pierces the pericardium (*see* Fig. 15.1).

Relations

Anteriorly: Oesophagus.
Posteriorly:
1 Lower eight thoracic vertebrae.
2 Right posterior intercostal arteries.

To the right:
1 Right lung and pleura.
2 Greater splanchnic nerve.

To the left:
1 Thoracic duct and aorta in lower part.
2 Oesophagus, trachea and vagus in the upper part.

Tributaries

1 Right superior intercostal vein formed by union of the second, third and fourth posterior intercostal veins.
2 Fifth to eleventh right posterior intercostal veins (Fig. 14.10).
3 Hemiazygos vein at the level of lower border of eighth thoracic vertebra.
4 Accessory hemiazygos vein at the level of upper border of eighth thoracic vertebra.
5 Right bronchial vein, near the terminal end of the azygos vein.
6 Several oesophageal, mediastinal, pericardial veins.

HEMIAZYGOS VEIN

Hemiazygos vein is also called the *inferior hemiazygos vein*. It is the mirror image of the lower part of the azygos vein. The *hemiazygos* is formed by the union of the left lumbar azygos, left ascending lumbar, and left subcostal veins.

Course

Hemiazygos vein pierces the left crus of the diaphragm, ascends on the left side of the vertebra overlapped by the aorta. At the level of eighth thoracic vertebra, it turns to the right, passes behind the oesophagus and the thoracic duct, and joins the azygos vein (Fig. 14.10).

Tributaries

Ninth to eleventh left posterior intercostal veins and oesophageal veins.

ACCESSORY HEMIAZYGOS VEIN

Accessory hemiazygos vein is also called the *superior hemiazygos vein*. It is the mirror image of the upper part of the azygos vein.

Course

Accessory hemiazygos vein begins at the medial end of the fourth or fifth intercostal space, and descends on the left side of the vertebral column. At the level of eighth thoracic vertebra, it turns to the right, passes behind the aorta and the thoracic duct, and joins the azygos vein.

Tributaries

1 Fifth to eighth left posterior intercostal veins.
2 Sometimes the left bronchial veins.

THORACIC SYMPATHETIC TRUNK

Features

The thoracic sympathetic trunk is a ganglionated chain situated one on each side of the thoracic vertebral column. Superiorly, it is continuous with the cervical part of the chain and inferiorly with the lumbar part (Figs 14.13 and 14.14).

Theoretically, the chain bears 12 ganglia corresponding to the 12 thoracic nerves. The first thoracic ganglion is commonly fused with the inferior cervical ganglion to form the cervicothoracic, or *stellate ganglion*. The remaining thoracic ganglia generally lie at the levels of the corresponding intervertebral discs and the intercostal nerves.

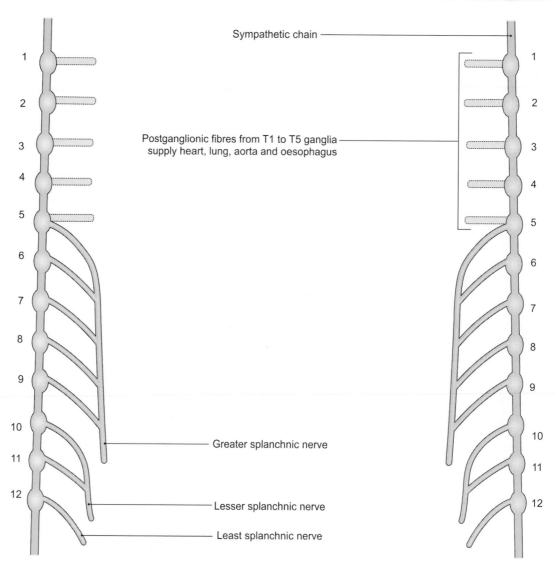

Sympathetic chain

Postganglionic fibres from T1 to T5 ganglia supply heart, lung, aorta and oesophagus

Greater splanchnic nerve

Lesser splanchnic nerve

Least splanchnic nerve

Fig. 14.13: The thoracic part of the sympathetic trunk and its splanchnic branches

Course and Relations

The chain crosses the neck of the first rib, the heads of the second to tenth ribs, and bodies of the eleventh and twelfth thoracic vertebrae. The whole chain descends in front of the posterior intercostal vessels and the intercostal nerves, and passes deep to the medial arcuate ligament to become continuous with the lumbar part of the sympathetic chain.

Branches

Lateral Branches for the Limbs and Body Wall

Each ganglion is connected with its corresponding spinal nerve by two rami, the *white* (preganglionic) and *grey* (postganglionic) rami communicantes. The white ramus is distal to the grey ramus (*see* Fig. A2.3). The grey rami communicantes along with spinal nerves supply structures in the skin and blood vessels of skeletal muscles of the whole body (Fig. 14.14).

Medial Branches for the Viscera

1 Medial branches from the upper 5 ganglia are postganglionic and get distributed to the heart, the great vessels, the lungs and the oesophagus, through the following.
   a. Pulmonary branches to the pulmonary plexuses.
   b. Cardiac branches to the deep cardiac plexus.
   c. Aortic branches to thoracic aortic plexus.
   d. Oesophageal branches which join the oesophageal plexus (Fig. 14.13).
2 Medial branches from the lower 7 ganglia are preganglionic and form three splanchnic nerves.
   a. *The greater splanchnic nerve* is formed by 5 roots from ganglia 5 to 9. It descends obliquely on the vertebral bodies, pierces the crus of the diaphragm, and ends (in the abdomen) mainly in the coeliac ganglion, and partly in the aortico-renal ganglion and the *suprarenal gland*.

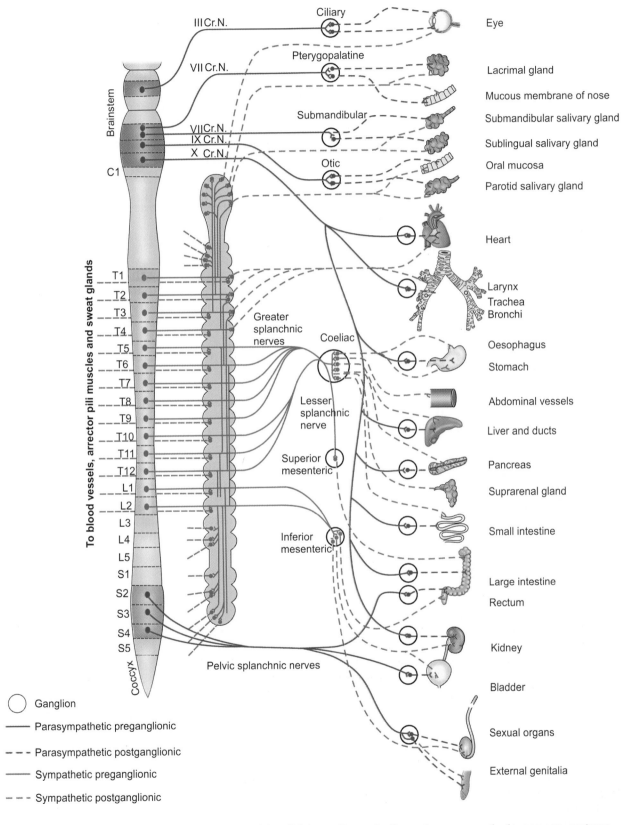

Fig. 14.14: Autonomic nervous system and its divisions: Sympathetic and parasympathetic nervous systems

b. *The lesser splanchnic nerve* is formed by two roots from ganglia 10 and 11. Its course is similar to that of the greater splanchnic nerve. It pierces the crus of the diaphragm, and ends in the coeliac ganglion (Fig. 14.14).

c. *The least (lowest) splanchnic nerve (renal nerve)* is tiny. It arises by one root from ganglion 12. It pierces the corresponding crus of the diaphragm. The sympathetic nervous system may be revised from Chapter 7 of BD Chaurasia's Handbook of General Anatomy, 5th edition.

CLINICAL ANATOMY

• Cardiac pain is an ischaemic pain caused by incomplete obstruction of a coronary artery.

Axons of pain fibres conveyed by the sensory sympathetic cardiac nerves reach thoracic one to thoracic five segments of spinal cord mostly through the dorsal root ganglia of the left side. Since these dorsal root ganglia also receive sensory impulses from the medial side of arm, forearm and upper part of front of chest, the pain gets referred to these areas as depicted in Fig. 18.27.

Though the pain is usually referred to the left side, it may even be referred to right arm, jaw, epigastrium or back.

FACTS TO REMEMBER

• Intercostal spaces are 11 on the back and only 9 in front of chest.

• Intercostal muscles are in 3 layers, external, internal and transversus. These correspond to the muscle layers of anterior abdominal wall.

• Neurovascular bundle lies in the upper part of the intercostal space in between internal and innermost intercostal muscles.

• Posterior intercostal artery and its collateral branch supplies two-thirds of the intercostal space.

• Right posterior intercostal arteries are longer than the left ones.

• Accessory hemiazygos drains 5–8 left intercostal and hemiazygos vein drains 9–11 left intercostal spaces. Corresponding veins on right side drain into vena azygos.

CLINICOANATOMICAL PROBLEM

One student is climbing the stairs at a fast pace as he is late for his examination and the lift got out of order. His heart is beating fast against his chest wall. He has dryness of mouth and sweating of the palm.

• What is the reason for rapid heart beat (tachycardia)?
• What is the effect of sympathetic on the skin?

Ans: As he is late for the examination, the sympathetic system gets overactive, increasing the heart rate, and blood pressure.

Sympathetic has three fold effect on the skin, i.e. vasomotor, pilomotor and sudomotor. The sweat secretion is markedly increased, including the pale skin with hair standing erect.

Sympathetic activity decreases the secretion of the glands. Dryness of mouth results from decreased salivary secretion.

FREQUENTLY ASKED QUESTIONS

1. Describe the course, branches of a typical thoracic spinal nerve. What is its applied anatomy.
2. Describe the internal thoracic artery under following headings: Origin, course, termination and branches.
3. Write short notes on:
   a. Posterior intercostal arteries
   b. Vena azygos
   c. Splanchnic nerves
   d. Cardiac pain referred to medial side of left arm
   e. Structures in the costal groove in order
   f. Name the parts of parietal pleura with their nerve supply
   g. Name the recesses of the pleura. What is their clinical importance?

MULTIPLE CHOICE QUESTIONS

1. The order of structures in the upper part of intercostal space from above downwards is:
   a. Vein, artery and nerve
   b. Artery, vein and nerve
   c. Vein, nerve and artery
   d. Vein, nerve, artery and vein

2. Parts of transversus thoracis are all, *except*:
   a. Subcostalis
   b. Intercostalis intimi
   c. Sternocostalis
   d. Serratus posterior superior

3. Which of the following arteries are enlarged in coarctation of aorta?
   a. Subclavian
   b. Internal mammary
   c. Posterior intercostals
   d. Anterior intercostals

4. Which posterior intercostal veins of left side drain into accessory hemiazygos vein?
   a. 1st to 5th
   b. 2nd to 4th
   c. 9th to 11th
   d. 5th to 8th

5. Which one is not a branch of internal thoracic artery?
   a. Superior epigastric
   b. Musculophrenic
   c. Anterior intercostal
   d. Posterior intercostal

6. Thoracolumbar outflow starts from lateral horn of which segments of spinal cord?
   a. T1–L1 segments
   b. T1–T12 segments
   c. T1–L2 segments
   d. T1–L5 segments

7. Following are the effects of sympathetic on skin, *except*:
   a. Sudomotor
   b. Vasomotor
   c. Pilomotor
   d. Decreases pigmentation

ANSWERS

1. a	2. d	3. c	4. d	5. d	6. c	7. d

Thoracic Cavity and Pleurae

Laughter is the best medicine but being seldom used

INTRODUCTION

The spongy lungs occupying a major portion of thoracic cavity are enveloped in a serous cavity—the pleural cavity. There is always slight negative pressure in this cavity. During inspiration, the pressure becomes more negative, and air is drawn into the lungs covered with its visceral and parietal layers. Visceral layer is inseparable from the lung and is supplied and drained by the same arteries, veins and nerves as lungs. In a similar manner, the parietal pleura follows the walls of the thoracic cavity with cervical, costal, diaphragmatic and mediastinal parts. Pleural cavity limits the expansion of the lungs.

THORACIC CAVITY

DISSECTION

Divide the manubrium sterni transversely immediately inferior to its junction with the first costal cartilage. Cut through the parietal pleura in the first intercostal space on both sides as far back as possible. Cut sternum at the level of xiphisternal joint. Use a bone cutter to cut 2nd to 7th ribs in midaxillary line on each side of thorax. Separate intercostal muscles in 1–6 spaces from underlying pleura.

Lift the inferior part of manubrium and body of sternum with ribs and costal cartilages and reflect it towards abdomen. Identify the pleura extending from the back of sternum onto the mediastinum to the level of lower border of heart. Note the smooth surface of pleura where it lines the thoracic wall and covers the lateral aspects of mediastinum. Trace the surface marking of parietal pleura on the skeleton.

Remove the pleura and the endothoracic fascia from the back of sternum and costal cartilages which is reflected towards abdomen. Identify the transversus thoracis muscle and internal thoracic vessels.

Note the origin of diaphragm from the xiphoid process and divide it. Identify the course and branches of intercostal nerve again. Trace the nerve medially superficial to the internal thoracic vessels.

Pull the lung laterally from the mediastinum and find its root with the pulmonary ligament extending downwards from it. Cut through the structures, i.e. bronchus/bronchi, pulmonary vessels, nerves, comprising its root from above downwards close to the lung. Remove the lung on each side. Be careful not to injure the lung or your hand from the cut ends of the ribs.

Identify the phrenic nerve with accompanying blood vessels anterior to the root of the lung. Make a longitudinal incision through the pleura only parallel to and on each side of the phrenic nerve. Strip the pleura posterior to the nerve backwards to the intercostal spaces. Pull the anterior flap forwards to reveal part of the pericardium with the heart. Identify the following structures seen through the pleura.

Right side

1. Bulge of the heart and pericardium anteroinferior to the root of the lung (Fig. 15.1).
2. A longitudinal ridge formed by right brachiocephalic vein down to first costal cartilage and by superior vena cava up to the bulge of the heart.
3. A smaller longitudinal ridge formed by inferior vena cava formed between the heart and the diaphragm.
4. Phrenic nerve with accompanying vessels forming a vertical ridge on these two venae cavae passing anterior to root of the lung.
5. Vena azygos arching over root of the lung to enter the superior vena cava.
6. Trachea and oesophagus posterior to the phrenic nerve and superior vena cava.
7. Right vagus nerve descending posteroinferiorly across the trachea, behind the root of the lung.

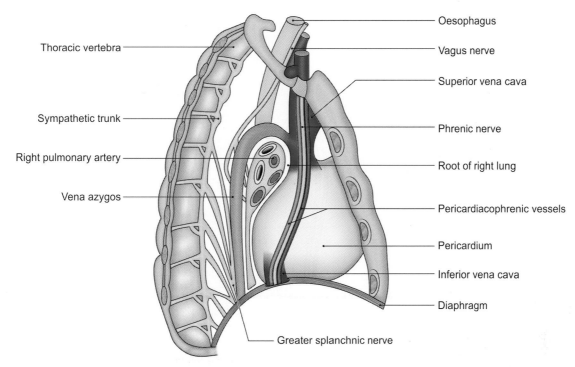

Fig. 15.1: Mediastinum as seen from the right side

8. Bodies of the thoracic vertebrae behind oesophagus with posterior intercostal vessels and azygos vein lying over them.
9. Sympathetic trunk on the heads of the upper ribs and on the sides of the vertebral bodies below this, anterior to the posterior intercostal vessels and intercostal nerves.

Left side
1. Bulge of the heart (Fig. 15.2).
2. Root of lung posterosuperior to it.
3. Descending aorta between (1) and (2) in front and vertebral column behind.
4. Arch of aorta over the root of the lung.
5. Left common carotid and left subclavian arteries passing superiorly from the arch of aorta.
6. Phrenic and vagus nerves descending between these vessels and the lateral surface of the aortic arch.
7. Sympathetic trunk same as on right side.

Identify longitudinally running sympathetic trunk on the posterior part of thoracic cavity. Find delicate greater and lesser splanchnic nerves arising from the trunk on the medial side. Look carefully for grey and white rami communicantes between the intercostal nerve and the ganglia on the sympathetic trunk (see Fig. 14.3).

Trace the intercostal vessels above the intercostal nerve. The order being vein, artery and nerve (VAN). On the right side, identify and follow one of the divisions of trachea to the lung root and the superior and inferior venae cavae till the pericardium.

On the left side of thoracic cavity, dissect the arch of aorta. Identify the superior cervical cardiac branch of the left sympathetic trunk and the inferior cervical cardiac branch of the left vagus on the arch of the aorta between the vagus nerve posteriorly and phrenic nerve anteriorly (cardiac nerves) (see Fig. 19.9).

The cavity of the thorax contains the right and left pleural cavities which are completely invaginated and occupied by the lungs. The right and left pleural cavities are separated by a thick median partition called the mediastinum. The heart lies in the mediastinum.

PLEURA

Features
Like the peritoneum, the pleura is a serous membrane which is lined by mesothelium (flattened epithelium). There are two pleural sacs, one on either side of the mediastinum. Each pleural sac is invaginated from its medial side by the lung, so that it has an outer layer, the *parietal pleura,* and an inner layer, the *visceral* or *pulmonary pleura.* The two layers are continuous with each other around the hilum of the lung, and enclose between them a potential space, the pleural cavity.

Table 15.1 shows comparison between visceral pleura and parietal pleura.

Section 2   Thorax

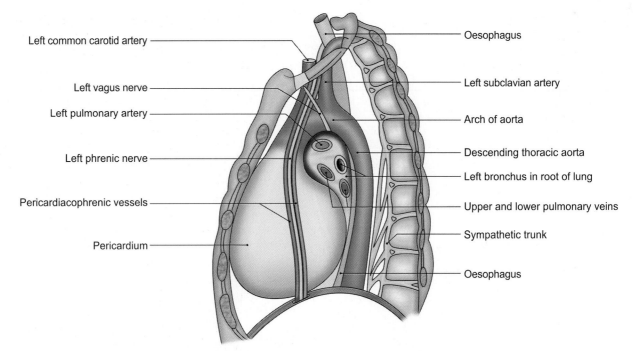

Fig. 15.2: Mediastinum as seen from the left side

Labels (clockwise): Left common carotid artery, Left vagus nerve, Left pulmonary artery, Left phrenic nerve, Pericardiacophrenic vessels, Pericardium, Oesophagus, Left subclavian artery, Arch of aorta, Descending thoracic aorta, Left bronchus in root of lung, Upper and lower pulmonary veins, Sympathetic trunk, Oesophagus

	Table 15.1: Comparison of visceral and parietal pleurae	
	Visceral	*Parietal*
Development	Splanchnopleuric mesoderm	Somatopleuric mesoderm
Position	Lines surface of lung including the fissures	Lines thoracic wall, mediastinum and diaphragm
Nerve supply	Sympathetic nerves from T2–T5 ganglia Parasympathetic from vagus nerve	Thoracic nerves and phrenic nerves
Sensitivity	Insensitive to pain	Sensitive to pain which may be referred.
Blood supply	Bronchial vessels	Intercostal and pericardiacophrenic vessels
Lymph drainage	Tracheobronchial lymph nodes	Intercostal lymph nodes

Pulmonary/Visceral Pleura

The serous layer of pulmonary pleura covers the surfaces and fissures of the lung, except at the hilum and along the attachment of the pulmonary ligament where it is continuous with the parietal pleura. It is firmly adherent to the lung and cannot be separated from it.

Surface Marking of the Lung/Visceral Pleura

The *apex* of the visceral pleura coincides with the cervical pleura, and is represented by a line convex upwards with a point rising 2.5 cm above the medial one-third of the clavicle (Fig. 15.5).

The *anterior border of the right visceral pleura* corresponds very closely to the anterior margin or costomediastinal line of the pleura and is obtained by joining:

- A point at the sternoclavicular joint,
- A point 3 in the median plane at the sternal angle,
- A point 4 in the median plane just above the xiphisternal joint.

The *anterior border of the left visceral pleura* corresponds to the anterior margin of the pleura up to the level of the fourth costal cartilage points I–IV left side.

In the lower part, it presents a cardiac notch of variable size. From the level of the fourth costal cartilage, it passes laterally for 3.5 cm from the sternal margin (V), and then curves downwards and medially to reach the sixth costal cartilage 4 cm from the median plane (VI). In the region of the cardiac notch, the pericardium is covered only by a double layer of pleura. The area of the cardiac notch is dull on percussion and is called the *area of superficial cardiac dullness* (Fig. 15.5).

The *lower border* of each visceral pleura lies two ribs higher than the parietal pleural reflection. It crosses the sixth rib in the midclavicular line (5), the eighth rib in the midaxillary line (6 and VII), the tenth rib at the lateral border of the erector spinae, and ends 2 cm lateral to the tenth thoracic spine .

Parietal Pleura

The parietal pleura is thicker than the pulmonary pleura, and is subdivided into the following four parts.
1 Costal
2 Diaphragmatic
3 Mediastinal
4 Cervical (Figs 15.3 and 15.4)

The *costal pleura* lines the thoracic wall which comprises ribs and intercostal spaces to which it is loosely attached by a layer of areolar tissue called the endothoracic fascia.

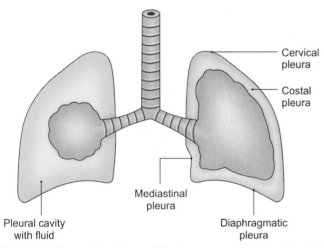

Fig. 15.3: The parietal pleura. The lung represented on the right is the early stage

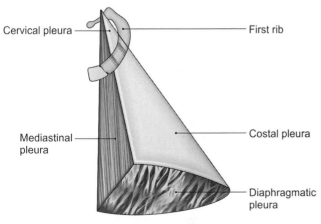

Fig. 15.4: The parietal pleura as a half cone

The *mediastinal pleura* lines the corresponding surface of the mediastinum. It is reflected over the root of the lung and becomes continuous with the pulmonary pleura around the hilum.

The *cervical pleura* extends into the neck, nearly 5 cm above the first costal cartilage and 2.5 cm above the medial one-third of the clavicle, and covers the apex of the lung (*see* Fig. 12.10). It is covered by the suprapleural membrane. Cervical pleura is related anteriorly to the subclavian artery and the scalenus anterior; posteriorly to the neck of the first rib and structures lying over it; laterally to the scalenus medius; and medially to the large vessels of the neck (*see* Fig. 12.10).

Diaphragmatic pleura lines the superior aspect of diaphragm. It covers the base of the lung and gets continuous with mediastinal pleura medially and costal pleura laterally.

Features of Parietal Pleura

The *cervical pleura* is represented by a curved line forming a dome over the medial one-third of the clavicle with a height of about 2.5 cm above the clavicle (Figs 15.5 and 21.1). Pleura lies in the root of neck on both sides.

The *anterior margin,* or the costomediastinal line of pleural reflection is as follows: On the right side, it extends from the sternoclavicular joint downwards and medially to the midpoint of the sternal angle. From here, it continues vertically downwards to the midpoint of the xiphisternal joint crosses to right of xiphicostal angle. On the left side, the line follows the same course up to the level of the fourth costal cartilage. It then arches outwards and descends along the sternal margin up to the sixth costal cartilage.

The *inferior margin,* or the costodiaphragmatic line of pleural reflection passes laterally from the lower limit of its anterior margin, so that it crosses the eighth rib in the midclavicular line, the tenth rib in the midaxillary line, and the twelfth rib at the lateral border of the sacrospinalis muscle. Further it passes horizontally a little below the 12th rib to the lower border of the twelfth thoracic vertebra, 2 cm lateral to the upper border of the twelfth thoracic spine (*see* Fig. 13.8a).

Thus the parietal pleurae descend below the costal margin at three places, at the right xiphicostal angle, and at the right and left costovertebral angles, below the twelfth rib behind the upper poles of the kidneys. The latter fact is of surgical importance in exposure of the kidney. The pleura may be damaged at this site (Fig. 15.5 and *see* Fig. 21.1).

The *posterior margins* of the pleura pass from a point 2 cm lateral to the twelfth thoracic spine to a point 2 cm lateral to the seventh cervical spine. The costal pleura becomes the mediastinal pleura along this line.

Thorax

Section 2

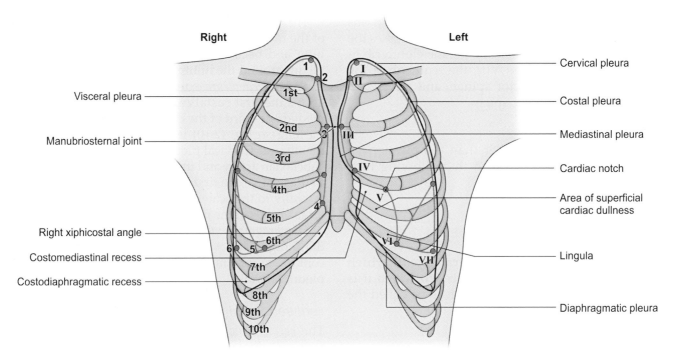

Fig. 15.5: Surface projection of the parietal pleura (black); visceral pleura and lung (pink) on the front of thorax

Pulmonary Ligament

The parietal pleura surrounding the root of the lung extends downwards beyond the root as a fold called the *pulmonary ligament*. The fold contains a thin layer of loose areolar tissue with a few lymphatics. Actually, it provides a dead space into which the pulmonary veins can expand during increased venous return as in exercise. The lung roots can also descend into it with the descent of the diaphragm (Fig. 15.6).

Recesses of Pleura

There are two recesses of parietal pleura, which act as 'reserve spaces' for the lung to expand during deep inspiration (Figs 15.5, 15.7 and 15.8).

The *costomediastinal recess* lies anteriorly, behind the sternum and costal cartilages, between the costal and mediastinal pleurae, particularly in relation to the cardiac notch of the left lung. This recess is filled up by the anterior margin of the lungs even during quiet breathing. It is only obvious in the region of the cardiac notch of the lung.

The *costodiaphragmatic/costovertebral recess* lies inferiorly between the costal and diaphragmatic pleurae. Vertically, it measures about 5 cm, and extends from the eighth to tenth ribs along the midaxillary line (Fig. 15.7).

During inspiration, the lungs expand into these recesses. So these recesses are obvious only in expiration and not in deep inspiration.

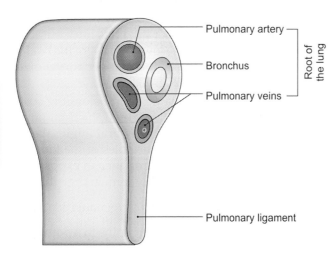

Fig. 15.6: Pleura at root of lung

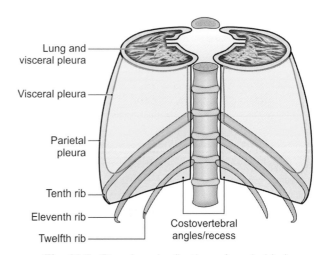

Fig. 15.7: The pleural reflections, from behind

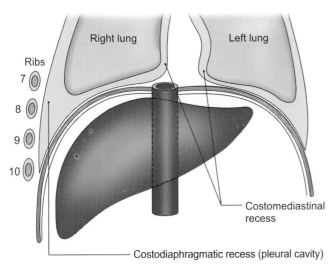

Fig. 15.8: Reflections of the pleura to show costodiaphragmatic and costomediastinal recesses

Nerve Supply of the Pleura

The parietal pleura develops from the somatopleuric layer of the lateral plate mesoderm, and is supplied by the somatic nerves. These are the intercostal and phrenic nerves. The parietal pleura is pain sensitive. The costal and peripheral parts of the diaphragmatic pleurae are supplied by the intercostal nerves, and the mediastinal pleura and central part of the diaphragmatic pleurae by the phrenic nerves (C4).

The pulmonary pleura develops from the splanchnopleuric layer of the lateral plate mesoderm, and is supplied by autonomic nerves. The sympathetic nerves are derived from second to fifth sympathetic ganglia while parasympathetic nerves are drawn from the vagus nerve. The nerves accompany the bronchial vessels. This part of the pleura is not sensitive to pain.

Sympathetic dilates the bronchi. The parasympathetic narrows the bronchial tree and is also secretory to the glands.

Blood Supply and Lymphatic Drainage

The parietal pleura is a part and parcel of the thoracic wall. Its blood supply and lymphatic drainage are, therefore, the same as that of the body wall. It is thus supplied by intercostal, internal thoracic and musculophrenic arteries.

The veins drain mostly into the azygos and internal thoracic veins. The lymphatics drain into the intercostal, internal mammary, posterior mediastinal and diaphragmatic nodes.

The pulmonary pleura, like the lung, is supplied by the bronchial arteries while the veins drain into bronchial veins. It is drained by the bronchopulmonary lymph nodes.

CLINICAL ANATOMY

- Aspiration of any fluid from the pleural cavity is called *paracentesis thoracis*. It is usually done in the eighth intercostal space in the midaxillary line (Fig. 15.9). The needle is passed through the lower part of the space to avoid injury to the principal neurovascular bundle, i.e. vein, artery and nerve (VAN).
- Some clinical conditions associated with the pleura are as follows.
  a. *Pleurisy:* This is inflammation of the pleura. It may be dry, but often it is accompanied by collection of fluid in the pleural cavity. The condition is called the pleural effusion (Fig. 15.10). Dry pleurisy is more painful because during inspiration both layers come in contact and there is friction.
  b. *Pneumothorax:* Presence of air in the pleural cavity.
  c. *Haemothorax:* Presence of blood in the pleural cavity.
  d. *Hydropneumothorax:* Presence of both fluid and air in the pleural cavity.
  e. *Empyema:* Presence of pus in pleural cavity.
- Costal and peripheral parts of diaphragmatic pleurae are innervated by intercostal nerves (Fig. 15.11). Hence irritation of these regions cause referred pain along intercostal nerves to throacic or abdominal wall. Mediastinal and central part of diaphragmatic pleurae are innervated by phrenic nerve (C4). Hence irritation here causes referred pain on tip of shoulders.
- Pain on right shoulder occurs due to inflammation of gallbladder, while on left shoulder is due to splenic rupture.
- Pleural effusion causes obliteration of costodiaphragmatic recess.
- Pleura extends beyond the thoracic cage at following areas:
  – Right xiphicostal angle (Fig. 15.5)
  – Right and left costovertebral angles (Fig. 15.7)
  – Right and left sides of root of neck as cervical dome of pleura (Fig. 15.5).

  The pleura may be injured at these sites during surgical procedures. These sites have to be remembered.
- During inspiration, pure air is withdrawn in the lungs. At the same time, deoxygenated blood is received through the pulmonary arteries. Thus an exchange of gases occurs at the level of alveoli. The deoxygenated blood gets oxygenated and sent via pulmonary veins to the left atrium of heart. The impure air containing carbon dioxide gets expelled during expiration.

Section 2 | Thorax

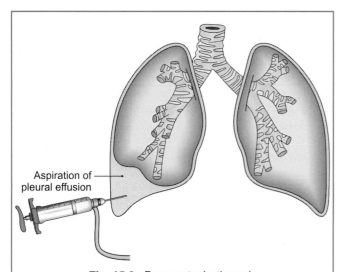

Fig. 15.9: Paracentesis thoracis

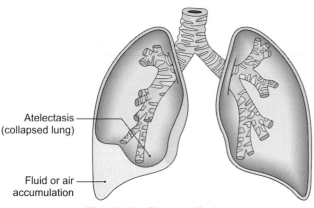

Fig. 15.10: Pleural effusion

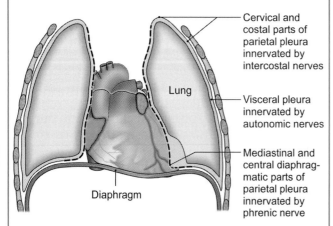

Fig. 15.11: Nerve supply of parietal pleura. Costal pleura and cervical pleura innervated by intercostal nerves, and mediastinal pleura and most of diaphragmatic pleura innervated by phrenic nerve

FACTS TO REMEMBER

- Parietal pleura limits the expansion of the lungs.
- Visceral pleura behaves in same way as the lung.
- Parietal pleura has same nerve supply and blood supply as the thoracic wall.
- Pleural cavity normally contains a minimal serous fluid for lubrication during movements of thoracic cage.
- Pleura lies beyond the thoracic cage at 5 places. These are right and left cervical pleurae above the 1st rib and the clavicle; right and left costovertebral angles and only right xiphicostal angle. Pleura is likely to be injured at these places.
- Paracentesis thoracis is done in the lower part of the intercostal space to avoid injury to the main intercostal vessels and nerve.
- Pleural effusion is one of the sign of tuberculosis of the lung.

CLINICOANATOMICAL PROBLEM

A child about 10 years of age had been having sore throat, cough and fever. On the third day, he developed severe cough, difficulty in breathing and high temperature, with pain in his right side of chest, right shoulder and around umbilicus.
- What is the probable diagnosis?
- Why does pain radiate to right shoulder and periumbilical region?

Ans: The most probable diagnosis is pneumonia of the right lung. The infection from pharynx spread down to the lungs. Pleura consists of two layers, visceral and parietal; the former is insensitive to pain and the latter is sensitive to pain. The costal part of parietal pleura is supplied by intercostal nerves and the mediastinal and central parts of diaphragmatic pleurae are supplied by phrenic (C4) nerve.

In pneumonia, there is always an element of pleural infection. The pain of pleuritis radiates to other areas. Due to infection in mediastinal and central part of diaphragmatic pleura, the pain is referred to tip of the right shoulder as this area is supplied by supraclavicular nerves with the same root value as phrenic nerve (C4).

The costal pleura is supplied by intercostal nerves. These nerves also supply the skin of anterior abdominal wall. So the pain of lower part of costal pleura gets referred to skin of abdomen, in the periumbilical area.

FREQUENTLY ASKED QUESTION

1. Write short notes on:
   a. Comparison of visceral and parietal pleura
   b. Paracentesis thoracis
   c. Name four clinical conditions associated with the pleura
   d. Sites where pleura (parietal) lies beyond the thoracic cage

MULTIPLE CHOICE QUESTIONS

1. Which of the following nerves innervate the costal pleura?
   a. Vagus
   b. Intercostal
   c. Splanchnic
   d. Phrenic

2. Which of the following nerves innervate the mediastinal pleura?
   a. Vagus
   b. Phrenic
   c. Intercostal
   d. Splanchnic

3. All the following arteries supply parietal pleura, *except*:
   a. Musculophrenic
   b. Internal thoracic
   c. Intercostal
   d. Bronchial

4. One of the following arteries supplies the visceral pleura:
   a. Bronchial
   b. Musculophrenic
   c. Internal thoracic
   d. Superior epigastric

5. All are main big recesses of pleura, *except*:
   a. Right costodiaphragmatic recess
   b. Left costodiaphragmatic recess
   c. Right costomediastinal recess
   d. Left costomediastinal recess

ANSWERS

| 1. b | 2. b | 3. d | 4. a | 5. c |

Lungs

One thousand Americans and same number of Indians stop smoking everyday – by dying
—Anonymous

INTRODUCTION

The lungs occupying major portions of the thoracic cavity, leave little space for the heart, which excavates more of the left lung. The two lungs hold the heart tight between them, providing it, the protection it rightly deserves. There are ten bronchopulmonary segments in each lung.

The lungs are a pair of respiratory organs situated in the thoracic cavity. Each lung invaginates the corresponding pleural cavity. The right and left lungs are separated by the mediastinum.

The lungs are spongy in texture. In the young, the lungs are brown or grey in colour. Gradually, they become mottled black because of the deposition of inhaled carbon particles. The right lung weighs about 700 g; it is about 50 to 100 g heavier than the left lung.

LUNGS

DISSECTION

Identify the lungs by the thin anterior border, thick posterior border, conical apex, wider base, medial surface with hilum and costal surface with impressions of the ribs and intercostal spaces. In addition, the right lung is distinguished by the presence of three lobes, whereas left lung comprises two lobes only.

On the mediastinal part of the medial surface of right lung identify two bronchi—the eparterial and hyparterial bronchi, with bronchial vessels and posterior pulmonary plexus, the pulmonary artery between the two bronchi on an anterior plane. The upper pulmonary vein is situated still on an anterior plane while the lower pulmonary vein is identified below the bronchi.

The impressions on the right lung in front of root of lung are of superior vena cava, inferior vena cava, and right ventricle. The impressions behind the root of lung are those of vena azygos and oesophagus.

Hilum of the left lung shows the single bronchus situated posteriorly, with bronchial vessels and posterior pulmonary plexus. The pulmonary artery lies above the bronchus. Anterior to the bronchus is the upper pulmonary vein, while the lower vein lies below the bronchus.

The mediastinal surface of left lung has the impression of left ventricle, ascending aorta. Behind the root of the left lung are the impressions of descending thoracic aorta while oesophagus leaves an impression in the lower part only.

Features

Each lung is conical in shape (Fig. 16.1). It has:
1 An apex at the upper end.
2 A base resting on the diaphragm.
3 Three borders, i.e. anterior, posterior and inferior.
4 Two surfaces, i.e. costal and medial. The medial surface is divided into vertebral and mediastinal parts.

The *apex* is blunt and lies above the level of the anterior end of the first rib. It reaches nearly 2.5 cm above the medial one-third of the clavicle, just medial to the supraclavicular fossa. It is covered by the cervical pleura, the suprapleural membrane, and is grooved by the subclavian artery on the medial side and anteriorly (*see* Fig. 12.10).

The *base* is semilunar and concave. It rests on the diaphragm which separates the right lung from the right lobe of the liver, and the left lung from the left lobe of the liver, the fundus of the stomach, and the spleen (*see* Fig. 15.8).

The *anterior border* is very thin (Figs 16.2 and 16.3). It is shorter than the posterior border. On the right side, it is vertical and corresponds to the anterior or costomediastinal line of pleural reflection. The anterior border of the left lung shows a wide cardiac notch below the level of the fourth costal cartilage. The heart and

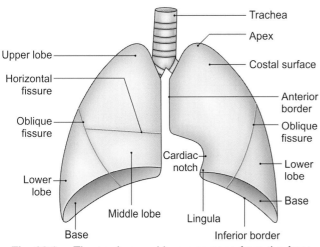

Fig. 16.1a: The trachea and lungs as seen from the front

pericardium are not covered by the lung in the region of this notch.

The *posterior border* is thick and ill defined. It corresponds to the medial margins of the heads of the ribs. It extends from the level of the seventh cervical spine to the tenth thoracic spine.

The *inferior border* separates the base from the costal and medial surfaces.

The *costal surface* is large and convex. It is in contact with the costal pleura and the overlying thoracic wall.

The *medial surface* is divided into a posterior or vertebral part, and an anterior or mediastinal part. The vertebral part is related to the vertebral bodies, intervertebral discs, the posterior intercostal vessels and the splanchnic nerves (*see* Figs 15.1 and 15.2). The mediastinal part is related to the mediastinal septum, and shows a cardiac impression, the hilum and a number of other impressions which differ on the two

sides. Various relations of the mediastinal surfaces of the two lungs are listed in Table 16.1.

Fissures and Lobes of the Lungs

The right lung is divided into 3 lobes (upper, middle and lower) by two fissures (oblique and horizontal). The left lung is divided into two lobes by the oblique fissure (Fig. 16.1).

The *oblique fissure* cuts into the whole thickness of the lung, except at the hilum. It passes obliquely downwards and forwards, crossing the posterior border about 6 cm below the apex and the inferior border about 5 cm from the median plane. Due to the oblique plane of the fissure, the lower lobe is more posterior and the upper and middle lobe more anterior.

In the right lung, the *horizontal fissure* passes from the anterior border up to the oblique fissure and separates a wedge-shaped middle lobe from the upper lobe. The fissure runs horizontally at the level of the fourth costal cartilage and meets the oblique fissure in the midaxillary line.

The tongue-shaped projection of the left lung below the cardiac notch is called the *lingula*. It corresponds to the middle lobe of the right lung.

The lungs expand maximally in the inferior direction because movements of the thoracic wall and diaphragm are maximal towards the base of the lung. The presence of the oblique fissure of each lung allows a more uniform expansion of the whole lung.

Surface Marking of the Lung

Surface marking of lung is same as that of visceral pleura described in Chapter 15. The surface marking of oblique and horizontal fissures is mentioned here.

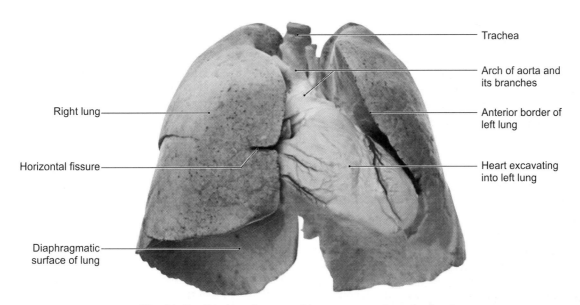

Fig. 16.1b: Trachea, lungs and heart as seen from the front

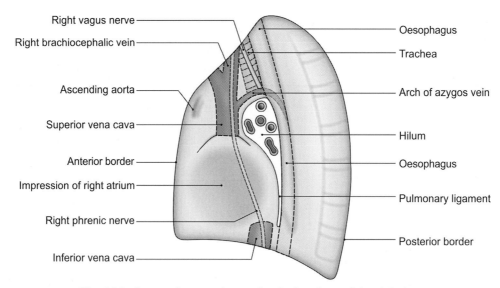

Fig. 16.2: Impressions on the mediastinal surface of the right lung

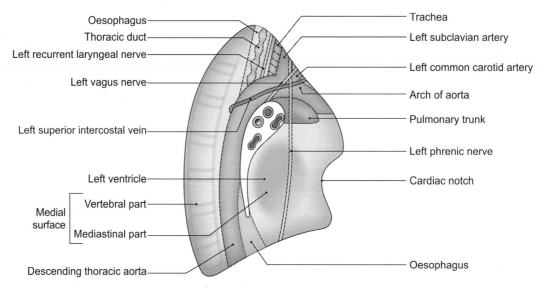

Fig. 16.3: Impressions on the mediastinal surface of the left lung

The *oblique fissure* can be drawn by joining:
a. A point 2 cm lateral to the third thoracic spine.
b. Another point on the fifth rib in the midaxillary line (*see* Fig. 21.2).
c. A third point on the sixth costal cartilage 7.5 cm from the median plane.

The *horizontal fissure* is represented by a line joining:
a. A point on the anterior border of the right lung at the level of the fourth costal cartilage.
b. A second point on the fifth rib in the midaxillary line.

Root of the Lung

Root of the lung is a short, broad pedicle which connects the medial surface of the lung to the mediastinum. It is formed by structures which either enter or come out of the lung at the hilum (Latin *depression*). The roots of the lungs lie opposite the bodies of the fifth, sixth and seventh thoracic vertebrae.

Contents

The root is made up of the following structures.

1 Principal bronchus on the left side, and eparterial and hyparterial bronchi on the right side.
2 One pulmonary artery.
3 Two pulmonary veins, superior and inferior.
4 Bronchial arteries, one on the right side and two on the left side.
5 Bronchial veins.

Table 16.1: Structures related to the mediastinal surfaces of the right and left lungs

Right side (Fig.16.2)	Left side (Fig.16.3)
1. Right atrium and auricle	1. Left ventricle, left auricle, infundibulum and adjoining part of the right ventricle
2. A small part of the right ventricle	2. Pulmonary trunk
3. Superior vena cava	3. Arch of aorta
4. Lower part of the right brachiocephalic vein	4. Descending thoracic aorta
5. Azygos vein	5. Left subclavian artery
6. Oesophagus	6. Thoracic duct
7. Inferior vena cava	7. Oesophagus
8. Trachea	8. Left brachiocephalic vein
9. Right vagus nerve	9. Left vagus nerve
10. Right phrenic nerve	10. Left phrenic nerve
	11. Left recurrent laryngeal nerve

6 Anterior and posterior pulmonary plexuses of nerves.
7 Lymphatics of the lung.
8 Bronchopulmonary lymph nodes.
9 Areolar tissue.

Arrangement of Structures in the Root

1 From anterior to posterior. It is similar on the two sides (Fig. 16.4a).
   a. Superior pulmonary vein
   b. Pulmonary artery
   c. Bronchus
2 From above downwards. It is different on the two sides.

Right side
   a. Eparterial bronchus (Fig. 16.4a)
   b. Pulmonary artery
   c. Hyparterial bronchus
   d. Inferior pulmonary vein

Left side
   a. Pulmonary artery
   b. Bronchus
   c. Inferior pulmonary vein (Fig. 16.4b)

Relations of the Root

Anterior
1 *Common on the two sides*
   a. Phrenic nerve
   b. Pericardiacophrenic vessels
   c. Anterior pulmonary plexus
2 *On the right side*
   a. Superior vena cava (Fig. 16.2)
   b. A part of the right atrium.

Posterior
1 *Common on the two sides:*
   a. Vagus nerve
   b. Posterior pulmonary plexus
2 *On left side:* Descending thoracic aorta

Superior
1 *On right side:* Terminal part of azygos vein
2 *On left side:* Arch of the aorta.

Inferior
Pulmonary ligament.

Differences between the Right and Left Lungs

These are given in Table 16.2.

Arterial Supply

The bronchial arteries supply nutrition to the bronchial tree and to the pulmonary tissue. These are small arteries that vary in number, size and origin, but usually they are as follows:
1 On the right side, there is one bronchial artery which arises from the third right posterior intercostal artery.
2 On the left side, there are two bronchial arteries, both of which arise from the descending thoracic aorta, the upper opposite fifth thoracic vertebra and the lower just below the left bronchus.

Deoxygenated blood is brought to the lungs by the two pulmonary arteries and oxygenated blood is returned to the heart by the four pulmonary veins.

There are precapillary anastomoses between bronchial and pulmonary arteries. These connections enlarge when any one of them is obstructed in disease.

Venous Drainage of the Lungs

The venous blood from the first and second divisions of the bronchi is carried by bronchial veins. Usually there are two bronchial veins on each side. The right bronchial veins drain into the azygos vein. The left bronchial veins drain into the hemiazygos vein.

The greater part of the venous blood from the lungs is drained by the pulmonary veins.

Table 16.2: Differences between the right and left lungs

Right lung	Left lung
1. It has 2 fissures and 3 lobes	1. It has only one fissure and 2 lobes
2. Anterior border is straight	2. Anterior border is interrupted by the cardiac notch
3. Larger and heavier, weighs about 700 g	3. Smaller and lighter, weighs about 600 g
4. Shorter and broader	4. Longer and narrower

Lymphatic Drainage

There are two sets of lymphatics, both of which drain into the bronchopulmonary nodes.

1 Superficial vessels drain the peripheral lung tissue lying beneath the pulmonary pleura. The vessels pass round the borders of the lung and margins of the fissures to reach the hilum.

2 Deep lymphatics drain the bronchial tree, the pulmonary vessels and the connective tissue septa. They run towards the hilum where they drain into the bronchopulmonary nodes (Fig. 16.4a).

The superficial vessels have numerous valves and the deep vessels have only a few valves or no valves at all. Though there is no free anastomosis between the

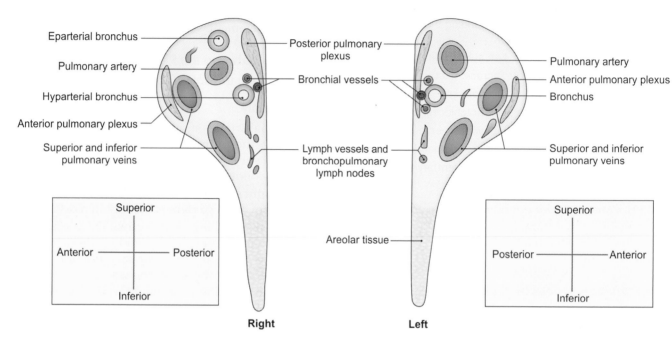

Fig. 16.4a: Roots of the right and left lungs

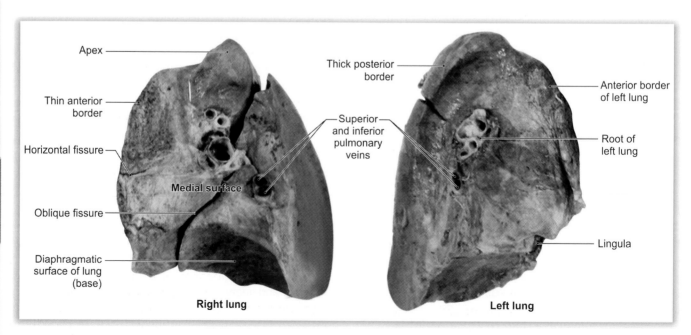

Fig. 16.4b: Gross anatomy of lungs including their roots

superficial and deep vessels, some connections exist which can open up, so that lymph can flow from the deep to the superficial lymphatics when the deep vessels are obstructed in disease of the lungs or of the lymph nodes.

Nerve Supply

1 Parasympathetic nerves are derived from the vagus. These fibres are:
   a. Motor to the bronchial muscles, and on stimulation cause bronchospasm.
   b. Secretomotor to the mucous glands of the bronchial tree.
   c. Sensory fibres are responsible for the stretch reflex of the lungs, and for the cough reflex.
2 Sympathetic nerves are derived from second to fifth sympathetic ganglia. These are inhibitory to the smooth muscle and glands of the bronchial tree. That is how sympathomimetic drugs, like adrenaline, cause bronchodilatation and relieve symptoms of bronchial asthma.

Both parasympathetic and sympathetic nerves first form anterior and posterior pulmonary plexuses situated in front of and behind the lung roots: From the plexuses nerves are distributed to the lungs along the blood vessels and bronchi (Fig. 16.4).

BRONCHIAL TREE

DISSECTION

Dissect the principal bronchus into the left lung. Remove the pulmonary tissue and follow the main bronchus till it is seen to divide into two lobar bronchi. Try to dissect till these divide into the segmental bronchi (Fig. 16.5).

Dissect the principal bronchus into the right lung. Remove the pulmonary tissue and follow the main bronchus till it is seen to divide into three lobar bronchi. Try to dissect till these divide into segmental bronchi.

Features

The *trachea* divides at the level of the lower border of the fourth thoracic vertebra into two primary principal bronchi, one for each lung. The *right principal bronchus* is 2.5 cm long. It is shorter, wider and more in line with the trachea than the left principal bronchus (Fig. 16.5). Inhaled particles or foreign bodies therefore, tend to pass more frequently to the right lung, with the result that infections are more common on the right side than on the left.

The *left principal bronchus* is 5 cm. It is longer, narrower and more oblique than the right bronchus. Right bronchus makes an angle of 25° with tracheal bifurcation, while left bronchus makes an angle of 45° with the trachea.

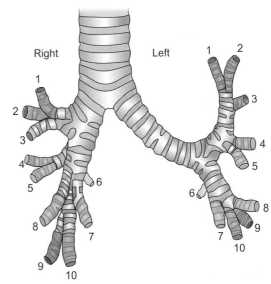

Fig. 16.5: Bronchopulmonary segments of the lungs (both sides 1 to 10, *see* Table 16.3)

Table 16.3: The bronchopulmonary segments	
Right lung	
Lobes	Segments
A. Upper	1. Apical
	2. Posterior
	3. Anterior
B. Middle	4. Lateral
	5. Medial
C. Lower	6. Superior
	7. Medial basal
	8. Anterior basal
	9. Lateral basal
	10. Posterior basal
Left lung	
A. Upper	
• Upper division	1. Apical
	2. Posterior
	3. Anterior
• Lower division	4. Superior lingular
	5. Inferior lingular
B. Lower	6. Superior
	7. Medial basal
	8. Anterior basal
	9. Lateral basal
	10. Posterior basal

Each principal bronchus enters the lung through the hilum, and divides into *secondary lobar bronchi*, one for each lobe of the lungs. Thus there are three lobar bronchi on the right side, and only two on the left side. Each lobar bronchus divides into *tertiary or segmental bronchi*, one for each bronchopulmonary segment; which are 10 on the right side and 10 on the left side. The segmental bronchi divide repeatedly to form very small branches called *terminal bronchioles*.

Section 2 Thorax

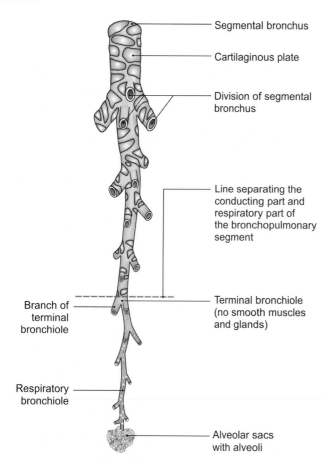

Fig. 16.6: Bronchial tree

Labels: Segmental bronchus; Cartilaginous plate; Division of segmental bronchus; Line separating the conducting part and respiratory part of the bronchopulmonary segment; Branch of terminal bronchiole; Terminal bronchiole (no smooth muscles and glands); Respiratory bronchiole; Alveolar sacs with alveoli

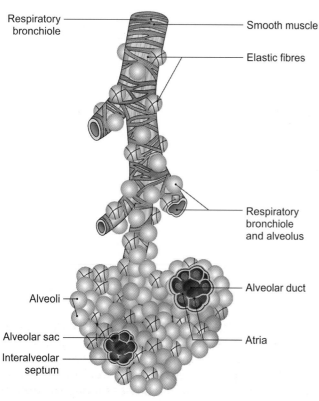

Fig. 16.7: Parts of a pulmonary unit

Labels: Respiratory bronchiole; Smooth muscle; Elastic fibres; Respiratory bronchiole and alveolus; Alveolar duct; Atria; Alveoli; Alveolar sac; Interalveolar septum

Still smaller branches are called *respiratory bronchioles* (Fig. 16.6).

Each respiratory bronchiole aerates a small part of the lung known as a *pulmonary unit*. The respiratory bronchiole ends in microscopic passages which are termed:

1 Alveolar ducts (Fig. 16.7)
2 Atria
3 Air saccules
4 Pulmonary alveoli (Latin *small cavity*). Gaseous exchanges take place in the alveoli.

Bronchopulmonary Segments

The most widely accepted classification of segments is given in Table 16.3. There are 10 segments on the right side and 10 on the left side (Figs 16.5 and 16.8).

Definition

1 These are well-defined anatomic, functional and surgical sectors of the lung.
2 Each one is aerated by a tertiary or segmental bronchus.
3 Each segment is pyramidal in shape with its apex directed towards the root of the lung (Fig. 16.8).
4 Each segment has a segmental bronchus, segmental artery, autonomic nerves and lymph vessels.
5 The segmental venules lies in the connective tissue between adjacent pulmonary units of bronchopulmonary segments.
6 During segmental resection, the surgeon works along the segmental veins to isolate a particular segment.

Relation to Pulmonary Artery

The branches of the pulmonary artery accompany the bronchi. The artery lies dorsolateral to the bronchus. Thus each segment has its own separate artery (Fig. 16.9).

Relation to Pulmonary Vein

The pulmonary veins do not accompany the bronchi or pulmonary arteries. They run in the intersegmental planes. Thus each segment has more than one vein and each vein drains more than one segment. Near the hilum, the veins are ventromedial to the bronchus.

It should be noted that the bronchopulmonary segment is not a bronchovascular segment because it does not have its own vein.

DEVELOPMENT OF RESPIRATORY SYSTEM

The lower respiratory tract primordium appears in the third week of intrauterine life in the form of an

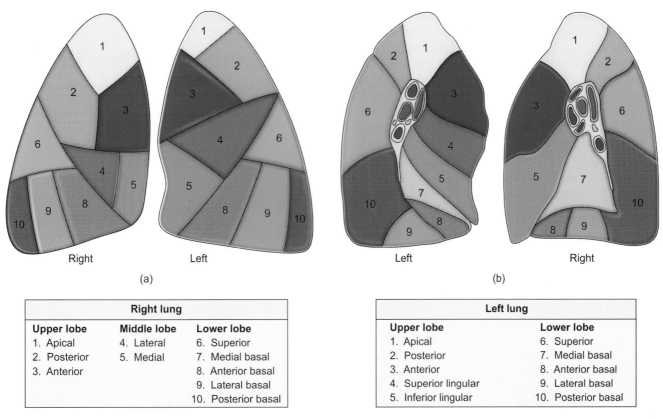

Figs 16.8a and b: The bronchopulmonary segments as seen on: (a) The costal aspects of the right and left lungs. Medial basal segments (no. 7) are not seen, and (b) segments seen on the medial surface of left and right lungs. Lateral segment of middle lobe (no. 4) is not seen on right side

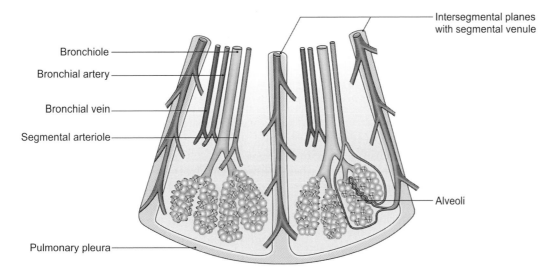

Fig. 16.9: Distal portions of adjacent bronchopulmonary segments

outgrowth (respiratory diverticulum) from the ventral wall of the primitive pharynx, i.e. the part of the foregut caudal to the hypobranchial eminence. Hence epithelial lining of the respiratory system is endodermal in origin. It forms the lining of the larynx, the trachea, the bronchi and the pulmonary alveoli.

The connective tissue, cartilage and smooth muscles of these structures develop from splanchnic mesenchyme surrounding the foregut. As development progresses, the diverticulum separates from the foregut by the tracheo-oesophageal septum (except at the entrance to the larynx).

The respiratory diverticulum below the larynx grows caudally and forms the trachea in the midline. This bifurcates into two lateral outpocketings; the lung buds. In the fifth week of intrauterine life, the proximal parts of each lung bud forms the principal bronchi. Each of these grows laterally and invaginates the pericardio-peritoneal canals (primitive pleural cavities). Following this, the primary bronchi divide into secondary bronchi (3 on the right side and 2 on the left side). These divide dichotomously into tertiary bronchi. Each tertiary bronchus with its surrounding mesenchyme forms a bronchopulmonary segment. By 24th week, about 17 orders of branches are formed and the lung parenchyma develops in four stages.

1 Pseudoglandular stage (between 5 and 17 weeks). In this stage developing lung resembles a gland.
2 Canalicular stage (between 16 and 25 weeks), the lumina of bronchi and bronchioles become larger and tissue becomes more vascular.
3 Terminal sac stage (between 24 weeks to birth). Many saccules appear at the ends of terminal bronchioles (terminal sacs). Capillaries bulge into these sacs.
4 Alveolar stage (late fetal period to 8 years after birth). The epithelial lining of the sacs becomes an extremely thin squamous layer and the alveolocapillary membrane allows exchange of gases.

The four stages overlap each other because the cranial segments of the lungs mature faster than the caudal ones.

By 28–32 weeks, some of the alveolar epithelial cells secrete a substance which is capable of lowering the surface tension at the air–alveolar interface and thus helps maintaining the patency of the alveoli: this is known as pulmonary surfactant.

Table 16.4 and Flowchart 16.1 show the development of respiratory system.

Congenital Anomalies

1 Tracheo-oesophageal fistula: This abnormal communication between the trachea and the oesophagus is due to a deviation of the oesophago-tracheal septum or from mechanical factor pushing the dorsal wall of the foregut anteriorly.
2 Tracheal stenosis.
3 Azygos lobe of lung around vena azygos: This may be due to a additional respiratory buds which develop independently of the main respiratory system.
4 Hyaline membrane disease or distress syndrome: This is due to a deficiency of pulmonary surfactant.
5 Agenesis of lung.

HISTOLOGY

In a section of the lung, the mesothelial covering of visceral pleura may be visible. The structure of the lung

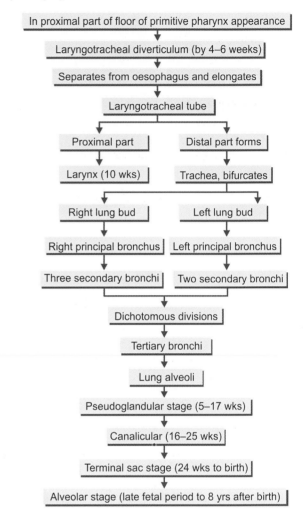

Flowchart 16.1: Quick review of sequence of development of respiratory system

In proximal part of floor of primitive pharynx appearance

Laryngotracheal diverticulum (by 4–6 weeks)

Separates from oesophagus and elongates

Laryngotracheal tube

Proximal part → Larynx (10 wks)

Distal part forms → Trachea, bifurcates

Right lung bud

Left lung bud

Right principal bronchus

Left principal bronchus

Three secondary bronchi

Two secondary bronchi

Dichotomous divisions

Tertiary bronchi

Lung alveoli

Pseudoglandular stage (5–17 wks)

Canalicular (16–25 wks)

Terminal sac stage (24 wks to birth)

Alveolar stage (late fetal period to 8 yrs after birth)

is a lacework of alveoli separated by thin walled septa. This is traversed by system of intrapulmonary bronchi, bronchioles and alveolar ducts, into which atria, alveolar sacs and alveoli open.

Intrapulmonary Bronchus

Intrapulmonary bronchus is lined by *pseudostratified ciliated columnar epithelium* with **goblet cells** resting on a thin basement membrane. **Cilia** prevent the accumulation of mucus in the bronchial tree. The **lamina propria** consists of reticular and elastic fibres. The **submucous coat** contains both mucous and serous acini. A complete layer of smooth muscle fibres is present which is responsible for infoldings of the mucous membrane. Outermost is the hyaline cartilage which is visible as small cartilaginous plates of varying sizes and shapes (Fig. 16.10) with tunica adventitia.

Terminal bronchiole is part of the conducting system of respiratory pathway which is less than 1 mm in diameter. It is lined by simple columnar epithelium.

Table 16.4: Development of components of respiratory system

S. no.	Component	Developed from
1	Epithelium of larynx, trachea bronchi and alveoli	Endoderm of foregut
2	Muscles of larynx	Branchial mesoderm of IVth and VIth
3	Cartilages of larynx-thyroid	IV arch cartilage
	• Cricoid	VI arch cartilage
	• Arytenoid	
4	Epiglottis	Dorsal part of hypobranchial eminence (fused ventral part of III and IV arches)
5	Glands of respiratory tract	Endoderm
6	Muscles, cartilages and connective tissue of trachea and bronchi	Splanchnic mesoderm

The lamina propria contains elastic and smooth muscle fibres. Both the glands and cartilage plates are absent (Fig. 16.11).

Respiratory Bronchiole

Respiratory bronchiole is lined by cuboidal epithelium. The walls consist of collagenous connective tissue containing bundles of interlacing smooth muscle fibres and elastic fibres. At number of places, the alveolar sacs and alveoli arise from the respiratory bronchiole and its cuboidal epithelium is continuous with the squamous epithelium of alveolar sacs and alveoli.

Alveoli

Alveoli are thin-walled polyhedral sacs. The alveoli are lined by two types of cells, which rest on a basement membrane. The main support of the alveoli is provided by elastic fibres. Majority of cells lining the alveoli are the *squamous cells* or *type I pneumocytes*. A few cells are larger cells or *type II pneumocytes*. Type II cells secrete the *surfactant* which lowers surface tension and prevents alveoli from collapsing.

The interalveolar septum containing numerous capillaries lined by continuous non-fenestrated endothelial cells is present between the adjacent alveoli.

CLINICAL ANATOMY

- Usually the infection of a bronchopulmonary segment remains restricted to it, although tuberculosis and bronchogenic carcinoma may spread from one segment to another.
- Knowledge of the detailed anatomy of the bronchial tree helps considerably in:
  a. Segmental resection (Fig. 16.12).
  b. Visualising the interior of the bronchi through a bronchoscope passed through the mouth and trachea. The procedure is called bronchoscopy.

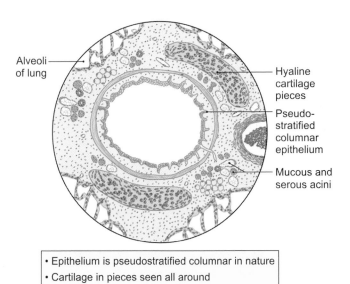

- Epithelium is pseudostratified columnar in nature
- Cartilage in pieces seen all around
- Mucous and serous acini also seen

Fig. 16.10: Intrapulmonary bronchus

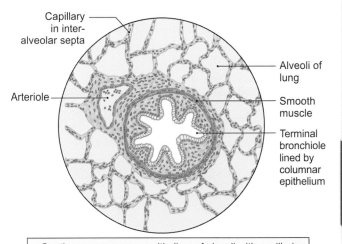

- Continuous squamous epithelium of alveoli with capillaries in interalveolar septa
- Bronchioles do not have glands or cartilages
- Arteriole seen adjacent to bronchiole

Fig. 16.11: Structure of terminal bronchiole

Section 2   Thorax

- Carina is a hook-shaped process projecting backwards from the lower margin of lowest tracheal ring. It helps to divide trachea into two primary bronchi. Right bronchus makes an angle of 25°, while left one makes an angle of 45°. Foreign bodies mostly descend into right bronchus (Fig. 16.13) as it is wider and more vertical than the left bronchus. Enlarged lymph nodes present in this area may distort the carina.
- Carina (Latin *keel*) of the trachea is a sensitive area. When patient is made to lie on her/his left side, secretions from right bronchial tree flow towards the carina due to effect of gravity. This stimulates the cough reflex, and sputum is brought out. This is called *postural drainage* (Fig. 16.14).
- Paradoxical respiration: During inspiration, the flail (abnormally mobile) segments of ribs are pulled inside the chest wall while during expiration the ribs are pushed out (Fig. 16.15).
- Tuberculosis of lung is one of the commonest diseases. A complete course of treatment must be taken under the guidance of a physician.
- *Bronchial asthma* is a common disease of respiratory system. It occurs due to bronchospasm of smooth muscles in the wall of bronchioles. Patient has difficulty especially during expiration. It is accompanied by wheezing. Epinephrine, a sympathomimetic drug, relieves the symptoms.
- *Auscultation of lung:* Upper lobe is auscultated above 4th rib on both sides; lower lobes are best heard on the back. Middle lobe is auscultated between 4th and 6th ribs on right side.
- Superior segment of lower lobe is the most dependent bronchopulmonary segment in supine position. Foreign bodies are likely to be lodged here.

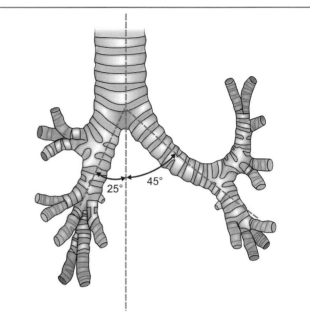

Fig. 16.13: Angles of right and left bronchi with carina

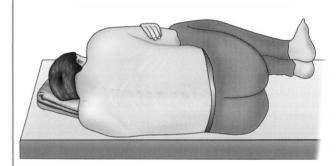

Fig. 16.14: Postural drainage from right lung

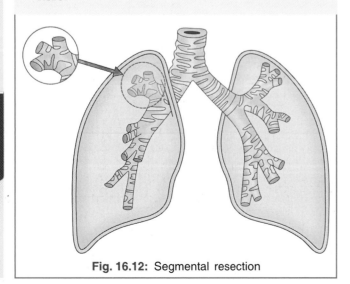

Fig. 16.12: Segmental resection

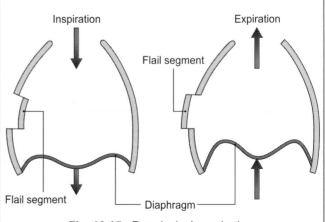

Fig. 16.15: Paradoxical respiration

FACTS TO REMEMBER

- Large spongy lungs occupy almost whole of thoracic cage leaving little space for the heart and accompanying blood vessels, etc.
- Bronchopulmonary segments are independent functional units of lung.
- Lungs are subjected to lot of insult by the smoke of cigarette/bidis/pollution.
- Tuberculosis of lung is one of the commonest killer in an underdeveloped or a developing country.

Complete treatment of TB is a must, otherwise the bacteria become resistant to antitubercular treatment. People harbouring resistant bacteria spread the disease to people around through their sputum.

CLINICOANATOMICAL PROBLEMS

Case 1

A young boy with sore throat while playing with small coins, puts 3 coins in his mouth. When asked by his mother, he takes out two of them, and is not able to take out one.

- Where is the third coin likely to pass?
- What can be the dangers to the boy?

Ans: Since the boy was having sore throat, it is likely the coin has been inhaled into his respiratory passages. The coin would pass down the larynx, trachea, right principal bronchus, as it is in line with trachea. The coin further descends into lower lobe bronchus, and into its posterior basal segment. That segment of the lung would get blocked, causing respiratory symptoms.

If the coin goes into oropharynx and oesophagus, it will comfortably travel down whole of digestive tract and would come out in the faecal matter next day.

Case 2

A 45-year-old man complained of severe cough, loss of weight, alteration of his voice. He has been smoking for last 25 years. Radiograph of the chest followed by biopsy revealed bronchogenic carcinoma in the left upper lobe of the lung.

- Where did the cancer cells metastasise?
- What caused alteration of his voice?

Ans: The bronchogenic carcinoma spreads to the bronchomediastinal lymph nodes. The left supraclavicular nodes are also enlarged and palpable; so these are called 'sentinal nodes'. The enlarged bronchomediastinal lymph nodes may exert pressure on the left recurrent laryngeal nerve in the thorax causing alteration of voice. The cancer of lung is mostly due to smoking.

FREQUENTLY ASKED QUESTIONS

1. Describe the gross anatomy of the lungs. Define a bronchopulmonary segment. Enumerate the segments of the lungs. What is the clinical importance of these segments
2. Write short notes on:
   a. Comparison of the roots of right and left lung
   b. Carina of trachea
   c. Postural drainage
   d. Effects of parasympathetic nerves on the lung
   e. Various subdivision of a segmental bronchus
   f. Intrapulmonary bronchus

MULTIPLE CHOICE QUESTIONS

1. Which one of the following structures is not related to medial surface of right lung?
   a. Superior vena cava
   b. Thoracic duct
   c. Trachea
   d. Oesophagus
2. Which of the following structures is single at the root of each lung?
   a. Pulmonary vein
   b. Pulmonary artery
   c. Bronchus
   d. Bronchial artery
3. Which one of the following is not a common relation to the roots of both lungs?
   a. Anterior pulmonary plexus
   b. Pericardiacophrenic vessels
   c. Superior vena cava
   d. Phrenic nerve

4. Part of lung aerated by a respiratory bronchiole is:
   a. A lobule
   b. A segment
   c. Alveolus
   d. Pulmonary unit

5. Respiratory bronchiole ends in all microscopic passages *except*:
   a. Alveolar ducts
   b. Atria
   c. Pulmonary alveoli
   d. Terminal bronchiole

6. The effects of parasympathetic on lungs are all *except:*
   a. Motor to bronchial muscle
   b. Secretomotor to mucous glands of bronchial tree
   c. Responsible for cough reflex
   d. Causes bronchodilation

7. Which of the following structures run in the intersegmental planes of the lungs?
   a. Segmental venules
   b. Bronchial vessels
   c. Pulmonary arteries
   d. Bronchus

8. Order of origin of segmental bronchi in lower lobe of lung is:
   a. Superior, anterior basal, medial basal, lateral basal and post basal
   b. Superior, medial basal, anterior basal and lateral basal and posterior basal
   c. Medial basal, superior, anterior basal, lateral basal and post basal
   d. Anterior basal, superior, medial basal, lateral basal and post basal

9. Permanent over distension of alveoli is known as:
   a. Empyema
   b. Emphysema
   c. Pneumothorax
   d. Dyspnoea

10. Angles of right and left bronchi at carina are:
    a. 20° and 40°   b. 25° and 45°
    c. 40° and 40°   d. 45° and 25°

ANSWERS									
1. b	2. b	3. c	4. d	5. d	6. d	7. a	8. b	9. b	10. b

Mediastinum

Amitabh Bachhan, the great actor suffered from myasthenia gravis, a disorder of thymus, present in the anterior mediastinum

INTRODUCTION

Mediastinum (plural—mediastina) (Latin *intermediate*) is the middle space left in the thoracic cavity in between the lungs. Its most important content is the heart, enclosed in the pericardium in the middle part of the inferior mediastinum or the middle mediastinum. Above it lies superior mediastinum. Anterior and posterior to the heart are anterior mediastinum and posterior mediastinum, respectively.

The mediastinum is the median septum of the thorax between the two lungs. It includes the mediastinal pleurae.

SUPERIOR AND INFERIOR MEDIASTINA

DISSECTION

Reflect the upper half of manubrium sterni upwards and study the boundaries and contents of superior and three divisions of the inferior mediastinum.

Boundaries

Anteriorly: Sternum

Posteriorly: Vertebral column

Superiorly: Thoracic inlet

Inferiorly: Diaphragm

On each side: Mediastinal pleura.

Divisions

For descriptive purposes, the mediastinum is divided into the *superior mediastinum* and the *inferior mediastinum*. The inferior mediastinum is further divided into the *anterior, middle* and *posterior* mediastina (Fig. 17.1).

The superior mediastinum is separated from the inferior by an imaginary plane passing through the

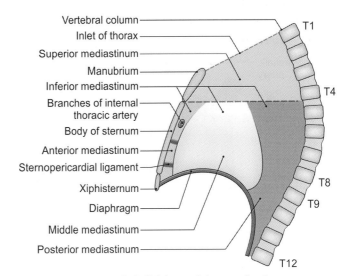

Fig. 17.1: Subdivisions of the mediastinum

sternal angle anteriorly and the lower border of the body of the fourth thoracic vertebra posteriorly. The inferior mediastinum is subdivided into three parts by the pericardium. The area in front of the pericardium is the anterior mediastinum. The area behind the pericardium is the posterior mediastinum. The pericardium and its contents form the middle mediastinum.

SUPERIOR MEDIASTINUM

Boundaries

Anteriorly: Manubrium sterni (Fig. 17.1)

Posteriorly: Upper four thoracic vertebrae

Superiorly: Plane of the thoracic inlet

Inferiorly: An imaginary plane passing through the sternal angle in front, and the lower border of the body of the fourth thoracic vertebra behind.

On each side: Mediastinal pleura.

Contents

1 *Trachea and oesophagus.*
2 *Muscles:* Origins of (i) sternohyoid, (ii) sterno-thyroid, (iii) lower ends of longus colli.
3 *Arteries:* (i) Arch of aorta, (ii) brachiocephalic artery, (iii) left common carotid artery, (iv) left subclavian artery (Fig. 17.2).
4 *Veins:* (i) Right and left brachiocephalic veins, (ii) upper half of the superior vena cava, (iii) left superior intercostal vein.
5 *Nerves:* (i) Vagus, (ii) phrenic, (iii) cardiac nerves of both sides, (iv) left recurrent laryngeal nerve.
6 *Thymus*
7 *Thoracic duct*
8 *Lymph nodes:* Paratracheal, brachiocephalic, and tracheobronchial.

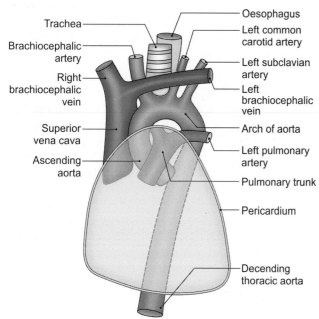

Fig. 17.2: Arrangement of the large structures in the superior mediastinum. Note the relationship of superior vena cava, ascending aorta and pulmonary trunk to each other in the middle mediastinum, i.e. within the pericardium. The bronchi are not shown

INFERIOR MEDIASTINUM

The inferior mediastinum is divided into—anterior, middle and posterior mediastina.

Anterior Mediastinum

Anterior mediastinum is a very narrow space in front of the pericardium, overlapped by the thin anterior borders of both lungs. It is continuous through the superior mediastinum with the pretracheal space of the neck. It contains areolar tissue and part of thymus gland.

Boundaries

Anteriorly: Body of sternum

Posteriorly: Pericardium

Superiorly: Imaginary plane separating the superior mediastinum from the inferior mediastinum.

Inferiorly: Superior surface of diaphragm.

On each side: Mediastinal pleura.

Contents

1 Sternopericardial ligaments (Fig. 17.1)
2 Lymph nodes with lymphatics
3 Small mediastinal branches of the internal thoracic artery.
4 The lowest part of the thymus
5 Areolar tissue.

Middle Mediastinum

Middle mediastinum is occupied by the pericardium and its contents, along with the phrenic nerves and the pericardiacophrenic vessels.

Boundaries

Anteriorly: Sternopericardial ligaments.

Posteriorly: Oesophagus, descending thoracic aorta, azygos vein (*see* Figs 15.1 and 15.2).

On each side: Mediastinal pleura.

Contents

1 *Heart* enclosed in pericardium (Fig. 17.2)
2 *Arteries:* (i) Ascending aorta, (ii) pulmonary trunk, (iii) two pulmonary arteries (Fig. 17.3)
3 *Veins:* (i) Lower half of the superior vena cava, (ii) terminal part of the azygos vein, and (iii) right and left pulmonary veins.

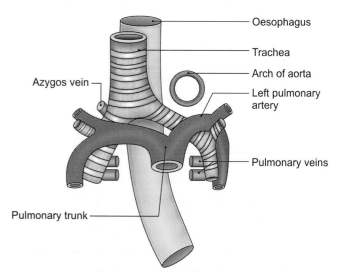

Fig. 17.3: Some structures present in superior, middle and posterior mediastina

4 *Nerves:* (i) Phrenic and (ii) deep cardiac plexus.
5 *Lymph nodes:* Tracheobronchial nodes.
6 *Tubes:* (i) Bifurcation of trachea and (ii) the right and left principal bronchi.

Posterior Mediastinum

Boundaries

Anteriorly: (i) Pericardium, (ii) bifurcation of trachea, (iii) pulmonary vessels, and (iv) posterior part of the upper surface of the diaphragm.

Posteriorly: Lower eight thoracic vertebrae and intervening discs.

On each side: Mediastinal pleura.

Contents

1 *Oesophagus* (Fig. 17.4).
2 *Arteries:* Descending thoracic aorta and its branches.
3 *Veins:* (i) Azygos vein, (ii) hemiazygos vein, and (iii) accessory hemiazygos vein.
4 *Nerves:* (i) Vagi, (ii) splanchnic nerves, greater, lesser and least, arising from the lower eight thoracic ganglia of the sympathetic chain (*see* Fig. 15.1).
5 *Lymph nodes and lymphatics:*
   a. Posterior mediastinal lymph nodes lying alongside the aorta.
   b. The thoracic duct (Fig. 17.4).

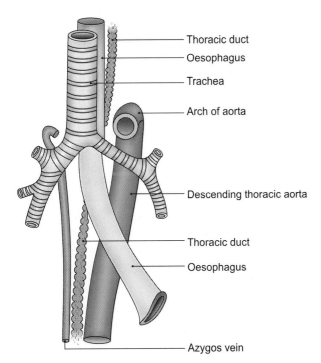

Thoracic duct
Oesophagus
Trachea
Arch of aorta
Descending thoracic aorta
Thoracic duct
Oesophagus
Azygos vein

Fig. 17.4: Structures in the posterior part of the superior mediastinum, and their continuation into the posterior mediastinum. Note the relationship of the arch of the aorta to the left bronchus, and that of the azygos vein to the right bronchus

- The prevertebral layer of the deep cervical fascia extends to the superior mediastinum, and is attached to the fourth thoracic vertebra. An infection present in the neck behind this fascia can pass down into the superior mediastinum but not lower down.

   The pretracheal fascia of the neck also extends to the superior mediastinum, where it blends with the arch of the aorta. Neck infections between the pretracheal and prevertebral fasciae can spread into the superior mediastinum, and through it into the posterior mediastinum. Thus mediastinitis can result from infections in the neck (*see* Chapter 3 of Volume 3).

- There is very little loose connective tissue between the mobile organs of the mediastinum. Therefore, the space can be readily dilated by inflammatory fluids, neoplasms, etc.

- In the superior mediastinum, all large veins are on the right side and the arteries on the left side. During increased blood flow, veins expand enormously, while the large arteries do not expand at all. Thus there is much 'dead space' on the right side and it is into this space that tumour or fluids of the mediastinum tend to project (Fig. 17.5).

- Compression of mediastinal structures by any tumour gives rise to a group of symptoms known as *mediastinal syndrome*. The common symptoms are as follows:

   a Obstruction of superior vena cava gives rise to engorgement of veins in the upper half of the body.

   b. Pressure over the trachea causes dyspnoea, and cough.

   c. Pressure on oesophagus causes dysphagia.

   d. Pressure or the left recurrent laryngeal nerve gives rise to hoarseness of voice (dysphonia).

   e. Pressure on the phrenic nerve causes paralysis of the diaphragm on that side.

   f. Pressure on the intercostal nerves gives rise to pain in the area supplied by them. It is called *intercostal neuralgia*.

   g. Pressure on the vertebral column may cause erosion of the vertebral bodies.

   The common causes of mediastinal syndrome are bronchogenic carcinoma, Hodgkin's disease causing enlargement of the mediastinal lymph nodes, aneurysm or dilatation of the aorta, etc.

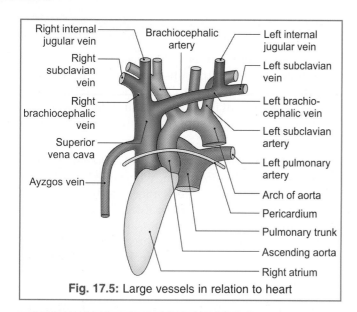

Right internal jugular vein
Brachiocephalic artery
Left internal jugular vein
Right subclavian vein
Left subclavian vein
Right brachiocephalic vein
Left brachio-cephalic vein
Superior vena cava
Left subclavian artery
Ayzgos vein
Left pulmonary artery
Arch of aorta
Pericardium
Pulmonary trunk
Ascending aorta
Right atrium

Fig. 17.5: Large vessels in relation to heart

Mnemonics

***Superior Mediastinum Contents:* PVT Left BATTLE**

Phrenic nerve
Vagus nerve
Thoracic duct
Left recurrent laryngeal nerve (not the right)
Brachiocephalic veins
Aortic arch (and its 3 branches)
Thymus   **L**ymph nodes
Trachea   **E**sophagus

FACTS TO REMEMBER

- Mediastinum is the middle space between the lungs.
- It is chiefly occupied by the heart enclosed in pericardium with blood vessels and nerves.
- Unit structures in the superior mediasternum are trachea, oesophagus, left recurrent laryngeal nerve between the two tubes and thoracic duct on the left of the oesophagus.

CLINICOANATOMICAL PROBLEM

A patient presents with lots of dilated veins in the front of chest and anterior thoracic wall

- What is the reason for so many veins seen on the anterior body wall?
- How does venous blood go back in circulation?

Ans: This appears to be a case of blockage of superior vena cava after the entry of vena azygos. The blood needs to return to heart and it is done through inferior vena cava. The backflow occurs:

Superior vena cava blockage → brachiocephalic veins → subclavian veins → axillary veins → lateral thoracic veins → thoracoepigastric veins → superficial epigastric veins → great saphenous veins → femoral veins → common iliac veins → inferior vena cava → right atrium of heart (*see* Fig. 14.6).

Many veins open up to assist the drainage

FREQUENTLY ASKED QUESTIONS

1. Enumerate the boundaries and contents of superior mediastinum
2. Enumerate the boundaries of mediastinum and its subdivisions.
3. Enumerate:
   a. Contents of middle mediastinum
   b. Contents of posterior mediastinum

MULTIPLE CHOICE QUESTIONS

1. Boundaries of mediastinum are all *except*:
   a. Sternum   b. Cervical vertebrae
   c. Thoracic inlet   d. Diaphragm
2. Inferior mediastinum is divided into:
   a. Anterior   b. Middle
   c. Posterior   d. Posteroinferior
3. Contents of middle mediastinum are all *except*:
   a. Heart with pericardium
   b. Pulmonary arteries
   c. Lower half of superior vena cava
   d. Bifurcation of trachea

4. Which one is not a content of superior mediastinum?
   a. Arch of aorta   b. Lower half of superior vena cava
   c. Trachea   d. Oesophagus
5. Which one is not a content of posterior mediastinum?
   a. Oesophagus   b. Descending thoracic aorta
   c. Arch of vena azygos   d. Vagus nerve

ANSWERS

1. b   **2.** d   **3.** d   **4.** b   **5.** c

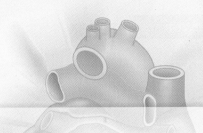

Pericardium and Heart

When there is room in the heart, there is room in the house
—Anonymous

INTRODUCTION

Pericardium, comprising fibrous and serous layers, encloses the heart pulsating from 'womb to tomb'.

Heart is a vital organ, pumping blood to the entire body (Figs 18.1 and 18.2). Its pulsations are governed by the brain through various nerves. Since heartbeat is felt or seen against the chest wall, it appears to be more active than the 'quiet brain' controlling it. That is why there are so many songs on the heart and few on the brain. Meditation, *yoga* and exercise help in regulating the heart beat through the brain.

PERICARDIUM

DISSECTION

Make a vertical cut through each side of the pericardium immediately anterior to the line of the phrenic nerve. Join the lower ends of these two incisions by a transverse cut approximately 1 cm above the diaphragm. Turn the flap of pericardium upwards and sideways to examine the pericardial cavity. See that the turned flap comprises fibrous and parietal layer of visceral pericardium. The pericardium enclosing the heart is its visceral layer (Fig. 18.3).

Pass a probe from the right side behind the ascending aorta and pulmonary trunk till it appears on the left just to the right of left atrium. This probe is in the *transverse sinus of the pericardium* (Fig. 18.4).

Lift the apex of the heart upwards. Put a finger behind the left atrium into a cul-de-sac, bounded to the right and below by inferior vena cava and above and to left by lower left pulmonary vein. This is the *oblique sinus of pericardium*.

Define the borders, surfaces, grooves, apex and base of the heart.

Features

The pericardium (Greek *around heart*) is a fibroserous sac which encloses the heart and the roots of the great vessels. It is situated in the middle mediastinum. It consists of the *fibrous pericardium* and the *serous pericardium* (Figs 18.1b and 18.2).

Fibrous pericardium encloses the heart and fuses with the vessels which enter/leave the heart. Heart is situated within the fibrous and serous pericardial sacs. As heart develops, it invaginates itself into the serous sac, without causing any breach in its continuity. The last part to enter the region of atria, from where the visceral pericardium is reflected as the parietal pericardium. Thus parietal layer of serous pericardium gets adherent to the inner surface of fibrous pericardium, while the visceral layer of serous pericardium gets adherent to the outer layer of heart and forms its epicardium.

FIBROUS PERICARDIUM

Fibrous pericardium is a conical sac made up of fibrous tissue. The parietal layer of serous pericardium is attached to its deep surface. The following features of the fibrous pericardium are noteworthy.

1 The apex is blunt and lies at the level of the sternal angle. It is fused with the roots of the great vessels and with the pretracheal fascia.
2 The base is broad and inseparably blended with the central tendon of the diaphragm.
3 Anteriorly, it is connected to the upper and lower ends of body of the sternum by weak superior and inferior *sternopericardial ligaments* (Fig. 18.3).
4 Posteriorly, it is related to the principal bronchi, the oesophagus with the nerve plexus around it and the descending thoracic aorta.
5 On each side, it is related to the mediastinal pleura, the mediastinal surface of the lung, the phrenic nerve, and the pericardiacophrenic vessels.
6 It protects the heart against sudden overfilling and prevents over expansion of the heart.

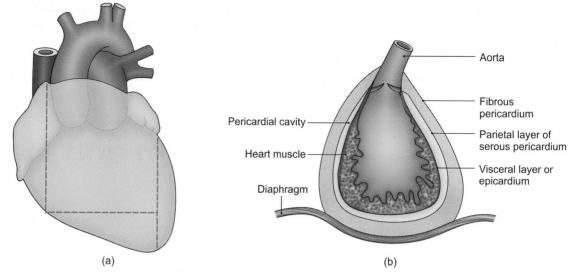

Figs 18.1a and b: (a) Lines of incision, and (b) layers of the pericardium

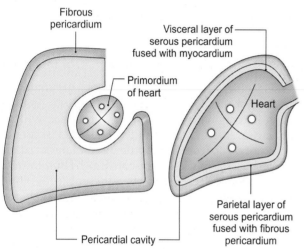

Fig. 18.2: Development of the layers of serous pericardium

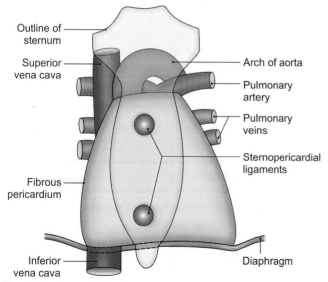

Fig. 18.3: The relations of the fibrous pericardium to the roots of the great vessels, to the diaphragm and sternum

SEROUS PERICARDIUM

Serous pericardium is thin, double-layered serous membrane lined by mesothelium. The outer layer or parietal pericardium is fused with the fibrous pericardium. The inner layer or the visceral pericardium, or epicardium is fused to the heart, except along the cardiac grooves, where it is separated from the heart by blood vessels. The two layers are continuous with each other at the roots of the great vessels, i.e. ascending aorta, pulmonary trunk, two venae cavae, and four pulmonary veins.

The *pericardial cavity* is a potential space between the parietal pericardium and the visceral pericardium. It contains only a thin film of serous fluid which lubricates the apposed surfaces and allows the heart to beat smoothly.

Sinuses of Pericardium

The epicardium at the roots of the great vessels is arranged in form of two tubes. The arterial tube encloses the ascending aorta and the pulmonary trunk at the arterial end of the heart tube, and the venous tube encloses the venae cavae and pulmonary veins at the venous end of the heart tube. The passage between the two tubes is known as the *transverse sinus* of pericardium. During development, to begin with, the veins of the heart are crowded together. As the heart increases in size and these veins separate out, a pericardial reflection surrounds all of them and forms the *oblique pericardial sinus*. This cul-de-sac is posterior to the left atrium (Fig. 18.4).

The *transverse sinus* is a horizontal gap between the arterial and venous ends of the heart tube. It is bounded anteriorly by the ascending aorta and pulmonary trunk, and posteriorly by the superior vena cava and inferiorly by the left atrium; on each side, it opens into the general pericardial cavity (Fig. 18.5). It develops from degeneration of the central part of dorsal mesocardium.

The *oblique sinus* is a narrow gap behind the heart. It is bounded anteriorly by the left atrium, and posteriorly by the parietal pericardium and oesophagus. On the right and left sides, it is bounded by reflections of pericardium as shown in Fig. 18.5. Below and to the left, it opens into the rest of the pericardial cavity. The oblique sinus permits pulsations of the left atrium to take place freely (Figs 18.4 and 18.5). It develops due to rearrangement of veins at the venous end.

Contents of the Pericardium

1 Heart with cardiac vessels and nerves.
2 Ascending aorta.
3 Pulmonary trunk.
4 Lower half of the superior vena cava.

5 Terminal part of the inferior vena cava
6 The terminal parts of the pulmonary veins.

Blood Supply

The fibrous and parietal pericardia are supplied by branches from:

1 Internal thoracic
2 Musculophrenic arteries
3 The descending thoracic aorta
4 Veins drain into corresponding veins.

Nerve Supply

The fibrous and parietal pericardia are supplied by the phrenic nerves. They are sensitive to pain. The epicardium is supplied by autonomic nerves of the heart and is not sensitive to pain. Pain of pericarditis originates in the parietal pericardium alone. On the other hand, cardiac pain or angina originates in the cardiac muscle or in the vessels of the heart.

Development

Fibrous pericardium develops from septum transversum.

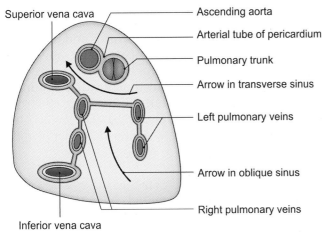

Fig. 18.4: The pericardial cavity seen after removal of the heart. Note the reflections of pericardium, and the mode of formation of the transverse and oblique sinuses

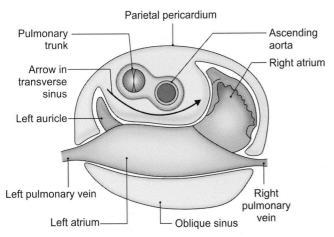

Fig. 18.5: Transverse section through the upper part of the heart. Note that oblique sinus forms posterior boundary of left atrium

---

CLINICAL ANATOMY

- Collection of fluid in the pericardial cavity is referred to as *pericardial effusion* or cardiac tamponade. The fluid compresses the heart and restricts venous filling during diastole. It also reduces cardiac output. Pericardial effusion can be drained by puncturing the left fifth or sixth intercostal space just lateral to the sternum, or in the angle between the xiphoid process and left costal margin, with the needle directed upwards, backwards and to the left (Fig. 18.6).

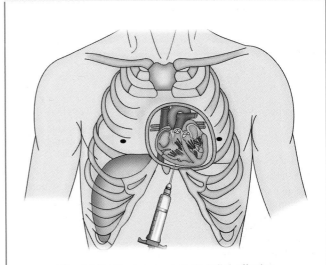

Fig. 18.6: Drainage of pericardial effusion

Section **2** **Thorax**

- In mitral stenosis, left atrium enlarges and compresses the oesophagus causing dysphagia.
- During heart surgery, the ligature is passed through the transverse sinus around aorta and the pulmonary trunk.

HEART

The heart is a conical hollow muscular organ situated in the middle mediastinum. It is enclosed within the pericardium. It pumps blood to various parts of the body to meet their nutritive requirements. The Greek name for the heart is *cardia* from which we have the adjective *cardia*. The Latin name for the heart is *cor* from which we have the adjective *coronary*.

The heart is placed obliquely behind the body of the sternum and adjoining parts of the costal cartilages, so that one-third of it lies to the right and two-thirds to the left of the median plane. The direction of blood flow, from atria to the ventricles is downwards forwards and to the left. The heart measures about 12 × 9 cm and weighs about 300 g in males and 250 g in females.

EXTERNAL FEATURES

The human heart has four chambers. These are the right and left atria and the right and left ventricles. The atria (Latin *chamber*) lie above and behind the ventricles. On the surface of the heart, they are separated from the ventricles by an atrioventricular groove. The atria are separated from each other by an interatrial groove. The ventricles are separated from each other by an interventricular groove, which is subdivided into anterior and posterior parts (Fig. 18.7). The heart has:

- An apex directed downwards, forwards and to the left.
- A base (posterior surface) directed backwards
- Three surfaces—anterior/sternocostal, inferior and left lateral
- *Borders:* The surfaces are demarcated by upper, inferior, right and left borders.

Grooves or Sulci

The atria are separated from the ventricles by a circular *atrioventricular* or *coronary sulcus*, which is divided into anterior and posterior parts. Anterior part consists of right and left halves. Right half is oblique between right auricle and right ventricle, lodging right coronary artery. Left part is small between left auricle and left ventricle, lodges circumflex branch of left coronary.

The coronary sulcus is overlapped anteriorly by the ascending aorta and the pulmonary trunk. The *interatrial groove* is faintly visible posteriorly, while anteriorly, it is hidden by the aorta and pulmonary trunk. The *anterior interventricular groove* is nearer to the left margin of the heart. It runs downwards and to the left. The lower end of the groove separates the apex from the rest of the inferior border of the heart. The *posterior interventricular groove* is situated on the diaphragmatic or inferior surface of the heart. It is nearer to the right margin of this surface (Fig. 18.8). The two interventricular grooves meet at the inferior border near the apex.

Apex of the Heart

Apex of the heart is formed entirely by the left ventricle. It is directed downwards, forwards and to the left and is overlapped by the anterior border of the left lung. It is situated in the left fifth intercostal space 9 cm lateral to the midsternal line just medial to the midclavicular

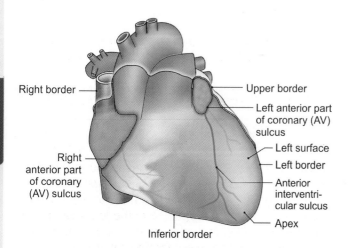

Fig. 18.7: Gross features: Sternocostal surface of heart

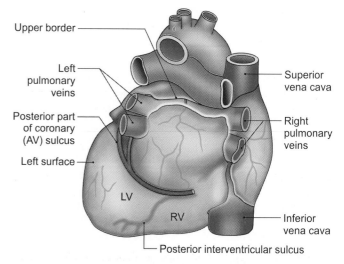

Fig. 18.8: The posterior base and inferior surface of the heart

line. In the living subject, pulsations may be seen and felt over this region (Fig. 18.7).

In children below 2 years, apex is situated in the left fourth intercostal space in midclavicular line.

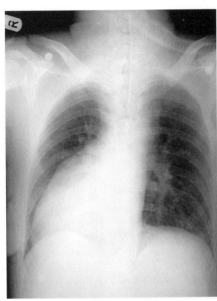
Base of the Heart

The *base* of the heart is also called its posterior surface. It is formed mainly by the left atrium and by a small part of the right atrium.

In relation to the base one can see the openings of four pulmonary veins which open into the left atrium; and of the superior and inferior venae cavae (Latin, *empty vein*) which open into the right atrium. It is related to thoracic five to thoracic eight vertebrae in the lying posture, and descends by one vertebra in the erect posture. It is separated from the vertebral column by the pericardium, the right pulmonary veins, the oesophagus and the aorta (*see* Figs 15.2 and 17.2).

Borders of the Heart

1 The *upper border* is slightly oblique, and is formed by the two atria, chiefly the left atrium.

2 The *right border* is more or less vertical and is formed by the right atrium. It extends from superior vena cava to inferior vena cava (IVC).

3 The *inferior border* is nearly horizontal and is formed mainly by the right ventricle. A small part of it near the apex is formed by left ventricle. It extends from IVC to apex.

4 The *left border* is oblique and curved. It is formed mainly by the left ventricle, and partly by the left auricle. It separates the anterior and left surfaces of the heart (Fig. 18.7). It extends from apex to left auricle.

Surfaces of the Heart

The *anterior* or *sternocostal surface* is formed mainly by the right atrium and right ventricle, and partly by the left ventricle and left auricle (Fig. 18.7). The left atrium is not seen on the anterior surface as it is covered by the aorta and pulmonary trunk. Most of the sternocostal surface is covered by the lungs, but a part of it that lies behind the cardiac notch of the left lung is uncovered. The uncovered area is dull on percussion. Clinically, it is referred to as the *area of superficial cardiac dullness.*

The *inferior* or *diaphragmatic surface* rests on the central tendon of the diaphragm. It is formed in its left two-thirds by the left ventricle, and in its right one-third by the right ventricle. It is traversed by the posterior interventricular groove, and is directed downwards and slightly backwards (Fig. 18.8).

The *left surface* is formed mostly by the left ventricle, and at the upper end by the left auricle. In its upper part, the surface is crossed by the coronary sulcus. It is related to the left phrenic nerve, the left pericardiacophrenic vessels and the pericardium.

Crux of the Heart

Crux of the heart is the meeting point of interatrial, atrioventricular and posterior interventricular grooves.

Types of Circulation

There are two main types of circulations, systemic and pulmonary. Table 18.1 shows their comparison.

RIGHT ATRIUM

Table 18.1: Comparing the systemic circulation and pulmonary circulation

Systemic circulation	Pulmonary circulation
Left ventricle	Right ventricle
↓	↓
Aortic valve	Pulmonary valve
↓	↓
Aorta	Pulmonary trunk and pulmonary arteries
↓	↓
Oxygenated blood to all tissues except lungs	Only to lungs
↓	↓
Venous blood collected	Deoxygenated blood gets oxygenated
↓	↓
Superior vena cava and inferior vena cava	4 pulmonary veins
↓	↓
Right atrium	left atrium

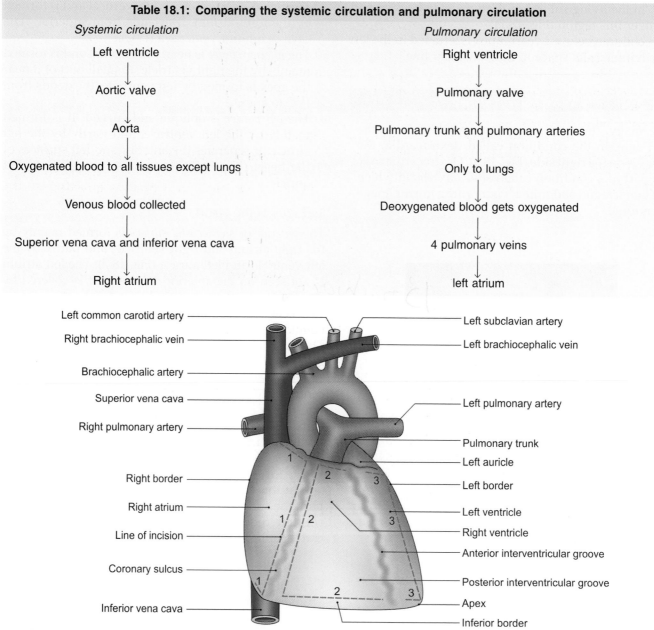

Fig. 18.10: External features of heart: (1) Line of incision for right atrium, (2) for right ventricle, and (3) for left ventricle

On its internal surface, see the vertical crista terminalis and horizontal pectinate muscles.

The fossa ovalis is on the interatrial septum and the opening of the coronary sinus is to the left of the inferior vena caval opening.

Define the three cusps of tricuspid valve.

Position

The right atrium is the right upper chamber of the heart. It receives venous blood from the whole body, pumps it to the right ventricle through the right atrioventricular or tricuspid opening. It forms the right border, part of the upper border, the sternocostal surface and the base of the heart (Fig. 18.7).

External Features

1 The chamber is elongated vertically, receiving the superior vena cava at the upper end and the inferior vena cava at the lower end (Fig. 18.11).
2 The upper end is prolonged to the left to form the right *auricle* (Latin *little ear*). The auricle covers the root of the ascending aorta and partly overlaps the infundibulum of the right ventricle. Its margins are notched and the interior is sponge-like, which prevents free flow of blood.

3 Along the right border of the atrium, there is a shallow vertical groove which passes from the superior vena cava to the inferior vena cava. This groove is called the *sulcus terminalis*. It is produced by an internal muscular ridge called the *crista terminalis* (Fig. 18.11a). The upper part of the sulcus contains the *sinuatrial* or *SA node* which acts as the pacemaker of the heart.

4 The right atrioventricular groove separates the right atrium from the right ventricle. It is more or less vertical and lodges the right coronary artery and the small cardiac vein.

Tributaries or Inlets of the Right Atrium

1 Superior vena cava.
2 Inferior vena cava.
3 Coronary sinus.
4 Anterior cardiac veins.
5 Venae cordis minimae (thebesian veins).
6 Sometimes the right marginal vein.

Right Atrioventricular Orifice

Blood passes out of the right atrium through the right atrioventricular or tricuspid orifice and goes to the right ventricle. The tricuspid orifice is guarded by the

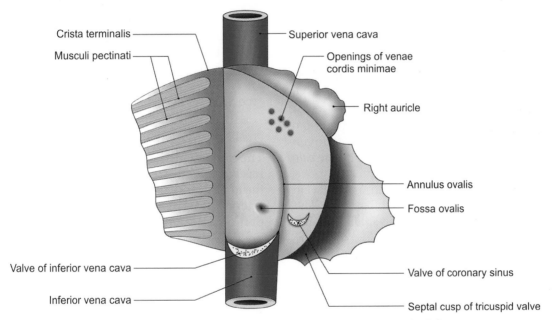

Fig. 18.11a: Interior of right atrium (cut along sulcus terminalis)

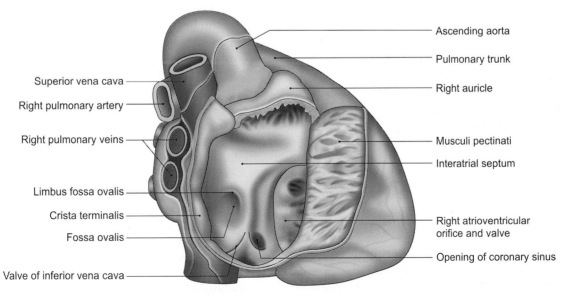

Fig. 18.11b: Interior of right atrium (cut along coronary sulcus)

Section 2 Thorax

tricuspid valve which maintains unidirectional flow of blood (Fig. 18.11b).

Internal Features

The interior of the right atrium can be broadly divided into the following three parts:

Smooth Posterior Part or Sinus Venarum

1 Developmentally, it is derived from the right horn of the sinus venosus.
2 Most of the tributaries except the anterior cardiac veins open into it.
   a The *superior vena cava* opens at the upper end.
   b The *inferior vena cava* opens at the lower end (Fig. 18.1a).

   The opening of inferior vena cava is guarded by a rudimentary valve of the inferior vena cava or *eustachian valve*. During embryonic life, the valve guides the inferior vena caval blood to the left atrium through the *foramen ovale*.
   c. The *coronary sinus* opens between the opening of the inferior vena cava and the right atrioventricular orifice. The opening is guarded by the *valve of the coronary sinus* or *thebesian valve*.
   d. The venae cordis minimae are numerous small veins present in the walls of all the four chambers. They open into the right atrium through small foramina.
3 The *intervenous tubercle* of *Lower* is a very small projection, scarcely visible, on the posterior wall of the atrium just below the opening of the superior vena cava. During embryonic life, it directs the superior caval blood to the right ventricle.

Rough Anterior Part or Pectinate Part, including the Auricle

1 Developmentally, it is derived from the primitive atrial chamber.
2 It presents a series of transverse muscular ridges called *musculi pectinati* (Figs 18.11a and b).

   They arise from the crista terminalis and run forwards and downwards towards the atrioventricular orifice, giving the appearance of the teeth of a comb. In the auricle, the muscles are interconnected to form a reticular network.

Interatrial Septum

1 Developmentally, it is derived from the *septum primum* and *septum secundum*.
2 It presents the *fossa ovalis*, a shallow saucer-shaped depression, in the lower part. The fossa represents the site of the embryonic septum primum.
3 The *annulus ovalis* or *limbus* (Latin *a border) fossa ovalis* is the prominent margin of the fossa ovalis. It represents the lower free edge of the septum

secundum. It is distinct above and at the sides of the fossa ovalis, but is deficient inferiorly. Its anterior edge is continuous with the left end of the valve of the inferior vena cava.
4 The remains of the *foramen ovale* are occasionally present. This is a small slit-like valvular opening between the upper part of the fossa and the limbus. It is normally occluded after birth, but may sometimes persist.

RIGHT VENTRICLE

DISSECTION

Incise along the ventricular aspect of right AV groove, till you reach the inferior border. Continue to incise along the inferior border till the inferior end of anterior interventricular groove. Next cut along the infundibulum.

Now the anterior wall of right ventricle is reflected to the left to study its interior (Fig. 18.10).

Position

The right ventricle is a triangular chamber which receives blood from the right atrium and pumps it to the lungs through the pulmonary trunk and pulmonary arteries. It forms the inferior border and a two-thirds part of the sternocostal surface and one-third part of inferior surface of the heart (Fig. 18.7).

External Features

1. Externally, the right ventricle has two surfaces—anterior or sternocostal and inferior or diaphragmatic.
2. The interior has two parts:
   a. The *inflowing part* is rough due to the presence of muscular ridges called *trabeculae carneae*. It develops from the proximal part of bulbus cordis of the heart tube.
   b. The *outflowing part* or *infundibulum* is smooth and forms the upper conical part of the right ventricle which gives rise to the pulmonary trunk. It develops from the mid portion of the bulbus cordis.

The two parts are separated by a muscular ridge called the *supraventricular crest* or infundibuloventricular crest situated between the tricuspid and pulmonary orifices.

Internal Features

1 The interior shows two orifices:
   a The right atrioventricular or tricuspid orifice, guarded by the tricuspid valve.
   b. The pulmonary orifice guarded by the pulmonary valve (Fig. 18.12).
2 The interior of the inflowing part shows *trabeculae carneae* or muscular ridges of three types:

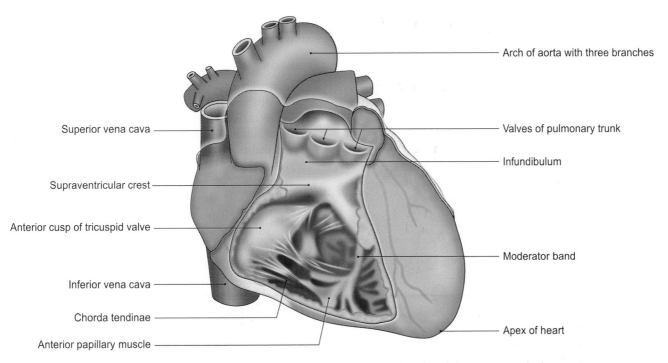

Fig. 18.12: Interior of the right ventricle. Note the moderator band and the supraventricular crest

a. *Ridges* or fixed elevations
b. *Bridges*
c. *Pillars* or *papillary muscles* with one end attached to the ventricular wall, and the other end connected to the cusps of the tricuspid valve by chordae tendinae (Latin *strings to stretch*). There are three papillary muscles in the right ventricle, anterior, posterior and septal. The anterior muscle is the largest (Fig. 18.12). The posterior or inferior muscle is small and irregular. The septal muscle is divided into a number of little nipples. Each papillary muscle is attached by chordae tendinae to the contiguous sides of two cusps (Fig. 18.13).

3 The septomarginal trabecula or moderator band is a muscular ridge extending from the ventricular septum to the base of the anterior papillary muscle. It contains the right branch of the AV bundle (Figs 18.12 and 18.14).

4 The cavity of the right ventricle is crescentic in section because of the forward bulge of the interventricular septum (Fig. 18.15).

5 The wall of the right ventricle is thinner than that of the left ventricle in a ratio of 1:3.

Interventricular Septum

The septum is placed obliquely. Its one surface faces forwards and to the right and the other faces backwards and to the left. The upper part of the septum is thin and membranous and separates not only the two ventricles but also the right atrium and left ventricle. The lower part is thick muscular and separates the two ventricles

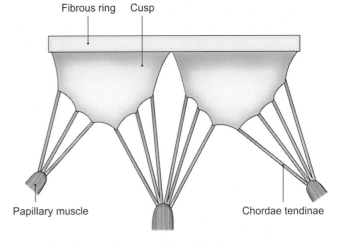

Fig. 18.13: Structure of an atrioventricular valve

(Fig. 18.15). Its position is indicated by the anterior and posterior interventricular grooves.

LEFT ATRIUM

DISSECTION

Cut off the pulmonary trunk and ascending aorta, immediately above the three cusps of the pulmonary and aortic valves. Remove the upper part of the left atrium to visualise its interior (Fig. 18.8). See the upper surface of the cusps of the mitral valve. Revise the fact that left atrium forms the anterior wall of the oblique sinus of the pericardium (Fig. 18.5).

Section 2   Thorax

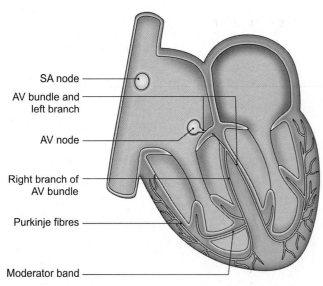

Fig. 18.14: The conducting system of the heart

Position

The left atrium is a quadrangular chamber situated posteriorly. Its appendage, the *left auricle* projects anteriorly to overlap the infundibulum of the right ventricle. The left atrium forms the left two-thirds of the base of the heart, the greater part of the upper border, parts of the sternocostal and left surfaces and the left border. It receives oxygenated blood from the lungs through four pulmonary veins, and pumps it to the left ventricle through the left atrioventricular or bicuspid (Latin *two tooth point*) or mitral orifice (Latin

like bishop's mitre) which is guarded by the valve of the same name.

Features

1 The posterior surface of the atrium forms the anterior wall of the oblique sinus of pericardium (Fig. 18.5).
2 The anterior wall of the atrium is formed by the interatrial septum.
3 Two pulmonary veins open into the atrium on each side of the posterior wall (Fig. 18.8).
4 The greater part of the interior of the atrium is smooth walled. It is derived embryologically from the absorbed pulmonary veins which open into it. Musculi pectinati are present only in the auricle where they form a reticulum. This part develops from the original primitive atrial chamber of the heart tube. The septal wall shows the fossa lunata corresponding to the fossa ovalis of the right atrium. In addition to the four pulmonary veins, the tributaries of the atrium include a few venae cordis minimae.

Table 18.2 compares the right atrium and the left atrium.

LEFT VENTRICLE

DISSECTION

Open the left ventricle by making a bold incision on the ventricular aspect of atrioventricular groove below left auricle and along whole thickness of left ventricle from above downwards till its apex. Curve the incision

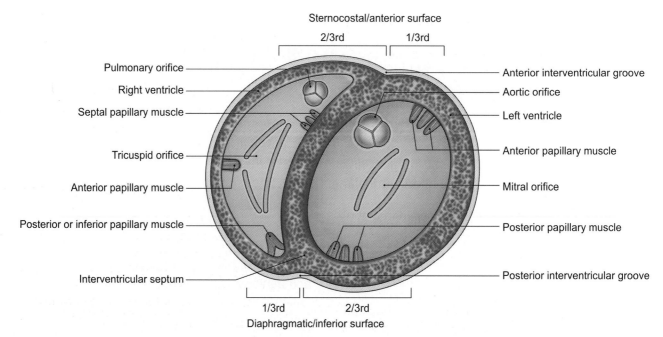

Fig. 18.15: Schematic transverse section through the ventricles of the heart showing the atrioventricular orifices, papillary muscles, and the pulmonary and aortic orifices

Table 18.2: Comparison of right atrium and left atrium

Right atrium	Left atrium
Receives venous blood of the body	Receives oxygenated blood from lungs
Pushes blood to right ventricle through tricuspid valve	Pushes blood to left ventricle through bicuspid valve
Forms right border, part of sternocostal and small part of base of the heart	Forms major part of base of the heart
Enlarged in tricuspid stenosis	Enlarged in mitral stenosis

towards right till the inferior end of anterior interventricular groove. Reflect the flap to the right and clean the atrioventricular and aortic valves (Fig. 18.10).

Remove the surface layers of the myocardium. Note the general directions of its fibres and the depth of the coronary sulcus, the wall of the atrium passing deep to the bulging ventricular muscle. Dissect the musculature and the conducting system of the heart.

Position

The left ventricle receives oxygenated blood from the left atrium and pumps it into the aorta. It forms the apex of the heart, a part of the sternocostal surface, most of the left border and left surface, and the left two-thirds of the diaphragmatic surface (Figs 18.7 and 18.8).

Features

1 Externally, the left ventricle has three surfaces—anterior or sternocostal, inferior or diaphragmatic, and left.

2 The interior is divisible into two parts:
   a. The lower rough part with trabeculae carneae develops from the primitive ventricle of the heart tube (Fig. 18.16).
   b. The upper smooth part or aortic vestibule gives origin to the ascending aorta: It develops from the mid portion of the bulbus cordis. The vestibule lies between the membranous part of the interventricular septum and the anterior or aortic cusp of the mitral valve.

3 The interior of the ventricle shows two orifices:
   a. The left atrioventricular or bicuspid or mitral orifice, guarded by the bicuspid or mitral valve.
   b. The aortic orifice, guarded by the aortic valve (Fig. 18.15).

4 There are two well-developed papillary muscles, anterior and posterior. Chordae tendinae from both muscles are attached to both the cusps of the mitral valve.

5 The cavity of the left ventricle is circular in cross-section (Fig. 18.15).

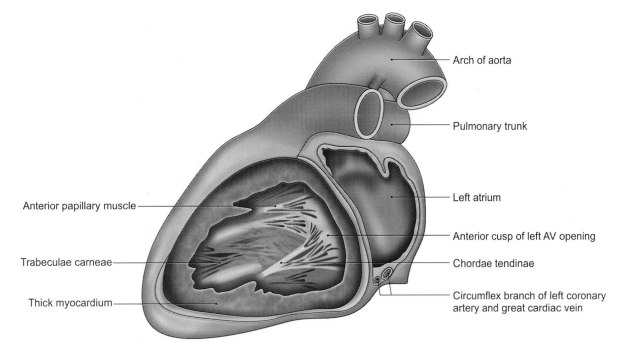

Anterior papillary muscle

Trabeculae carneae

Thick myocardium

Arch of aorta

Pulmonary trunk

Left atrium

Anterior cusp of left AV opening

Chordae tendinae

Circumflex branch of left coronary artery and great cardiac vein

Fig. 18.16: Interior of left atrium and left ventricle

Thorax

Section 2

6 The walls of the left ventricle are three times thicker than those of the right ventricle.

Table 18.3 compares the right ventricle and the left ventricle.

CLINICAL ANATOMY

- The area of the chest wall overlying the heart is called the *precordium*.
- Rapid pulse or increased heart rate is called *tachycardia* (Greek *rapid heart*).
- Slow pulse or decreased heart rate is called *bradycardia* (Greek *slow heart*).
- Irregular pulse or irregular heart rate is called *arrhythmia*.
- Consciousness of one's heartbeat is called *palpitation*.
- Inflammation of the heart can involve more than one layer of the heart. Inflammation of the pericardium is called *pericarditis;* of the myocardium is *myocarditis;* and of the endocardium is *endocarditis.*
- Normally, the diastolic pressure in ventricles is zero. A positive diastolic pressure in the ventricle is evidence of its failure. Any one of the four chambers of the heart can fail separately, but ultimately the rising back pressure causes right sided failure (congestive cardiac failure or CCF) which is associated with increased venous pressure, oedema on feet, and breathlessness on exertion. Heart failure (right sided) due to lung disease is known as *cor pulmonale.*

STRUCTURE OF HEART

VALVES

The valves of the heart maintain unidirectional flow of the blood and prevent its regurgitation in the opposite direction. There are two pairs of valves in the heart, a pair of atrioventricular valves and a pair of semilunar valves. The right atrioventricular valve is known as the tricuspid valve because it has three cusps. The left atrioventricular valve is known as the bicuspid valve because it has two cusps. It is also called the mitral valve. The semilunar valves include the aortic and pulmonary valves, each having three semilunar cusps. The cusps are folds of endocardium, strengthened by an intervening layer of fibrous tissue (Figs 18.17a and b).

Atrioventricular Valves

1 Both valves are made up of the following components.
   a. A *fibrous ring* to which the cusps are attached (Fig. 18.13).
   b. The *cusps* are flat and project into the ventricular cavity. Each cusp has an attached and a free margin, and an atrial and a ventricular surface. The atrial surface is smooth (Fig. 18.16). The free margins and ventricular surfaces are rough and irregular due to the attachment of chordae tendinae. *The valves are closed during ventricular systole* (Greek *contraction*) by apposition of the atrial surfaces near the serrated margins (Fig. 18.15).
   c. The *chordae tendinae* connect the free margins and ventricular surfaces of the cusps to the apices of the papillary muscles. They prevent eversion of the free margins and limit the amount of ballooning of the cusps towards the cavity of the atrium.
   d. The atrioventricular valves are kept competent by active contraction of the *papillary muscles*, which pull on the chordae tendinae during ventricular systole. Each papillary muscle is connected to the contiguous halves of two cusps (Fig. 18.13).
2 Blood vessels are present only in the fibrous ring and in the basal one-third of the cusps. Nutrition to the central two-thirds of the cusps is derived directly from the blood in the cavity of the heart.

Table 18.3: Comparison of right ventricle and left ventricle

Right ventricle	Left ventricle
Thinner than left, 1/3 thickness of left ventricle	Much thicker than right, 3 times thicker than right ventricle
Pushes blood only to the lungs	Pushes blood to top of the body and down to the toes
Contains three small papillary muscles	Contains two strong papillary muscles
Cavity is crescentic	Cavity is circular
Contains deoxygenated blood	Contains oxygenated blood
Forms 2/3rd sternocostal and 1/3rd diaphragmatic surfaces	Forms 1/3rd sternocostal and 2/3rd diaphragmatic surfaces

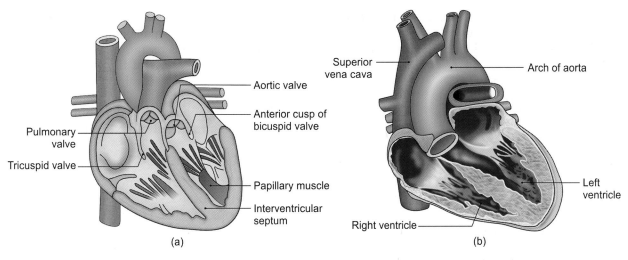

Figs 18.17a and b: (a) Interior of heart, and (b) the cusps of atrioventricular valves

3 The tricuspid valve has three cusps and can admit the tips of three fingers. The three cusps: the anterior, posterior or inferior, and septal. These lie against the three walls of the ventricle. Of the three papillary muscles, the anterior is the largest, the inferior is smaller and irregular, and the septal is represented by a number of small muscular elevations.

4 The mitral or bicuspid valve has two cusps—a large anterior or aortic cusp, and a small posterior cusp. It admits the tips of two fingers. The anterior cusp lies between the mitral and aortic orifices. The mitral cusps are smaller and thicker than those of the tricuspid valve.

Semilunar Valves

1 The aortic and pulmonary valves are called semilunar valves because their cusps are semilunar in shape. Both valves are similar to each other (Figs 18.17a and b).

2 Each valve has three cusps which are attached directly to the vessel wall, there being no fibrous ring. The cusps form small pockets with their mouths directed away from the ventricular cavity. The free margin of each cusp contains a central fibrous *nodule* from each side of which a thin smooth margin *the lunule* extends up to the base of the cusp. These *valves are closed during ventricular diastole* when each cusp bulges towards the ventricular cavity (Fig. 18.17).

3 Opposite the cusps the vessel walls are slightly dilated to form the aortic and pulmonary sinuses. The coronary arteries arise from the anterior and the left posterior aortic sinuses (Fig. 18.18).

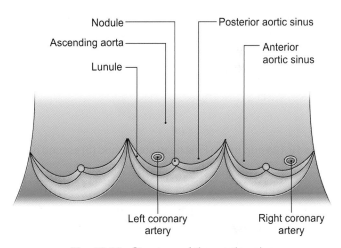

Fig. 18.18: Structure of the aortic valve

sound is produced by closure of the semilunar valves (Figs 18.19a and b).

- Narrowing of the valve orifice due to fusion of the cusps is known as 'stenosis', viz. mitral stenosis, aortic stenosis, etc.

- Dilatation of the valve orifice, or stiffening of the cusps causes imperfect closure of the valve leading to back flow of blood. This is known as incompetence or regurgitation, e.g. aortic incompetence or aortic regurgitation.

FIBROUS SKELETON

The fibrous rings surrounding the atrioventricular and arterial orifices, along with some adjoining masses of fibrous tissue, constitute the fibrous skeleton of the heart. It provides attachment to the cardiac muscle and keeps the cardiac valve competent (Fig. 18.20).

The *atrioventricular fibrous rings* are in the form of the figure of 8. The atria, the ventricles and the membranous part of the interventricular septum are

---

CLINICAL ANATOMY

- The first heart sound is produced by closure of the atrioventricular valves. The second heart

Section 2 · Thorax

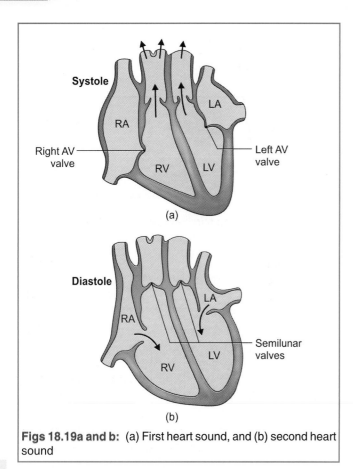

Figs 18.19a and b: (a) First heart sound, and (b) second heart sound

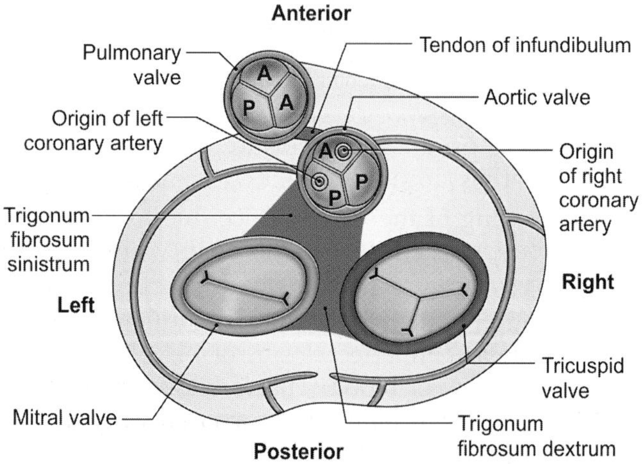

Fig. 18.20: Heart seen from above after removing the atria. The mitral, tricuspid, aortic and pulmonary orifices and their valves are seen. The fibrous skeleton of the heart is also shown (anatomical position)

attached to them. There is no muscular continuity between the atria and ventricles across the rings except for the atrioventricular bundle or *bundle of His*.

There is large mass of fibrous tissue between the atrioventricular rings behind and the aortic ring in front.

It is known as the *trigonum fibrosum dextrum*. In some mammals like sheep, a small bone the *os cordis* is present in this mass of fibrous tissue.

Another smaller mass of fibrous tissue is present between the aortic and mitral rings. It is known as the *trigonum fibrosum sinistrum. The tendon of the infundibulum* (close to pulmonary valve) binds the posterior surface of the infundibulum to the aortic ring.

MUSCULATURE OF THE HEART

Cardiac muscle fibres form long loops which are attached to the fibrous skeleton. Upon contraction of the muscular loops, the blood from the cardiac chambers is wrung out like water from a wet cloth. The atrial fibres are arranged in a superficial transverse layer and a deep anteroposterior (vertical) layer.

The ventricular fibres are arranged in superficial and deep layers.

The superficial fibres arise from skeleton of the heart to undergo a spiral course. First these pass across the inferior surface, wind round the lower border and then across the sternocostal surface to reach the apex of heart, where these fibres form a vortex and continue with the deep layer.

Superficial fibres are:
a. Fibres start from tendon of infundibulum (1) pass across the diaphragmatic surface, curve around inferior border to reach the sternocostal surface. Then these fibres cross the anterior interventricular groove to reach the apex, where these form a vortex and end in anterior papillary muscle of left ventricle (Fig. 18.21a).
b. Fibres arise from right AV ring take same course as (2) but end in posterior papillary muscle (Fig. 18.21a).
c. Fibres arise from left AV ring, lie along the diaphragmatic surface, cross the posterior interventricular groove to reach the papillary muscles of right ventricle (Fig. 18.21b).
d. Deep fibres are 'S' shaped. These arise from papillary muscle of one ventricle, turn in interventricular groove, to end in papillary muscle of other ventricle. Fibres of first layer circle RV, cross through interventricular septum and end in papillary muscle of LV. Layers two and three have decreasing course in RV and increasing course in LV (Fig. 18.21c).

CONDUCTING SYSTEM

The conducting system is made up of myocardium that is specialised for initiation and conduction of the cardiac impulse. Its fibres are finer than other myocardial fibres, and are completely cross-striated. The conducting system has the following parts.

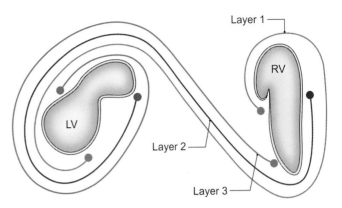

Fig. 18.21c: Deep fibres of ventricles in three layers

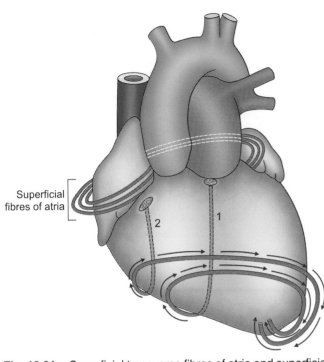

Fig. 18.21a: Superficial transverse fibres of atria and superficial fibres of ventricles 1, 2

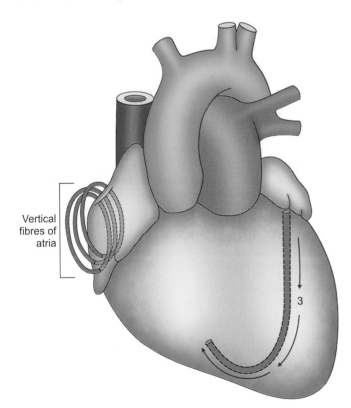

Fig. 18.21b: Vertical fibres of atria and superficial fibres of ventricle 3

1 *Sinuatrial node or SA node:* It is known as the 'pacemaker' of the heart. It generates impulses at the rate of about 70–100 beats/min and initiates the heartbeat. It is horseshoe-shaped and is situated at the atriocaval junction in the upper part of the sulcus terminals. The impulse travels through the atrial wall to reach the AV node (Fig. 18.14).

2 *Atrioventricular node or AV node:* It is smaller than the SA node and is situated in the lower and dorsal part of the atrial septum just above the opening of the coronary sinus. It is capable of generating impulses at a rate of about 40 to 60 beats/min.

3 *Atrioventricular bundle or AV bundle or bundle of His:* It is the only muscular connection between the atrial and ventricular musculatures. It begins as the atrioventricular (AV) node crosses AV ring and descends along the posteroinferior border of the membranous part of the ventricular septum. At the upper border of the muscular part of the septum, it divides into right and left branches.

4 *The right branch* of the AV bundle passes down the right side of the interventricular septum. A large part enters the moderator band to reach the anterior wall of the right ventricle where it divides into Purkinje fibres.

5 *The left branch* of the AV bundle descends on the left side of the interventricular septum and is distributed to the left ventricle after dividing into Purkinje fibres.

6. *The Purkinje fibres* form a subendocardial plexus. They are large pale fibres striated only at their margins. They usually possess double nuclei. These generate impulses at the rate of 20–35 beats/minute.

CLINICAL ANATOMY

Defects of or damage to conducting system results in cardiac arrhythmias, i.e. defects in the normal rhythm of contraction. Except for a part of the left branch of the AV bundle supplied by the left coronary artery, the whole of the conducting system

Section **2** **Thorax**

is usually supplied by the right coronary artery. Vascular lesions of the heart can cause a variety of arrhythmias.

ARTERIES SUPPLYING THE HEART

The heart is supplied by two coronary arteries, arising from the ascending aorta. Both arteries run in the coronary sulcus.

Features of Coronary Arteries

i. The blood flows through these arteries during diastole of heart
ii. Diameter is 1.5–5.2 mm
iii. Left coronary is larger in calibre and supplies more myocardium
iv. These arteries are "functional end arteries". Though their branches anastomose with each other but one cannot compensate for the other artery in case of thrombosis.
v. The origin of posterior interventricular artery determines the dominance of the artery.
vi. Sympathetic stimulation dilates the intramuscular arteries and constricts the epicardial arteries.

RIGHT CORONARY ARTERY

DISSECTION

Carefully remove the fat from the coronary sulcus. Identify the right coronary artery in the depth of the right part of the atrioventricular sulcus (Figs 18.22a and b).

Trace the right coronary artery superiorly to its origin from the right aortic sinus and inferiorly till it turns onto the posterior surface of the heart to lie in its atrioventricular sulcus. It gives off the posterior interventricular branch which is seen in posterior interventricular groove.

The right coronary artery ends by anastomosing with the circumflex branch of left coronary artery or by dipping itself deep in the myocardium there.

Position

Right coronary artery is smaller than the left coronary artery. It arises from the anterior aortic sinus (Figs 18.22a and b) of ascending aorta.

Course

1 It first passes forwards and to the right to emerge on the surface of the heart between the root of the pulmonary trunk and the right auricle.

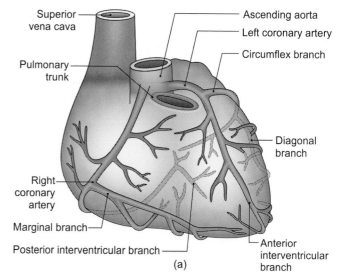

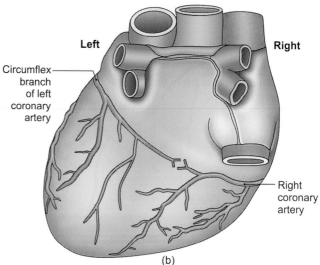

Figs 18.22a and b: Arterial supply of heart: (a) Sternocostal surface, and (b) diaphragmatic surface

2 It then runs downwards in the right anterior coronary sulcus to the junction of the right and inferior borders of the heart.

3 It winds round the inferior border to reach the diaphragmatic surface of the heart. Here it runs backwards and to the left in the right posterior coronary sulcus to reach the posterior interventricular groove.

4 It terminates by anastomosing with the circumflex branch of left coronary artery at the crux.

Branches

• Atrial branches are anterior, posterior and lateral. One of the anterior atrial branches is called SA nodal artery. It arises from right coronary artery in 60% cases.

• Right conus artery forms an arterial circle around pulmonary trunk with a similar branch from the left coronary artery. The circle is called, "annulus of Vieussens".

- Ventricular branches are as anterior and posterior group. The anterior group lies on the sternocostal surface while posterior group traverses the diaphragmalic surface of the heart.
- Right marginal artery arises as the right coronary artery crosses the right border of heart. It runs along its inferior border till the apex of heart.
- Posterior interventricular branch arises close to the crus of heart and lies in the posterior interventicular groove. It gives septal branches to posterior 1/3rd of interventricular septum. It also supplies AV node.

Area of Distribution

1 Right atrium
2 Ventricles
   a. Greater part of the right ventricle, except the area adjoining the anterior interventricular groove.
   b. A small part of the left ventricle adjoining the posterior interventricular groove.
3 Posterior 1/3rd part of the interventricular septum.
4 Whole of the conducting system of the heart except a part of the left branch of the AV bundle. The SA node is supplied by the left coronary artery in about 40% of cases.

LEFT CORONARY ARTERY

DISSECTION

Strip the visceral pericardium from the sternocostal surface of the heart. Expose the anterior interventricular branch of the left coronary artery and the great cardiac vein by carefully removing the fat from the anterior interventricular sulcus. Note the branches of the artery to both ventricles and to the interventricular septum which lies deep to it. Trace the artery inferiorly to the diaphragmatic surface and superiorly to the left of the pulmonary trunk (Figs 18.22a and b).

Trace the circumflex branch of left coronary artery on the left border of heart into the posterior part of the sulcus, where it may end by anastomosing with the right coronary artery or by dipping into the myocardium.

Position

Left coronary artery is larger than the right coronary artery. It arises from the left posterior aortic sinus of ascending aortic.

Course

1 The artery first runs forwards and to the left and emerges between the pulmonary trunk and the left auricle. Here it gives the anterior *interventricular branch* which runs downwards in the groove of the same name. The further continuation of the left coronary artery is called the *circumflex artery* (Figs 18.22a and b and 18.23).

2 After giving off the anterior interventricular branch, the artery runs to the left in the left anterior coronary sulcus.

3 It winds round the left border of the heart and continues in the left posterior coronary sulcus. Near the posterior interventricular groove, it terminates by anastomosing with the right coronary artery.

Branches

- Anterior interventricular branch is a large branch. It descends in the anterior interventricular groove. It gives following branches:
   i. Anterior ventricular branches for the ventricles. The large branch is called "left diagonal artery".
   ii. Septal branches which supply anterior 2/3rd of the interventricular septum.
   iii. Left conus artery forms an arterial ring around the pulomonary trunk with a similar branch from right coronary artery.
- Circumflex branch is the terminal part of left coronary artery after it has given off the large anterior interventricular branch. Circumflex branch runs in the left anterior coronary sulcus, then curves around the left border of heart to lie in the left posterior coronary sulcus. It ends by anastomosing with the terminal part of right coronary artery, a little to the left of the crux. Its branches are:
   i. Left marginal artery which lies along the left border of heart till the apex of heart.

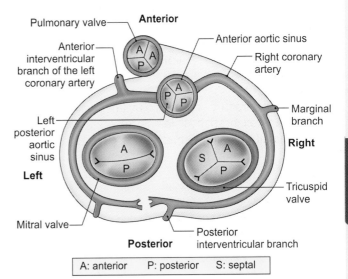

Fig. 18.23: Origin of the coronary arteries from the aortic sinuses and their course in the coronary sulcus, as seen after removal of the atria (anatomical position)

ii. Anterior and posterior ventricular branches
iii. Atrial branches which are in anterior, posterior and lateral groups.

Area of Distribution

1 Left atrium
2 Ventricles
   a. Greater part of the left ventricle, except the area adjoining the posterior interventricular groove.
   b. A small part of the right ventricle adjoining the anterior interventricular groove.
3 Anterior part of the interventricular septum (Fig. 18.24).
4 A part of the left branch of the AV bundle.

CARDIAC DOMINANCE

In about 10% of hearts, the right coronary is rather small and is not able to give the posterior interventricular branch. In these cases, the circumflex artery, the continuation of left coronary, provides the posterior interventricular branch as well as to the AV node. Such cases are called left dominant.

Mostly, the right coronary gives posterior interventricular artery. Such hearts are right dominant. Thus the artery giving the posterior interventricular branch is the dominant artery.

Collateral Circulation

Cardiac Anastomoses

The two coronary arteries anastomose with each other in myocardium.

Extracardiac Anastomoses

The coronary arteries anastomose with the following:
1 Vasa vasorum of the aorta.

2 Vasa vasorum of the pulmonary arteries.
3 The internal thoracic arteries.
4 The bronchial arteries.
5 The pericardiacophrenic arteries.

The last three anastomose through the pericardium. These channels may open up in emergencies when both coronary arteries are obstructed.

Retrograde flow of blood in the veins may irrigate the myocardium.

These anastomoses are of little practical value. They are not able to provide an alternative source of blood in case of blockage of a branch of a coronary. Blockage of arteries or coronary thrombosis usually leads to death of myocardium. The condition is called myocardial infarction.

CLINICAL ANATOMY

- Thrombosis of coronary artery is a common cause of sudden death in persons past middle age. This is due to myocardial infarction and ventricular fibrillation (Fig. 18.25).
- Incomplete obstruction, usually due to spasm of the coronary artery causes *angina pectoris*, which is associated with agonising pain in the precordial region and down the medial side of the left arm and forearm (Fig. 18.26). Pain gets relieved by putting appropriate tablets below the tongue.
- Coronary angiography determines the site(s) of narrowing or occlusion of the coronary arteries or their branches.
- Angioplasty helps in removal of small blockage. It is done using small stent or small inflated balloon (Fig. 18.27) through a catheter passed upwards through femoral artery, aorta, into the coronary artery.
- If there are large segments or multiple sites of blockage, coronary bypass is done using either great saphenous vein or internal thoracic artery as graft(s) (Fig. 18.28).

VEINS OF THE HEART

These are the great cardiac vein, the middle cardiac vein, the right marginal vein, the posterior vein of the left ventricle, the oblique vein of the left atrium, the anterior cardiac veins, and the venae cordis minimae (Figs 18.29a and b). All veins except the last two drain into the coronary sinus which opens into the right atrium. The anterior cardiac veins and the venae cordis minimae open directly into the right atrium.

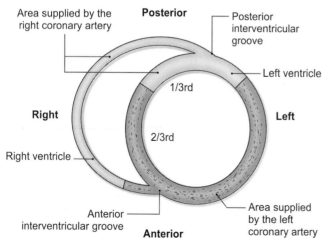

Fig. 18.24: Transverse section through the ventricles showing the areas supplied by the two coronary arteries

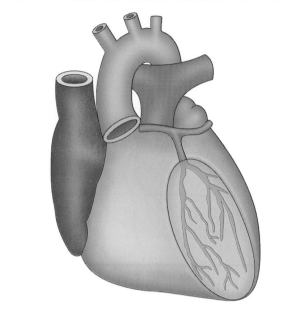

Fig. 18.25: Myocardial infarction due to blockage of anterior interventricular branch of left coronary artery

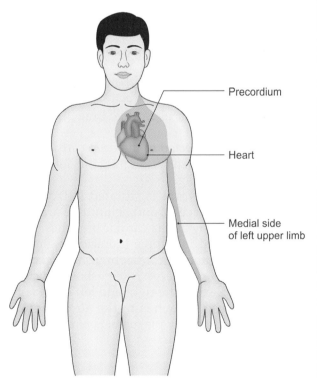

Fig. 18.26: Pain of angina pectoris felt in precordium and along medial border of left arm

Precordium

Heart

Medial side of left upper limb

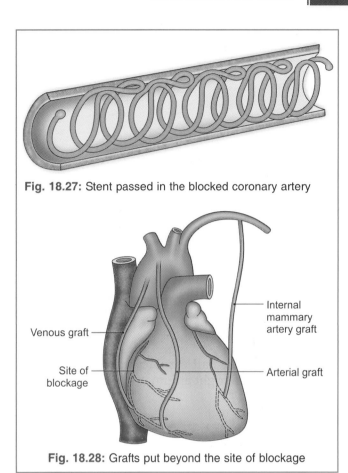

Fig. 18.27: Stent passed in the blocked coronary artery

Fig. 18.28: Grafts put beyond the site of blockage

Venous graft

Site of blockage

Internal mammary artery graft

Arterial graft

Coronary Sinus

The coronary sinus is the largest vein of the heart. It is situated in the left posterior coronary sulcus. It is about 3 cm long. It ends by opening into the posterior wall of the right atrium. It receives the following tributaries:

1 The *great cardiac vein* accompanies first the anterior interventricular artery and then the left coronary artery to enter the left end of the coronary sinus (Fig. 18.29a).

2 The *middle cardiac vein* accompanies the posterior interventricular artery, and joins the middle part of the coronary sinus.

3 The *small cardiac vein* accompanies the right coronary artery in the right posterior coronary sulcus and joins the right end of the coronary sinus. The right marginal vein may drain into the small cardiac vein (Fig. 18.29b).

4 The *posterior vein of the left ventricle* runs on the diaphragmatic surface of the left ventricle and ends in the coronary sinus.

5 The *oblique vein of the left atrium of Marshall* is a small vein running on the posterior surface of the left atrium. It terminates in the left end of the coronary sinus. It develops from the left common cardinal vein or duct of Cuvier which may sometimes form a large left superior vena cava.

6 The *right marginal vein* accompanies the marginal branch of the right coronary artery. It may either

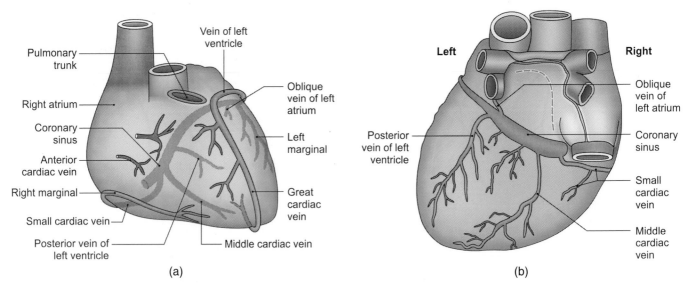

Figs 18.29a and b: Veins of the heart: (a) Sternocostal surface, and (b) diaphragmatic surface

drain into the small cardiac vein, or may open directly into the right atrium.

Anterior Cardiac Veins

The *anterior cardiac veins* are three or four small veins which run parallel to one another on the anterior wall of the right ventricle and usually open directly into the right atrium through its anterior wall.

Venae Cordis Minimae

The *venae cordis minimae* or *thebesian veins* or *smallest cardiac veins* are numerous small valveless veins present in all four chambers of the heart which open directly into the cavity. These are more numerous on the right side of the heart than on the left. This may be one reason why left sided infarcts are more common.

LYMPHATICS OF HEART

Lymphatics of the heart accompany the coronary arteries and form two trunks. The right trunk ends in the brachiocephalic nodes, and the left trunk ends in the tracheobronchial lymph nodes at the bifurcation of the trachea.

NERVE SUPPLY OF HEART

Parasympathetic nerves reach the heart via the vagus. These are cardioinhibitory; on stimulation they slow down the heart rate.

Sympathetic nerves are derived from the upper four to five thoracic segments of the spinal cord. These are cardio-acceleratory, and on stimulation, they increase the heart rate, and also dilate the coronary arteries.

Both parasympathetic and sympathetic nerves form the superficial and deep cardiac plexuses, the branches of which run along the coronary arteries to reach the myocardium.

The *superficial cardiac plexus* is situated below the arch of the aorta in front of the right pulmonary artery. It is formed by:

a. The superior cervical cardiac branch of the left sympathetic chain.
b. The inferior cervical cardiac branch of the left vagus nerve.

The plexus is connected to the deep cardiac plexus, the right coronary artery, and to the left anterior pulmonary plexus (Fig. 18.30).

The *deep cardiac plexus* is situated in front of the bifurcation of the trachea, and behind the arch of the aorta. It is formed by all the cardiac branches derived from all the cervical and upper thoracic ganglia of the sympathetic chain, and the cardiac branches of the vagus and recurrent laryngeal nerves, except those which form the superficial plexus. The right and left halves of the plexus distribute branches to the corresponding coronary and pulmonary plexuses. Separate branches are given to the atria.

CLINICAL ANATOMY

- Cardiac pain is an ischaemic pain caused by incomplete obstruction of a coronary artery.
- Axons of pain fibres conveyed by the sensory sympathetic cardiac nerves reach thoracic one to thoracic five segments of spinal cord mostly through the dorsal root ganglia of the left side. Since these dorsal root ganglia also receive sensory

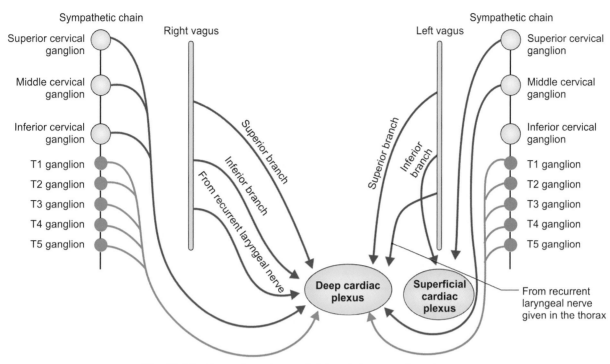

Fig. 18.30: Formation of superficial and deep cardiac plexuses

impulses from the medial side of arm, forearm and upper part of front of chest, the pain gets referred to these areas as depicted in Fig. 18.26.

• Though the pain is usually referred to the left side, it may even be referred to right arm, jaw, epigastrium or back. Viscera have low amount of sensory output whereas skin is an area of high amount of sensory output. So pain arising from area of low sensory output area is projected as coming from high sensory output area.

Developmental Components

1 Right atrium (Fig. 18.11)
   a. Rough anterior part—atrial chamber proper.
   b. Smooth posterior part—
      – Absorption of right horn of sinus venosus
      – Interatrial septum
   Demarcating part—crista terminalis.
2 Left atrium (Figs 18.16 and 18.29b)
   a. Rough part—atrial chamber proper
   b. Smooth part—
      – Absorption of pulmonary veins.
      – Interatrial septum.
3 Right ventricle
   a. Rough part—proximal portion of bulbus cordis (Fig. 18.12).
   b. Smooth part—the conus cordis or middle portion of bulbus cordis.
4 Left ventricle (Fig. 18.16)

   a. Rough part—whole of primitive ventricular chamber.
   b. The conus cordis or the middle portion of bulbus cordis forms the smooth part.
5 Interatrial septum
   a. Septum primum—fossa ovalis.
   b. Septum secundum—limbus fossa ovalis.
6 Interventricular septum
   a. Thick muscular in lower part by the two ventricles.
   b. Thin membranous in upper part by fusion of inferior atrioventricular cushion and right and left conus swelling. Membranous part not only separates the two ventricles, but also separates right atrium from left ventricle.
7 Truncus arteriosus or distal part of bulbus cordis forms the ascending aorta and pulmonary trunk, as separated by spiral septum.

Spiral septum is responsible for triple relation of ascending aorta and pulmonary trunk. At the beginning, pulmonary trunk is anterior to ascending aorta, then it is to the left and finally the right pulmonary artery is posterior to ascending aorta (Fig. 18.10).

Heart is fully functional at the end of second month of intrauterine life.

FOETAL CIRCULATION

The foetus (Greek *offspring*) is dependent for its entire nutrition on the mother, and this is achieved through the placenta attached to the uterus. As the lungs are not functioning, the blood needs to bypass the pulmonary circuit. The oxygenated blood reaches the foetus through the single 'umbilical vein'. This vein containing oxygenated blood traverses the umbilical cord to reach the liver. The oxygenated blood bypasses the liver via 'the ductus venosus' to join inferior vena cava. As inferior vena cava drains into the right atrium, the oxygenated and nutrient rich blood brought by it enters the right atrium. Then it passes into the left atrium through 'foramen ovale', thus bypassing the pulmonary circuit (Figs 18.31 and 18.32).

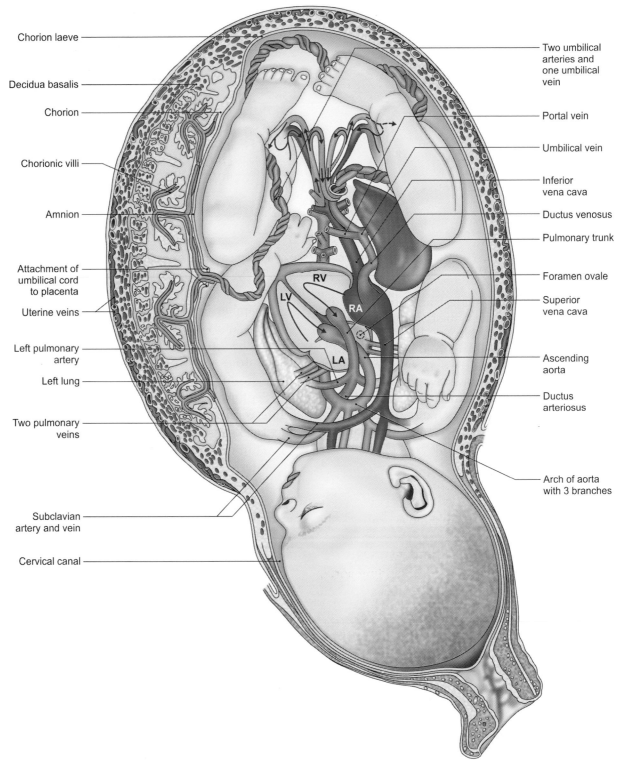

Fig. 18.31: Foetal circulation *in situ* (schematic)

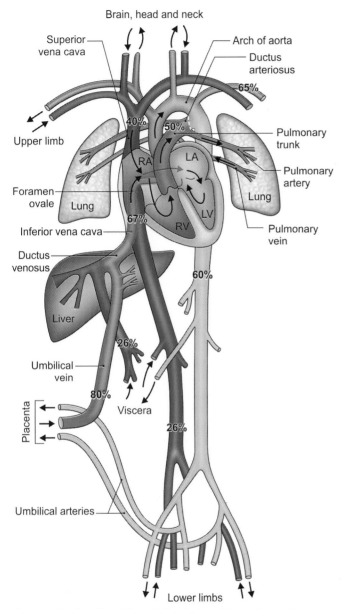

Fig. 18.32: Details of foetal circulation. Percentage of oxygen in blood vessels is put in numbers

From the left atrium, it enters the left ventricle and traverses the systemic circuit via the ascending aorta, arch of aorta and descending thoracic and descending abdominal aortae. The last mentioned vessel divides into common iliac arteries. Each common iliac artery terminates by dividing into external and internal iliac arteries. Arising from two internal iliac arteries are the two umbilical arteries which in turn pass through the umbilical cord to end in the placenta.

The deoxygenated blood from the viscera, lower limbs, head and neck and upper limbs also enters the right atrium via both the inferior and superior venae cavae. This venous blood gains entry into the right ventricle and leaves it via the pulmonary trunk and

left pulmonary artery. The left pulmonary artery is joined to the left end of arch of aorta via the 'ductus arteriosus'. Thus the venous blood traversing through the left pulmonary artery and ductus arteriosus enters the left end of arch of aorta. So the descending thoracic and abdominal aortae get mixed blood. At the internal iliac end, it passes via the two umbilical arteries to reach the placenta for oxygenation.

So for bypassing the lungs and for providing oxygen and nutrition to the developing embryo and foetus, the following structures had to be improvised.

a. One umbilical vein
b. Ductus venosus
c. Foramen ovale
d. Ductus arteriosus
e. Two umbilical arteries.
Flowchart 18.1 shows the details of foetal circulation.

Flowchart 18.1: Foetal circulation

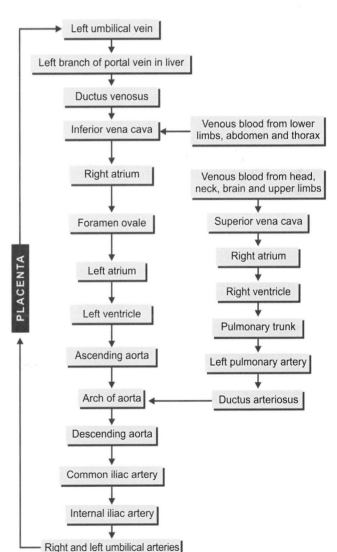

Flowchart 18.2: Postnatal circulation

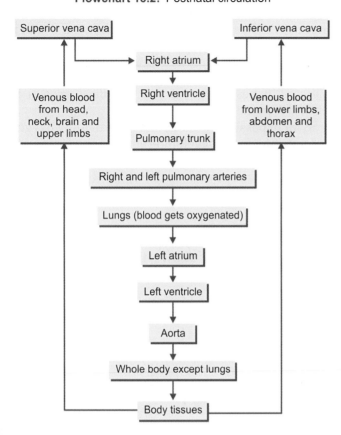

- Heart is a pump for pushing blood to the lungs and for rest of the organs of the body. Due to sympathetic stimulation, it is felt thumping against the chest wall.
- All the components of left ventricle are thicker as it has to push the blood from top of head to the toes of foot.
- Left atrium forms most of the base of the heart.
- Coronary arteries are functional end arteries.
- Pain of heart due to myocardial infarction is referred to left side of chest between 3rd and 6th intercostal spaces. It also get extended to medial side of left upper limb in the area of distribution of C8 and T1 spinal segments.

At the time of birth, with the start of breathing process, these structures (a–e) retrogress and gradually the adult form of circulation takes over (Flowchart 18.2).

Changes at birth:

Lungs start functioning.

a. Umbilical vein forms ligamentum teres.

b. Ductus venosus forms ligamentum venosum.

c. Foramen ovale closes.

d. Ductus arteriosus forms ligamentum arteriosum.

e. Umbilical arteries form medial umbilical ligaments.

Placenta is delivered and removed.

Mnemonics

Heart valves "**T**ry **P**ulling **M**y **A**orta"

Tricuspid
Pulmonary
Mitral
Aorta

CLINICOANATOMICAL PROBLEMS

Case 1

An adult man was stabbed on his upper left side of chest. He was taken to the casualty department of the hospital. The casualty physician noted that the stab wound was in left third intercostal space close to the sternum. Further the patient has engorged veins on the neck and face.

- What is the site of injury?
- Why are the veins of the neck and face engorged?
- What procedure would be done as an emergency measure before taking him to operation theatre?

Ans: The injury is in left third intercostal space injuring the pericardium and right ventricle, causing *haemopericardium*. Veins of the neck and face are engorged as the venae cavae are not able to pour blood in the right atrium. Pericardial tapping is done to take out the blood from the pericardial cavity. It is done as an emergency measure.

Case 2

A 40-year-old lady while playing tennis, suddenly fell down, holding onto her chest and left arm due to severe pain.

- Why is the pain in her chest?
- Why is the pain in her left arm?

Ans: Tennis is a very strenuous game. The lady fainted as there was more need for the oxygen. Since it could not be supplied, the myocardium got ischaemic which caused visceral pain. The pain is carried by afferents which travel mostly with left side sympathetic nerves to the thoracic one and thoracic 2–5 segments of the spinal cord. Since somatic nerves (T1–T5) also travel to the same segments, the pain is referred to the skin area. T1 supplies the medial side of arm and T2–T5 supply the intercostal spaces.

Case 3

A 10-year-old boy had mild cough and fever. The physician could feel the increased rate of his pulse, but could not hear the heartbeat on the left side of his chest. After some thought the physician was able to feel the heart beat as well.

• Where is the normal apex beat heard?
• Name the congenital anomaly of the heart which could cause inability of heart beat to be felt on the left side.

Ans: Apex beat is normally heard in the left fifth intercostal space, 9 cm from midsternal line, within the left lateral line. The congenital anomaly in this case is dextrocardia, when the heart is placed on the right side of the heart. The apex beat is heard in right fifth intercostal space to the right of the inferior end of the sternum. In few cases not only the heart but the viscera of abdomen and thorax are a mirror image of normal. The condition is called "situs inversus".

FREQUENTLY ASKED QUESTIONS

1. Describe the gross features of heart like apex, base, borders, surfaces and grooves.
2. Describe the right ventricle under following heads: External features, openings, internal features, conducting tissue
3. Write short notes on:
   a. Sinuses of pericardium
   b. Interventricular septum
   c. Valves of the heart
   d. Comparison of right and left coronary arteries
   e. Coronary sinus

MULTIPLE CHOICE QUESTIONS

1. The structures covering the heart are:
   a. Fibrous pericardium
   b. Parietal layer of serous pericardium
   c. Pericardial cavity
   d. All of the above
2. Boundaries of oblique sinus are all *except:*
   a. Superior and inferior venae cavae on right side
   b. Anteriorly by left atrium
   c. Posteriorly by right atrium
   d. Left side by left pulmonary veins
3. Boundaries of base of heart are formed by all *except:*
   a. Four pulmonary veins
   b. Oesophagus and descending aorta
   c. Pericardium
   d. Ascending aorta
4. Apex of the heart is felt at:
   a. 8 cm lateral to midclavicular line in left 5th intercostal space
   b. 9 cm lateral to midclavicular line in left 5th intercostal space
   c. 9 cm lateral to midclavicular line in left 6th intercostal space
   d. 9 cm lateral to midclavicular line in right 5th intercostal space
5. Entry channels of heart are all *except:*
   a. Superior vena cava   b. Inferior vena cava
   c. 4 pulmonary veins   d. Pulmonary trunk

6. Trabeculae carneae of right ventricle are in all following forms *except:*
   a. Ridges   b. Bridges
   c. Papillary muscles   d. Chordae tendinae
7. Right coronary artery arises from which sinus?
   a. Anterior aortic sinus
   b. Right posterior aortic sinus
   c. Left posterior aortic sinus
   d. From anterior and posterior aortic sinuses
8. Blood to the interventricular septum is supplied by:
   a. Only right coronary artery
   b. Only left coronary artery
   c. Anterior half by right coronary artery and posterior half by left coronary artery
   d. Anterior 2/3rd by left coronary artery and posterior 1/3rd by right coronary artery
9. Coronary arteries anastomose with all the following arteries *except:*
   a. Vasa vasorum of the aorta
   b. Vasa vasorum of pulmonary arteries
   c. Bronchial arteries
   d. Anterior intercostal arteries
10. Rough part of left ventricle develops from:
    a. Whole of primitive ventricular chamber
    b. Proximal part of bulbus cordis
    c. Middle part of bulbus cordis
    d. Distal part of bulbus cordis

ANSWERS

1. d	2. c	3. d	4. b	5. d	6. d	7. a	8. d	9. d	10. a

Section **2** Thorax

Superior Vena Cava, Aorta and Pulmonary Trunk

Blood is meant to circulate, otherwise it forms clots blocking the vessels.

INTRODUCTION

Superior vena cava brings deoxygenated blood from the head and neck, upper limbs and thorax to the heart. Aorta and pulmonary trunk are the only two exit channels from the heart, developing from a single truncus arteriosus. The two are intimately related to each other.

LARGE BLOOD VESSELS

DISSECTION

Trace superior vena cava from level of first right costal cartilage where it is formed by union of left and right brachiocephalic veins till the third costal cartilage where it opens into right atrium (Fig. 19.1).

Trace the ascending aorta from the vestibule of left ventricle upwards between superior vena cava and pulmonary trunk (Fig. 19.2).

Arch of aorta is seen above the bifurcation of pulmonary trunk.

Cut ligamentum arteriosum as it connects the left pulmonary artery to the arch of aorta.

Trace the left recurrent laryngeal nerve to the medial aspect of arch of aorta.

Lift the side of oesophagus forwards to expose the anterior surface of the descending aorta.

Lift the diaphragm forwards and expose the aorta in the inferior part of the posterior mediastinum.

SUPERIOR VENA CAVA

Superior vena cava is a large venous channel which collects blood from the upper half of the body and drains it into the right atrium. It is formed by the union of the right and left brachiocephalic or innominate veins behind the lower border of the first right costal cartilage close to the sternum. Each brachiocephalic vein is formed behind the corresponding sternoclavicular joint by the union of the internal jugular and subclavian veins (Fig. 19.1).

Course

The superior vena cava is about 7 cm long. It begins behind the lower border of the sternal end of the first right costal cartilage, pierces the pericardium opposite the second right costal cartilage, and terminates by opening into the upper part of the right atrium behind the third right costal cartilage (Fig. 19.2). It has no valves.

Relations

1 *Anterior*
   a. Chest wall.
   b. Internal thoracic vessels.
   c. Anterior margin of the right lung and pleura.
   d. The vessel is covered by pericardium in its lower half (Fig. 19.2).
2 *Posterior*
   a. Trachea and right vagus (posteromedial to the upper part of the vena cava) (*see* Fig. 16.2).
   b. Root of right lung posterior to the lower part.
3 *Medial*
   a. Ascending aorta.
   b. Brachiocephalic artery.
4 *Lateral*
   a. Right phrenic nerve with accompanying vessels.
   b. Right pleura and lung (Fig. 19.3).

Tributaries

1 The azygos vein arches over the root of the right lung and opens into the superior vena cava at the level of the second costal cartilage, just before the latter enters the pericardium.
2 Several small mediastinal and pericardial veins drain into the vena cava.

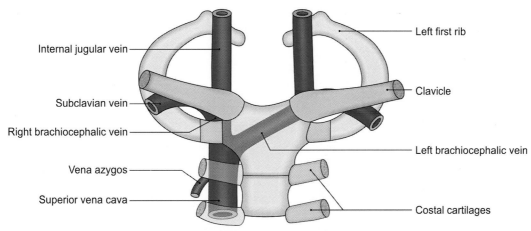

Fig. 19.1: Formation of superior vena cava

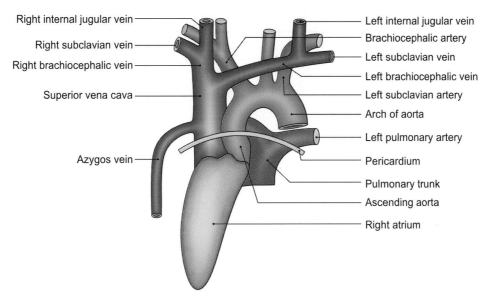

Fig. 19.2: The superior vena cava and its relations

CLINICAL ANATOMY

- When the superior vena cava is obstructed above the opening of the azygos vein, the venous blood of the upper half of the body is returned through the azygos vein; and the superficial veins are dilated on the chest up to the costal margin (Fig. 19.4). Blood from upper limb is returned through the communicating veins joining the veins around the scapula with the intercostal veins. The latter veins of both sides drain into vena azygos (*see* Flowchart 14.1).

- When the superior vena cava is obstructed below the opening of the azygos veins, the blood is returned through the inferior vena cava via the femoral vein; and the superior veins are dilated on both the chest and abdomen up to the saphenous opening in the thigh. The superficial vein connecting the lateral thoracic vein with the superficial epigastric vein is known as the *thoracoepigastric* vein (Fig. 19.5) (*see* Flowchart 14.2).

- In cases of mediastinal syndrome, the signs of superior vena caval obstruction are the first to appear.

AORTA

The aorta is the great arterial trunk which receives oxygenated blood from the left ventricle and distributes it to all parts of the body. It is studied in thorax in the following three parts:

1 Ascending aorta.
2 Arch of the aorta.
3 Descending thoracic aorta.

Section 2   Thorax

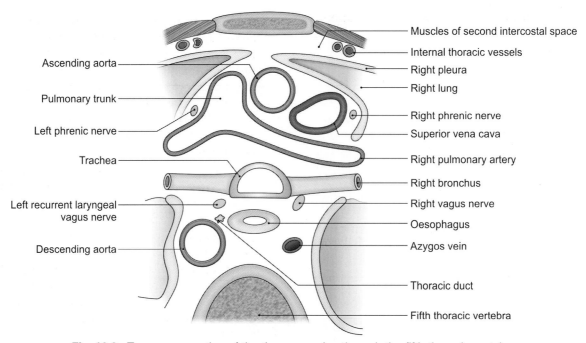

Fig. 19.3: Transverse section of the thorax passing through the fifth thoracic vertebra

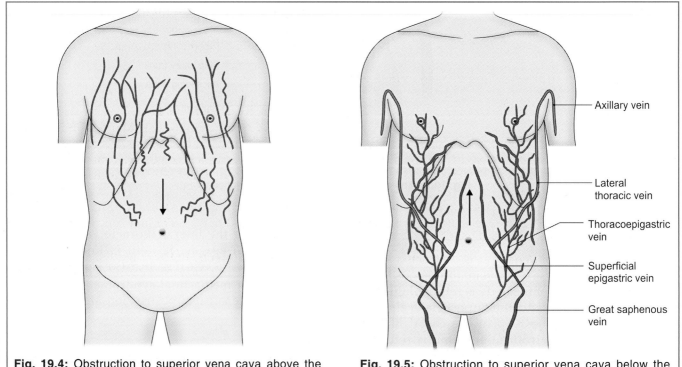

Fig. 19.4: Obstruction to superior vena cava above the opening of vena azygos

Fig. 19.5: Obstruction to superior vena cava below the opening of vena azygos

ASCENDING AORTA

Origin and Course

The ascending aorta arises from the upper end of the left ventricle. It is about 5 cm long and is enclosed in the pericardium (Fig. 19.2).

It begins behind the left half of the sternum at the level of the lower border of the third costal cartilage. It runs upwards, forwards and to the right and becomes continuous with the arch of the aorta at the sternal end of the upper border of the second right costal cartilage.

At the root of the aorta, there are three dilatations of the vessel wall, called the *aortic sinuses*. The sinuses are anterior, left posterior and right posterior.

Relations

Anterior

1 Sternum
2 Right lung and pleura
3 Infundibulum of the right ventricle
4 Root of the pulmonary trunk (Fig. 19.3)
5 Right auricle

Posterior

1 Transverse sinus of pericardium
2 Left atrium
3 Right pulmonary artery
4 Right bronchus (Fig. 19.3)

To the Right

1 Superior vena cava
2 Right atrium

To the Left

1 Pulmonary trunk above
2 Left atrium below

Branches

1 The right coronary artery arises from anterior aortic sinus (*see* Fig. 18.18).
2 Left coronary artery arises from the left posterior aortic sinus.

CLINICAL ANATOMY

- *Aortic knuckle:* In posteroanterior view of radiographs of the chest, the arch of the aorta is seen as a projection beyond the left margin of the mediastinal shadow. The projection is called the aortic knuckle. It becomes prominent in old age (*see* Fig. 21.12).
- *Coarctation of the aorta* is a localised narrowing of the aorta opposite to or just beyond the attachment of the ductus arteriosus. An extensive collateral circulation develops between the branches of the subclavian arteries and those of the descending aorta. These include the anastomoses between the anterior and posterior intercostal arteries. These arteries enlarge greatly and produce a characteristic notching on the ribs (Figs 19.6a and b).
- *Ductus arteriosus, ligamentum arteriosum and patent ductus arteriosus:* During foetal life, the *ductus arteriosus* (Fig. 19.7) is a short wide channel connecting the beginning of the left pulmonary artery with the arch of the aorta immediately distal to the origin of the left subclavian artery. It conducts most of the blood from the right ventricle into the aorta, thus short circuiting the lungs. After birth, it is closed functionally within about a week and anatomically within about eight weeks. The remnants of the ductus form a fibrous band called the *ligamentum arteriosum*. The left recurrent laryngeal nerve hooks around the ligamentum arteriosum.

The ductus may remain patent after birth. The condition is called *patent ductus arteriosus* and may cause serious problems. The condition can be surgically treated.

- *Aortic arch aneurysm* is a localised dilatation of the aorta which may press upon the left recurrent laryngeal nerve leading to paralysis of left vocal cord and hoarseness. It may also press upon the surrounding structures and cause the mediastinal syndrome (Fig. 19.8), i.e. dyspnoea, dysphagia, dysphonia, etc.

ARCH OF THE AORTA

Arch of the aorta is the continuation of the ascending aorta. It is situated in the superior mediastinum behind the lower half of the manubrium sterni.

Course

1 It begins behind the upper border of the second right sternochondral joint (*see* Figs 17.2 and 17.4).
2 It runs upwards, backwards and to the left across the left side of the bifurcation of trachea. Then it passes downwards behind the left bronchus and on the left side of the body of the fourth thoracic vertebra. It thus arches over the root of the left lung.
3 It ends at the lower border of the body of the fourth thoracic vertebra by becoming continuous with the descending aorta.

Thus the beginning and the end of arch of aorta are at the same level, although it begins anteriorly and ends posteriorly.

Relations

Anteriorly and to the Left

1 Four nerves from before backwards:
   a. Left phrenic.
   b. Lower cervical cardiac branch of the left vagus.
   c. Superior cervical cardiac branch of left sympathetic chain.
   d. Left vagus (Fig. 19.9).
2 Left superior intercostal vein, deep to the phrenic nerve and superficial to the vagus nerve.
3 Left pleura and lung.
4 Remains of thymus.

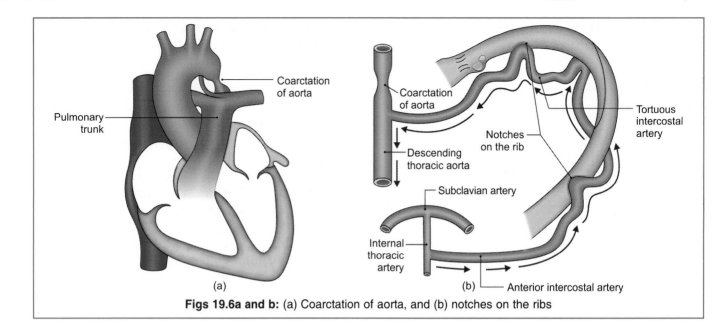

Figs 19.6a and b: (a) Coarctation of aorta, and (b) notches on the ribs

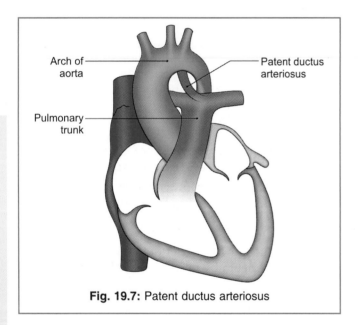

Fig. 19.7: Patent ductus arteriosus

Posteriorly and to the Right

1 Trachea, with the deep cardiac plexus and the tracheobronchial lymph nodes.
2 Oesophagus
3 Left recurrent laryngeal nerve
4 Thoracic duct
5 Vertebral column

Superior

1 Three branches of the arch of the aorta:
a. Brachiocephalic
b. Left common carotid
c. Left subclavian arteries (Fig. 19.10)

2 All three arteries are crossed close to their origin by the left brachiocephalic vein.

Inferior

1 Bifurcation of the pulmonary trunk (Fig. 19.2).
2 Left bronchus
3 Ligamentum arteriosum with superficial cardiac plexus on it.
4 Left recurrent laryngeal nerve.

Branches

1 Brachiocephalic artery which divides into the right common carotid and right subclavian arteries (Fig. 19.2).
2 Left common carotid artery.
3 Left subclavian artery.

DESCENDING THORACIC AORTA

Descending thoracic aorta is the continuation of the arch of the aorta. It lies in the posterior mediastinum (*see* Fig. 17.4). It continues as abdominal aorta which ends by dividing into right and left common iliac arteries.

Course

1 It begins on the left side of the lower border of the body of the fourth thoracic vertebra.
2 It descends with an inclination to the right and terminates at the lower border of the twelfth thoracic vertebra.

Relations

Anterior

1 Root of left lung

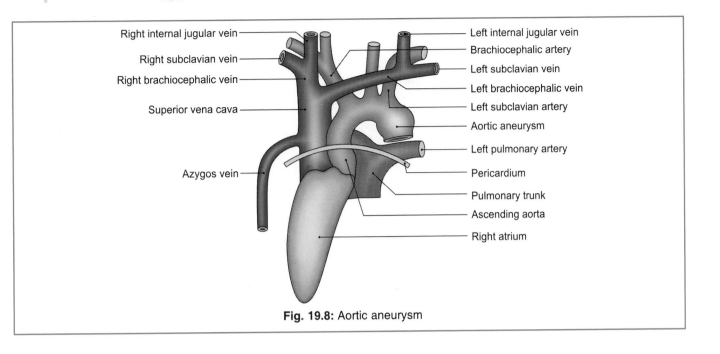

Right internal jugular vein
Right subclavian vein
Right brachiocephalic vein
Superior vena cava
Azygos vein

Left internal jugular vein
Brachiocephalic artery
Left subclavian vein
Left brachiocephalic vein
Left subclavian artery
Aortic aneurysm
Left pulmonary artery
Pericardium
Pulmonary trunk
Ascending aorta
Right atrium

Fig. 19.8: Aortic aneurysm

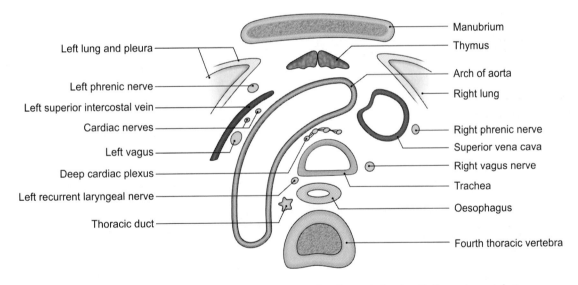

Left lung and pleura
Left phrenic nerve
Left superior intercostal vein
Cardiac nerves
Left vagus
Deep cardiac plexus
Left recurrent laryngeal nerve
Thoracic duct

Manubrium
Thymus
Arch of aorta
Right lung
Right phrenic nerve
Superior vena cava
Right vagus nerve
Trachea
Oesophagus
Fourth thoracic vertebra

Fig. 19.9: Transverse section of the thorax passing through the fourth thoracic vertebra

2 Pericardium and heart.
3 Oesophagus in the lower part.
4 Diaphragm.

Posterior

1 Vertebral column.
2 Hemiazygos veins.

To the Right Side

1 Oesophagus in the upper part.
2 Azygos vein.

3 Thoracic duct (Fig. 19.3).
4 Right lung and pleura.

To the Left Side

Left lung and pleura.

Branches

1 Nine posterior intercostal arteries on each side for the third to eleventh intercostal spaces.

2 The subcostal artery on each side (*see* Fig. 14.8).

3 Two left bronchial arteries. The right bronchial artery arises from the third right posterior intercostal artery.

Section 2 **Thorax**

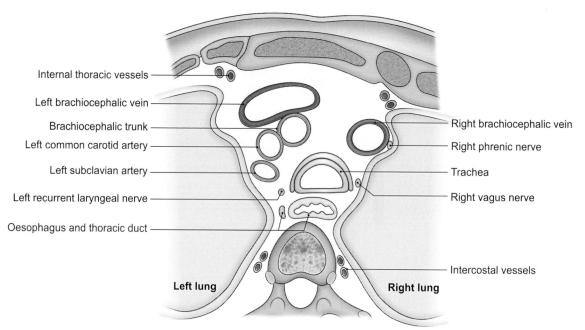

Internal thoracic vessels
Left brachiocephalic vein
Brachiocephalic trunk
Left common carotid artery
Left subclavian artery
Left recurrent laryngeal nerve
Oesophagus and thoracic duct

Right brachiocephalic vein
Right phrenic nerve
Trachea
Right vagus nerve

Intercostal vessels

Left lung   Right lung

Fig. 19.10: Transverse section of thorax passing through the third thoracic vertebra

4 Oesophageal branches, supplying the middle one-third of the oesophagus.
5 Pericardial branches, to the posterior surface of the pericardium.
6 Mediastinal branches, to lymph nodes and areolar tissue of the posterior mediastinum.
7 Superior phrenic arteries to the posterior part of the superior surface of the diaphragm. Branches of these arteries anastomose with those of the musculo-phrenic and pericardiacophrenic arteries.

PULMONARY TRUNK

The wide pulmonary trunk starts from the summit of infundibulum of right ventricle. Both the ascending aorta and pulmonary trunk are enclosed in a common sleeve of serous pericardium, in front of transverse sinus of pericardium. Pulmonary trunk carrying deoxygenated blood, overlies the beginning of ascending aorta. It courses to the left and divides into right and left pulmonary arteries under the concavity of aortic arch at the level of sternal angle (Figs 19.2 and 19.3).

The right pulmonary artery courses to the right behind ascending aorta, and superior vena cava and anterior to oesophagus to become part of the root of the lung. It gives off its first branch to the upper lobe before entering the hilum. Within the lung the artery descends posterolateral to the main bronchus and divides like the bronchi into lobar and segmental arteries.

The left pulmonary artery passes to the left anterior to descending thoracic aorta to become part of the root of the left lung. At its beginning, it is connected to the inferior aspect of arch of aorta by ligamentum arteriosus, a remnant of ductus arteriosus. Rest of the course is same as of the right branch.

FACTS TO REMEMBER

- Superior vena cava is the second largest vein of the body.
- Vena azygos brings the venous blood from the posterior parts of thoracic and abdominal wall.
- Aorta is the largest elastic artery of the body. It takes oxygenated blood to all parts of the body except the lungs.
- There is a gradual transition from its elastic nature to muscular nature of its branches.
- Pulmonary trunk arises from the right ventricle. It soon divides into right and left pulmonary arteries which carry deoxygenated blood from right ventricle to the lungs for oxygenation.
- Pulmonary trunk and ascending aorta develop from a common source, the truncus arteriosus.
- There is triple relationship between these two vessels:
  - Close to heart, pulmonary trunk lies anterior to ascending aorta.
  - At upper border of heart, pulmonary trunk lies to the left of ascending aorta (Fig. 19.2).
  - A little above this, the right pulmonary artery lies posterior to the ascending aorta.

Section 2 Thorax

CLINICOANATOMICAL PROBLEM

A teenage girl was complaining of breathlessness. The physician heard a 'machine like murmur' during auscultation on the second left intercostal space, close to the margin of sternum. There was continuous thrill on the same site. On getting radiographs of chest and angiocardiography, a diagnosis of patent ductus arteriosus was made.
- What is the 'machine-like' murmur?
- How can the shunting of blood be prevented
- Describe briefly the function of ductus arteriosus during prenatal life. When does it close?

Ans: The ductus arteriosus is a patent channel during fetal life for conducting the blood from left pulmonary artery to arch of aorta beyond the origin of left subclavian artery. The ductus carries blood from right ventricle to descending thoracic aorta. This is necessary as lungs are not functioning. After birth, with the functioning of lungs, ductus arteriosus obliterates and becomes ligamentum arteriosus. If this does not take place (as it occurs in one out of 3000 births), there is back flow of blood from aorta into pulmonary artery giving rise to 'machine-like' murmur. The treatment is surgical.

FREQUENTLY ASKED QUESTIONS

1. Name the parts of aorta. Describe arch of aorta under the following heading:
   a. Beginning
   b. Course
   c. Relations
   d. Branches

2. Describe the foetal circulation
3. Write short notes on:
   a. Branches of descending thoracic aorta
   b. Patent ductus arteriosus
   c. Obstruction of superior vena cava

MULTIPLE CHOICE QUESTIONS

1. Branches of arch of aorta are all *except*:
   a. Brachiocephalic trunk
   b. Left common carotid
   c. Left subclavian
   d. Vertebral

2. How many pairs of posterior intercostal arteries arise from descending thoracic aorta?
   a. Nine   b. Eleven
   c. Ten   d. Twelve

3. Aortic aneurysm may cause following symptoms:
   a. Dyspnoea   b. Dysphagia
   c. Dysphonia   d. All of the above

4. Posterior relations of ascending aorta are all *except*:
   a. Transverse sinus of pericardium
   b. Right atrium
   c. Right pulmonary artery
   d. Right bronchus

ANSWERS

1. d   **2.** a   **3.** d   **4.** b

Trachea, Oesophagus and Thoracic Duct

The best thing about animals is that they don't talk much
—T. Wilder

INTRODUCTION

Trachea or windpipe is the patent tube for passage of air to and from the lungs. In contrast, oesophagus lying behind the trachea opens only while drinking or eating. Thoracic duct brings the lymph from major part of the body to the root of the neck.

TRACHEA

The trachea (Latin *air vessel*) is a wide tube lying more or less in the midline, in the lower part of the neck and in the superior mediastinum. Its upper end is continuous with the lower end of the larynx. The trachea in the neck is covered by the isthmus of the thyroid gland and acts as a shield for trachea. At its lower end, the trachea ends by dividing into the right and left principal bronchi (Fig. 20.1).

The trachea is 10 to 15 cm in length. Its external diameter measures about 2 cm in males and about 1.5 cm in females. The lumen is smaller in the living than in the cadaver. It is about 3 mm at one year of age. During childhood, it corresponds to the age in years, with a maximum of about 12 mm in adults, i.e. it increases 1 mm per year up to 12 years.

The upper end of the trachea lies at the lower border of the cricoid cartilage, opposite the sixth cervical vertebra. In the cadaver its bifurcated lower end lies at the lower border of the fourth thoracic vertebra, corresponding in front to the sternal angle. However, in living subjects, in the erect posture, the bifurcation lies at the lower border of the sixth thoracic vertebra and descends still further during inspiration.

Over most of its length, the trachea lies in the median plane, but near the lower end it deviates slightly to the right. As it runs downwards, the trachea passes slightly backwards following the curvature of the spine.

Relations of the Thoracic Part

Anteriorly

1 Manubrium sterni.
2 Sternothyroid muscles.
3 Remains of the thymus.
4 Left brachiocephalic and inferior thyroid veins.
5 Aortic arch, brachiocephalic and left common carotid arteries.
6 Deep cardiac plexus (*see* Fig. 19.9).
7 Some lymph nodes.

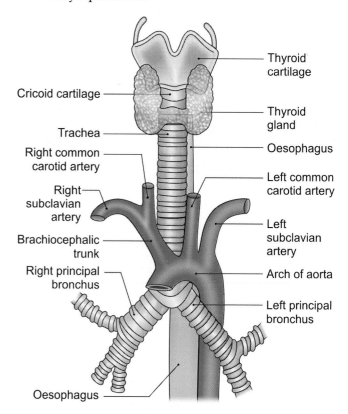

Fig. 20.1: Trachea and its relations

Posteriorly

1 Oesophagus
2 Vertebral column

On the Right Side

1 Right lung and pleura
2 Right vagus
3 Azygos vein (Fig. 20.2)

On the Left Side

1 Arch of aorta, left common carotid and left sub-clavian arteries.
2 Left recurrent laryngeal nerve (Fig. 20.3).

Structure

The trachea has a fibroelastic wall supported by a cartilaginous skeleton formed by C-shaped rings. The rings are about 16 to 20 in number and make the tube convex anterolaterally. Posteriorly, there is a gap which is closed by a fibroelastic membrane and contains transversely arranged smooth muscle known as the *trachealis*. The lumen is lined by ciliated columnar epithelium and contains many mucous and serous glands.

Arterial Supply

Inferior thyroid arteries.

Venous Drainage

Into the left brachiocephalic vein.

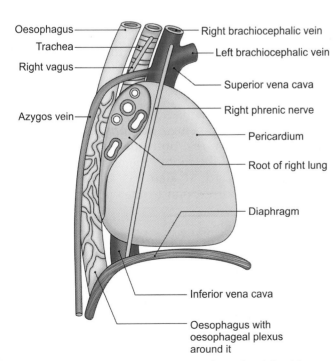

Fig. 20.2: Mediastinum as seen from the right side

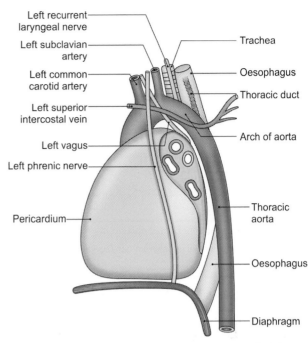

Fig. 20.3: Mediastinum as seen from the left side

Lymphatic Drainage

To the pretracheal and paratracheal nodes.

Nerve Supply

1 *Parasympathetic:* Nerves through vagi and recurrent laryngeal nerves. It is:
   a. Sensory and secretomotor to the mucous membrane.
   b. Motor to the trachealis muscle.
2 *Sympathetic:* Fibres from the middle cervical ganglion reach, it along the inferior thyroid arteries and are vasomotor.

DEVELOPMENT

Development of trachea is described in respiratory system (*see* Chapter 16).

HISTOLOGY OF TRACHEA

Trachea is a thin walled flexible tube. The trachea is lined by *pseudostratified ciliated columnar epithelium* with interspersed goblet cells resting on a basement membrane. The *lamina propria* consists of elastic fibres, lymphocytes both segregated and aggregated and short ducts of the glands (Fig. 20.4). The *submucosa* which contains both mucous and serous acini that keep the epithelium moist. The most characteristic feature of trachea is its supporting framework of 16–20 C-shaped hyaline cartilages that encircle it on its ventral and lateral aspects. The cartilage is covered by perichondrium on all sides which separates it from the neighbouring structures. The outermost layer is the adventitia which contains blood vessels and nerves.

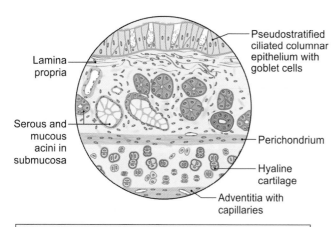

Fig. 20.4: Various layers of wall of trachea

- Pseudostratified columnar ciliated epithelium
- Serous and mucous acini in between cartilage and epithelium
- C-shaped hyaline cartilage outside

CLINICAL ANATOMY

- In radiographs, the trachea is seen as a vertical translucent shadow due to the contained air in front of the cervicothoracic spine (*see* Fig. 21.12).
- Clinically, the trachea is palpated in the suprasternal notch. Normally, it is median in position. Shift of the trachea to any side indicates a mediastinal shift.
- During swallowing when the larynx is elevated, the trachea elongates by stretching because the tracheal bifurcation is not permitted to move by the aortic arch. Any downward pull due to sudden and forced inspiration, or aortic aneurysm will produce the physical sign known as 'tracheal tug'.
- *Tracheostomy:* It is a surgical procedure which allows air to enter directly into trachea. It is done in cases of blockage of air pathway in nose or larynx.
- As the tracheal rings are incomplete posteriorly, the oesophagus can dilate during swallowing. This also allows the diameter of the trachea to be controlled by the trachealis muscle. This muscle narrows the caliber of the tube, compressing the contained air, if the vocal cords are closed. This increases the explosive force of the blast of compressed air, as occurs in coughing and sneezing.
- Mucus secretions help in trapping inhaled foreign particles, and the soiled mucus is then expelled by coughing. The cilia of the mucous membrane beat upwards, pushing the mucus towards the pharynx.
- The trachea may get compressed by pathological enlargements of the thyroid, the thymus, lymph nodes and the aortic arch. This causes dyspnoea, irritative cough, and often a husky voice.

OESOPHAGUS

DISSECTION

Remove the posterior surface of the parietal pericardium between the right and left pulmonary veins. This uncovers the anterior surface of the oesophagus in the posterior mediastinum.

Find the azygos vein and its tributaries on the vertebral column to the right of the oesophagus. Find and follow the thoracic duct on the left of azygos vein.

Identify the sternal, sternocostal, interchondral and costochondral joints on the anterior aspect of chest wall which was reflected downwards.

Expose the ligaments which unite the heads of the ribs to the vertebral bodies and intervertebral discs.

Features

The oesophagus is a narrow muscular tube, forming the food passage between the pharynx and stomach. It extends from the lower part of the neck to the upper part of the abdomen (Fig. 20.2). The oesophagus is about 25 cm long. The tube is flattened anteroposteriorly and the lumen is kept collapsed; it dilates only during the passage of the food bolus. The pharyngo-oesophageal junction is the narrowest part of the alimentary canal except for the vermiform appendix.

The oesophagus begins in the neck at the lower border of the cricoid cartilage, where it is continuous with the lower end of the pharynx.

It descends in front of the vertebral column through the superior and posterior parts of the mediastinum, and pierces the diaphragm at the level of tenth thoracic vertebra. It ends by opening into the stomach at its cardiac end at the level of eleventh thoracic vertebra.

Curvatures

In general, the oesophagus is vertical, but shows slight curvatures in the following directions. There are two side to side curvatures, both towards the left (*see* Fig. 17.4). One is at the root of the neck and the other near the lower end. It also has anteroposterior curvatures that correspond to the curvatures of the cervicothoracic spine.

Constrictions

Normally, the oesophagus shows four constrictions levels.

1 At its beginning, 15 cm/6-inch from the incisor teeth, where it is crossed by cricopharyngeus muscle.
2 Where it is crossed by the aortic arch, 22.5 cm/9-inch from the incisor teeth.
3 Where it is crossed by the left bronchus, 27.5 cm/11-inch from the incisor teeth (Fig. 20.9).

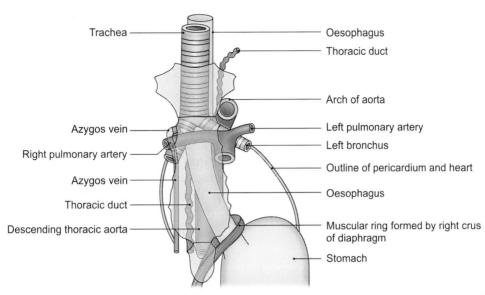

Fig. 20.5: Structures in the posterior mediastinum seen after removal of the heart and pericardium

4 Where it pierces the diaphragm 37.5 cm/15-inch from the incisor teeth.

The distance from the incisor teeth are important in passing instruments like endoscope into the oesophagus.

For the sake of convenience, the relations of the oesophagus may be studied in three parts—cervical, thoracic and abdominal. The relations of the cervical part are described in Volume 3, and those of the abdominal part in Volume 2 of BD Chaurasia's Human Anatomy.

Relations of the Thoracic Part of the Oesophagus

Anteriorly

1 Trachea
2 Right pulmonary artery
3 Left bronchus
4 Pericardium with left atrium
5 The diaphragm (Figs 20.2 and 20.3).

Posteriorly

1 Vertebral column
2 Right posterior intercostal arteries
3 Thoracic duct
4 Azygos vein with the terminal parts of the hemi-azygos veins
5 Thoracic aorta
6 Right pleural recess
7 Diaphragm (Fig. 20.5)

To the Right

1 Right lung and pleura
2 Azygos vein
3 The right vagus (Figs 20.6a to c)

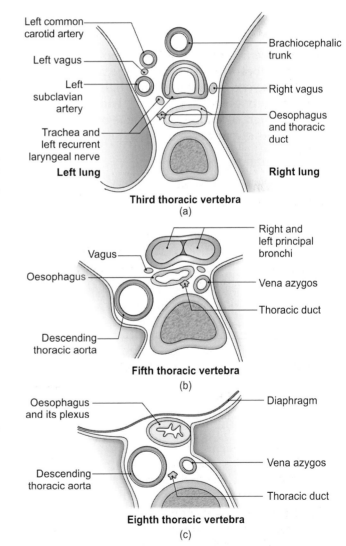

Figs 20.6a to c: Outline drawings of three sections through the oesophagus at different levels of thoracic vertebrae

Section 2 | Thorax

To the Left

1 Aortic arch
2 Left subclavian artery
3 Thoracic duct
4 Left lung and pleura
5 Left recurrent laryngeal nerve, all in the superior mediastinum (*see* Figs 19.3 and 19.9)

In the posterior mediastinum, it is related to:

1 The descending thoracic aorta
2 The left lung and mediastinal pleura (*see* Fig. 16.3)

Arterial Supply

1 The cervical part including the segment up to the arch of aorta is supplied by the inferior thyroid arteries.
2 The thoracic part is supplied by the oesophageal branches of the aorta.
3 The abdominal part is supplied by the oesophageal branches of the left gastric artery.

Venous Drainage

Blood from the upper part of the oesophagus drains into the brachiocephalic veins; from the middle part it goes to the azygos veins; and from the lower end it goes to the left gastric vein and vena azygos via hemiazygos vein. The lower end of the oesophagus is one of the sites of portosystemic anastomoses.

Lymphatic Drainage

The cervical part drains to the deep cervical nodes; the thoracic part to the posterior mediastinal nodes; and the abdominal part to the left gastric nodes.

Nerve Supply

1 *Parasympathetic nerves:* The upper half of the oesophagus is supplied by the recurrent laryngeal nerves, and the lower half by the oesophageal plexus formed mainly by the two vagi. Parasympathetic nerves are sensory, motor and secretomotor to the oesophagus.

2 *Sympathetic nerves:* For upper half of oesophagus, the fibres come from middle cervical ganglion and run with inferior thyroid arteries. For lower half, the fibres come directly from upper four thoracic ganglia, to form oesophageal plexus before supplying the oesophagus. Sympathetic nerves are vasomotor.

The *oesophageal plexus* is formed mainly by the parasympathetic through vagi but sympathetic fibres are also present. Towards the lower end of the oesophagus; the vagal fibres form the anterior and posterior gastric nerves which enter the abdomen through the oesophageal opening of the diaphragm.

DEVELOPMENT

Described in Chapter 19; Volume 2.

HISTOLOGY OF OESOPHAGUS

The oesophagus is a muscular tube that rapidly propels the food from pharynx into the stomach. It is about 25 cm long. The **mucous membrane** is thrown into longitudinal folds when empty. The epithelium is *stratified squamous non-keratinised* in character and protective in function. The lamina propria sends papillae into the epithelium. The muscularis mucosae is indistinct at the beginning of oesophagus, but becomes distinct lower down (Fig. 20.7). The **submucosa** contains *oesophageal glands*. These are mucus secreting glands with acini which are round or oval in shape. The **muscularis externa** has striated muscle fibres in upper third, mixed, i.e. both striated and smooth muscle fibres in the middle third and smooth muscle fibres in the lower third of oesophagus.

The outermost layer is the **adventitia** which is made up of loose connective tissue with capillaries and nerves.

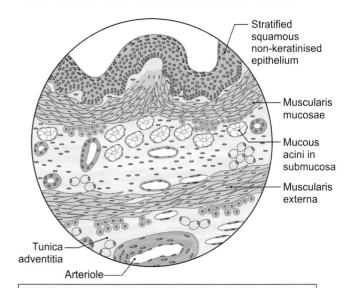

Labels: Stratified squamous non-keratinised epithelium; Muscularis mucosae; Mucous acini in submucosa; Muscularis externa; Tunica adventitia; Arteriole

- Epithelium is stratified squamous non-keratinised
- Oesophageal mucous glands in submucosa
- Lower one-third shows smooth muscle in muscularis externa

Fig. 20.7: Histology of oesophagus

CLINICAL ANATOMY

- In portal hypertension, the communications between the portal and systemic veins draining the lower end of the oesophagus dilate. These dilatations are called *oesophageal varices*. Rupture of these varices can cause serious haematemesis

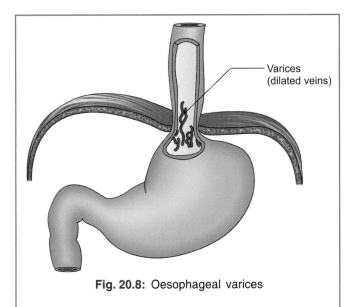

Fig. 20.8: Oesophageal varices

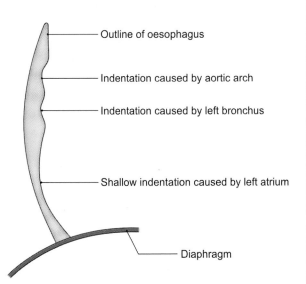

- Outline of oesophagus
- Indentation caused by aortic arch
- Indentation caused by left bronchus
- Shallow indentation caused by left atrium
- Diaphragm

Fig. 20.9: Normal indentations of oesophagus

or vomiting of blood. The oesophageal varices can be visualised radiographically by barium swallow; they produce worm-like shadows (Fig. 20.8).

- Left atrial enlargement as in mitral stenosis can also be visualised by barium swallow. The enlarged atrium causes a shallow depression on the front of the oesophagus. Barium swallow also helps in the diagnosis of oesophageal strictures, carcinoma and achalasia cardia (Fig. 20.9).
- The normal indentations on the oesophagus should be kept in mind during oesophagoscopy (Fig. 20.9).
- The lower end of the oesophagus is normally kept closed. It is opened by the stimulus of a food bolus. In case of neuromuscular incoordination,

the lower end of the oesophagus fails to dilate with the arrival of food which, therefore, accumulates in the oesophagus. This condition of neuromuscular incoordination characterised by inability of the oesophagus to dilate is known as 'achalasia cardia' (Fig. 20.10). It may be due to congenital absence of nerve cells in wall of oesophagus.

- Improper separation of the trachea from the oesophagus during development gives rise to tracheo-oesophageal fistula (Fig. 20.11).
- Compression of the oesophagus in cases of mediastinal syndrome causes dysphagia or difficulty in swallowing.

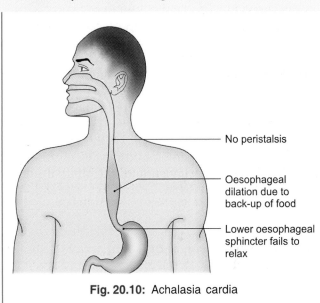

- No peristalsis
- Oesophageal dilation due to back-up of food
- Lower oesophageal sphincter fails to relax

Fig. 20.10: Achalasia cardia

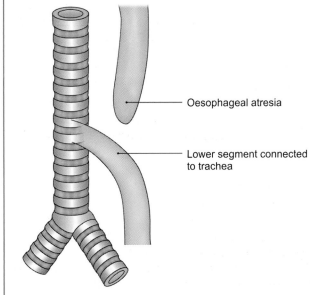

- Oesophageal atresia
- Lower segment connected to trachea

Fig. 20.11: Tracheo-oesophageal fistula

Section **2** Thorax

THORACIC DUCT

Features

The thoracic duct is the largest lymphatic vessel in the body. It extends from the upper part of the abdomen to the lower part of the neck, crossing the posterior and superior parts of the mediastinum. It is about 45 cm/ 18 inch long. It has a beaded appearance because of the presence of many valves in its lumen (Fig. 20.12).

Course

The thoracic duct begins as a continuation of the upper end of the cisterna chyli near the lower border of the twelfth thoracic vertebra and enters the thorax through the aortic opening of the diaphragm (see Fig. 12.16).

It then ascends through the posterior mediastinum from level of 12th thoracic vertebra to 5th thoracic vertebra, where it crosses from the right side to the left side. Then it courses through the superior mediastinum along the left edge of the oesophagus and reaches the neck.

In the neck, it arches laterally at the level of the transverse process of seventh cervical vertebra. Finally it descends in front of the first part of the left subclavian artery and ends by opening into the angle of junction between the left subclavian and left internal jugular veins (Fig. 20.12).

Relations

At the Aortic Opening of the Diaphragm

Anteriorly: Diaphragm

Posteriorly: Vertebral column

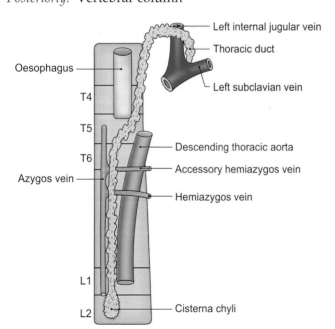

Fig. 20.12: The course of the thoracic duct

To the right: Azygos vein

To the left: Aorta (Fig. 12.16)

In the Posterior Mediastinum

Anteriorly

1 Diaphragm (Figs 20.6c)
2 Oesophagus
3 Right pleural recess

Posteriorly

1 Vertebral column
2 Right posterior intercostal arteries
3 Terminal parts of the hemiazygos veins.

To the right: Azygos vein

To the left: Descending thoracic aorta (Fig. 20.6c).

In the Superior Mediastinum

Anteriorly

1 Arch of aorta
2 The origin of the left subclavian artery (Fig. 20.6a)

Posteriorly: Vertebral column

To the right: Oesophagus

To the left: Pleura

In the Neck

The thoracic duct forms an arch rising about 3–4 cm above the clavicle. The arch has the following relations.

Anteriorly

1 Left common carotid artery
2 Left vagus
3 Left internal jugular vein

Posteriorly

1 Vertebral artery and vei.
2 Sympathetic trunk
3 Thyrocervical trunk and its branches
4 Left phrenic nerve
5 Medial border of the scalenus anterior
6 Prevertebral fascia covering all the structures mentioned
7 The first part of the left subclavian artery.

Tributaries

The thoracic duct receives lymph from, roughly, both halves of the body below the diaphragm and the left half above the diaphragm (Fig. 20.13).

In the thorax, the thoracic duct receives lymph vessels from the posterior mediastinal nodes and from small intercostal nodes. At the root of the neck, efferent

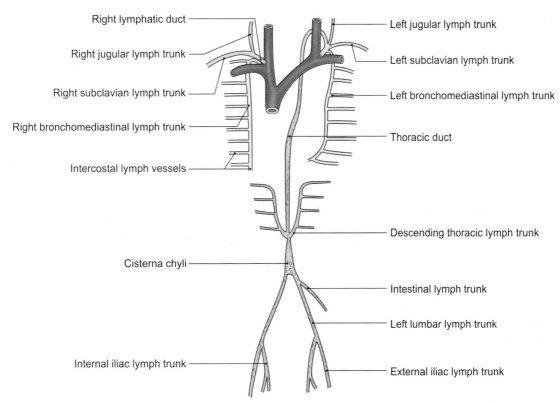

Right lymphatic duct

Right jugular lymph trunk

Right subclavian lymph trunk

Right bronchomediastinal lymph trunk

Intercostal lymph vessels

Cisterna chyli

Internal iliac lymph trunk

Left jugular lymph trunk

Left subclavian lymph trunk

Left bronchomediastinal lymph trunk

Thoracic duct

Descending thoracic lymph trunk

Intestinal lymph trunk

Left lumbar lymph trunk

External iliac lymph trunk

Fig. 20.13: The tributaries of the thoracic duct

vessels of the nodes in the neck form the *left jugular trunk,* and those from nodes in the axilla form the *left subclavian trunk.* These trunks end in the thoracic duct. The *left bronchomediastinal trunk* drains lymph from the left half of the thorax and ends in the thoracic duct. On the right side there is right lymphatic duct into which right broncho-mediastinal, right jugular and right subclavian lymph trunks drain. The right lymphatic trunk ends in the right brachiocephalic vein at the junction of right subclavian and right internal jugular veins.

FACTS TO REMEMBER

- Trachea contains C-shaped hyaline cartilaginous rings which are deficient posteriorly, so that the oesophagus situated behind the trachea is not compressed by trachea.
- Trachea begins at 6th cervical vertebra and ends at thoracic 4 (in expiration) by dividing into two principal bronchi. Trachea is always patent.
- Oesophagus is 25 cm long, like duodenum and ureter. Its maximum part about 20 cm/8" lie in thoracic cavity.
- There is no digestive activity in the oesophagus. Lower part of oesophagus is a site of portocaval anastomoses.

- Thoracic duct drains lymph from both lower limbs, abdominal cavity, left side of thorax, left upper limb and left side of head and neck.

CLINICOANATOMICAL PROBLEM

A young lady during her midpregnancy period complained of rapid breathing and difficulty in swallowing. She also gave a history of sore throat with pains in her joints during childhood.

- What is the likely diagnosis?
- What is the explanation for her symptoms?

Ans: The diagnosis most likely is rheumatic heart. It occurs due to streptococcal infection in the throat. Its toxins affect the mitral valve of the heart and kidney as well. In this case her mitral valve got affected, leading to mitral stenosis which causes left atrial enlargement due to its incomplete emptying into the left ventricle.

The enlarged left atrium presses on the oesophagus, as it passes behind the heart and pericardium. So the patient complains of dysphagia. A simple barium swallow can show the enlarged left atrium causing pressure on the oesophagus.

As enough blood is not reaching the lungs, there is anoxia in the body, leading to rapid breathing.

Section **2** Thorax

FREQUENTLY ASKED QUESTIONS

1. Describe trachea. Give the relations of thoracic part of trachea. Add a note on tracheostomy
2. Describe oesophagus under following headings:
   a. Beginning
   b. Course
   c. Termination
   d. Relations of the thoracic part
   e. Clinical anatomy
3. Write short notes on:
   a. Thoracic duct and its tributaries
   b. Achalasia cardia
   c. Normal indentations of oesophagus

MULTIPLE CHOICE QUESTIONS

1. Indentations in the oesophagus are caused by all *except*:
   a. Aortic arch   b. Left bronchus
   c. Left atrium   d. Left ventricle
2. In mitral stenosis, barium swallow is done to see compression of oesophagus due to enlargement of:
   a. Right atrium
   b. Left atrium
   c. Left ventricle
   d. Right ventricle
3. Oesophageal varices are seen in which part of oesophagus?
   a. Upper end
   b. Middle region
   c. Lower end
   d. Whole of oesophagus
4. Right side relations of thoracic part of oesophagus are all *except*:
   a. Right lung and pleura   b. Azygos vein
   c. Right vagus   d. Left vagus

ANSWERS

1. d   2. b   3. c   4. d

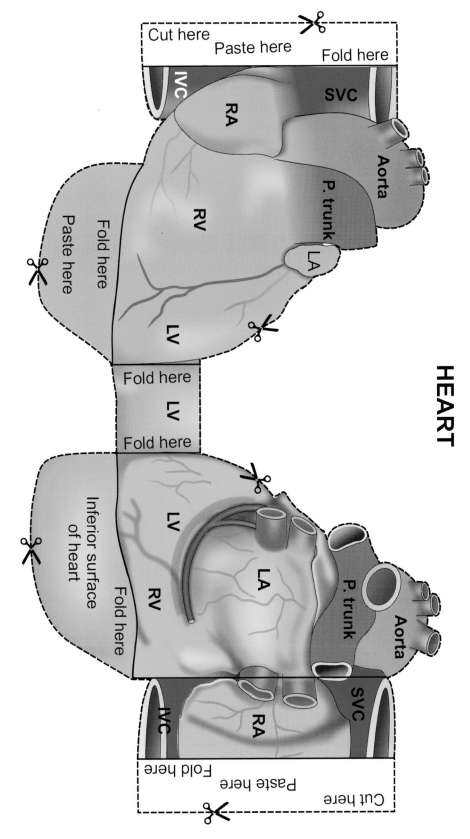

HEART

- Cut, fold and paste at the appropriate sites
- Fill it with cotton carefully

Surface Marking and Radiological Anatomy of Thorax

Tuberculosis not only affects the poor, but rich as well in same quantum

INTRODUCTION

Surface marking is the projection of deeper structures on the surface of body.

SURFACE MARKING

The bony and soft tissue surface landmarks have been described in Chapter 12.

The surface marking of important structures is described here.

- Parietal pleura (Fig. 21.1)
- Lungs (Figs 21.2 to 21.4)
- Heart (Fig. 21.5)
- Cardiac valves and ascultatory areas (Fig. 21.6)

Surface Marking of Parietal Pleura

The *cervical pleura* is represented by a curved line forming a dome over the medial one-third of the clavicle with a height of about 2.5 cm above the clavicle. Pleura lies in the root of neck on both sides (points 1 and I) (Fig. 21.1).

The *anterior margin,* the costomediastinal line of pleural reflection is as follows: *On the right side,* it extends from the sternoclavicular joint downwards and medially to the midpoint of the sternal angle (point 2). From here it continues vertically downwards to the midpoint of the xiphisternal joint crosses to right of xiphicostal angle (point 3). *On the left side,* the line follows the same course up to the level of the fourth costal cartilage. It then arches outwards and descends along the sternal margin up to the sixth costal cartilage (points I–IV).

The *inferior margin,* or the costodiaphragmatic line of pleural reflection (same on both sides) passes laterally from the lower limit of its anterior margin, so that it crosses the eighth rib in the midclavicular line (Fig. 21.2), the tenth rib in the midaxillary line, and the twelfth rib at the lateral border of the sacrospinalis muscle (Fig. 21.3). Further it passes horizontally a little below

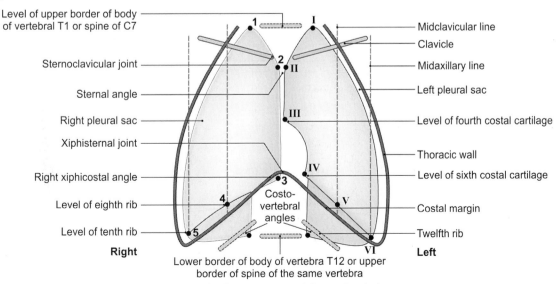

Fig. 21.1: Surface marking of the parietal pleura

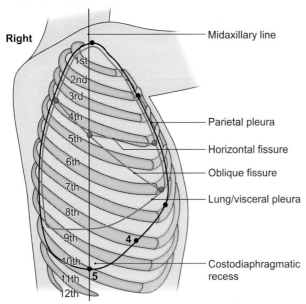

Fig. 21.2: Parietal (black) and visceral pleurae and lung (pink) from the lateral aspect. Costodiaphragmatic recess is seen

the 12th rib to the lower border of the twelfth thoracic vertebra, 2 cm lateral to the upper border of the twelfth thoracic spine (Fig. 21.3).

Thus the pleurae descend below the costal margin at three places, at the right xiphicostal angle, and at the right and left costovertebral angles below the twelfth rib behind the upper poles of the kidneys. The latter fact is of surgical importance in exposure of the kidney. The pleura may be damaged at these sites (Fig. 21.1).

The *posterior margins* of the pleura pass from a point 2 cm lateral to the twelfth thoracic spine to a point 2 cm lateral to the seventh cervical spine. The costal pleura becomes the mediastinal pleura along this line.
- Points 4 and 5 in Fig. 21.2—right side
- Points 6 and 7 in Fig. 21.3—right side
- Points V and VI in Fig. 21.1—left side
- Points VII and VIII in Fig. 21.3—left side

Surface Making of the Lungs

The *apex* of the lung coincides with the cervical pleura, and is represented by a line convex upwards rising 2.5 cm above the medial one-third of the clavicle point 1 on right and I on left side (Fig. 21.4).

The *anterior border of the right lung* corresponds very closely to the anterior margin or costomediastinal line of the pleura and is obtained by joining:
- Point 2 at the sternoclavicular joint,
- Point 3 in the median plane at the sternal angle,
- Point 4 in the median plane just above the xiphisternal joint.

The *anterior border of the left lung* corresponds to the anterior margin of the pleura up to the level of the fourth costal cartilage points II–IV.

In the lower part, it presents a cardiac notch of variable size. From the level of the fourth costal cartilage, it passes laterally for 3.5 cm from the sternal margin, and then curves downwards and medially to reach the sixth costal cartilage 4 cm from the median plane (points V and VI). In the region of the cardiac notch, the pericardium is covered only by a double layer

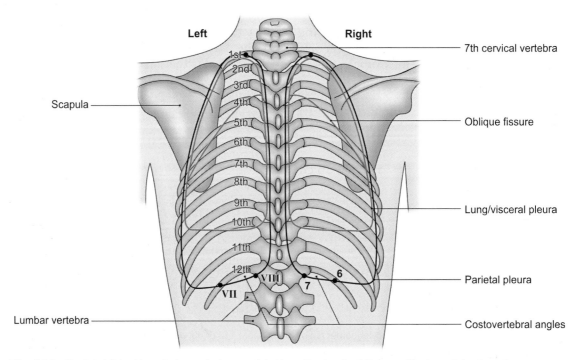

Fig. 21.3: Parietal (black) and visceral pleurae (pink) on the back of thorax. Costovertebral angles are seen

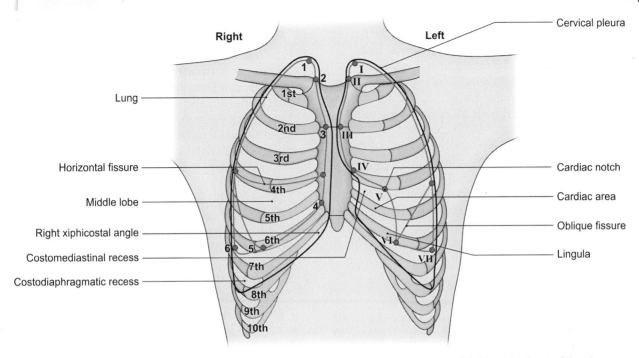

Fig. 21.4: Surface projection of the parietal pleura (black), visceral pleura and lung (pink) on the front of the thorax

of pleura. The area of the cardiac notch is dull on percussion and is called the *area of superficial cardiac dullness.*

The *lower border* of each lung (same on both the sides) lies two ribs higher than the parietal pleural reflection. It crosses the sixth ribs (points 5 and VI) in the midclavicular line, the eighth rib (points 6 and VII) in the midaxillary line (Fig. 21.4), the tenth rib at the lateral border of the erector spinae, and ends 2 cm lateral to the tenth thoracic spine (Fig. 21.3).

The *posterior border* coincides with the posterior margin of the pleural reflection except that its lower end lies at the level of the tenth thoracic spine (Fig. 21.3).

The *oblique fissure* can be drawn on both sides by joining:
- A point 2 cm lateral to the third thoracic spine.
- Another point on the fifth rib in the midaxillary line (Figs 21.2 and 21.4).
- A third point on the sixth costal cartilage 7.5 cm from the median plane.

The *horizontal fissure* is represented only on right side by a line joining:
- A point on the anterior border of the right lung at the level of the fourth costal cartilage.
- A second point on the fifth rib in the midaxillary line (Fig. 21.2).

Between the visceral and parietal pleurae, the recesses are present. Costodiaphragmatic recesses are present on both sides and are about 4–5 cm deep. Costomediastinal recess is prominent on left side, to left of sternum between 4th and 6th costal cartilages.

Surface Marking of the Borders of the Heart

- Point 1 at the lower border of the second left costal cartilage about 1.3 cm from the sternal margin (Fig. 21.5).
- Point 2 at the upper border of the third right costal cartilage 0.8 cm from the sternal margin.
- Point 3 in the right 4th intercostal space 3.8 cm from median plane.
- Point 4 at the lower border of the sixth right costal cartilage 2 cm from the sternal margin.

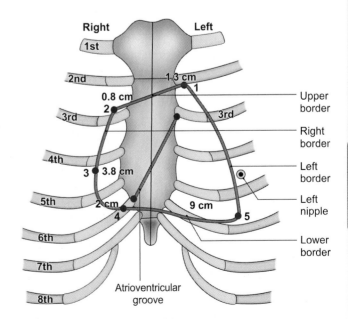

Fig. 21.5: Surface projection of the borders of the heart

- Point 5 at the apex of the heart in the left fifth intercostal space 9 cm from the midsternal line.
- Joining of points 1 and 2 forms upper border.
- The right border is marked by a line, slightly convex to the right, joining the points 2, 3 and 4. The maximum convexity is about 3.8 cm from the median plane in the fourth space.
- The inferior border is drawn by joining points 4 and 5.
- The left border is marked by a line, fairly convex to the left, joining the points 1 and 5.

Atrioventricular groove is marked by a line drawn from the sternal end of left 3rd costal cartilage to the sternal end of right sixth costal cartilage.

The area of the chest wall overlying the heart is called the *precordium*.

Surface Marking of the Cardiac Valves and the Auscultatory Areas

Sound produced by closure of the valves of the heart can be heard using a stethoscope. The sound arising in relation to a particular valve are best heard not directly over the valve, but at areas situated some distance away from the valve in the direction of blood flow through it. These are called auscultatory areas. The position of the valves in relation to the surface of the body, and of the auscultatory areas is given in Table 21.1 and Fig. 21.6.

Arteries

Internal Mammary (Thoracic) Artery

It is marked by joining the following points (Fig. 21.7).
- First point 1 cm above the sternal end of the clavicle, 3.5 cm from the median plane.
- Next points 2–7 marked over the upper 6 costal cartilages at a distance of 1.25 cm from the lateral sternal border.
- The last point 8 is marked in the sixth intercostal space 1.25 cm from the lateral sternal border.

Pulmonary Trunk

1 First mark the pulmonary valve by a horizontal line 2.5 cm long, mainly along the upper border of the left 3rd costal cartilage and partly over the adjoining part of the sternum (Fig. 21.6).
2 Then mark the pulmonary trunk by two parallel lines 2.5 cm apart from the pulmonary orifice upwards to the left 2nd costal cartilage.

Ascending Aorta

1 First mark the aortic orifice by a slightly oblique line 2.5 cm long running downwards and to the right over the left half of the sternum beginning at the level of the lower border of the left 3rd costal cartilage (Fig. 21.6).
2 Then mark the ascending aorta by two parallel lines 2.5 cm apart from the aortic orifice upwards to the right half of the sternal angle (Fig. 21.6).

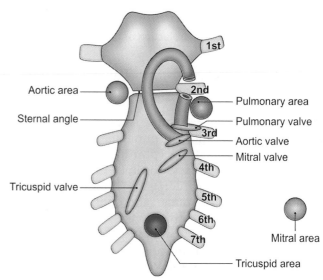

Fig. 21.6: Surface projection of the cardiac valves. The position of the auscultatory areas is also shown

Valve	Diameter of orifice	Surface marking	Auscultatory area
		Table 21.1: Surface marking of the cardiac valves and the sites of the auscultatory areas (Fig. 21.6)	
1. Pulmonary	2.5 cm	A horizontal line, 2.5 cm long, behind the upper border of the third left costal cartilage and adjoining part of the sternum	Second left intercostal space near the sternum
2. Aortic	2.5 cm	A slightly oblique line, 2.5 cm long, behind the left half of the sternum at the level of the lower border of the left third costal cartilage	Second right costal cartilage near the sternum
3. Mitral	3 cm	An oblique line, 3 cm long, behind the left half of the sternum opposite the left fourth costal cartilage	Cardiac apex
4. Tricuspid	4 cm	Most oblique of all valves, being nearly vertical, 4 cm long, behind the right half of the sternum opposite the fourth and fifth spaces	Lower end of the sternum

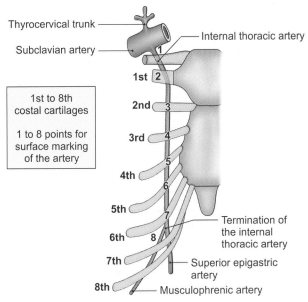

Thyrocervical trunk
Subclavian artery
Internal thoracic artery

1st to 8th costal cartilages

1 to 8 points for surface marking of the artery

1st
2nd
3rd
4th
5th
6th
7th
8th

Termination of the internal thoracic artery

Superior epigastric artery

Musculophrenic artery

Fig. 21.7: The origin, course and terminations of the internal thoracic artery (1st–8th costal cartilages)

Arch of the Aorta

Arch of the aorta lies behind the lower half of the manubrium sterni. Its upper convex border is marked by a line which begins at the right end of the sternal angle, arches upwards and to the left through the centre of the manubrium, and ends at the sternal end of the left second costal cartilage. Note that the beginning and the end of the arch lie at the same level. When marked on the surface as described above, the arch looks much smaller than it actually is because of foreshortening (Fig. 21.8).

Descending Thoracic Aorta

Descending thoracic aorta is marked by two parallel lines 2.5 cm apart, which begin at the sternal end of the left second costal cartilage, pass downwards and medially, and end in the median plane 2.5 cm above the transpyloric plane (Fig. 21.8).

Brachiocephalic Artery

Brachiocephalic artery is marked by a broad line extending from the centre of the manubrium to the right sternoclavicular joint (Fig. 21.8).

Left Common Carotid Artery

The thoracic part of this artery is marked by a broad line extending from a point a little to the left of the centre of the manubrium to the left sternoclavicular joint.

Left Subclavian Artery

The thoracic part of the left subclavian artery is marked by a broad vertical line along the left border of the manubrium a little to the left of the left common carotid artery.

Veins

Superior Vena Cava

Superior vena cava is marked by two parallel lines 2 cm apart, drawn from the lower border of the right first costal cartilage to the upper border of the third right costal cartilage, overlapping the right margin of the sternum (Fig. 21.9).

Right Brachiocephalic Vein

It is marked by two parallel lines 1.5 cm apart, drawn from the medial end of the right clavicle to the lower border of the right first costal cartilage close to the sternum (Fig. 21.9).

Left Brachiocephalic Vein

It is marked by two parallel lines 1.5 cm apart, drawn from the medial end of the left clavicle to the lower

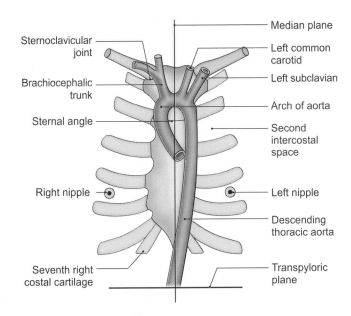

Median plane
Sternoclavicular joint
Left common carotid
Brachiocephalic trunk
Left subclavian
Sternal angle
Arch of aorta
Second intercostal space
Right nipple
Left nipple
Descending thoracic aorta
Seventh right costal cartilage
Transpyloric plane

Fig. 21.8: Surface marking of some arteries of thorax

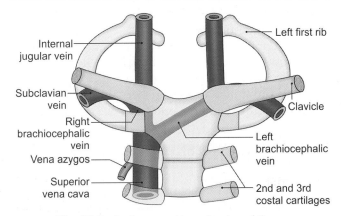

Internal jugular vein
Left first rib
Subclavian vein
Clavicle
Right brachiocephalic vein
Left brachiocephalic vein
Vena azygos
Superior vena cava
2nd and 3rd costal cartilages

Fig. 21.9: Surface marking of veins of thorax

Section 2 Thorax

border of the first right costal cartilage. It crosses the left sternoclavicular joint and the upper half of the manubrium (Fig. 21.9).

Trachea (Thoracic Part)

Trachea is marked by two parallel lines 2 cm apart, drawn from the lower border of the cricoid cartilage (2 cm below the thyroid notch) to the manubrio sternal angle, inclining slightly to the right (Fig. 21.10).

Right Bronchus

Right bronchus is marked by a broad line running downwards and to the right for 2.5 cm from the lower end of the trachea to the sternal end of the right third costal cartilage.

Left Bronchus

Left bronchus is marked by a broad line running downwards and to the left for 5 cm from the lower end of the trachea to the left third costal cartilage 4 cm from the median plane (Fig. 21.10).

Oesophagus

It is marked by one on each side two parallel lines 2.5 cm apart by joining the following points:
1 Two points (one on each side) 2.5 cm apart at the lower border of the cricoid cartilage across the median plane (Fig. 21.11).
2 Two points (one on each side) 2.5 cm apart at the root of the neck a little to the left of the median plane one on each side.
3 Two points (one on each side) 2.5 cm apart at the sternal angle across the median plane.
4 Two points (one on each side) 2.5 cm apart at the left 7th costal cartilage 2.5 cm from the median plane.

Thoracic Duct

It is marked by joining the following points.
1 A point 2 cm above the transpyloric plane slightly to the right of the median plane (Fig. 21.10).
2 A second point 2 cm to right of median plane below manubriosternal angle.
3 A third point across to left side at same level.
4 A fourth point 2.5 cm above the left clavicle 2 cm from the median plane.
5 A fifth point just above the sternal angle 1.3 cm to the left of the median plane.

RADIOLOGICAL ANATOMY

The most commonly taken radiographs are described as posteroanterior (PA) views. X-rays travel from posterior to the anterior side. A study of such radio-

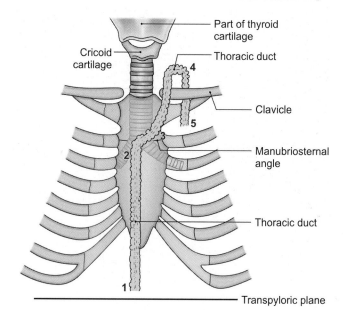

Fig. 21.10: Surface marking of trachea, bronchi and thoracic duct

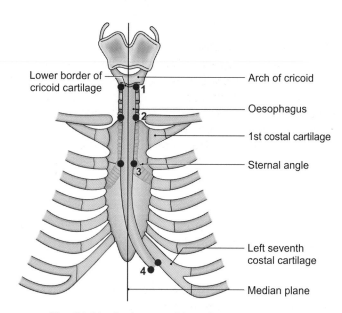

Fig. 21.11: Surface marking of the oesophagus

graphs gives information about the lungs, the diaphragm, the mediastinum, the trachea, and the skeleton of the region (Fig. 21.12). Take radiograph keeping both hands on waist to clear lung fields from scapula.

Following structures have to be examined in posteroanterior view of the thorax.

Soft Tissues

Nipples in both the sexes may be seen over the lung fields. The female breasts will also be visualised over the lower part of the lung fields. The extent of the overlap varies according to the size and pendulance of the breasts.

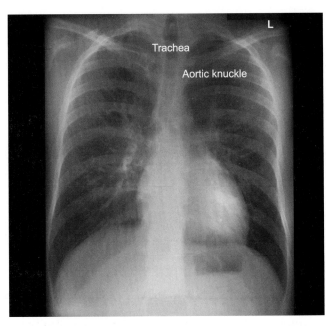

Fig. 21.12: Posteroanterior view of the thorax

Bones

The bones of the vertebrae are partially visible. Costo-transverse joints are seen on each side. The posterior parts of the ribs are better seen because of the large amounts of calcium contained in them. The ribs get wider and thinner as they pass anteriorly. Costal cartilages are not seen unless these are calcified. The medial borders of the scapulae may overlap the periphery of the lung fields.

Trachea

Trachea is seen as air-filled shadow in the midline of the neck. It lies opposite the lower cervical and upper thoracic vertebrae (Fig. 21.12).

Diaphragm

Diaphragm casts dome-shaped shadows on the two sides. The shadow on the right side is little higher than on the left side. The angles where diaphragm meets the thoracic cage are the costophrenic angles—the right and the left. Under the left costophrenic angle is mostly the gas in the stomach, while under the right angle is the smooth shadow of the liver.

Lungs

The dense shadows are cast by the lung roots due to the presence of the large bronchi, pulmonary vessels, bronchial vessels and lymph nodes. The lungs readily permit the passage of the X-rays and are seen as translucent shadows during full inspiration. Both blood vessels and bronchi are seen as series of shadows radiating from the lung roots. The smaller bronchi are not seen. The lung is divided into three zones—upper zone is from the apex till the second costal cartilage. Middle zone extends from the second to the fourth costal cartilage. It includes the hilar region. Lower zone extends from the fourth costal cartilage till the bases of the lungs.

Mediastinum

Shadow is produced by the superimpositions of structures in the mediastinum. It is chiefly produced by the heart and the vessels entering or leaving the heart. The transverse diameter of heart is half the transverse diameter of the thoracic cage. During inspiration, heart descends down and acquires tubular shape. Right border of the mediastinal shadow is formed from above downwards by right brachiocephalic vein, superior vena cava, right atrium and inferior vena cava. The left border of mediastinal shadow is formed from above downwards by aortic arch (aortic knuckle), left margin of pulmonary trunk, left auricle and left ventricle. The inferior border of the mediastinal shadow blends with the liver and diaphragm.

TOMOGRAPHY

Tomography is a radiological technique by which radiograms of selected layers (depths) of the body can be made. Tomography is helpful in locating deeply situated small lesions which are not seen in the usual radiograms.

NUMERICALS

- Anteroposterior diameter of inlet of thorax—5 cm.
- Transverse diameter of inlet of thorax—10 cm.
- Suprasternal notch—T2 vertebra.
- Sternal angle—disc between T4 and T5 vertebra. 2nd costal cartilage articulates with the sternum.
- Xiphisternal joint—T9 vertebra.
- Subcostal angle—between sternal attachments of 7th costal cartilages.
- Vertebra prominence—7th cervical spine.
- Superior angle of scapula—level of T2 spine.
- Root of spine of scapula—level of T3 spine.
- Inferior angle of scapula—level of T7 spine.
- Length of oesophagus—25 cm:
  - Cervical part—4 cm.
  - Thoracic part—20 cm.
  - Abdominal part—1.25 cm.
  - Beginning of oesophagus—C6 vertebra.
  - Termination of oesophagus—T11 vertebra.
- Beginning of trachea—C6 vertebra:
  - Length of trachea—10–15 cm.
  - Bifurcation of trachea—upper border of T5 vertebra.
  - Length of right principal bronchus—2.5 cm.
  - Length of left principal bronchus—5 cm.

Appendix 2

The disappointment at losing a patient lasts longer than joy in saving one

INTRODUCTION

Appendix 2 at the end of the section on thorax gives a bird's eye view of the sympathetic component of the autonomic nervous system. The course of the typical and atypical intercostal nerves is described briefly. Arteries of thorax have been tabulated. Clinical terms are also given.

AUTONOMIC NERVOUS SYSTEM

The autonomic nervous system comprises sympathetic and parasympathetic components. Sympathetic component is active during *fright, flight or fight*. During any of these activities, the pupils dilate, skin gets pale, blood pressure rises, blood vessels of skeletal muscles, heart, and brain dilate. The person is tense and gets tired soon (Fig. A2.1). There is hardly any activity in the digestive tracts due to which the individual does not feel hungry.

Parasympathetic component has the opposite effects of sympathetic component. This component is sympathetic to the digestive tract. In its activity,

digestion and metabolism of food occurs. Heart beats normally. Person is relaxed and can do creative work (Fig. A2.2).

Autonomic nervous system is controlled by brainstem and cerebral hemispheres. These include reticular formation of brainstem, thalamic and hypothalamic nuclei, limbic lobe and prefrontal cortex including the ascending and descending tracts interconnecting these regions.

Sympathetic Nervous System

Sympathetic nervous system is the larger of the two components of autonomic nervous system. It consists of two ganglionated trunks, their branches, prevertebral ganglia, plexuses. It supplies all the viscera of thorax, abdomen and pelvis, including the blood vessels of head and neck, brain, limbs, skin and the sweat glands as well as arrector pilorum muscle of skin of the whole body.

The preganglionic fibres are the axons of neurons situated in the lateral horns of T1–L2 segments of spinal cord. They leave spinal cord through their respective

Fig. A2.1: Actions of sympathetic system

Fig. A2.2: Actions of parasympathetic system

4 These may synapse in the corresponding ganglia and pass medially to the viscera like heart, lungs, oesophagus.

5 These white rami communicantes (wrc) pass to corresponding ganglia and emerge from these as wrc (unrelayed) in the form of splanchnic nerves to supply abdominal and pelvic viscera after synapsing in the ganglia situated in the abdominal cavity. Some fibres of splanchnic nerves pass express to *adrenal medulla*.

Sympathetic trunk on either side of the body extends from cervical region to the coccygeal region where both trunks fuse to form a single *ganglion impar*. Sympathetic trunk has cervical, thoracic, lumbar, sacral and coccygeal parts.

ventral roots, to pass in their nerve trunks, and beginning of ventral rami via white ramus communicans (wrc). There are 14 wrc on each side. These fibres can have following alternative routes.

1 They relay in the ganglion of the sympathetic trunks, postganglionic fibres pass via the grey rami communicantes and get distributed to the blood vessels of muscles, skin, sweat glands and to arrector pili muscles (Fig. A2.3).

2 These may pass through the corresponding ganglion and ascend to a ganglion higher before terminating in the above manner.

3 These may pass through the corresponding ganglion and descend to a ganglion lower and then terminate in the above manner.

Thoracic Part of Sympathetic Trunk

There are usually 11 ganglia on the sympathetic trunk of thoracic part. The first ganglion lies on neck of Ist rib and is usually fused with inferior cervical ganglion and forms *stellate ganglion*. The lower ones lie on the heads of the ribs. The sympathetic trunk continues with its abdominal part by passing behind the medial arcuate ligament.

The ganglia are connected with the respective spinal nerves via the white ramus communicans (from the spinal nerve to the ganglion) and the grey ramus communicans (from the ganglion to the spinal nerve, i.e. ganglion gives grey).

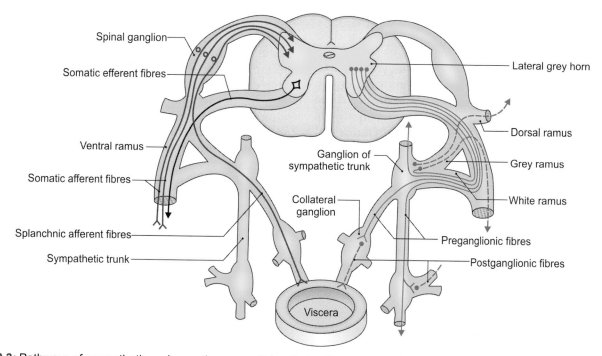

Fig. A2.3: Pathways of sympathetic and somatic nerves: Splanchnic afferent fibres and somatic afferent fibres (green); sympathetic preganglionic efferent fibres (red); sympathetic postganglionic efferent fibres (red dotted); and somatic efferent fibres (black)

Section 2 Thorax

Branches

1 Grey rami communicantes to all the spinal nerves, i.e. T1–T12. The postganglionic fibres pass along the spinal nerves to supply cutaneous blood vessels, sweat glands and arrector pili muscles.
2 Some white rami communicantes from T1 to T5 ganglia travel up to the cervical part of sympathetic trunk to relay in the three cervical ganglia. Fibres from the lower thoracic ganglia T10–L2 pass down as preganglionic fibres to relay in the lumbar or sacral ganglia.
3 The first five thoracic ganglia give postganglionic fibres to heart, lungs, aorta and oesophagus.
4 Lower eight ganglia give fibres which are preganglionic (unrelayed) for the supply of abdominal viscera. These are called splanchnic (visceral) nerves.

Ganglia 5–9 give fibres which constitute greater splanchnic nerve. Some fibres reach *adrenal medulla*.

Ganglia 9–10 give fibres that constitute lesser splanchnic nerve.

Ganglion 11 gives fibres that constitute lowest splanchnic nerve.

Nerve Supply of Heart

Preganglionic sympathetic neurons are located in lateral horns T1–T5 segments of spinal cord. These fibres pass along the respective ventral roots of thoracic nerves, to synapse with the respective ganglia of the sympathetic trunk. After relay, the postganglionic fibres form thoracic branches which intermingle with the vagal fibres, to form cardiac plexus.

Some fibres from T1 to T5 segments of spinal cord reach their respective ganglia. These fibres then travel up to the cervical part of the sympathetic chain and relay in superior, middle and inferior cervical ganglia. After relay, the postganglionic fibres form the three cervical cardiac nerves. Preganglionic parasympathetic neurons for the supply of heart are situated in the dorsal nucleus of vagus nerve.

Sympathetic activity increases the heart rate. Larger branches of coronary are mainly supplied by sympathetic. It causes vasodilatation of coronary arteries. Impulses of pain travel along sympathetic fibres. These fibres pass mostly through left sympathetic trunk and reach the spinal cord via T1–T5 spinal nerves. Thus the pain may be referred to the area of skin supplied by T1–T5 nerves, i.e. retrosternal, medial side of the upper limbs. Since one is more conscious of impulses coming from skin than the viscera, one feels as if the pain is in the skin. This is the basis of the *referred pain*.

Smaller branches of coronary artery are supplied by parasympathetic nerves. These nerves are concerned with slowing of the cardiac cycle.

The nerves reach the heart by the following two plexuses.

Superficial Cardiac Plexus

Superficial cardiac plexus is formed by the following:
1 Superior cervical cardiac branch of left sympathetic trunk.
2 Inferior cervical cardiac branch of left vagus nerve.

Deep Cardiac Plexus

Deep cardiac plexus consists of two halves which are interconnected and lie anterior to bifurcation of trachea (Table A2.1).

Branches from the cardiac plexus give extensive branches to pulmonary plexuses, right and left coronary plexuses. Branches from the coronary plexuses supply both the atria and the ventricles. Left ventricle gets richer nerve supply because of its larger size.

Nerve Supply of Lungs

The lungs are supplied from the anterior and posterior pulmonary plexuses. Anterior plexus is an extension of deep cardiac plexus. The posterior part is formed from branches of vagus and T2–T5 sympathetic ganglia. Small ganglia are found on these nerves for the relay of parasympathetic impulses brought via vagus nerve fibres. Parasympathetic system is bronchoconstrictor or motor, whereas sympathetic system is inhibitory. Sympathetic stimulation causes relaxation of smooth

Table A2.1: Components of deep cardiac plexus	
Right half	*Left half*
1. Superior, middle, inferior cervical cardiac branches of right sympathetic trunk	Only middle and inferior branches
2. Cardiac branches of T2–T4 ganglia of right side	Same
3. Superior and inferior cervical cardiac branches of right vagus	Only the superior cervical cardiac branch of left vagus
4. Thoracic cardiac branch of right vagus	Same
5. Two branches of right recurrent laryngeal nerve arising from neck region	Same, but coming from thoracic region

Table A2.2: Arteries of thorax

Artery	Origin, course and termination	Area of distribution
INTERNAL THORACIC (*see* Figs 14.11 and 21.7)	Arises from inferior aspect of 1st part of subclavian artery. Its origin lies 2 cm above the sternal end of the clavicle. It runs downwards, forwards and medially behind the clavicle and behind the 1–6 costal cartilages and 1–5 intercostal spaces to terminate in the 6th intercostal space by dividing into superior epigastric and musculophrenic arteries	It supplies pericardium, thymus, upper six intercostal spaces in their anterior parts, mammary gland, rectus sheath and also 7–9 intercostal spaces. Thus it supplies anterior thoracic and anterior abdominal walls from the clavicle to the umbilicus
Pericardiacophrenic artery	Branch of internal thoracic artery	Supplies fibrous and parietal layer of serous pericardia and the diaphragm
Mediastinal arteries	Small branches of internal thoracic artery	Supply thymus and fat in the mediastinum
Two anterior intercostal arteries	Two arteries each arise in 1–6 upper intercostal spaces from internal thoracic	Supply muscles of the 1–6 intercostal spaces and parietal pleura
Perforating arteries	Arise from internal thoracic artery in 2nd, 3rd and 4th spaces	They are large enough to supply the mammary gland
Superior epigastric artery	Terminal branch of internal thoracic artery. Enters the rectus sheath and ends by anastomosing with inferior epigastric artery, a branch of external iliac artery	Supplies the aponeuroses which form the rectus sheath, including the rectus abdominis.
Musculophrenic artery	This is also the terminal branch of internal thoracic artery. Ends by giving 2 anterior intercostal arteries in 7–9 intercostal spaces and by supplying the thoraco-abdominal diaphragm	Supplies the muscles of anterior parts of 7–9 intercostal spaces, and the muscle fibres of the thoracoabdominal diaphragm
ASCENDING AORTA (*see* Fig. 19.2)	Arises from the upper end of left ventricle. It is about 5 cm long and is enclosed in the pericardium. It runs upwards, forwards and to the right and continues as the arch of aorta at the sternal end of upper border of 2nd right costal cartilage. At the root of aorta, there are three dilatations of the vessel wall called the aortic sinuses. These are anterior, left posterior and right posterior	Supplies the heart musculature with the help of right coronary and left coronary arteries, described later.
ARCH OF AORTA (*see* Fig. 19.2)	It begins behind the upper border of 2nd right sterno-chondral joint. Runs upwards, backwards and to left across the left side of bifurcation of trachea. Then it passes behind the left bronchus and on the left side of body of T4 vertebra by becoming continuous with the descending thoracic aorta	Through its three branches, namely brachio-cephalic, left common carotid and left subclavian arteries, arch of aorta supplies part of brain, head, neck and upper limb
Brachiocephalic artery	1st branch of arch of aorta. Runs upwards and soon divides into right common carotid and right subclavian arteries	Through these two branches, part of the right half of brain, head, and neck are supplied. The distribution of 2 branches on right side is same as on the left side
Left common carotid artery	It runs upwards on the left side of trachea and at upper border of thyroid cartilage. The artery ends by dividing into internal carotid and external carotid arteries	The two branches supply brain, structures in the head and neck
Left subclavian artery	It is the last branch of arch of aorta. Runs to left in the root of neck behind scalenus anterior muscle, then on the upper surface of 1st rib. At the outer border of 1st rib, it continues as the axillary artery	Gives branches which supply part of brain, part of thyroid gland, muscles around scapula, 1st and 2nd posterior intercostal spaces
DESCENDING THORACIC AORTA (*see* Fig. 14.8)	Begins on the left side of the lower border of body of T4 vertebra. Descends with inclination to right and ends at the lower border of T12 vertebra by continuing as abdominal aorta	3–11 posterior intercostal spaces, subcostal area, lung tissue, oesophagus, pericardium, mediastinum and diaphragm

Section 2 Thorax

Contd...

Table A2.2: Arteries of thorax (Contd.)

Artery	Origin, course and termination	Area of distribution
3–11 posterior intercostal arteries (*see* Fig. 14.9)	3–11 posterior intercostal arteries of both right and left sides arise from the descending thoracic aorta. Right branches are little longer than the left. Each intercostal artery and its collateral branch end by anastomosing with the two anterior intercostal arteries	Supply the muscles of these intercostal spaces. Each of these arteries gives a collateral branch, which runs along the lower border of the respective intercostal space
Bronchial arteries	Two left bronchial arteries arise from descending aorta	Bronchial tree
Oesophageal branches	2–3 oesophageal branches arise from descending aorta	Supply the oesophagus
Pericardial branches	Branches of descending aorta, run on the pericardium	Fibrous and parietal layer of serous pericardia
Mediastinal branches	Arise from descending aorta	Supply lymph nodes and fat in posterior mediastinum
Superior phrenic arteries	Two branches of descending aorta. End in the superior surface of diaphragm. These arteries anastomose with branches of musculophrenic and pericardiacophrenic arteries.	Supply the thoracoabdominal diaphragm

Table A2.3: Comparison of right and left coronary arteries

Right coronary artery	Left coronary artery
1. Origin: Anterior aortic sinus of ascending aorta	1. Left posterior aortic sinus of ascending aorta
2. Course: Between pulmonary trunk and right auricle	2. Between pulmonary trunk and left auricle
3. Descends in atrioventricular groove on the right side	3. Descends in atrioventricular groove on the left side
4. Turns at the inferior border to run in posterior part of atrioventricular groove	4. Turns at left border to run in posterior part of atrioventricular groove. It is called circumflex branch
5. Termination: Ends by anastomosing with the circumflex branch of left coronary artery	5. Its circumflex branch ends by anastomosing with right coronary artery
6. Branches: To right atrium, right ventricle (marginal artery) and posterior interventricular branch for both ventricles and posterior 1/3rd of interventricular septa	6. Left atrium, left ventricle and anterior interventricular branch for both ventricles and anterior 2/3rd of interventricular septa. Anterior interventricular branch ends by anastomosing with posterior interventricular branch
7. Supplies sinuatrial node, atrioventricular (AV) node, AV bundle, right branch of AV bundle including its Purkinje fibres	7. Supplies left branch of atrioventricular bundle including its Purkinje fibres

muscles of bronchial tubes or bronchodilator. The pressure of inspired air also causes bronchodilatation.

TYPICAL INTERCOSTAL NERVE

Typical intercostal nerve is any of the nerves belonging to 3rd to 6th intercostal spaces.

Beginning

Typical thoracic spinal nerve after it has given off dorsal primary ramus or dorsal ramus is called the intercostal nerve. It runs in the intercostal space, i.e. between the lower border of rib above and upper border of rib below (*see* Fig. 14.3).

Course

Typical intercostal nerve enters the posterior part of intercostal space by passing behind the posterior intercostal vessels. So the intercostal nerve lies lowest in the neurovascular bundle. The order from above downwards is vein, artery and nerve (VAN). At first the bundle runs between posterior intercostal membrane and subcostalis, then between inner intercostal and innermost intercostal and lastly between inner intercostal and sternocostalis muscles (*see* Fig. 14.2).

At the anterior end of intercostal space, the intercostal nerve passes in front of internal thoracic vessels, pierces internal intercostal muscle and anterior intercostal membrane to continue as anterior cutaneous branch which ends by dividing into medial and lateral cutaneous branches (*see* Fig. 14.4).

Branches

1. Communicating branches to the sympathetic ganglion close to the beginning of ventral ramus. The anterior or ventral ramus containing sympathetic fibres from lateral horn of spinal cord gives off a *white ramus communicans* to the sympathetic ganglion. These fibres get relayed in the ganglion. Some of these relayed fibres pass via *grey ramus communicans* to ventral ramus. A few pass backwards in the dorsal ramus and rest pass through the ventral ramus. These sympathetic fibres are sudomotor, pilomotor and vasomotor to the skin and vasodilator to the skeletal vessels (*see* Fig. 14.3).
2. Before the angle, nerve gives a collateral branch that runs along the upper border of lower rib. This branch supplies intercostal muscles, costal pleura and periosteum of the rib.
3. Lateral cutaneous branch arises along the midaxillary line. It divides into anterior and posterior branches.
4. The nerve keeps giving muscular, periosteal, and branches to the costal pleura during its course.
5. Anterior cutaneous branch is the terminal branch of the nerve. It divides into anterior and posterior branches.

ATYPICAL INTERCOSTAL NERVES

The thoracic spinal nerves and their branches which do not follow absolutely thoracic course are designated as atypical intercostal nerves. Thus first and second intercostal nerves are atypical as these two nerves partly supply the upper limb.

The first thoracic nerve entirely joins the brachial plexus as its last rami or root. It gives no contribution to the first intercostal space. That is why the nerve supply of skin of first intercostal space is from the supraclavicular nerves (C3, C4) (*see* Fig. 3.4).

The second thoracic or second intercostal nerve runs in the second intercostal space. But its lateral cutaneous branch as *intercostobrachial nerve* is rather big and it supplies skin of the axilla as well. Third to sixth intercostal nerves are typical (*see* Fig. 7.1).

Also seventh, eight, ninth, tenth, eleventh intercostal nerves are atypical, as these course partly through thoracic wall and partly through anterolateral abdominal wall. Lastly the twelfth thoracic is known as subcostal nerve. It also passes through the anterolateral abdominal muscles. These nerves supply parietal peritoneum, muscles of the anterolateral abdominal wall and overlying skin.

ARTERIES

The arteries of thorax are internal thoracic artery, ascending aorta, arch of aorta, descending thoracic aorta and coronary arteries. These have been described with their origin, course, termination and area of distribution in Tables A2.2 and A2.3.

CLINICAL TERMS

Site of pericardial tapping: Removal of pericardial fluid is done in left *4th* or *5th intercostal* spaces just to the left of the sternum as pleura deviates exposing the pericardium against the medial part of left 4th and 5th intercostal spaces. Care should be taken to avoid injury to internal thoracic artery lying at a distance of 1 cm from the lateral border of sternum. Needle can also be passed upwards and posteriorly from the left xiphicostal angle to reach the pericardial cavity (*see* Fig. 18.6).

Foreign bodies in trachea: Foreign bodies like pins, coins entering the trachea pass into right bronchus; Right bronchus wider shorter, more vertical and is in line with trachea, so the foreign bodies in the trachea travel down into right bronchus and then into posterior basal segments of the lower lobe of the lung (*see* Fig. 16.5).

Site of bone marrow puncture: The manubrium sterni is the favoured site for bone *marrow puncture* in adults. Manubrium is subcutaneous and easily approachable (*see* Fig. 13.14). Bone marrow studies are done for various haematological disorders. Another site is the iliac crest; which is the preferred site in children.

Posture of a patient with respiratory difficulty: Such a patient finds comfort while sitting, as diaphragm is lowest in this position. In lying position, the diaphragm is highest, and patient is very uncomfortable (*see* Fig. 13.32).

In standing position, the diaphragm level is midway, but the patient is too sick to stand.

Patient also fixes the arms by holding the arms of a chair, so that serratus anterior and pectoralis major can move the ribs and help in respiration.

Paracentesis thoracis or pleural tapping: Aspiration of any fluid from the pleural cavity is called *paracentesis thoracis*. It is usually done in the eighth intercostal space in midaxillary line. The needle is passed through lower part of space to avoid injury to the principal neurovascular bundle (*see* Fig. 15.9).

Section 2 Thorax

Some clinical conditions associated with the pleura are as follows:

Pleurisy: This is inflammation of the pleura. It may be dry, but often it is accompanied by collection of fluid in the pleural cavity. The condition is called the pleural effusion.

Pneumothorax: Presence of air in the pleural cavity.

Haemothorax: Presence of blood in the pleural cavity.

Hydropneumothorax: Presence of both fluid and air in the pleural cavity.

Empyema: Presence of pus in the pleural cavity.

Coronary artery: Thrombosis of a coronary artery is a common cause of sudden death in persons past middle age. This is due to myocardial infarction and ventricular fibrillation.

Incomplete obstruction, usually due to spasm of the coronary artery causes angina pectoris, which is associated with agonising pain in the precordial region and down the medial side of the left arm and forearm.

Coronary angiography determines the site(s) of narrowing or occlusion of the coronary arteries or their branches.

Angioplasty helps in removal of small blockage. It is done using small stent or small inflated balloon (*see* Fig. 18.27).

If there are large segments or multiple sites of blockage, coronary bypass is done using either great saphenous vein or internal thoracic artery as graft(s) (*see* Fig. 18.28).

Cardiac pain is an ischaemic pain caused by incomplete obstruction of a coronary artery.

Viscera usually have low amount of sensory output, whereas skin is an area of high amount of sensory output. So pain arising from low sensory output area is projected as coming from high sensory output area.

Axons of pain fibres conveyed by the sensory sympathetic cardiac nerves reach thoracic one to thoracic five segments of spinal cord mostly through the dorsal root ganglia of the left side. Since these dorsal root ganglia also receive sensory impulses from the medial side of arm, forearm and upper part of front of chest, the pain gets referred to these areas as depicted in Fig. 18.26.

Though the pain is usually referred to the left side, it may even be referred to right arm, jaw, epigastrium or back.

Oesophageal varices: In portal hypertension, the communications between the portal and systemic veins draining the lower end of the oesophagus dilate. These dilatations are called *oesophageal varices* (*see* Fig. 20.8). Rupture of these varices can cause serious haematemesis or vomiting of blood. The oesophageal varices can be visualised radiographically by barium swallow; they produce worm-like shadows.

Barium swallow: Left atrial enlargement as in mitral stenosis can also be visualised by barium swallow. The enlarged atrium causes a shallow depression on the front of the oesophagus. Barium swallow also helps in the diagnosis of oesophageal strictures, carcinoma and achalasia cardia.

Coarctation of the aorta: *Coarctation of the aorta* is a localised narrowing of the aorta opposite to or just beyond the attachment of the ductus arteriosus. An extensive collateral circulation develops between the branches of the subclavian arteries and those of the descending aorta. These include the anastomoses between the anterior and posterior intercostal arteries. These arteries enlarge greatly and produce a characteristic notching on the ribs (*see* Fig. 19.6).

Aortic aneurysm: *Aortic aneurysm* is a localised dilatation of the aorta which may press upon the surrounding structures and cause the mediastinal syndrome (*see* Fig. 19.8).

FREQUENTLY ASKED QUESTIONS

1. Describe the thoracic part of sympathetic system.
2. Discuss the nerve supply of lung. What is the clinical importance of these nerves.
3. Components of deep cardiac plexus on the right and left sides.
4. Superficial cardiac plexus.
5. Atypical intercostal nerves.
6. Cardiac pain referred to medial side of left arm.

MULTIPLE CHOICE QUESTIONS

A. **Match the following on the left side with their appropriate answers on the right side.**

1. Arteries and their branches:
   a. Internal thoracic   i. Posterior interventricular
   b. Descending aorta   ii. Posterior intercostal
   c. Right coronary   iii. Anterior interventricular
   d. Left coronary   iv. Anterior intercostal

2. Ribs:
   a. True ribs   i. 8th, 9th and 10th
   b. Atypical ribs   ii. 1st, 11th, 12th
   c. Least fractured ribs   iii. 1st–7th
   d. Vertebrochondral ribs   iv. 1st, 2nd, 10th, 12th

3. Vertebral levels:
   a. Aortic opening in diaphragm   i. T8
   b. Oesophageal opening in diaphragm   ii. T10
   c. Inferior vena cava in diaphragm   iii. T11
   d. Gastro-oesophageal junction   iv. T12

4. Mediastinum:
   a. Anterior mediastinum   i. Trachea
   b. Middle mediastinum   ii. Azygos vein
   c. Posterior mediastinum   iii. Heart
   d. Superior mediastinum   iv. Sternopericardial ligaments

B. **For each of the incomplete statements or questions below, one or more answers given is/ are correct. Select**

A. If only a, b and c are correct
B. If only a and c are correct
C. If only b and d are correct
D. If only d is correct
E. If all are correct

1. The apex of the heart:
   a. is formed only by left ventricle
   b. is situated in the left 5th intercostal space
   c. is just medial to midclavicular line
   d. is directed downwards, backwards and to the left

2. The aortic opening in the diaphragm:
   a. lies at the lower border of 12th thoracic vertebra
   b. transmits aorta, thoracic duct and azygos vein
   c. lies in the central tendinous part of the diaphragm
   d. is quadrangular in shape

3. The trachea:
   a. extends in cadaver from C6 to T4.
   b. deviates to the right at its termination
   c. is lined by ciliated pseudostratified epithelium
   d. is seen as a vertical radiopaque shadow in radiograph.

4. Thoracic duct:
   a. begins at the lower border of L1
   b. is the upward continuation of cisterna chyli
   c. enters the thorax through vena caval opening in the diaphragm
   d. ends by opening at the junction of left subclavian and left internal jugular veins

5. Bronchopulmonary segment:
   a. is aerated by a segmental bronchus
   b. is pyramidal in shape with its base directed towards periphery
   c. is an independent respiratory unit
   d. is supplied by its own separate branch of pulmonary artery and vein

6. Visceral pleura:
   a. is pain insensitive
   b. develops from splanchnopleuric mesoderm
   c. covers all the surfaces of the lung including fissures but not the hilum
   d. is innervated by autonomic nerves

Section 2   Thorax

ANSWERS

A. 1. a – iv, b – ii,   c – i,   d – iii,   2. a – iii, b – iv,   c – ii,   d – i
    3. a – iv, b – ii,   c – i,   d – iii,   4. a – iv, b – iii,   c – ii,   d – i
B. 1. A   2. A   3. A   4. C   5. B   6. E.

FURTHER READING

1. Anderson RH, Ho SY, Becker AE. The surgical anatomy of the conduction tissues. *Thorax* 1983; 38: 408–20.

2. Armstrong P. The normal chest. In: Armstrong P, Wilson AG, Dee P, Hansell DM (eds) *Images of the Diseases of the Chest*. London: Mosby: 2000; 12–62.

3. Celli B. The diaphragm and respiratory muscles. *Chest Surg Clin N Am* 1998; 8:207–24.

4. Kumar H, Rath G, Kowle M and Vidya Ram. Bilateral sternalis with unusual left-sided presentation: A clinical perspective. *Yonsei Medical Journal* 2003; 44: 719–722.

5. Kurihara Y, Yakushiji, Matsumoto J, Ishikawa T, Hirata K. The ribs: anatomic and radiologic considerations: *Radiographics* 1999; 19:105–19.

6. Mizeres NJ. The cardiac plexus in man. *Am J Anat* 1963; 112:141–51.

7. Peterson WG. The normal antireflux mechanism. *Chest Surg Clin N Am* 2001; 11:473–83.

8. Rajanna MJ. Anatomical and surgical considerations of the phrenic and accessory phrenic nerves. *J Inter Coll Surg* 1947; 60:42–52.

1. a. Identify the part of the bone.
    b. Name the structures related to it.

2. a. Name the joint shown.
    b. Name its type.

3. a. Identify the part shown.
    b. Name the structures present.

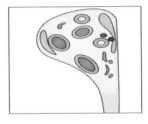

4. a. Identify the part shown.
    b. Name its three branches.

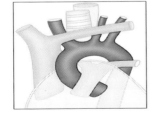

5. a. Identify the sulcus.
    b. Name the structures present.

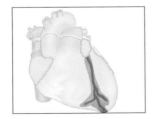

6. a. Identify the structure.
    b. Name its main branches.

7. a. Identify the part.
    b. Name its segments.

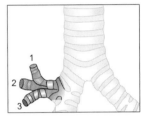

8. a. Name the structure.
    b. Name its 3 openings.

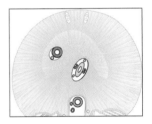

9. a. Identify the part.
    b. Name its boundaries.

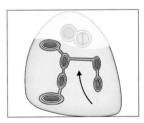

10. a. Identify the ganglion.
    b. Name the connections with the ventral ramus.

Section 2 Thorax

ANSWERS: SPOTS ON THORAX

1. a. Neck of 1st rib
   b. • Sympathetic trunk
      • Posterior intercostal vein
      • Superior intercostal artery

2. a. Manubriosternal joint
   b. Secondary cartilaginous joint

3. a. Hilum of right lung
   b. • Eparterial bronchus
      • Pulmonary artery
      • Hyparterial bronchus
      • Upper and lower pulmonary veins

4. a. Arch of aorta
   b. • Brachiocephalic trunk
      • Left common carotid artery
      • Left subclavian artery

5. a. Anterior interventricular sulcus
   b. • Anterior interventricular branch of left coronary artery
      • Great cardiac vein

6. a. Right coronary artery
   b. • Marginal artery
      • Posterior interventricular branch
      • Branch to SA node, AV node

7. a. Upper lobar segment
   b. 1 Apical
      2 Posterior
      3 Anterior

8. a. Thoracoabdominal diaphragm
   b. • Aortic opening
      • Venacaval opening
      • Oesophageal opening

9. a. Oblique sinus of pericardium
   b. • Inferior vena cava—below and to right
      • Pulmonary veins—above and to left
      • Left atrium—anterior
      • Fibrous pericardium and oesophagus—posterior

10. a. Sympathetic ganglion
    b. • Grey ramus communicans
       • White ramus communicans

Index